A BOYS' TREASURY OF
SEA STORIES

The *Adventure Galley*

A BOYS' TREASURY OF SEA STORIES

Illustrated by

WILL NICKLESS

GOLDEN PLEASURE BOOKS · LONDON

Published by

GOLDEN PLEASURE BOOKS LTD
DRURY HOUSE · RUSSELL STREET · LONDON WC2

© Copyright 1966 Golden Pleasure Books Ltd

Printed in Czechoslovakia by Tisk, Brno

T 1659

CONTENTS

Famous Ships

by

FRANK KNIGHT

The Adventure Galley
of Captain Kidd the Pirate, 1696

There have always been pirates. Julius Caesar was once captured by them. King Alfred and many other English kings had to build ships to drive them out of the Channel. In Queen Elizabeth I's time pirates from Algiers used to raid English towns, and once sailed right into the Thames.

But the great days of pirates were from about 1650 to 1720, and their chief hunting grounds were among the West Indies and off the coasts of North America.

They came because Spain refused to let ships of other nations trade with her American colonies. Many seamen defied the ban, and the Spaniards called them pirates. Most of them, however, had commissions from their governments, as Drake did. Strictly, they were privateers, or private warships, not pirates.

Elizabeth issued many such commissions. But James I, anxious to make peace with Spain, cancelled them. Many seamen who held them decided to remain in the West Indies to become real pirates.

They had chosen a hard life. No ports would receive them.

For food they caught wild cattle, roasting the meat over wood fires in the open. The Spanish-Indian word for such a fire was boucan, and so the pirates came to be called boucaniers, or buccaneers.

But their numbers grew. They were joined by runaway slaves, deserting seamen and soldiers, and unemployed seamen from Europe. They took possession of some islands which were almost deserted, such as St Kitts, Antigua, Tortuga. Many English pirates went to Jamaica, which Oliver Cromwell's ships captured from the Spaniards. One famous buccaneer, Henry Morgan, became governor of Jamaica, with the task of putting an end to piracy!

Pirates, like burglars, can only make a living if they can sell the goods they steal. The pirates' best customers were the colonists, Spanish in the south, English in the north.

England made the same mistake as Spain. Only British ships were allowed to trade with British colonies. But few ships came, and the pirates captured many that did. Then the pirates sold their cargoes to the hungry colonies much cheaper than honest merchants would have done.

In return the colonists welcomed pirate ships to their harbours. The pirates spent their money in the growing American towns such as New York, Boston, Philadelphia. Some pirates built fine houses there and lived like lords. They made friends with colonial governors and got bankers to invest money in their voyages. Piracy became big business.

Soon the pirates became more ambitious. They made longer voyages. From their American homes they went all the way to the Indian Ocean and Persian Gulf. They took possession of the island of Madagascar and set their own 'king' to rule it.

Incredibly rich cargoes went home to America. In 1694 Thomas Tew sailed into Boston with a cargo worth £1000,000. Two years later Henry Avery came in with goods worth £300,000.

8

This sort of thing could not last. Many of the goods had been stolen from the powerful East India Company, or from their Indian friends. They told the British government it must send out warships to stop the traffic.

Britain was at war with France and could not spare a warship. The government told the Earl of Bellomont, who was governor in chief of the American colonies, he must do something about it from his side of the Atlantic. Bellomont decided to send out a private warship, a privateer.

The ship he chose was called *Adventure Galley*, an armed merchant ship of about 300 tons, mounting thirty guns. She was a sailing ship, but was called 'galley' because she also had big oars for moving her in harbour or in a flat calm. She was not a galley at all in the old-fashioned sense of a rowing ship.

The man he chose to command her was a retired merchant skipper named Captain Kidd, a most respectable man by all accounts, who had lived in New York for many years.

Captain Kidd sailed. Little was heard of him for almost a year. And then, suddenly, came the news that instead of catching pirates, Kidd was indulging in piracy himself. The East India Company angrily demanded that real warships be sent out — and this time they went.

Meanwhile Captain Kidd was on his way home with the *Adventure Galley*. He sailed innocently into New York, and was promptly arrested, and was then sent to England for trial.

Was he really a pirate? His crew said he was, and he had forced them to be pirates too. One man who refused was killed by Captain Kidd 'with a bucket worth eightpence'.

Captain Kidd said he was not. He said his crew mutinied and forced him to seize other ships. And, in any case, two ships he took were carrying French cargoes, which made them enemies. He said he had given the French papers of those ships to the Earl of Bellomont.

9

But the Earl of Bellomont had died and the papers could not be found. After more than two years of argument Captain Kidd was tried, found guilty, and hanged. Right to the end he protested: 'I am the innocentist person of them all, only I have been sworn against by perjured persons.'

Perhaps he was. Two hundred years after his death those French papers were found in the Public Records Office in London.

Nobody believed him innocent at the time. In fact the newspapers and story-writers of his day turned him into the greatest pirate who ever lived, which he certainly was not. Horrible crimes were invented for him. Books were written about his career, quite untrue. His imaginary life was even acted on the stage.

In fact much of the nonsense written about pirates began with these stories of Captain Kidd.

The truth is that pirates were not very romantic. They were not even particularly bloodthirsty. They never killed people if they could avoid it, for they knew they would be hanged for it if they were caught. Captain Kidd was hanged for killing that man with a bucket, not for piracy. Piracy was sometimes pardoned, but not murder.

Pirates did not make people walk the plank. Some story-writer invented that. Nor did pirates fight if they could avoid it. Even the famous Blackbeard Teach, who loved to decorate himself with cutlasses and pistols, fireworks and lighted candles, was only in one serious fight. It was with a young naval officer, and Blackbeard was killed.

Pirates did not make a habit of burying their treasure. They spent it on gay living. But they did sometimes pretend they had buried it when they were captured, so that their lives might be spared. They hoped to be given a chance to dig it up; in other words a chance to escape. Captain Kidd tried that, but nobody believed him.

Some later pirates were much more bloodthirsty: the pirates of the China Sea, Borneo and Java, for instance. They killed for the love of killing. And there was the famous Benito de Soto who was a pirate in the Atlantic not much more than a hundred years ago. He once locked all the passengers of a sailing-ship under hatches, opened the sea-cocks, and set fire to the ship as well. Captain Kidd would never have done that.

The Victory
Nelson's flagship at Trafalgar, 1805

The old wooden sailing-ships had long lives. Merchant ships might remain in service for a hundred years. Even warships might last fifty years.

Nelson's *Victory* was ordered to be built in 1758, the year of Nelson's birth. She was launched in 1765, forty years before Trafalgar. She was kept afloat in harbour for 120 years after that. Now she is preserved in a dry-dock, but she is still an admiral's flagship, as she was during most of her active life.

The best ships were built of oak. But oak is an expensive timber. An oak tree must grow for a hundred years before it is ready for cutting. In those days nearly all oak trees were reserved for the use of the Navy, and were marked with the Government's 'broad arrow'. Some old trees may still be seen bearing this mark.

Admiral Collingwood, who was second in command to Nelson at Trafalgar, used to carry acorns in his pocket and plant them in any likely spot. He did not dream that long before his trees had grown, all warships would be built of iron or steel.

Because oak was valuable, and scarce, ships could not be scrapped when they became old-fashioned. Even when a ship was rotten and falling to pieces, any good timber in her was carefully removed and used again. That happened in the case of the *Royal George*, and with many others.

Nor did ships easily become old-fashioned. Drake's *Revenge* was not very different from the frigates of Nelson's day, more than two centuries later. Sails and rigging had improved, and so had guns; but the hulls were very similar. There was no machinery of any kind to become out of date. Drake could have sailed the *Victory*, or Nelson the *Revenge*. Both men would have been lost aboard the steamers which came only a few years after Trafalgar.

The *Victory* was practically rebuilt twice in her fifty years of active life. This was partly because she was such a popular ship. Many admirals besides Nelson chose her for their flagship, including Admiral Kempenfeldt who went down with the *Royal George*, Admiral Keppel who had been one of Anson's midshipmen aboard the *Centurion*, Lord Howe, Lord Hood, and Lord St Vincent.

Once the Admiralty converted the *Victory* into a prison ship; but such a shout of protest arose that they had to fit her out as a flagship again. And that was before Nelson made her famous at Trafalgar.

When Nelson heard she was to be his flagship he wrote to a friend, 'I am very pleased, for I know the weight of the *Victory* in the Mediterranean.' That is, even her name added something to the importance of his appointment as Admiral in Command. Friends and enemies alike knew that whoever flew his flag in the *Victory* must be an important man.

Nelson's job in the Mediterranean was to keep the French fleet shut up in Toulon, or to fight it if it came out. For Na-

12

poleon was hoping to invade Britain, but could not do so without his warships.

In the summer of 1803 Nelson vowed 'never to go into port till after the battle, if they make me wait a year'. But they made him wait much longer than that. Next summer he was writing, 'If I should miss these fellows my heart will break.' And in another letter he said that the French admiral 'sometimes plays bo-peep in and out of Toulon, like a mouse at the edge of a hole.'

But at Christmas 1804 they did slip out, and Nelson missed them in bad weather.

His own ships were terribly battered by then. Most of them had not been in dock for two years. Some of the best had gone to watch the Spanish fleet, for Spain was also at war with Britain.

Rumours and false reports came in. Someone said the French had gone to Italy. Nelson chased them there, but did not find them. Then he thought they might have gone to Egypt, so he went there to look for them. Not until March did he learn that they had passed Gibraltar, bound out into the Atlantic.

The wind turned against him. He fretted and fumed, and after weeks managed to reach Gibraltar. More delays — and then the wind changed and off Nelson went, not even bothering to wait for the ships' laundry to come back from the shore.

He guessed now that the French meant to attack the West Indies, and he was right. His fleet crossed the Atlantic in twenty-four days, and so frightened the French that they hurried back across the Atlantic again.

This time they escaped into Spanish ports. The British frigates could see the combined French and Spanish fleets in Cadiz harbour. But Napoleon wanted both fleets in the English Channel, and said he would sack the admiral in command if he did not make a move.

They made a move on October 19, 1805. The watching

The *Victory* (right)

frigates saw their topsails being hoisted. Nelson prepared for battle.

The British fleet formed into two parallel lines, one led by Nelson in the *Victory*, the other by Collingwood in the *Royal Sovereign*. But there was scarcely any wind. Not until the morning of October 21 could Nelson get his ships near enough to open fire. The *Victory* was moving at about two knots.

Nelson's plan was to smash the long enemy line in two places, and so break the big fleet up into small groups. The plan worked perfectly. The two British lines sailed majestically on, ignoring the French guns, until they crashed in among the enemy ships. The *Victory* came under fire from seven or eight French ships at once. From one came the bullet which killed Lord Nelson in his hour of triumph.

Every history book tells of the Battle of Trafalgar. But here is a letter from a young sailor who took part in it, written to his father just after the battle.

'This comes to tell you that I am alive and hearty except three fingers; but that's not much, it might have been my head. I told brother Tom I should like to see a great battle, and I have seen one, and we have peppered the enemy rarely; and for matter of that, they fought us pretty tightish for French and Spanish. Three of our mess are killed, and four more of us winged.

'How my fingers got knocked overboard I don't know; but off they are, and I never missed them till I wanted them. You see by my writing it was my left hand, so I can write to you, and fight for my King yet. We have taken a rare parcel of ships, but the wind is so rough we cannot bring them home, else I should roll in prize-money. So we are busy smashing 'em, and blowing 'em up wholesale.

'Our dear Admiral Nelson is killed, so we have paid pretty sharply for licking 'em. I never set eyes on him, for which I am both sorry and glad; for, to be sure, I should like to have seen him. But then, all the men in our ship who have seen him are such soft toads, they have done nothing but blast their eyes and cry ever since he was killed. God bless you, chaps that fought like the Devil, sit down and cry like a wench.

'I am still in the Royal Sovereign, but the Admiral has left her. He is in a frigate so that he may be here and there and everywhere. For he's as cute and bold as a lion, for all he can cry! I saw tears with my own eyes, when the boat hailed and said my Lord was dead. So no more at present — Sam.'

The Mary Celeste
Heroine of the most famous
sea mystery, 1872

She was a very ordinary little sailing tramp, owned in the U.S.A., built in Nova Scotia, of about 230 tons. Her skipper, Captain Benjamin Briggs, was also part-owner of her. He was a very respectable man, by all accounts, and religious.

The *Mary Celeste* sailed from New York for Genoa, Italy, on November 7, 1872. She had a cargo of oil and raw alcohol in barrels. Captain Briggs had his wife and two-year-old daughter with him. There were a mate, second mate, cook and four seamen.

Twenty-eight days later, on December 5, the *Mary Celeste* was found drifting helplessly about 600 miles west of Gibraltar, with no one on board.

16

Why? A court of enquiry was held, books have been written about it, men have puzzled about it ever since. Nobody knows.

She was found by the brig *Dei Gratia* which had been in New York with her. In fact Captain and Mrs Briggs had dined with Captain Morehouse of the *Dei Gratia* just before sailing. So Captain Morehouse sent his mate on board the mystery ship.

The mate found very little wrong. The sails were set, though some were torn and one had been let down on deck, perhaps in a hurry. It had not been stowed away. There was water in the ship's bilges, but not a lot. She was not sinking. The ship's only small boat was missing.

Some hatch covers were off, but the cargo in the hold seemed undamaged. The cabin skylight was open, and everything was wet inside, from rain or spray. But on the whole things were in good order.

The ship's log was in the mate's cabin. It showed no unusual entry. But the ship's other papers and the captain's navigation instruments were missing.

There was plenty of food on board, and water. There was no sign of fire or other calamity. In short there was nothing to show why the ship had been abandoned.

Yet she had been, and in a hurry. The seamen had left their pipes and tobacco in the fo'c'sle, and their oilskins. Why had that sail been dropped in haste? On the other hand the captain had had time to collect his papers and instruments.

The mate of the *Dei Gratia* sailed the *Mary Celeste* to Gibraltar. There she was handed over to the port authorities. Captain Morehouse claimed salvage money in the usual way.

Of course everyone expected the *Mary Celeste's* crew to turn up somewhere. But they never did. No trace of their boat was ever found.

Those are the plain facts. Unfortunately they were much too

plain for some people. 'Experts' busied themselves with the mystery, and found sinister clues.

There was a cut in the ship's rail which must have been made with an axe. Why? There were two long scratches in the ship's bow planking. How did they get there? There were some nasty brown stains on deck which must be blood. There was actually a bloodstained sword in the captain's cabin, which someone had tried to clean! Biggest mystery of all, the clock in the cabin was hanging upside down.

Alas for the 'experts', most of these clues came to nothing. The axe cut might have been made years ago. The scratches in the planking were merely where splinters had been torn away by the sea. A doctor said the blood was not blood, whatever else it might be.

As for the sword, it was an ancient curio, no more than an ornament. Its stains were only rust; and the person who had tried to clean it was the mate of the *Dei Gratia*, to pass the time away. He had also tried to get the clock going, but could not, so put it back on the wall in disgust, not noticing and not caring that it was upside down.

Naturally the experts were annoyed at having their clues blown away like this. They bullied the mate of the *Dei Gratia* unmercifully, almost accusing him of murder. As to the remaining owner of the *Mary Celeste*, who had come from America to give evidence, he wrote to a friend:

'They were going to arrest me for hiring the crew to make away with the officers. I did not know but they might do it, as they seem to do just as they like. So I decided to come home.'

In despair the experts of the court of enquiry gave up. But not so the amateurs. The mystery was too intriguing to be dropped. Strange theories were put forward, none of which fitted the facts.

One was that an octopus had removed the crew one by

The *Marie Celeste*

one — and presumably the boat as well! But why an octopus should need navigation instruments nobody explained.

Another was that plague had broken out. Or the captain had gone mad and killed everybody, including himself. Or the entire crew had gone swimming, and the ship had sailed away from them.

Most fantastic, one theory was that the baby on board was really a baby-grand piano. It had broken adrift and so frightened the crew that they all jumped overboard.

Other investigators picked on Captain Morehouse and his crew. They were mere pirates, who had killed the crew of the *Mary Celeste* for the sake of the salvage money. Or perhaps a gang of toughs joined the *Mary Celeste* in New York and did away with the regular crew.

There were even 'confessions' of stories like that, published in newspapers as coming from 'survivors'. But strangest of all, perhaps, are the details which have been invented to make the mystery more mysterious.

The mate of the *Dei Gratia* said clearly enough that there was nothing on the cabin table except the racks, or 'fiddles', to keep things from sliding off in bad weather. And the ship had been in bad weather, for everything was wet.

But someone invented the story that there was a meal on the table, ready to be eaten. Says one writer, 'Three cups of tea were standing on the table. They were still warm!' And the same writer tells how newly washed shirts were hanging on a line, and there was a chicken frying on the galley stove.

Another writer has 'a phial of sewing-machine oil still standing upright by a reel of cotton and a thimble'.

All this is nonsense. But the mystery remains. What did happen? The answers given by two practical seamen are worth quoting.

One was the mate of the *Dei Gratia*. He said that when someone on board the *Mary Celeste* tested the depth of water in her bilge that morning, water had surged up the pipe, giving an entirely false reading. He said it had happened to him sometimes, when the ship was rolling. The water surged up and the reading on the line became ten or twelve feet instead of two or three. So the crew panicked, thinking the ship was sinking under them, and left her.

The other man was the part-owner of the *Mary Celeste*, himself an old seaman. He thought gas from the cargo of alcohol might have caused an explosion which blew those hatch covers off. So the crew hastily took to the boat in case a worse explosion was to follow.

In either case, then, the ship must have sailed away on her own, and the boat been swamped by the bad weather which came soon afterwards.

It is a tame ending to a mystery story, but at least it fits the facts. And the other mystery of the *Mary Celeste* remains. Why pick on her? Why has she become the most famous mystery ship of all time?

The Titanic
The unsinkable ship, 1912

The White Star Line boasted that their great ship was unsinkable. Her bottom was divided into sixteen separate watertight compartments. If any one became holed it could be shut off from the rest, and the ship would still float.

But on her maiden voyage an iceberg ripped through five of those compartments, and she did sink. More than 1,500 people were drowned.

She was the biggest and most luxurious liner that had yet been built: 46,000 tons, 880 feet long, she could carry 2,000 passengers besides her crew of 800. Her speed was 24 knots, and on this first voyage she was trying to break the Atlantic speed record.

Famous and wealthy people, American and British, had booked passages in her. But in addition there were hundreds of poor emigrants from Europe, going to America to find new homes and fortune.

It happened on a fine, calm, but very cold night, April 14, 1912. Icebergs were about, as the captain of the *Titanic* had been told by wireless — and not many ships had wireless in those days. But the *Titanic* rushed on, out to break the record. And, of course, she was unsinkable.

Suddenly, just before midnight, the look-outs shouted that there was an iceberg right ahead. The helm was put over, the engines reversed. But it was too late. The berg slid along the ship's side, slopping tons of ice on to her decks.

Not many people heard or felt the shock. Most people were in bed. A few who happened to be on deck thought it was a great joke, and began playing with the ice. But far down below stokers were horrified to see the Atlantic water pouring in.

Half an hour later Captain Smith realised the awful truth. The unsinkable *Titanic* was sinking. He ordered the boats to be got ready, the passengers mustered on deck. The first wireless call for assistance went out.

Captain Smith knew what the passengers did not. There were only half enough boats to go round. Moreover there had been no boat-drill on board. Even the crew did not know to which boats they were supposed to go. As to the passengers, they were only annoyed at being turned out on deck in the cold. Many refused to go. The ship was unsinkable.

In their cabin high on the bridge the two wireless operators were having trouble, too. Other ships heard their distress call,

22

but refused to believe it. They thought it was a leg-pull and refused to wake their captains.

One ship, the *Californian*, a big cargo liner, could actually see the *Titanic*. Sensibly, she had stopped because there was so much ice about, and was waiting for daylight. Her wireless operator was asleep, and her captain. Her officers watched the big ship arrive, and also stop. Later, when the *Titanic* fired distress rockets, the *Californian's* people thought they were fireworks to amuse the passengers! When the *Titanic's* lights went out they thought she had steamed away.

In fact only one ship took the *Titanic's* calls seriously. She was the small and old Cunarder *Carpathia*, bound from New York on a sunshine cruise to the Mediterranean.

The *Carpathia* was built to do fourteen knots. That night her aged engines pushed her along at seventeen. Steam was cut off from the passengers' radiators to give more for the engines. But she was sixty miles away from the *Titanic* when she heard the call.

The *Titanic's* passengers refused to worry. They played cards in the saloon. The band was playing. But down below third-class and emigrant passengers found the water rising in their cabins. They rushed about blindly, not even knowing where the boat-deck was. The huge ship seemed a maze of alleyways and staircases leading nowhere.

The first boats were lowered almost empty. The first-class passengers refused to leave the warm saloon. But the officers knew the boats must be put in the water, even if they went empty. Better that than let them go down with the ship.

Then the ship began to tilt, and suddenly people realised the matter was serious. Now they rushed for the boats, and the trouble was to keep them back. Men tried to crowd in with the women and children. But some women refused to leave their menfolk, preferring to drown with them.

By that time, too, people were finding their way up from far below. Officers had to bring out their revolvers. A few shots were fired into the air. The last boat was lowered, and there were still about 1,600 people on board the ship. Hundreds were still trying to find the boat-deck.

Two hours after hitting the berg the ship's foredeck dipped under water. The band began playing hymns. Officers and seamen struggled desperately to clear collapsible boats and rafts so that they would float when the ship sank. Inside the ship furniture and fittings began to slide.

At two o'clock the captain told the two wireless operators to save themselves. They ignored him and went on working. But a few minutes later they heard the sea swishing over the top bridge. Then they went.

People fought their way towards the stern, which was rising high into the air as the ship stood on her head. Everything inside slid down in a tremendous avalanche. One of the four huge funnels toppled over.

At twenty minutes past two the *Titanic* vanished. The unsinkable ship had sunk — in less than three hours. On board the *Californian* an officer noted that the big ship's lights had disappeared. Twenty-seven miles to the southward the *Carpathia* was racing on.

The water felt like ice. Second Officer Lightoller said it felt like a thousand knives when he was plunged into it. He had just been sucked down into one of the sinking ship's big ventilators, and blown out again by a blast of hot air. He grabbed a collapsible boat with about thirty other men. The junior wireless operator fought his way out from underneath it and joined them.

Fifth Officer Rowe took one boat back to look for survivors. He found four. No other boat went back, but most of them held only women and children. In any case nobody could live long in that icy water.

At four in the morning the *Carpathia* arrived. Captain

The *Titanic*

Rostron had to take his ship to the lifeboats, for the frozen people in them could not row to the ship.

The *Carpathia* took on board 705 people. There had been 2,207 on board the *Titanic*. 1,502 were missing, for none was picked up by any other ship. At just about this time the White Star Line man in New York was telling newspaper reporters, 'We place absolute confidence in the *Titanic*. We believe her to be unsinkable.'

The truth horrified the world. Laws were hastily passed about lifeboats, boat-drills, wireless. Such a thing must never be allowed to happen again.

Perhaps it will not. At any rate nobody is likely to boast again that a ship is unsinkable.

Amyas and the Armada
from Westward Ho!

by
CHARLES KINGSLEY

Westward Ho! *tells of the exciting adventures of Amyas Leigh on the Spanish main in the years 1575 — 1588. Amyas' hatred of the Spanish is patriotic, but also personal. His lady-love was carried off by a Spanish cavalier named Don Guzman, who married the girl, but then left her to burn to death, along with Amyas' brother, at the hands of the Spanish Inquisition. The desire to revenge these deeds leads Amyas into the famous battle which is the climax of the book — the defeat of the Invincible Spanish Armada.*

The Spaniards are dispirited and battered, but unbroken still; and as they slide to their anchorage in Calais Roads on the Saturday evening of that most memorable week, all prudent men know well that England's hour is come, and that the bells which will call all at Christendom to church upon the morrow morn, will be either the death-knell or the triumphal peal of the Reformed faith throughout the world.

But where is Amyas Leigh all this while? Day after day he has been seeking the *Sta. Catharina* in the thickest of the press, and cannot come at her, cannot even hear of her; one moment he dreads that she has sunk by night, and balked him of his prey; the next, that she has repaired her damages, and will escape him after all. He is moody, discontented, restless, even (for the first time in his life) peevish with his men. He can talk of nothing but Don Guzman; he can find no better employment, at every spare moment, than taking his sword out of the sheath, and handling it, fondling it, talking to it even, bidding it not to fail him in the day of vengeance.

Amyas called for a boat and went on board Drake's ship to ask for news of the *Sta. Catharina*, and listened scowling to the loud chants and tinkling bells, which came across the water from the Spanish fleet. At last Drake was summoned by the Lord Admiral, and returned with a secret commission, which ought to bear fruit that night; and Amyas, who had gone with him, helped him till nightfall, and then returned to his own ship as Sir Amyas Leigh, Knight, to the joy and glory of every soul on board, except his moody self.

So there, the livelong summer Sabbath day, before the little high-walled town and the long range of yellow sand-hills, lie those two mighty armaments, scowling at each other, hardly out of gun-shot. Messenger after messenger is hurrying towards Bruges to the Duke of Parma, for light craft which can follow these nimble English somewhat better than their own floating castles; and above all, entreating him to put to sea at once with all his force. He returns for answer; first, that his victual is not ready; next, that his Dutch sailors, who have been kept at their post for many a week at the sword's point, have run away like water; and thirdly, that over and above all, he cannot come so 'strangely provided of great ordnance and musketeers' as those five-and-thirty Dutch ships, in which round-sterned and stubborn-hearted heretics watch, like terriers at a rat's hole, the entrance of Nieuwport and Dunkirk.

Lord Henry Seymour has brought Lord Howard a letter of command from Elizabeth's self; and Drake has been carrying out so busily all that Sunday long, that by two o'clock on the Monday morning, eight fire-ships 'besmeared with wildfire, brimstone, pitch and resin, and all their ordnance charged with bullets and with stones,' are stealing down the wind

28

straight for the Spanish fleet, guided by two valiant men of Devon, Young and Prowse. (Let their names live long in the land!) The ships are fired, the men of Devon steal back, and in a moment more, the heaven is red with glare from Dover Cliffs to Gravelines Tower.

And then breaks forth one of those disgraceful panics which so often follow overweening presumption; and shrieks, oaths, prayers, and reproaches make night hideous. Cutting all cables, hoisting any sails, the Invincible Armada goes lumbering wildly out to sea, every ship foul of her neighbour.

The largest of the four galliasses loses her rudder, and drifts helpless to and fro, hindering and confusing. The duke, having (so the Spaniards say) weighed his anchor deliberately instead of leaving it behind him, runs in again after a while and fires a signal for return; but his truant sheep are deaf to the shepherd's pipe, and swearing and praying by turns, he runs up the Channel towards Gravelines, picking up stragglers on his way, who are struggling as best they can among the flats and shallows: but Drake and Fenner have arrived as soon as he. When Monday's sun rises on the quaint old castle and muddy dykes of Gravelines town, the thunder of the cannon recommences, and is not hushed until the night. Drake can hang coolly enough in the rear to plunder when he thinks fit: but when the battle needs it none can fight more fiercely, among the foremost; and there is need now, if ever. That Armada must never be allowed to re-form. If it does, its left wing may yet keep the English at bay, while its right drives off the blockading Hollanders from Dunkirk port, and sets Parma and his flotilla free to join them, and to sail in doubled strength across to the mouth of the Thames.

So Drake has weighed anchor, and away up the Channel with all his squadron, the moment that he saw the Spanish fleet come up; and with him Fenner burning to redeem the honour, which indeed he had never lost; and ere Fenton,

29

Beeston, Crosse, Ryman and Lord Southwell can join them, the Devon ships have been worrying the Spaniards for two full hours into confusion worse confounded.

But what is that heavy firing behind them? Alas for the great galliasse! She lies, like a huge stranded whale, upon the sands where now stands Calais pier: and Amyas Preston is pounding her into submission, while a fleet of hoys and drumblers look on and help, as jackals might the lion.

Soon, on the southwest horizon, loom up larger and larger two mighty ships, and behind them sail on sail. As they near a shout greets the *Triumph* and the *Bear*; and on and in the Lord High Admiral glides stately into the thickest of the fight.

True, we have still but some three-and-twenty ships which can cope at all with some ninety of the Spaniards, but we have dash, and daring, and the inspiration of utter need. Now, or never, must the mighty struggle be ended. We worried them off Portland; we must rend them in pieces now; and in rushes ship after ship, to smash her broadsides through and through the wooden castles 'sometimes not a pike's-length asunder,' and then out to reload, and give place meanwhile to another. The smaller are fighting with all sails set; the few larger, who once in, are careless about coming out again, fight with topsails loose, and their main and foreyards close down on deck, to prevent being boarded. The duke, Oquenda and Recalde, having with much ado got clear of the shallows, bear the brunt of the fight to seaward; but in vain. The day goes against them more and more, as it runs on. Seymour and Winter have battered the great *San Philip* into a wreck; her masts are gone by the board: Pimintelli in the *San Matthew* comes up to take the mastiffs off the fainting bull, and finds them fasten on him instead; but the Evangelist, though smaller, is stouter than the Deacon, and of all the shot poured into him, not twenty 'lackt him through.' His masts are tottering; but sink or strike he will not.

'Go ahead, and pound his tough hide, Leigh,' roars Drake off the poop of his ship, while he hammers away at one of the great galliasses. 'What right has he to keep us all waiting?'

Amyas slips in as best he can between Drake and Winter; as he passes he shouts to his ancient enemy —

'We are with you, sir; all friends today!' and slipping round Winter's bows, he pours his broadside into those of the *San Matthew*, and then glides on to reload; but not to return. For, not a pistol shot to leeward, worried by three or four small craft, lies an immense galleon; and on her poop — can he believe his eyes for joy? — the maiden and the wheel he has sought so long!

'There he is!' shouts Amyas, springing to the starboard side of the ship. The men, too, have already caught sight of that hated sign; a cheer of fury bursts from every throat.

'Steady, men!' says Amyas in a suppressed voice. 'Not a shot! Reload, and be ready; I must speak with him first'; and silent as the grave, amid the infernal din, the *Vengeance* glides up to the Spaniard's quarter.

'Don Guzman Maria Magdalena Sotomayor de Soto!' shouts Amyas from the mizzen rigging, loud and clear amid the roar.

He has not called in vain. Fearless and graceful as ever, the tall mail-clad figure of his foe leaps up upon the poop-railing, twenty feet above Amyas's head, and shouts through his vizor —

'At your service, sir! whosoever you may be.'

A dozen muskets and arrows are levelled at him; but Amyas frowns down. 'No man strikes him but I. Spare him, if you kill every other soul on board. Don Guzman, I am Captain Sir Amyas Leigh; I proclaim you a traitor and a ravisher, and challenge you once more to single combat, when and where you will.'

'You are welcome to come on board to me, sir,' answer

'I proclaim you a traitor and a ravisher, and challenge you to combat.'

the Spaniard in a clear, quiet tone, 'bringing with you this answer, that you lie in your throat,' and lingering a moment, out of bravado, to arrange his scarf, he steps down slowly again behind the bulwarks.

'Coward!' shouts Amyas at the top of his voice.

The Spaniard reappears instantly. 'Why that name, Senor, of all others?' asks he in a cool, stern voice.

'Because we call men cowards in England, who leave their wives to be burnt alive by priests.'

The moment the words had passed Amyas's lips, he felt that they were cruel and unjust. But it was too late to recall them. The Spaniard started, clutched his sword-hilt, and then hissed back through his closed vizor —

'For that word, sirrah, you hang at my yard-arm, if Saint Mary gives me grace.'

'See that your halter be a silken one, then,' laughed Amyas, 'for I am just dubbed knight.' And he stepped down as a storm of bullets rang through the rigging round his head; the Spaniards are not as punctilious as he.

'Fire!' His ordnance crash through the stern-works of the Spaniard; and then he sails onward, while her balls go humming harmlessly through his rigging.

Half an hour has passed of wild noise and fury; three times has the *Vengeance*, as a dolphin might, sailed clean round and round the *Sta. Catharina*, pouring in broadside after broadside, till the guns are leaping to the deck-beams with their own heat, and the Spaniard's sides are slit and spotted in a hundred places. And yet, so high has been his fire in return, and so strong the deck defences of the *Vengeance*, that a few spars broken, and two or three men wounded by musketry, are all her loss. But still the Spaniard endures, magnificent as ever; it is the battle of the thresher and the whale; the end is certain, but the work is long.

A puff of wind clears away the sulphurous veil for a moment; the sea is clear of ships towards the land; the Spanish fleet are moving again up Channel, Medina bringing up the rear; only some two miles to their right hand, the vast hull the *San Philip* is drifting up the shore with the tide, and of somewhat nearer the *San Matthew* is hard at work with her pumps. They can see the white stream of water pouring down her side.

In the meanwhile, long ere the sun had set, comes down the darkness of the thunderstorm, attracted, as to a volcano's mouth, to that cast mass of sulphur-smoke which cloaks the sea for many a mile; and heaven's artillery above makes answer to man's below. But still, through the smoke and rain, Amyas clings to his prey. She too, has seen the northward movement of the Spanish fleet, and sets her topsails; Amyas calls to the men to fire high, and galleys, having forced their way at last over the shallows, coming flashing and sputtering up to the combatants, and take his fire off the galleon. Amyas grits his teeth, and would fain hustle into the thick of the press once more, in spite of the galley's beaks.

'Most heroical captain,' says Cary, pulling a long face, 'if we do, we are stove and sunk in five minutes; not to mention that Yeo says he hasn't twenty rounds of great cartridge left.'

So, surely and silent, the *Vengeance* sheers off, but keeps as near as she can to the little squadron, all through the night of rain and thunder which follows. Next morning the sun rises on a clear sky, with a strong west-north-west breeze, and all hearts are asking what the day will bring forth.

They are long past Dunkirk now; the German Ocean is opening before them. The Spaniards, sorely battered, and lessened in numbers, having during the night regained some sort of order. The English hang on their skirts a mile or two behind. They have no ammunition, and must wait for more. To Amyas's great disgust, the *Sta. Catharina* has rejoined her fellow during the night.

'Never mind,' says Cary; 'she can neither dive nor fly, and as long as she is above water, we — What is the Admiral about?'

He is signalling Lord Henry Seymour and his squadron. Soon they tack, and come down the wind for the coast of Flanders. Parma must be blockaded still; and the Hollanders are likely to be too busy with their plunder to do it effectually. Suddenly there is a stir in the Spanish fleet. Medina and the rearmost ships turn upon the English. What can it mean? Will they offer battle once more? If so, it were best to get out of their way for we have nothing wherewith to fight them. So the English lie close to the wind. They will let them pass, and return to their old tactic of following and harassing.

'Goodbye to Seymour,' says Cary, 'if he is caught between them and Parma's flotillas. They are going to Dunkirk.'

'Impossible! They will not have water enough to reach his light craft. Here comes a big ship right upon us! Give him all you have left lads; and if he will fight us, lay him alongside, and die boarding.'

They gave him what they had, and hulled him with every shot, but his huge side stood silent as the grave. He had not wherewithal to return the compliment.

'As I live, he is cutting loose the foot of his mainsail! the villain means to run.'

'There go the rest of them! Victoria!' shouted Cary, as one after another, every Spaniard set all the sail he could.

There was silence for a few minutes throughout the English fleet; and then cheer upon cheer of triumph rent the skies. It was over. The Spaniard had refused battle, and thinking only of safety, was pressing downward toward the Straits again. The Invincible Armada had cast away its name, and England was saved.

'But he will never get there, sir,' said old Yeo, who had come upon deck to murmur his *Nunc Domine,* and gaze upon that sight beyond all human faith and hope: 'Never, never will he weather the Flanders shore, against such a breeze as is coming up. Look to the eye of the wind sir, and see how the Lord is fighting for His people!'

Yes, down it came, fresher and stiffer every minute out of the grey northwest, as it does so often after a thunderstorm; and the sea began to rise high and white, till the Spaniards were fain to take in all spare canvas, and lie-to as best they could; while the English fleet, lying-to also, awaited an event which was in God's hands and not in theirs.

'They will all be ashore on Zealand before the afternoon,' murmured Amyas; 'and I have lost my labour! Oh, for powder, powder, powder! to go in and finish it at once!'

'Oh, sir,' said Yeo, 'don't murmur against the Lord in the very day of his mercies. It is hard; but His will be done.'

'Could we not borrow powder from Drake there?'

'Look at the sea, sir!'

And indeed, the sea was far too rough for any such attempt. The Spaniards neared and neared the fatal dunes, which fringed the shore for many a dreary mile; and Amyas had to wait weary hours, growling like a dog who has had the bone snatched out of his mouth, till the day wore on; when, behold, the wind began to fall as rapidly as it had risen. A savage joy rose in Amyas's breast.

'They are safe! safe for us! Who will go and beg us powder? A cartridge here and a cartridge there? — anything to set to work again!'

Cary volunteered, and returned in a couple of hours with some quantity: but he was on board again only just in time, for the southwester had recovered the mastery of the skies, and the Spaniards and the English were moving away; but this time northward. Whither now? To Scotland? Amyas knew not, and cared not, provided he was in the company of Don Guzman de Soto.

36

The Armada was defeated, and England saved.

Yes, it is over; and the great Armada is vanquished. As the medals struck on the occasion said, 'It came, it saw, and it fled!' And whither? Away and northward, like a herd of frightened deer, past the Orkneys and Shetlands, catching up a few hapless fishermen as guides; past the coast of Norway, there, too, refused water and food by the brave descendants of the Vikings; and on northward ever towards the lonely Faroes, and the everlasting dawn which heralds round the Pole the midnight sun.

Their water is failing; the cattle must go overboard and the wild northern sea echoes to the shrieks of drowning horses. They must homeward at least, somehow, each as best he can. Let them meet again at Cape Finisterre, if indeed they ever meet. Medina Sidiona, with some five and twenty of the soundest and best victualled ships, will lead the way, and leave the rest to their fate. He is soon out of sight; and forty more, the only remnant of the mighty host, come wandering wearily behind, hoping to make the southwest coast of Ireland, and have help, or at least, fresh water there, from their fellow-Romanists. Alas, for them! for now comes up from the Atlantic, gale on gale; and few of that hapless remnant reached the shores of Spain.

And where are Amyas and the *Vengeance* all this while?

At the fifty-seventh degree of latitude, the English fleet, finding themselves growing short of provision, and having been long since out of powder and ball, turned southward toward home. A few pinnaces are still sent onward to watch their course: and the English fleet, caught in the same storms which scattered the Spaniards, 'with great danger and industry reached Harwich port, and there provided themselves of victuals and ammunition,' in case the Spaniards should return; but there is no need for caution. The Armada is away on the other side of Scotland, and Amyas is following in its wake.

For when the Lord High Admiral determined to return, Amyas asked leave to follow the Spaniard; and asked too, of Sir John Hawkins, who happened to be at hand, such ammunition and provision as could be afforded to him, promising to repay the same like an honest man, out of his plunder if he lived, out of his estate if he died; after which, Amyas, calling his men together, reminded them once more of the story of the Rose of Torridge and Don Guzman de Soto, and then asked —

'Men of Bideford, will you follow me? There will be plunder for those who love plunder; revenge for those who love revenge; and for all of us (for we all love honour) the honour of having never left the chase as long as there was a Spanish flag in England's seas.'

And every soul on board replied that they would follow Sir Amyas Leigh around the world.

It was now the sixteenth day of the chase. They had seen, the evening before, St David's Head, and then the Welsh coast round Milford Haven, looming out black and sharp before the blaze of the inland thunderstorm.

In vain, they had strained their eyes through the darkness, to catch, by the fitful glare of the flashes the tall masts of the Spaniard. Of one thing at least they were certain, that with the wind as it was, she could not have gone far to the westward; and to attempt to pass them again and go northward was more than she dare do.

Amyas paced the sloppy deck fretfully and fiercely. He knew that the Spaniard could not escape; but he cursed every moment that lingered between him and that one great revenge which blackened all his soul. The men sat sulkily about the deck and whistled for a wind; the sails flapped idly against the masts; and the ship rolled in the long troughs of the sea, till her yard-arm almost dipped left and right.

So the morning wore away, without a sign of living thing,

not even the passing gull; and the black melancholy of the heaven reflected itself in the black melancholy of Amyas. Was he to lose his prey after all? The thought made him shudder with rage and disappointment. It was intolerable. Anything but that.

'No, God!' he cried, 'let me but once feel this in his accursed heart, and then — strike me dead, if Thou wilt!'

'The Lord have mercy on us,' cried John Brimblecombe. 'What have you said?'

'What is that to you, sir? They are piping to dinner. Go down. I shall not come.'

And Jack went down, and talked in a half-terrified whisper of Amyas's ominous words. All thought that they portended some bad luck, except old Yeo.

'Here she is!' thundered Amyas from the deck; and in an instant all were scrambling up the hatchway as fast as the frantic rolling of the ship would let them.

Yes, there she was. The cloud had lifted suddenly and to the south a ragged bore of blue sky let a long stream of sunshine down on her tall masts and stately hull, as she lay rolling some four or five miles to the eastward; but as for land, none was to be seen.

The weary day wore on. The strip of blue sky was curtained over again, and all was dismal as before, though it grew sultrier every moment; and now and then a distant mutter shook the air to westward. Nothing could be done to lessen the distance between the ships, for the *Vengeance* had had all her boats carried away but one, and that was much too small to tow her; and while the men went down again to finish dinner, Amyas sharpened his sword, looking up every now and then suddenly at the Spaniard, as if to satisfy himself that it was not a vision which had vanished.

About two, Yeo came up to him.

'He is ours safely now, sir. The tide has been running to

the eastward for this two hours, and there comes the breeze.'

'And there the storm, too.'

And with that strangely accelerating pace which some storms seem to possess, the thunder, which had been growling slow and seldom far away, now rang peal on peal along the cloudy floor above their heads.

'Here comes the breeze. Round with the yards, or we shall be taken aback.'

The yards creaked round; the sea grew crisp around them; the hot air swept their cheeks, tightened every rope, filled every sail, bent her over. A cheer burst from the men as the helm went up, and they staggered away before the wind, right down upon the Spaniard, who lay still becalmed.

'There is more behind, Amyas,' said Cary. 'Shall we not shorten sail a little?'

'No. Hold on every stitch,' said Amyas. 'Give me the helm, man. Boatswain, pipe away to clear for fight.'

It was done, and in ten minutes the men were all at quarters, while the thunder rolled louder and louder overhead, and the breeze freshened fast.

'The dog has it now. There he goes!' said Cary.

'Right before the wind. He has no liking to face us.'

'He is running into the jaws of destruction,' said Yeo. 'An hour more will send him either right up the Channel, or smack on shore somewhere.'

After two hours more, the four miles had diminished to one, while the lightning flashed nearer and nearer as the storm came up; and from the vast mouth of a black cloud-arch poured so fierce a breeze that Amyas yielded unwillingly to hints, which were growing into open murmurs, and bade shorten sail.

On they rushed with scarcely lessened speed, the black arch following fast, curtained by one flat grey sheet of pouring rain, before which the water was boiling in a long white line; while every moment behind the watery veil, a keen blue spark leapt down into the sea, or darted zigzag through the rain.

'We shall have it now, and with a vengeance; this will try your tackle, master,' said Cary.

The functionary answered with a shrug, and turned up the collar of his rough frock, as the first drops flew stinging round his ears. Another minute and the squall burst full upon them, in rain, which cut like hail — hail which lashed the sea into froth, and wind which whirled off the heads of the surges, and swept the waters into one white seething waste. And above them, and behind them, and before them, the lightning leapt and ran, dazzling and blinding, while the deep roar of the thunder was changed to sharp ear-piercing cracks.

On they swept, gaining fast on the Spaniard.

'Call the men up, and to quarters; the rain will be over in ten minutes.'

Yeo ran forward to the gangway; and sprang back again, with a face white and wild —

'Land right ahead! Port your helm sir! for the love of God, port your helm!'

Amyas, with the strength of a bull, jammed the helm down, while Yeo shouted to the men below.

She swung round. The masts bent like whips, crack went the foresail like a cannon. What matter? Within two hundred yards of them was the Spaniard; in front of her and above her, a huge dark bank rose through the dense hail, and mingled with the clouds; and at its foot, plainer every moment, pillars and spouts of leaping foam.

'What is it, Mort? Hartland?'

'It might be anything for thirty miles.'

'Lundy!' said Yeo. 'The south end! I see the head of the Shutter in the breakers! Hard a-port yet, and get her close-hauled as you can, and the Lord may have mercy on us still! Look at the Spaniard!'

Yes, look at the Spaniard!

He, too, had seen his danger, and tried to broach-to. But his clumsy mass refused to obey the helm; he struggled a moment, half hid in foam; fell away again, and rushed upon his doom.

'Lost! Lost! Lost!' cried Amyas madly, and throwing up his hands, let go the tiller. Yeo caught it just in time.

'Sir, what are you at? We shall clear the rock yet.'

'Yes!' shouted Amyas in his frenzy; 'but he will not!'

Another minute. The galleon gave a sudden jar, and stopped. Then one long heave and bound, as if to free herself and then her bows lighted clean upon the Shutter.

An awful silence fell on every English soul. They heard not the roaring of wind and surge. They saw not the blinding flashes of the lightning; but they heard one long ear-piercing wail to every saint in Heaven rise from five hundred human throats; they saw the mighty ship heel over from the wind, and sweep headlong down the cataract of the race. Plunging her yards into the foam and showing her whole black side even to her keel, till she rolled clean over and vanished forever and ever.

'Shame!' cried Amyas, hurling his sword far into the sea, 'to lose my right, my right! when it was in my very grasp! Unmerciful!'

A crack which rent the sky, and made the granite ring and quiver; a bright world of flame and then a blank of utter darkness, against which stood out, glowing red-hot, every mast and sail, and rock, and Salvation Yeo as he stood just in front of Amyas, the tiller in his hand. All red-hot, transfigured into fire; and behind, the black, black night.

Strange Tales of the Coast

by

GEORGE GOLDSMITH-CARTER

'The Greate Storme'

The shores of Britain have always been noted for wild weather — indeed, Spanish sailors of long ago christened the Thames' approaches 'The Black Deeps', because they so feared the fierce winds and furious currents. Nevertheless, in all our long history of tempest and shipwreck, there has never been such a fearful night as that of 23rd November, 1703.

There had been a full gale blowing from the south-west for nearly ten days previously but, on the night in question, the wind suddenly changed to the north-north-west, where it swiftly increased in fury from a mere gale to a hurricane — and then to a living, bellowing wall of fury which sent men, women and children cowering to their cellars.

Nothing could withstand the insane force of that killer-wind. Thousands of houses and buildings were reduced to piles of rubble; tiles hurtled through the air with such velocity that they were afterwards found buried *eight inches deep in the earth;* tens of thousands of great trees were torn out by the roots; and hundreds of people were killed by flying debris. The Bishop of Bath and his wife were killed instantly in the Bishop's Palace at Wells, Somerset, when a great chimney crashed through the roof; *fifteen thousand* sheep were hurled into the River Severn and drowned as a result of the wind-force; and, so great was the general carnage, Queen Anne called the entire nation to prayer and fasting in order to appease the Wrath of God.

Yet, terrible as things were on land, they were infinitely worse at sea. A few days previous to the hurricane, the famous engineer Henry Winstanley had finished his new Eddystone Lighthouse, and had decided to spend a few days in it to test its strength. Before he went, Winstanley was heard to say that he hoped to be in his lighthouse 'In the greatest storme under the Face of Heaven', such was his confidence in his work. His presumptuous wish was granted in the most terrible manner for, the day after 'The Greate Storme', watchers from Plymouth were horrified to see the dangerous Eddystone rocks swept clean by the great, smoking seas; the lighthouse — together with Winstanley, his workmen and the lighthouse-keepers — had been smashed into oblivion. In the meantime, *whole fleets* of merchant ships and warships had been hurled to destruction, the bodies of *8,000 drowned seamen* being ultimately cast up along our beaches.

The worst scene of the entire catastrophe, however, was on the Goodwin Sands. A few days before the killer-wind had struck, Admiral Basil Beaumont's fleet of thirteen men o' war had just returned from the Mediterranean, and were at anchor between the mainland and the Goodwin Sands. The sudden fury of that awful wind ripped the fleet from its moorings and blew the ships either ashore on the mainland, or on to the deadly Goodwins. Three 70-gun ships — the *Mary*, *Stirling Castle* and *Restoration* — were driven on to the Goodwins and totally wrecked, with the loss of nearly 2,000 officers and men, including Admiral Beaumont.

Daylight dawned on 24th November, to reveal a fearful scene of death and disaster. Boatmen watching from Deal

44

beach saw survivors from the three wrecks, racing madly up and down the sands, waving frantically for help before the returning tide swept them to death. The local men's boats were not seaworthy enough to face the enormous seas which were still running, so Simon Pritchard, leader of the boatmen, went to the Preventive Inspector with a request to be allowed to use the large and seaworthy Customs boats to snatch the pitiful survivors from the cruel sands before it became too late. The inhuman Customs official refused the request, however, saying that 'Her Majesty's boats are not for rescuing pressed scum, who would be better dead, anyway!'

Thomas Powell — the tough little Mayor of Deal — had other ideas about this matter, however. Taking the local boatmen in a body to the sheds where the big Customs boats were kept, he ordered them to break down the doors and launch off immediately, telling the protesting Customs officer, at the same time, that he, the Mayor, would assume full responsibility for the use of the boats.

Thanks to the determination of Thomas Powell, and the courage and magnificent seamanship of Simon Pritchard and his men, the shipwrecked sailors were snatched from the Goodwins just as the tide was about to carry them away.

So greatly did the townsfolk of Deal admire both Thomas Powell and Simon Pritchard, that their names have never been forgotten in the vicinity.

The Ghost Ship

A few years ago, lightshipmen aboard lightships stationed round the Goodwin Sands reported that strangely human cries were coming from the dreaded Goodwins. The source of these eerie sounds was never discovered; the incident was but one of many similar weird occurrences which, during the course of the centuries, have given this 10 by 4-mile graveyard of ships and men the reputation of being a haunted area.

The Goodwins — which, in just over 500 years, are estimated to have swallowed some 50,000 human lives — abound in ghost stories; but undoubtedly the most uncanny of all is the story of the ghostly schooner *Lady Lovibond*, which was seen every fifty years, over a period of two centuries — in each instance on 13th February.

On this day, in the year 1748, the three-masted schooner *Lady Lovibond*, carrying general cargo for Oporto, and commanded by Captain Simon Read, sailed down the Thames and around the North Foreland. Captain Read was a very proud and happy man, for he had just married a young and lovely girl; his bride, together with her mother and a small party of friends, were aboard the schooner. As the fine vessel sped through the water, the captain's cabin was the scene of happiness and revelry as people toasted the happy couple. On deck, however, the scene was a different one, for the first mate, John Rivers, was pacing the planks like an angry tiger. The reason was a simple one — namely, that he had been a rival for the hand of the captain's lovely wife, and he boiled with jealous anger to hear the happy laughter coming from the cabin below. True, he had been best man at the wedding, but this in no way eased the bitterness of his thoughts.

Glancing away to eastward, where the great breakers of the Goodwins rolled in smoky thunder, John Rivers suddenly conceived a devilish plan. Casually drawing a heavy, club-like belaying pin from the rail, the mate walked softly up behind the man at the steering wheel and felled him to the deck with one crushing blow. As the helmsman rolled into the scuppers, Rivers seized the steering wheel and, with a mad laugh, drove the speeding schooner hard on to the wicked sands, which are as hard as rock at low tide.

The captain was too occupied with his bride and wedding guests to notice the sudden change of course and, with a terrible grinding crash, and the awful tumult of rending timbers and toppling masts, the once proud schooner broke her back. Listening to the terrified screams of the trapped people in the flooded cabin below, John Rivers threw back his head and laughed with crazy triumph. He knew that he would die, too, but what matter — his vengeance was complete!

It was late evening when this awful tragedy occurred and, at daybreak the next day, there was nothing to be seen of the *Lady Lovibond*, her passengers or her crew, for the Goodwins had engulfed them.

Later, at an official enquiry into the incident, John Rivers's sorrowing mother, giving evidence, admitted that she had heard her son say that he would get even with Simon Read, even if it cost him his life.

The tragedy was nearly forgotten, but, in the year 1798, on 13th February, Captain James Westlake, of the trading brig *Edenbridge*, had a strange and terrifying experience. While skirting the Goodwins at the exact spot where Rivers had driven the *Lady Lovibond* to her doom, he saw a three-masted schooner with all sails set driving down on his vessel at fantastic speed. Cursing the captain of the hurtling schooner as a madman, Westlake ran to the wheel of his brig, and he and the helmsman put the helm hard over just in time to avert collision. As the schooner sheered past, Westlake and his helmsman both heard the sound of revelry and laughter coming from the schooner's cabin. By this time the entire crew of the *Eden-bridge* had rushed on deck and, to their horror, they saw the schooner strike the nearby Goodwins *and instantly vanish from sight*. This was no mere hallucination for, at a subsequent enquiry into the matter the crew of a fishing smack which had been nearby supported Captain Westlake's evidence, saying that they, too, had seen the schooner strike. They had lowered a boat as fast as they could to rescue survivors, but had had the unnerving experience of finding nothing but empty sand and sea.

Again the fearful incident was almost forgotten, until the day of 13th February, 1848, when Deal boatmen saw a schooner run aground on the identical spot where the *Lady Lovibond* had been lost. Launching their speedy sailing galleys to the rescue, the hardy boatmen were utterly confounded when they found — nothing! Again the frightening occurrence had been no mere hallucination, for the crew of a big American clippership, which had been passing near the spot, swore that they, too, had seen the schooner strike the sands and then vanish into thin air.

The last time the tragic phantom schooner was seen was on 13th February, 1898, when Deal boatmen again saw a three-masted vessel strike the fatal sands at the same ill-omened spot. Launching off at a speed for which they are still famous, the Deal boatmen again found nothing but the hard sand and empty sea.

The phantom of the *Lady Lovibond* has not been seen since that day, and the mystery of the ghostly schooner has remained unsolved. The Goodwins keep their secrets well.

Dogger Bank

On 5th March, 1883, a huge fleet of sailing trawlers, ranging from 40 to 80 tons burthen, and hailing from Hull, Grimsby, Yarmouth, Lowestoft and Colchester, lay becalmed off the northern extremity of the Dogger Bank. It was a place rich in fish, but very dangerous, for here, during northerly gales, huge seas burst in fury on the steep sides of the bank, creating a dangerous maelstrom which North Sea fishermen grimly named 'The Cemetery'.

Day had dawned with a leaden sky and, although there was no wind, an ugly surf was thundering across 'The Cemetery'. At 11 o'clock that night, the wind rose sufficiently to fill the sails of the becalmed smacks, giving them just enough speed to pull their cumbersome trawl nets along the bottom. Just before midnight, the light breeze increased with terrifying speed to a howling blizzard, which chopped the crests of the waves into flying spindrift and blotted everything from sight in a blinding mantle of whirling snow.

From mere gale force the north-east wind increased to hurricane force and, with stunning violence, it struck the huddle of unprepared fishing smacks, snapping their heavy trawl ropes like cotton threads and driving many of them into the frightful fury of 'The Cemetery'. The crews of those frail and tiny sailing craft had no chance whatever; men were swept headlong from the decks by giant masses of water topped with ghostly white surf, their cries unheard amid the roaring of wind and sea. Brother was torn from the side of brother, sons from the sides of their fathers and, incredible as it may seem, some lucky men were swept from the decks of sinking smacks on to the decks of craft which miraculously survived the dreadful carnage.

Other incredible things happened, too. One Grimsby smack, in spite of being ballasted by heavy stones, was rolled completely over by the giant seas, coming upright again with the stones, her catch and the wrecked ironwork of her keep all unbelievably mixed up — and not a single member of her crew harmed. Churned and tossed remorselessly in the cauldron of 'The Cemetery', smack after smack crammed on all the sail they could carry and vainly sought to sail clear of the smashing waves. All in vain, for many were smashed to matchwood by the fury of the waves, some being literally burst asunder by the weight of water which fell on them. Others were just sailed right under the water by their panic-stricken crews. The luckier ones wallowed off into the night, some dismasted, some with bare masts, and some with tiny storm sails set. In the terror of that raging night, one could not see, much less help, his neighbour. It was a case of every man and every ship for themselves.

Grey daylight brought no relief to the scene for, in those days, there was no radio to bring swift aid. As far as the eye could see, there was nothing in all the raging seas but wallowing, mastless hulks to which men grimly clung, the bottoms of upturned vessels, shattered spars and floating bodies. Some of the vessels just vanished without trace, but the fate of others has been recorded.

The 72-ton smack, *North Sea*, of the famous Red Cross Fleet, while sailing on the port tack, was seen to be hit by a huge sea which ripped out her masts and decking, leaving her to fill and sink within eight minutes. Only three of her crew were picked up.

The 72-ton smack *John Harker* of Grimsby, was seen with her sails ripped away, bulwarks and boat gone and her crew clinging to the sinking wreck shouting for help. Before help could be given, a driving snow-squall blotted the smack from sight and when it was gone, the *John Harker* had vanished.

50

The smack *Thomas and Florry*, her hatches stove-in, mizzen-mast and bulwarks ripped away, and 16 feet of her starboard side torn out, was abandoned by her crew. They were picked up from their sinking small boat in the nick of time by another smack, aptly named *Blessing*, then transferred to the smack *Energy*, of Grimsby, which eventually landed them at Hull on 8th March. Such were but a very few of the incidents which were observed. A great many of the trawlers were just driven away into the howling darkness never to reappear.

Day after day, damaged and undamaged trawlers sailed into the east-coast fishing ports, some crammed with survivors, some towing dismasted vessels. As the terrible extent of the disaster gradually became known, the fishing ports of the east coast were besieged by frantic women seeking amid the battered smacks for news of husbands, sons, brothers and sweethearts who had been out at sea.

After several weeks had passed, the appalling casualties of this one dreadful night became known. Forty-five trawlers had been lost in 'The Cemetery', some having been seen to sink, others just vanishing forever. Seven smacks had been abandoned by their crews, 38 had been badly damaged and 51 slightly damaged.

The total loss of life was truly shocking, for 255 men and boys had been drowned. Such was the effect of the disaster on many of the survivors, that they became shattered wrecks of their former robust selves, never daring to face the sea again.

A maritime disaster of such magnitude inevitably led to an official enquiry, which revealed that the majority of the smacks that had survived the fury of the Dogger Bank had been able to use their big trawl-nets as sea-anchors on which to ride out the fury of the sea and wind. Others had ridden out the hurricane-force wind on enormous lengths of stout rope attached to stockless anchors, which the crews had been naged to drop clear of the fury of 'The Cemetery'. The majority of the lost vessels had crammed on all sail in a desperate and losing race to gain sea-room before they were overwhelmed. Their crews had made the fatal blunder of imagining that they could outsail the very elements and, in making the attempt, had driven their smacks clean under.

At the same time of the disaster, the famous 'Short Blue'* fleet of smacks, sailing under the direction of senior skipper Skinley, was working on the southern edge of the Dogger Bank, and these smacks rode out the gale with very little damage. This was, indeed, a remarkable fact that emphasised the truly terrible reputation of 'The Cemetery'.

*So called from the short blue pennant these trawlers flew from the masts. Each fleet in the days of the sailing trawlers flew their own company flag.

The Wreck of the Indian Chief

Aided by a strong wind from the north-west, the 1,238-ton, full-rigged ship *Indian Chief*, bound from Middlesbrough to Yokohama with a general cargo, roared down the North Sea, the foam boiling under the graceful forefoot. At 2.30 a.m. on 5th January, 1881, the look-out sighted the swinging rays of the Kentish Knock light-vessel. Not long after this, the north-west wind flew to the eastward, bringing icy, snow-laden rain squalls — death in dreadful form to seventeen of the crew of the *Indian Chief*, and an awful suffering to those who survived.

With the sudden and deadly change of wind, the deeply-laden ship began to drift down on to the Longsand, which lay hard-a-lee. The early morning was as black as the pit, and the eerily-piping wind as bitter as death. Although the helm of the ship was instantly altered, the mainbraces of the mainsail suddenly fouled and, in turn, caused the spanker-boom to catch the steering wheel, which made the great sailing ship strike the Longsand broadside on.

Captain Fraser, the ship's master, ordered a large red distress flare to be burned and rockets to be fired. Cheered by the answering rockets, which mounted from the Kentish Knock and Sunk lightships, the crew went to the shelter of the deckhouse, confident that the lifeboat would rescue them within a few hours.

The savage, icy day turned to night, while the *Indian Chief*, her sails now in tatters and drumming like devil's coach whips, slowly beat her life out on the uncaring sands. In the deck-house, the still-confident crew waited without warmth or hot food, not knowing that the Aldeburgh and Harwich lifeboats had been launched, only to be beaten back into the raging surf by the ferocity of the ice-laden easterly wind. However, as dawn broke, one of the crew gave a hoarse cry of hope and staggered across the already-breaking deck planks. Half-blinded by spray which froze to ice pellets as it struck, the rest of the drenched crew went to the rail. They saw a small ship backing and filling just below the boiling, smashing surf that was hammering their great ship to kindling. Putting her helm over, the little vessel vanished into the welter. With despairing groans, the crew of the wrecked ship tottered back into the miserable shelter of the deckhouse. They thought that the little craft they had seen so briefly had been the lifeboat, and that they had callously been left to die. Actually, the vessel had been a small sailing coaster whose master, realising his inability to effect a rescue, did the next best thing and, clapping on all the sail he dared to carry, headed at speed to Ramsgate to call out the lifeboat there.

Slowly the bitter day passed and, as the tide rose, it gave brutal strength and weight to the awful seas which were hammering at the wreck. At midnight the wind and sea eased a trifle but, as the old sailors say in all truth: 'An easterly wind has more lives than a cat.'

Red and cruel, the bitter sun rose in a sky unnaturally clear, bringing with it a vicious and snowladen gale, and seas more wicked than ever.

Suddenly, amid the awful sounds of rending timber and groaning masts, there was a shattering report, followed by a series of horrifying rumbles from the heart of the dying ship.

Captain Fraser looked at the faces of his crew, haggard in the greenish glow of that terrible dawn. 'She's broken her back, lads, and the pressure is blowing her decks out. We'd better try to launch the boats.'

Three boats were lowered; the first, with two men in it, was instantly engulfed by the roaring sea; the other two filled and sank immediately. The remainder of the crew fled back to the disintegrating deckhouse, while cruel green water, rolling unchecked from stem to stern, battered savagely at their frail shelter.

A five o'clock that afternoon there rose a giant sea, whose terrible might dwarfed all that had gone before. Roaring into smoking surf, it thundered like a watery avalanche across the vanishing ship, sweeping away the deckhouse and leaving nothing but a few uprights to which the half-drowned, frozen men clung with a death-grip. The once-proud *Indian Chief* was a dead ship now, the mainmast a tottering ruin, the gaping holds filled with lapping water, and great, black watery gulfs where the decks had blown out. 'Take to the mizzen-mast,' Captain Fraser told his men. 'When the mainmast falls, it will take the foremast with it!' Some men did not hear his orders in the roar of the wind and sea. They scrambled into the foremast rigging, and thereby saved themselves from a ghastly death. Seventeen men, already doomed but unaware of it, took to the mizzen top-mast while Captain Fraser and his young brother Howard, the second mate, lashed themselves securely to the lower part of the mizzen-mast.

Night came again, bringing no relief from the deadly wind which gnawed the frozen faces of the survivors like a savage dog and, at three o'clock in the morning, the ferocious sea struck its most awful blow. A seething mountain of water ripped away the mizzen topmast, to which seventeen men had pinned their only hope of survival, tossing it like a twig overboard, to dangle by its rigging in the smashing surf.

Too weak to free themselves, seventeen men kicked away their lives, drowning slowly in the great surges beneath the horrified eyes of their shipmates, who were lashed helplessly to the foremast. Below the jagged break of the mizzen-mast, Howard Fraser spoke comforting words to his elder brother, who stared mutely ahead through a mask of brine and ice.

Suddenly a survivor croaked in a wild voice: '*A light — a light!*' Exposed to the vicious elements, men sometimes suffer from delusions — but this time it was no fantasy. The light was that of the paddle tug *Vulcan*, of Ramsgate, with the Ramsgate lifeboat *Bradford* in tow.

The sight of the sturdy *Vulcan* and the stalwart, life-jacketed figures in the wallowing, plunging *Bradford*, rising triumphantly from each watery valley of death, brought strength to the frozen limbs of the survivors. Somehow they cut themselves free from their lashing and, knotting a number of ropes together, they lashed the end to a piece of shattered timber, letting it drift down to the lifeboat. Soon, they were hauling back a massive hawser which meant all the difference between life and death.

Magnificent old Charles Fish, the giant coxswain of the

Bradford, pointed to a figure lashed to the splintered butt of the mizzen-mast — a figure which appeared to be making frantic but unavailing efforts to free itself. 'Help that man!' he thundered, in a voice which beat down even the raging of the wind and sea. 'No good...' came back the terrible cry. 'It's Captain Fraser... been dead for hours... we'll try to get his brother...!' *The awful shuddering and jarring of the wreck had imparted a macabre motion to Fraser's frozen corpse — movements so life-like that they had deceived even the hawk-eyes of Coxswain Fish.*

Somehow, the survivors managed to cut Howard Fraser from his last refuge against the sea. He was still alive but quite mad, crying like a child and struggling feebly as they took him from his dead brother's side. Gently the dedicated lifeboatmen laid him in the lifeboat's bottom, chafing his frozen limbs and trying to give him sips of rum. All in vain, for he died in half an hour. One by one, the survivors of the *Indian Chief* dropped into the tossing lifeboat, averting their eyes from the awful figure of their dead captain, his head crushed by a falling yard, his ice-rimed body lashed to the splintered mast, watching sightlessly for the help which came too late for him.

Even when the last survivor had been taken off, together with the captain's body, the danger was still fearful. The *Bradford* buried by the great seas which tumbled in smoking ruin across the Longsand, seemed in imminent danger of sinking. One survivor said afterwards that he was even more terrified in the lifeboat than he had been aboard the wreck, for it seemed quite impossible for the tiny, gallant craft to survive the terribly crippling weight of the monstrous seas.

Slowly, with her freight of half-drowned and frozen men, the *Bradford* was towed clear of the maelstrom by the labouring *Vulcan*, and back to Ramsgate. Watchers on the breakwater of Ramsgate Harbour marvelled when they saw the two rescue

56

vessels enter safe water. The paint had literally been washed from the lifeboat, and the *Vulcan* was a near-wreck, both sponsons and half her wheelhouse gone.

One by one, the survivors of the *Indian Chief* were helped ashore and supported by Captain Brain, the Harbour Master, and members of his staff, they stumbled along the breakwater to shelter, warmth and food. Shivering with bowed heads and flaccid limbs, they were helped from sight — the pitiful flotsam of Britain's most awful shipwreck.

Author's Note. In 1947, while aboard the Trinity House Vessel *Ready* which was servicing the Longsand Head Buoy, an ancient, worm-eaten and barnacle-covered topmast and yard was pulled up in the mooring chain of the buoy. Was it part of the fatal mast which, seventy-nine years ago, carried seventeen men to a fearful death in this terrible shipwreck?

Jackdaw Baits the Trap

by

JOHN E. EDWARDS

'Deck below! Squadron's making off, sir!'

Perched high in the rigging of the sloop of war *Jackdaw*, Midshipman Peter Busby, fourteen years old and on his first war patrol, balanced his brass-bound telescope against a handy stay and took another anxious look across the blue-white, sunlit Caribbean Ocean. Three British frigates, the fighting backbone of the West Indies Station and the most powerful squadron afloat in those waters, were spreading enormous wings of white canvas and skimming away like giant gulls towards the distant horizon. From the signal yard of the leading frigate a tiny cluster of brilliant colours burst suddenly against the cobalt background of the tropical blue sky.

'Flagship's signalling, sir' Peter frantically pictured to himself the diagrammed pages of the signal book over which he had pored for hours during the last few months. 'Good luck,' he read off loudly. 'You'll need it!'

'Acknowledge that signal!' The voice of Lieutenant Thatcher, captain of the *Jackdaw*, sharply addressed a seaman from the quarterdeck. There was a swift rush of hoists and a red swallowtail climbed to the *Jackdaw's* peak.

'Well, Mr Busby. What are you lying aloft like a dead cat on a yard for?' called Thatcher. 'Report to the deck in two seconds, or I'll take my sword and chase you three times round the world!'

Peter banged shut his telescope, scalded his hands in skidding down a stay and sprinted for the quarterdeck. Lieutenant Thatcher, tall, lean and darkly brooding, with hands clasped behind and head lowered in an habitual attitude of pessimism, awaited his arrival with impatience.

'So we're playing guessing games are we, Mr Busby?' said Thatcher, piercing eyes under thick, dark brows transfixing Peter as though he had committed some mortal sin. 'You wish me to hazard a guess as to what sail rig the squadron carried? Tempt me to a wager, perhaps, on what compass course the flagship's steering?'

'N-no, sir. 'Course not, sir.' Peter breathlessly hastened to complete his report. 'Squadron's settled to a nor'westerly course under full spread of sail.'

'Deserting us, you might say.' Thatcher sucked hollows in his cheeks and nodded gloomily. 'Abandoning us to the first powerful raider that slips from Cartagena harbour to blow us clear out of the water. You'd say that, now, wouldn't you, Mr Busby?'

'Abandoning us?' Peter gave a startled look towards the rapidly disappearing frigate group, now discernible only by the flash of sunlight on their white sails. To the southward, a purple smear on the horizon marked the Spanish fortress of Cartagena. In that moment, there seemed something ominous in the hiss of the trade wind about his ears and the shadows of the weather rigging swinging relentlessly back and forth over the deck. 'It — it would seem so, sir.'

The *Jackdaw* was a fifty ton sloop, an adapted merchantman; a good seaboat of small size and shallow draft, handy for dodging among the shoals and reefs of the Caribbean islands; a useful dogsbody to the West Indies Fleet, with four six-pounders and a crew of sixteen. But all the same a tiny force to be left on solitary guard against the guns and galleons concentrated in Cartagena harbour.

'And that would be your best estimate of our present situation?' Thatcher pressed him for an answer.

'I — I suppose it would, sir.'

'Aha!' said Thatcher abruptly. 'That's 'cos you're a fool, lad.' He gave his tricorne hat a thump to settle it more firmly on his head, hitched at his blue, knee-length coat and strode off across the quarterdeck.

Peter fell in beside him, vainly trying to match his steps, and settling finally for a trot that at least kept him abreast as Thatcher swung about at the port-side rail in a flurry of coat-tails and marched back across the quarterdeck.

'Now listen carefully, lad, and be swift with your answers. What's the reason for this squadron being at sea?'

Peter thought quickly. 'Attacks upon Spanish shipping — search and chase operations — destruction of Spanish raiders.'

'You do not have to remind me that England is at war with Spain,' said Thatcher testily. 'I myself have twice been sunk in frigates of the line, and endured months of imprisonment in stinking Spanish dungeons on the island of Cuba, before escaping with such useful information that my Lords of Admiralty were put to the painful embarrassment of recalling me to England and promoting me to my present command.' He checked at the starboard tail, twirled high on his toes and came down with a ringing crash of heels upon the deck. 'You'll tell me next it's May 3rd in the year 1710, and nigh on seven bells in the afternoon watch. Think again, Mr Busby!'

Peter jerked to a halt. Sturdily built for his age, with a stubborn jaw and a mop of copper-coloured hair tied behind with a black ribbon, he glared up at his captain with recklessly mutinous grey eyes. It was the same look he had given his own father when demanding to be allowed to join the British Navy. Peter's father, a prosperous Bristol merchant, had argued vainly against the hardships and dangers of the naval

60

service, then finally given way and procured him a berth as midshipman aboard the sloop of war *Jackdaw*, newly-commissioned at Portsmouth.

Peter's joy at realising his sea-going ambitions was somewhat dampened by his first meeting with Thatcher, a moody lieutenant of thirty-two, with neither family nor fortune, little hope of advancement, and an unfortunate reputation for being unlucky. Thatcher had been wearily amused by Peter's brand-new sea-chest, his much-prized telescope, and his most treasured keepsake, a captured Spanish flag given him by an Avonmouth captain, which he kept carefully stowed in waterproof wrappings. Nothing Thatcher said was ever hurtful or vicious; he was a good officer and the *Jackdaw* was a trim ship; but he had a discomfiting tongue that had more than once stirred Peter's temper.

'I am grateful for your efforts to teach me my duties,' said Peter angrily, 'but how can I be expected to know the contents of your secret sailing instructions?'

'Stop being so stiff, lad.' Thatcher stood over him, looking steadily down his long nose. But his voice was softer now, with a hint of approval in it. 'You're the nearest thing to an officer I possess aboard this lugger. Should I fall in the fighting, you must take command. Now tell me — what's the 'tween-deck buzz?'

Peter blinked. Like every vessel afloat, the *Jackdaw* was a hot-bed of sailors' gossip. But how on earth could the rumours of the lower deck be of any concern to her captain?

'There's — there's talk that we're hunting a renegade raider,' he began haltingly. 'Fast and heavily gunned — a ghost brig called *Sinbad*, impossible to capture.' He could feel his face crimsoning as he recounted these far-fetched scraps of seamen's yarns, but in response to Thatcher's grave nod he went on: 'Commanded by a bloodthirsty lunatic — bribed by Spanish gold to destroy English ships and ravage her colonies.'

'Quite right in every respect,' said Thatcher promptly. 'Let this be a lesson to you, lad. Forget your fancy notions about spies and ciphers and suchlike. My Lords Commissioners at Whitehall have been at great pains and much expense to discover what the *Jackdaw's* fo'c'sle could have told them for nothing.'

'You mean it's all true?' Peter's voice rose in astonishment.

'Every rum-soaked word of it. When war with Spain first broke out, most buccaneers and pirates in the Caribbean got letters of marque from one or other of the colonies' Governors, authorising them to loot Spanish shipping.' Thatcher's face hardened. 'Save for one — Jack Bendigo, master of the *Sinbad*, whose crimes were so foul and whose nature was so vicious that not even his fellow seawolves would run with him. After a year or two of lean pickings, with every man's hand against him, Bendigo quit these waters and took the *Sinbad* to Madagascar, where he terrorised the East India merchants — until a few months ago, when...'

'...when he returned to the Caribbean,' broke in Peter excitedly. 'But why did Bendigo come back?'

Thatcher shrugged. 'For gold, and the protection of Spanish bases from which to strike. Spain has bought herself a deadly weapon in Bendigo. He is mad for revenge against us. Already he has ravaged the colonies of the Windward Islands.'

'I still don't understand why —' Peter checked himself and looked southwards at the distant hump of Cartagena harbour towards which they were heading under light sail. 'Then Bendigo is lying at Cartagena,' he said in a rush of understanding. 'We've got him bottled up!'

'Not quite, Mr Busby.' Thatcher's voice was a silken purr. 'I am flattered by your confidence in my ability, but this lone sloop could hardly prevent Bendigo from breaking out of Cartagena whenever he had a mind to.'

'Then what are we doing here?' asked Peter. 'Why have the frigates gone off and left us alone?'

'To lay a trap for a ghost, of course.'

'Eh?' Peter stared at him with rounded eyes.

'They call *Sinbad* the ghost ship,' explained Thatcher, 'because she's so elusive — too speedy to be caught by heavy frigates, and too powerfully gunned to be fought by smaller vessels fast enough to catch her. Only thing left to do is to tempt Bendigo into a trap.'

'But the frigates will have been sighted from Cartagena's watchtowers,' said Peter.

'They will indeed, lad. Bendigo'll have seen them come, and watched them go away again.'

'Then he must know there's only the *Jackdaw* left to bar his way,' said Peter.

'Which will not strike Jack Bendigo as peculiar,' said Thatcher cynically, 'because he's profited all his rotten life from the Admiralty's patriotic notion that one British ship can do the work of a squadron.'

'But — but where's the trap?' asked Peter.

'That lies with the frigates, lad. Once their tops'ls have dipped below the horizon, they'll beat back to windward under cover of darkness and sweep inshore by first light. We've heard from friendly Indian tribes ashore that Bendigo's finished refitting and is now ready for sea. The Dons'll not pay him to sit in harbour. Besides which, Bendigo will leap at the chance of destroying a British sloop before the eyes of his Spanish paymasters.'

'Then Bendigo will bring out the *Sinbad*,' said Peter.

'On the flood tide at dawn tomorrow,' added Thatcher. 'And to make absolutely certain he does so...'

'We bait the trap with the *Jackdaw*?'

'But of course,' said Thatcher drily. 'What could be more dispensable than this tiny sloop and her miserable captain?'

'And when Bendigo comes to blow us out of the water,' said Peter, his spirits soaring at the prospect of action, 'the frigates will swoop down and batter him into submission.'

'While you and I are feeding the sharks in a welter of wreckage,' said Thatcher. 'Well done, Mr Busby. We'll make a Flag Officer of you yet — should you live so long!'

'It's a good plan,' said Peter, ignoring Thatcher's wry humour, 'but wouldn't it be even better if we stood in towards Cartagena and fired some challenging shots from our guns?'

Thatcher smiled and jerked his thumb forward. Peter glanced down the deck of the *Jackdaw* and saw to his surprise that the port-side forward six-pounder was already primed and about to be fired. The gun's-crew, burly, light-footed men, sunbronzed and pigtailed, were scampering about with rope-tackles to take up the recoil. The lighted linstock, a long iron plated pike staff with a forked prong at the end which held a rope match soused in saltpetre, already glowed in the mastergunner's hand.

'Quartermaster, I'll trouble you for a touch of starboard helm!' Thatcher turned and called to the poop. 'Lightly now, or I'll have you flogged round the sloop!'

The *Jackdaw* was steered by the wheel, as was now becoming the fashion, instead of the cumbersome tiller. Peter saw white teeth flash in a nut-brown face as the grinning quartermaster showed his appreciation of Thatcher's blood-curdling threat. The wheel-spokes blurred and steadied, and the *Jackdaw's* bowsprit swung gracefully over a serene ocean only lightly troubled by the easterly trades.

'Fire when you bear on the town!' Thatcher shook his fist at the gun's crew. 'A guinea apiece if you knock down the bell tower — a fortnight's hard tack if you miss!'

Peter heard the men chuckle as they crouched around the breech of their gun. He clasped his hands firmly behind and stiffened his legs to ramrod straightness, determined to show no reaction to the explosion. Practice guns fired during their Atlantic crossing from England had caused him to jump involuntarily. Thatcher had gaily offered to wager that the first broadside fired in anger would send 'Mr Leapfrog Busby' clear across Jamaica. He would give him no second chance to display his irritating wit.

But a more urgent thought made Peter swallow nervously as he stood on the deck. He would soon be in the thick of his first sea-fight. Thatcher would be strictly honest in the report he would make about him. A moment's hesitancy, a hint of cowardice, and there would be no second chance for Peter to redeem himself.

He looked at the vast loneliness of blue ocean that lay behind the tiny *Jackdaw*, then at the threatening ridge of the enemy coastline that they were approaching. He wondered if all men felt like this, putting on an outward show of courage when inside they felt weak and helpless.

The gun muzzle swung steadily in answer to the sloop's movement, traversing tiny dots of palms clusters and the low, humped shapes of buildings, settling finally upon the barely visible walls of Cartagena harbour. There was a stab of red flame. The six-pounder leaped back madly against its tackles, bellowing like a monster. A cloud of grey smoke hazed the shuddering deck for a moment, then swirled away before the breeze. The iron ball hummed away like an angry hornet and battered a huge spray of water out of a wavetop, woefully short of the Spanish fort.

'Ah, well,' said Thatcher pleasantly. 'The thought was there, and that's what counts.'

But when an answering growl of iron thunder came back from Cartagena, and balls from heavy guns raised distant but menacing plumes from the sea between, Thatcher became brusque and business-like.

'Bendigo's snuffling at the bait, Mr Busby. We must flirt

with him a little closer. I shall stand by the helm. Kindly put a good man in the bow chains, take constant soundings and relay them back to me. These are shoal waters we are entering, and we'd look foolish stranded on a sandbank just now!'

While a huge, blood-red sun rainbowed the western ocean and threatened them with the imminent downrush of tropical darkness, the *Jackdaw*, under easy sail, threaded a tortuous course over the treacherous waters before Cartagena harbour. Peter stood by the bow-rail. Below him, feet braced in the leadsman's chains, a seaman was swinging the leadline in wide circles, casting it forward into the sea, then reading off the depths when the sloop's passage brought the leadline vertical beneath him.

'By the mark four!' called the leadsman.

Peter cupped his hands and called back the sounding to the poop deck. They were in dangerously shoal water already. Thatcher was looking anxious.

'And a half two!'

Peter chewed at his lip. An abrupt change of depth, and now only fifteen feet of water below them. He conjured up a frightful vision of the *Jackdaw*, her mainmast snapped by the force of a sudden grounding, sails and shrouds trailing down. The next sounding would be crucial...

A sudden jar shook the *Jackdaw* along her length. Planking groaned below. The sloop heeled sickeningly, jib and mainsail flapping like the wings of a wounded bird. Then, with an audible sucking sound and a flurry of brown water along her sides, she broke clear and righted herself again.

Remembering to look down and assure himself that the leadsman, cursing and spluttering and fighting to regain his foothold in the chains, was safe, Peter faced the poop and made a jubilant thumbs-up signal. Thatcher smiled grimly and stabbed a finger stubbornly forward.

The leadsman was changed at half-hourly intervals, but

Peter, determined to show Thatcher what he was made of, kept to his station through the curiously chill hours of a jet-black tropical night. They beat backwards and forwards beneath a weirdly glowing moon and a glazed sprinkling of stars. Now and then an ominous vibration went through the *Jackdaw* as she grazed a sandbank. With nothing to guide them but the hoarse chanting of depths from the bows, they flitted like a grey moth over strangely lead-like, sullen waters.

But their luck held good. When Peter, cramped and shivering at the bow-rail, saw the eastern sky shimmer into pale light, he cheered himself with the thought that in an hour or two, under the stimulus of blazing sun, he would fling himself into his first fighting action. Thatcher was a pessimist. They would cover themselves in glory. He could almost see the despatches now. He bit thankfully into the slice of cold beef and the ship's biscuit that a seaman thrust into his hand. It was then that day broke, and he saw that their luck had disastrously run out.

The whole sea-scape was shrouded in a clammy white mist. They could see little farther than their bowsprit. They were blind and helpless as a moth in a paper bag.

Thatcher appeared suddenly beside him, three-cornered hat askew, bony face drawn with dismay.

'A typical stroke of fortune, Mr Busby,' he said bitterly. 'It is not for nothing, you see, that I am called the Jonah of the West Indies Fleet. God, what a mess!'

Peter frowned at him in puzzlement. What other naval officer but Lieutenant Thatcher would express his feelings so openly before a midshipman? But then, Thatcher broke every rule of behaviour. He harangued and threatened his crew — and they loved him for it, and served him willingly and well. He had driven and lashed his only midshipman with a cutting tongue — yet Peter found himself admiring and liking the man, even now feeling a sort of sympathy for him. Not that he would dare express it, but a show of confidence might not come amiss. Particularly with Thatcher's career threatened with dishonourable extinction at the failure of their mission.

'I'm ready to obey your orders, sir,' he said quietly.

'Recalling me to my duty, are you?' growled Thatcher in miserable indignation. 'You misbegotten midshipman. Utter another word and I'll drop you over the side!'

Peter's own disappointment at the frustration of their plan now broke his self-control.

'But you can't have it both ways, sir,' he said heatedly. 'Last night you were fuming about this being a suicide mission — now you're in a rage because Bendigo can't come out and attack us.'

For a moment it seemed that he had gone too far. Thatcher whipped round. He thrust his face close to Peter's.

'What would you have me do, Mr Busby? Put about like a whipped cur? Make for the open sea, seek out the waiting frigates, pay my respects to the Commodore and tell him I cannot accomplish my task 'cos the weather's turned foul?'

'N-no, of course not.' Peter was horrified.

'Then what's the alternative?' rapped Thatcher.

'Stand in for the shore, regardless — I suppose,' said Peter doubtfully. 'Force Bendigo out and —'

He staggered as Thatcher fetched him a resounding thump on the shoulder.

'My own thoughts precisely! Well done, Mr Busby!' Like magic, his mood of depression was instantly transformed into delight. 'We're already steering for the harbour mouth, lad.' He bent over the bow-rail and spoke to the chanting leadsman. 'Stop that silly racket, or I'll cut your tongue out! Get back aboard, my man, and dry your feet.' He turned back to Peter. 'We'll be in the harbour channel directly. Keep a sharp lookout forward. Scream your head off if you sight anything.'

Stiffly erect at the sharp angle of the bow-rail, Peter searched the mist through which they were creeping. At any moment death might strike at them — out of roaring carronades from the fortress walls towards which they were blindly groping; or from the reeking gun muzzles of the *Sinbad*, if Bendigo, infuriated by the *Jackdaw's* insolent invitation to a duel, should even now quit harbour with a Spanish pilot and steal out through the mist to destroy them.

He jumped when a seaman clapped his shoulder and thrust a pistol and cutlass into his hands. Stuffing the pistol into his coat pocket and wrapping his fingers about the cold cutlass-grip, he became aware of the intense activity on the deck behind him. Bare feet padded the boards. Gun truckles grumbled as all four six-pounders were cleared for action. Wraith-like figures, looking more like witches on Hallowe'en than naval gunners, swung lighted linstocks in gentle arcs to keep them glowing in the clammy atmosphere.

A sudden sound ahead of them sent alarm signals racing through his body. Leaping to the top of the bow-rail, he balanced against a slanting fore-stay, forcing himself to listen through and beyond the subdued mutter of the seamen, the noisy slap of sea against the *Jackdaw's* side, the creak and groan of the sloop's gear. Then it came again — the sound of high, nasal voices thinly penetrating the muggy air.

Peter twisted like a cat and gave a low hail towards the poop. He heard Thatcher rap a command. Blocks screeched as fore- and main-sail were hoisted to their limits, scooping every ounce of thrust from the wayward breeze that was tormenting the mist into fantastic patterns. There was a shrill, musical chatter from the bows beneath him. The sloop leaned slightly and sharpened her speed.

'Craft dead ahead!' The words ripped out of Peter's throat when the prow of a strange vessel took shape in the mist. The *Jackdaw's* bowsprit lunged towards her enemy. Thatcher was going to ram!

Peter dropped to the deck and wrapped one arm about the teak rail, leaving his cutlass hand free. A sudden chorus of shouts told him that they had been sighted. A fore-and-aft rigged vessel, much of the *Jackdaw's* size, collapsed her main-sail in a panic and sheered away — but too late. With a crunch of shattered timber, the *Jackdaw's* bow sliced like an eagle's beak into her enemy's port quarter.

Peter's body slammed against the rail. The port-side six-pounders thundered together, stabbing red flame. There was a rattle of musket fire from the *Jackdaw* as the two ships, locked in a rending agony of splintering planks and snapping cordage, swung their lengths around. Men screamed shrilly and slumped upon the strange craft's deck in grotesque attitudes of death.

Perched high in the *Jackdaw's* bows, Peter found himself rail to rail with their adversary's raised stern. Blinking the powder-haze out of his eyes, he desperately parried a ringing cutlass stroke from a swarthy villain fighting with lunatic energy and mouthing curses at him. He recovered, feeling as though his wrist were broken, and slashed back in a frenzy. A gaping red line striped down the bearded face and it dropped out of his blurred vision like a nightmare.

Pain flamed through his arm as another steel blade, hacking through the powder-streaked air, clashed upon his cutlass and beat it out of his hand. Peter thumbed back the heavy hammer, of his pistol, jammed the muzzle against a heaving chest and jerked at the trigger. The man's mouth flung open in a sound-less cry, his eyes rolled whitely in his head and he fell across the rail like a sack.

The six-pounders roared again, and this time, with a grinding wrench, the two ships parted. Peter's last sight of their stricken foe was the huge red and gold banner of Spain that drooped and fell when the sea rushed in through her riven hull and she sank stern-first.

'Dammit, we've turned about!' Thatcher was glaring up at

70

his sail spread when Peter came on to the poop deck to make his report. The steep, triangular areas of canvas were bulging tautly to a breeze that came fresher now from the starboard side. 'Now where the devil's Cartagena got to? Astern of us, for a wager. Blast this confounded mist!'

Peter had hoped for some congratulatory word after their successful action. It was, after all, his first taste of sea-fighting. But their victory seemed to have landed them in an even more dangerous predicament. They were now completely lost. All the same, he did have something to report.

'That was a Spanish vessel,' he said. 'I spotted her colours.'

'I did not believe her to be a Barbary corsair,' replied Thatcher coldly.

'But she wasn't cleared for action,' went on Peter. 'Her guns didn't fire. I think she was a pilot boat leading something out of harbour.'

'Leading something...?' Thatcher's eyes lighted with a sudden idea. He whirled to the taffrail and peered astern through the clammy grey curtain of mist at which the eager fingers of the lifting breeze were already tearing. 'God save us, boy, you were right! Look there!'

Peter turned. Less than a cable's length astern, revealed by a movement in the mist and then instantly obscured again, he made out the tall, pale ghost of a ship gliding towards them.

'It's Bendigo, right enough,' cried Thatcher. 'He's bringing the *Sinbad* out after us. And here we are, turned wrong ways round in the harbour channel with no room to manoeuvre!' He dashed his hat against the taffrail in a burst of bitter anger. 'My luck holds good, you will observe, Mr Busby!'

But Peter had already left his side. Winged by a sudden inspiration, he rattled down the 'tween-decks companionway, grabbed a precious bundle out of his sea chest, and was back on the poop before Thatcher had finished cursing his misfortune. He ripped back the wrappings and wordlessly thrust before Thatcher's astonished face the gold and crimson folds of the Spanish flag that was his treasured keep-sake.

'You're mad, Mr Busby; It'd never work.' Thatcher's response was predictably pessimistic, and then his quick intelligence asserted itself. 'I don't know, though. The mist's thick enough. I reckon I can still recall some of my prison dungeon Spanish.'

Taking this for an order, Peter raced to the signal halyards, lowered the British colours and hauled to the *Jackdaw's* peak the billowing red and gold of Spain.

'Shorten sail and shut your mouths!' Thatcher's command was low but incisive. 'Steady as she goes, quartermaster. Keep by me, Mr Busby. This was your idea, as I recall. Should Bendigo mislike my Spanish accent and fire off his bow-chasers, then I shall have the consolation of dying in your company.'

'It — it would be an honour,' said Peter, half in retort and half meaning it. To his surprise, Thatcher gave a dry chuckle before clapping his tricorne hat firmly upon his lean head and stepping up to the taffrail.

'Amigos!' he yelled, muffling his voice with the flat of one hand held before his mouth, and addressing the looming outlines of the *Sinbad* in garbled Spanish. 'Follow us closely — make more speed!'

A hoarse voice from the *Sinbad* demanded to know what the devil was happening.

'British sloop — we sink her — clear water ahead,' shouted back Thatcher, and quietly to Peter. 'The *Sinbad* draws a fathom more of water than we do. Please God we skid over a sandbank and run the renegade aground!'

Peter gripped his arm. 'Look sir. The mist is clearing!'

It was true. The freshening breeze was shredding the vapours into nothing. To seaward was a glint of dazzling sunshine and a prospect of blue and white ocean.

'Oh my God, that's torn it! They'll sight us now.' Before Thatcher could hail the *Sinbad* again, a ragged chorus of howls broke from the brig. 'Luff her, quartermaster. Take all the wind you can get. We'll have to run for it, Mr Busby. I'll trouble you to take the waist.'

'Aye, aye, sir.' Peter leaped down to the deck and stationed himself amidships. He was now in command of the sloop's battery of six-pounders. Should dire necessity demand that they fight the *Sinbad* ship to ship, it would be his responsibility, while Thatcher manoeuvred the sloop, to maintain a disciplined and accurate fire from all guns that would bear on their target.

There was a great crash from the *Sinbad*, and jets of orange flame shot out from her bow'-chasers. Almost instantly, so close behind them was Bendigo's white mountain of canvas, the air seemed filled with a savage, hurtling sound. There was a thunderous shock amidships. Great slivers of wood were torn from the *Jackdaw's* sides and waterline. The deadly whine of splinters scythed across their topdeck. Peter winced and staggered, clapping a hand to the sear of pain like a sharp nail being dragged across his forehead. His limbs trembled with nausea, and he struggled to stay erect with blood streaming down his cheek.

'Hard-a-starboard!' yelled Thatcher from the poop. 'Wear ship!'

The *Jackdaw* flung across wind and scurried away on the port tack. Peter clenched his teeth. This manoeuvre of Thatcher's would lay them open to the scalding weight of the *Sinbad's* starboard broadside. He peered through a hail of spray and readied his own gun's-crews, fiercely resolved to give back what fire he could.

'Ready to go about! Port your helm — wait for it, man — now!'

With a squeal and snap of gear, the boom mainsail thundered

73

over and took the wind on the opposite tack. The *Jackdaw* spun and checked and then darted back across the *Sinbad's* black, thrusting bows. Peter shook his head. They were fluttering aimlessly about the ocean like a sparrow hunted by a hawk. Enlightenment came with Thatcher's next shout.

'Satan's curse on you! Show yourselves, dammit!' Arms outstretched, the captain of the *Jackdaw* was bitterly eyeing the sun-dazzled waters over which they sped. His voice rang out beseechingly. 'Sandbanks ahoy!'

So that was it. They were still in shoal water, with Bendigo in hot pursuit. Thatcher was trying to run the renegade brig aground. If ever a captain needed luck...

Peter lurched headlong to the deck as a jarring blow struck their bottom. The sloop heeled steeply. Planking groaned under an unbearable strain and her mainmast quivered like a bowstring. With a shriek and thunder of truckles, the port-side guns hurtled backwards down the tilting deck and battled like stampeding elephants against their restraining tackles. Thatcher had succeeded too well — they were stuck fast.

The next instant, a heavy salvo from the *Sinbad's* bowchasers, double-shotted for close range fighting, smashed along their sides. Giant spouts of water, brown-stained with sand, leaped into the air. A heavy ball punched into their stern. Blindly obeying the impulse to rally his gunners for a last despairing defiance, Peter staggered to his feet — and then pitched across a hatch coaming when the *Jackdaw*, levered off the clutching sandbank by the very shots that were aimed to sink her, skidded into clear water again and groped for the singing breeze.

Peter scrambled to the starboard rail and looked behind them. For one moment the *Sinbad*, her bows creaming majestically and her rigging dotted with triumphantly howling men, bore down on them like a fury. Then she struck the sandbank in their wake.

74

The force of the collision killed the *Sinbad* as a fighting ship.

She might have collided with a mountain. Main and fore-topmast, with yards and sails, broke off and tumbled down in a dreadful tangle. She lifted in a great rending of timber, and canted sideways to bury her lee-rail in a welter of broken water. Men dropped from her rigging like flies. The force with which she had hit the sand had killed the *Sinbad* as a fighting ship. Bendigo was beaten.

'I'll not have my deck cluttered up by blood-stained mid-shipmen. We're a sorry enough looking sight as it is!'

Peter became aware that Thatcher was standing beside him. 'Here, take this, Mr Busby, and make yourself presentable.'

Peter accepted the handkerchief that Thatcher held out to him and wiped his face.

'The frigates, by some quaint error in the Commodore's reckoning,' went on Thatcher, lightly sarcastic, 'are close to hand and even now bearing down to surround the *Sinbad* — as you will observe, Mr Busby, if you can bear to leave off prettying yourself for one moment and cast your eyes to starboard.'

Peter looked. The three frigates had returned as promised to close the trap, and were now backing sail to form a crescent of doom about the stricken renegade.

'It would seem that my fortunes have changed at last,' said Thatcher pleasantly. 'I wonder whether the Commodore will run aground before my very eyes — but perhaps that is asking too much.' He turned his gaze upon Peter. 'They will promote me for this, you know — give me a bigger command, I mean. You have done very well today Mr Busby. I should —' He struggled in a mixed mood of new-found confidence and unaccustomed shyness. 'I should take it very kindly if you would consent to accompany me.'

Peter grinned at him. 'I'd like that very much, sir.'

Thatcher gave a satisfied nod. Then he looked away, and his eyes hardened. 'The flagship's signalling us, Mr Busby.

Smartly with your telescope, now. Read what she has to say.'

Peter levelled his telescope at the flagship's signal yard, where a string of coloured bunting fluttered gaily against the sun-bleached, blue sky.

'Strike — your — colours — this — instant,' he read slowly. A moment's puzzlement, then he glanced up at the *Jackdaw's* peak, where the flamboyant banner of Spain still flew arrogantly to the breeze. He looked at Thatcher. 'Beg to report, sir, that we're sailing under the enemy's flag.'

'Indeed, indeed — I had quite forgotten. Make what reply you will, Mr Busby. Those are your colours, and I fancy it's your day.'

It took Peter some time to assemble the correct flags, but when he finally bent to the halyard and hoisted the bunting aloft, he was well satisfied with his answer.

'Trophy — of — war,' was the signal he sent.

Midshipman Peter Busby was not lowering his colours that day — not even for a Commodore.

The Pirates

from Captain Singleton

by

DANIEL DEFOE

I shipped myself, in an evil hour to be sure, on a voyage to Cadiz, in a ship called the —, and in the course of our voyage, being on the coast of Spain, was obliged to put into the Groyn, by a strong southwest wind.

Here I fell into company with some masters of mischief; and, among them, one, forwarder than the rest, began an intimate confidence with me, so that we called one another brothers, and communicated all our circumstances to one another. His name was Harris. This fellow came to me one morning, asking me if I would go on shore, and I agreed; so we got the captain's leave for the boat, and went together. When we were together, he asked me if I had a mind for an adventure that might make amends for all past misfortunes. I told him, yes, with all my heart; for I did not care where I went, having nothing to lose, and no one to leave behind me.

He then asked me if I would swear to be secret, and that, if I did not agree to what he proposed, I would nevertheless never betray him. I readily bound myself to that, upon the most solemn imprecations and curses that the devil and both of us could invent.

He told me, then, there was a brave fellow in the other ship, pointing to another English ship which rode in the harbour, who, in concert with some of the men, had resolved to mutiny the next morning, and run away with the ship; and that, if we could get strength enough among our ship's company, we might do the same. I liked the proposal very well, and he got eight of us to join with him, and he told us, that as soon as his friend had begun the work, and was master of the ship, we should be ready to do the like. This was his plot; and I, without the least hesitation, either at the villainy of the fact or the difficulty of performing it, came immediately into the wicked conspiracy, and so it went on among us; but we could not bring our part to perfection.

Accordingly, on the day appointed, his correspondent in the other ship, whose name was Wilmot, began the work, and, having seized the captain's mate and other officers, secured the ship, and gave the signal to us. We were but eleven in our ship, who were in the conspiracy, nor could we get any more that we could trust; so that, leaving the ship, we all took the boat, and went off to join the other.

Having thus left the ship I was in, we were entertained with a great deal of joy by Captain Wilmot and his new gang; and, being well prepared for all manner of roguery, bold, desperate (I mean myself), without the least checks of conscience for what I was entered upon, or for anything I might do, much less with any apprehension of what might be the consequence of it; I say, having thus embarked with this crew, which at last brought me to consort with the most famous pirates of the age, some of whom have ended their journals at the gallows, I think the giving an account of some of my other adventures may be an agreeable piece of story; and this I may venture to say beforehand, upon the word of a pirate, that I shall not be able to recollect the full, no, not by far, of the great variety which has formed one of the most reprobate schemes that ever man was capable to present to the world.

I that was, as I have hinted before, an original thief, and a pirate, even by inclination before, was now in my element, and never undertook anything in my life with more particular satisfaction.

Captain Wilmot (for so we are now to call him) being thus possessed of a ship, and in the manner as you have heard, it may be easily concluded he had nothing to do to stay in the port, or to wait either the attempts that might be made from the shore, or any change that might happen among his men. On the contrary, we weighed anchor the same tide, and stood out to sea, steering away for the Canaries. Our ship had twenty-two guns, but was able to carry thirty; and besides, as she was fitted out for a merchant-ship only, she was not furnished either with ammunition or small-arms sufficient for our design, or for the occasion we might have in case of a fight. So we put into Cadiz, that is to say, we came to an anchor in the bay; and the captain, and one whom we called young Captain Kidd, who was the gunner, landed, and some of the men who could best be trusted, among whom was my comrade Harris, who was made second mate, and myself, who was made a lieutenant. Some bales of English goods were proposed to be carried on shore with us for sale, but my comrade, who was a complete fellow at his business, proposed a better way for it; and having been in the town before, told us, in short, that he would buy what powder and bullet, small-arms, or anything else we wanted, on his own word, to be paid for when they came on board, in such English goods as we had there. This was much the best way, and accordingly he and the captain went on shore by themselves, and having made such a bargain as they found for their turn, came away again in two hours' time, and bringing only a butt of wine and five casks of brandy with them, we all went on board again.

The next morning two *barcos longos* came off to us, deeply laden, with five Spaniards on board them, for traffic. Our captain sold them good pennyworths, and they delivered us sixteen barrels of powder, twelve small rundlets of fine powder for our small-arms, sixty muskets, and twelve fuses for the officers; seventeen ton of cannon-ball, fifteen barrels of musket-bullets, with some swords and twenty good pair of pistols. Besides this, they brought thirteen butts of wine (for we, that were now all become gentlemen, scorned to drink the ship's beer), also sixteen puncheons of brandy, with twelve barrels of raisins and twenty chests of lemons; all which we paid for in English goods; and, over and above, the captain received six hundred pieces of eight in money. They would have come again, but we would stay no longer.

From hence we sailed to the Canaries, and from thence onward to the West Indies, where we committed some depredation upon the Spaniards for provisions, and took some prizes, but none of any great value, while I remained with them, which was not long at that time; for, having taken a Spanish sloop on the coast of Carthagena, my friend made a motion to me, that we should desire Captain Wilmot to put us into the sloop, with a proportion of arms and ammunition, and let us try what we could do; she being much fitter for our business than the great ship, and a better sailer. This he consented to, and we appointed our rendezvous at Tobago, making an agreement, that whatever was taken by either of our ships should be shared among the ship's company of both; all which we very punctually observed, and joined our ships again, about fifteen months after, at the island of Tobago, as above.

We cruised near two years in those seas, chiefly upon the Spaniards; not that we made any difficulty of taking English ships, or Dutch, or French, if they came in our way; and particularly, Captain Wilmot attacked a New England ship bound from the Madeiras to Jamaica, and another bound from New York to Barbados, with provisions; which last was a very happy supply to us. But the reason why we meddled as little with English vessels as we could, was, first, because, if they were ships of any force, we were sure of more resistance from them; and, secondly, because we found the English ships had less booty when taken, for the Spaniards generally had money on board, and that was what we best knew what to do with. Captain Wilmot was, indeed, more particularly cruel when he took any English vessel, that they might not too soon have advice of him in England; and so the men-of-war had orders to look out for him. But this part I bury in silence for the present.

We increased our stock in these two years considerably, having taken 60,000 pieces of eight in one vessel, and 100,000 in another; and being thus first grown rich, we resolved to be strong too, for we had taken a brigantine built at Virginia, an excellent sea-boat, and a good sailer, and able to carry twelve guns; and a large Spanish frigate-built ship, that sailed incomparably well also, and which afterwards, by the help of good carpenters, we fitted up to carry twenty-eight guns. And now we wanted more hands, so we put away for the Bay of Campeachy, not doubting we should ship as many men there as we pleased; and so we did.

Here we sold the sloop that I was in; and Captain Wilmot keeping his own ship, I took the command of the Spanish frigate as captain, and my comrade Harris as eldest lieutenant, and a bold enterprising fellow he was, as any the world afforded. One culverdine* was put into the brigantine, so that we were now three stout ships, wellmanned, and victualled for twelve months; for we had taken two or three sloops from New England and New York, laden with flour, peas, and barrelled beef and pork, going for Jamaica and Barbados; and for more beef we went on shore on the island of Cuba, where we killed as many black cattle as we pleased, though we had very little salt to cure them.

Out of all the prizes we took here we took their powder and

*a large cannon

bullet, their small-arms and cutlasses; and as for their men, we always took the surgeon and the carpenter, as persons who were of particular use to us upon many occasions; nor were they always unwilling to go with us, though for their own security, in case of accidents, they might easily pretend they were carried away by force.

We had one very merry fellow here, a Quaker, whose name was William Walters, whom we took out of a sloop bound from Pennsylvania to Barbados. He was a surgeon, and they called him doctor; but he was not employed in the sloop as a surgeon, but was going to Barbados to get a berth, as the sailors call it. However, he had all his surgeon's chests on board, and we made him go with us, and take all his implements with him. He was a comic fellow indeed, a man of very good solid sense, and an excellent surgeon; but, what was worth all, very good-humoured and pleasant in his conversation, and a bold, stout, brave fellow too, as any we had among us.

I found William, as I thought, not very averse to go along with us, and yet resolved to do it so that it might be apparent he was taken away by force, and to this purpose he comes to me. 'Friend,' says he, 'thou sayest I must go with thee, and it is not in my power to resist thee if I would; but I desire thou wilt oblige the master of the sloop which I am on board to certify under his hand, that I was taken away by force and against my will.' And this he said with so much satisfaction in his face, that I could not but understand him. 'Ay, ay,' says I, 'whether it be against your will or no, I'll make him and all the men give you a certificate of it, or I'll take them all along with us, and keep them till they do.' So I drew up a certificate myself, wherein I wrote that he was taken away by main force, as a prisoner, by a pirate ship; that they carried away his chest and instruments first, and then bound his hands behind him and forced him into their boat; and this was signed by the master and all his men.

Accordingly I fell a-swearing at him, and called to my men to tie his hands behind him, and so we put him into our boat and carried him away. When I had him on board, I called him to me. 'Now, friend,' says I, 'I have brought you away by force, it is true, but I am not of the opinion I have brought you away so much against your will as they imagine. Come,' says I, 'you will be a useful man to us, and you shall have very good usage among us.' So I unbound his hands, and first ordered all things that belonged to him to be restored to him, and our captain gave him a dram.

'Thou hast dealt friendly by me,' says he, 'and I will be plain with thee, whether I came willingly to thee or not. I shall make myself as useful to thee as I can, but thou knowest it is not my business to meddle when thou are to fight.' 'No, no,' says the captain, 'but you may meddle a little when we share the money.' 'Those things are useful to furnish a surgeon's chest,' says William, and smiled, 'but I shall be moderate.'

In short, William was a most agreeable companion; but he had the better of us in this part, that if we were taken we were sure to be hanged, and he was sure to escape; and he knew it well enough. But, in short, he was a sprightly fellow, and fitter to be captain than any of us. I shall have often an occasion to speak of him in the rest of the story.

Our cruising so long in these seas began now to be so well known, that not in England only, but in France and Spain, accounts had been made public of our adventures, and many stories told how we murdered the people in cold blood, tying them back to back, and throwing them into the sea; one half of which, however, was not true, though more was done than is fit to speak of here.

The consequence of this, however, was, that several English men-of-war were sent to the West Indies, and were particularly instructed to cruise in the Bay of Mexico, and the Gulf of

Florida, and among the Bahama islands, if possible, to attack us. We were not so ignorant of things as not to expect this, after so long a stay in that part of the world; but the first certain account we had of them was at Honduras, when a vessel coming in from Jamaica told us that two English men-of-war were coming directly from Jamaica thither in quest of us. We were indeed as it were embayed, and could not have made the least shift to have got off, if they had come directly to us; but, as it happened, somebody had informed them that we were in the Bay of Campeachy, and they went directly thither, by which we were not only free of them, but were so much to the windward of them, that they could not make any attempt upon us, though they had known we were there.

We took this advantage, and stood away for Carthagena, and from thence with great difficulty beat it up at a distance from under the shore for St Martha, till we came to the Dutch island of Curaçao, and from thence to the island of Tobago, which, as before, was our rendezvous; which, being a deserted, uninhabited island, we at the same time made use of for a retreat. Here the captain of the brigantine died, and Captain Harris, at that time my lieutenant, took the command of the brigantine.

Here we came to a resolution to go away to the coast of Brazil, and from thence to the Cape of Good Hope, and so for the East Indies; but Captain Harris, as I have said, being now captain of the brigantine, alleged that his ship was too small for so long a voyage, but that, if Captain Wilmot would consent, he would take the hazard of another cruise, and he would follow us in the first ship he could take. So we appointed our rendezvous to be at Madagascar, which was done by my recommendation of the place, and the plenty of provisions to be had there.

Accordingly, he went away from us in an evil hour; for, instead of taking a ship to follow us, he was taken, as I heard afterwards, by an English man-of-war, and being laid in irons, died of mere grief and anger before he came to England. His lieutenant, I have heard, was afterwards executed in England for a pirate; and this was the end of the man who first brought me into this unhappy trade.

We parted from Tobago three days after, bending our course for the coast of Brazil, but had not been at sea above twenty-four hours, when we were separated by a terrible storm, which held three days, with very little abatement or intermission. In this juncture Captain Wilmot happened, unluckily, to be on board my ship, to his great mortification; for we not only lost sight of his ship, but never saw her more till we came to Madagascar, where she was cast away. In short, after having in this tempest lost our fore-topmast, we were forced to put back to the isle of Tobago for shelter, and to repair our damage, which brought us all very near our destruction.

We were no sooner on shore here, and all very busy looking out for a piece of timber for a topmast, but we perceived standing in for the shore an English man-of-war of thirty-six guns. It was a great surprise to us indeed, because we were disabled so much; but, to our great good fortune, we lay pretty snug and close among the high rocks, and the man-of-war did not see us, but stood off again upon his cruise. So we only observed which way she went, and at night, leaving our work, resolved to stand off to sea, steering the contrary way from that which we observed she went; and this, we found, had the desired success, for we saw him no more. We had gotten an old mizzen-topmast on board, which made us a jury fore-topmast for the present; and so we stood away for the isle of Trinidad, where, though there were Spaniards on shore, yet we landed some men with our boat, and cut a very good piece of fir to make us a new topmast, which we got fitted up effectually; and also we got some cattle here to eke out our provisions; and calling a council of war among ourselves, we resolved to quit those seas for the present, and steer away for the coast of Brazil.

The first thing we attempted here was only getting fresh water, but we learnt that there lay the Portuguese fleet at the bay of All Saints, bound for Lisbon, ready to sail, and only waited for a fair wind. This made us lie by, wishing to see them put to sea, and accordingly as they were with or without convoy, to attack or avoid them.

It sprung up a fresh gale in the evening at S.W. by W., which, being fair for the Portugal fleet, and the weather pleasant and agreeable, we heard the signal given to unmoor, and running in under the island of Si—, we hauled our mainsail and foresail up in the brails, lowered the topsails upon the cap, and clewed them up, that we might lie as snug as we could, expecting their coming out, and the next morning saw the whole fleet come out accordingly, but not all to our satisfaction, for they consisted of twenty-six sail, and most of them ships of force, as well as burthen, both merchantmen and men-of-war; so, seeing there was no meddling, we lay still where we were also, till the fleet was out of sight, and then stood off and on, in hopes of meeting with further purchase.

It was not long before we saw a sail, and immediately gave her chase; but she proved an excellent sailer, and, standing out to sea, we saw plainly she trusted to her heels — that is to say, to her sails. However, as we were a clean ship, we gained upon her, though slowly, and had we had a day before us, we should certainly have come up with her; but it grew dark apace, and in that case we knew we should lose sight of her.

Our merry Quaker, perceiving us to crowd still after her in the dark, wherein we could not see which way she went, came very dryly to me. 'Friend Singleton,' says he, 'dost thee know what we are a-doing?' Says I, 'Yes; why, we are chasing yon ship, are we not?' 'And how dost thou know that?' says he, very gravely still. 'Nay, that's true,' says I again; 'we cannot be sure.' 'Yes, friend,' says he, 'I think we may be sure that we are running away from her, not chasing her. I am afraid,' adds he, 'thou art turned Quaker, and hast resolved not to use the hand of power, or art a coward, and art flying from thy enemy.'

'What do you mean?' says I (I think I swore at him). 'What do you sneer at now? You have always one dry rub or another to give us.'

'Nay,' says he, 'it is plain enough the ship stood off to sea due east, on purpose to lose us, and thou mayest be sure her business does not lie that way; for what should she do at the coast of Africa in this latitude, which should be as far south as Congo or Angola? But as soon as it is dark, that we would lose sight of her, she will tack and stand away west again for the Brazil coast and for the bay, where thou knowest she was going before; and are we not, then, running away from her? I am greatly in hopes, friend,' says the dry, gibing creature, 'thou wilt turn Quaker, for I see thou art not for fighting.'

'Very well, William,' says I; 'then I shall make an excellent pirate.' However, William was in the right, and I apprehended what he meant immediately; and Captain Wilmot, who lay very sick in his cabin, overhearing us, understood him as well as I, and called out to me that William was right, and it was our best way to change our course, and stand away for the bay, where it was ten to one but we should snap her in the morning.

Accordingly we went about-ship, got our larboard tacks on board, set the top-gallant sails, and crowded for the bay of All Saints, where we came to an anchor early in the morning, just out of gunshot of the forts; we furled our sails with rope-yarns, that we might haul home the sheets without going up to loose them, and, lowering our main and foreyards, looked just as if we had lain there a good while.

In two hours afterwards we saw our game standing in for the bay with all the sail she could make, and she came innocently into our very mouths, for we lay still till we saw her almost within gunshot, when, our foremast gears being stretched fore and aft, we first ran up our yards, and then hauled home the top-sail sheets, the rope-yarns that furled them giving way of themselves; the sails were set in a few minutes; at the same time slipping our cable, we came upon her before she could get under way upon the other tack. They were so surprised that they made little or no resistance, but struck after the first broadside.

We were considering what to do with her, when William came to me. 'Hark thee, friend,' says he, 'thou hast made a fine piece of work of it now, hast thou not, to borrow thy neighbour's ship here just at thy neighbour's door, and never ask him leave? Now, dost thou not think there are some men-of-war in the port? Thou hast given them the alarm sufficiently; thou wilt have them upon thy back before night, depend upon it, to ask thee wherefore thou didst so.'

'Truly, William,' said I, 'for aught I know, that may be true; what, then, shall we do next?' Says he, 'Thou hast but two things to do: either to go in and take all the rest, or else get thee gone before they come out and take thee; for I see they are hoisting a topmast to yon great ship, in order to put to sea immediately, and they won't be long before they come to talk with thee, and what wilt thou say to them when they ask thee why thou borrowedst their ship without leave?'

As William said, so it was. We could see by our glasses they were all in a hurry, manning and fitting some sloops they had there, and a large man-of-war, and it was plain they would soon be with us. But we were not at a loss what to do; we found the ship we had taken was laden with nothing considerable for our purpose, except some cocoa, some sugar, and twenty barrels of flour; the rest of her cargo was hides; so we took out all we thought fit for our turn, and, among the rest, all her ammunition, great shot, and small-arms, and turned her off. We also took a cable and three anchors she had, which were for our purpose, and some of her sails. She had enough left just to carry her into port, and that was all.

Having done this, we stood on upon the Brazil coast, southward, till we came to the mouth of the river Janeiro. But as we had two days the wind blowing hard at S.E. and S.S.E., we were obliged to come to an anchor under a little island, and wait for a wind. In this time the Portuguese had, it seems, given notice over land to the governor there, that a pirate was upon the coast; so that, when we came in view of the port, we saw two men-of-war riding just without the bar, whereof one, we found, was getting under sail with all possible speed, having slipped her cable on purpose to speak with us; the other was not so forward, but was preparing to follow. In less than an hour they stood both fair after us, with all the sail they could make.

Had not the night come on, William's words had been made good; they would certainly have asked us the question what we did there, for we found the foremost ship gained upon us, especially upon one tack, for we plied away from them to windward; but in the dark losing sight of them, we resolved to change our course and stand away directly for sea, not doubting that we should lose them in the night.

Whether the Portuguese commander guessed we would do so or no, I know not; but in the morning when the daylight appeared, instead of having lost him, we found him in chase of us about a league astern; only, to our great good fortune, we could see but one of the two. However, this one was a great ship, carried six-and-forty guns, and an admirable sailer, as appeared by her outsailing us; for our ship was an excellent sailer too, as I have said before.

When I found this, I easily saw there was no remedy, but

we must engage; and as we knew we could expect no quarter from those scoundrels the Portuguese, a nation I had an original aversion to, I let Captain Wilmot know how it was. The captain, sick as he was, jumped up in the cabin, and would be led out upon the deck (for he was very weak) to see how it was. 'Well,' says he, 'we'll fight them!'

Our men were all in good heart before, but to see the captain so brisk, who had lain ill of a calenture ten or eleven days, gave them double courage, and they went all hands to work to make a clear ship and be ready. William, the Quaker, comes to me with a kind of a smile. 'Friend,' says he, 'what does yon ship follow us for?' 'Why,' says I, 'to fight us, you may be sure.' 'Well,' says he, 'and will he come up with us, dost think?' 'Yes,' said I, 'you see she will.' 'Why, then, friend,' says the dry wretch, 'why dost thou run from her still, when thou seest she will overtake thee? Will it be better for us to be overtaken farther off than here?' 'Much as one for that,' says I; 'why, what would you have us do?' 'Do!' says he; 'let us not give the poor man more trouble than needs must; let us stay for him and hear what he has to say to us.' 'He will talk to us in powder and ball,' said I. 'Very well, then,' says he, 'if that be his country language, we must talk to him in the same, must we not? or else how shall he understand us?' 'Very well, William,' says I, 'we understand you.' And the captain, as ill as he was, called to me, 'William's right again,' says he; 'as good here as a league farther.' So he gives a word of command, 'Haul up the mainsail; we'll shorten sail for him.'

Accordingly we shortened sail, and as we expected her upon our lee-side, we being then upon our starboard tack, brought eighteen of our guns to the larboard side, resolving to give him a broadside that should warn him. It was about half-an-hour before he came up with us, all which time we luffed up, that we might keep the wind of him, by which he was obliged to run up under our lee, as we designed him; when we got him upon our quarter, we edged down, and received the fire of five or six of his guns. By this time you may be sure all our hands were at their quarters, so we clapped our helm hard a-weather, let go the lee-braces of the maintop sail, and laid it a-back, and so our ship fell athwart the Portuguese ship's hawse; then we immediately poured in our broadside, raking them fore and aft, and killed them a great many men.

The Portuguese, we could see, were in the utmost confusion; and not being aware of our design, their ship having fresh way, ran their bowsprit into the fore part of our main shrouds, as that they could not easily get clear of us, and so we lay locked after that manner. The enemy could not bring above five or six guns, besides their small-arms, to bear upon us, while we played our whole broadside upon him.

In the middle of the heat of this fight, as I was very busy upon the quarter-deck, the captain calls to me, for he never stirred from us, 'What the devil is friend William a-doing yonder?' says the captain; 'has he any business upon deck?' I stepped forward, and there was friend William, with two or three stout fellows, lashing the ship's bowsprit fast to our main-mast, for fear they should get away from us; and every now and then he pulled a bottle out of his pocket, and gave the men a dram to encourage them. The shot flew about his ears as thick as may be supposed in such an action, where the Portuguese, to give them their due, fought very briskly, believing at first they were sure of their game, and trusting to their superiority; but there was William, as composed, and in as perfect tranquillity as to danger, as if he had been over a bowl of punch, only very busy securing the matter, that a ship of forty-six guns should not run away from a ship of eight-and-twenty.

This work was too hot to hold long; our men behaved bravely: our gunner, a gallant man, shouted below, pouring in his shot at such a rate, that the Portuguese began to slacken

The Portuguese ran their bowsprit into our main shrouds.

their fire; we had dismounted several of their guns by firing in at their forecastle, and raking them, as I said, fore and aft. Presently comes William up to me. 'Friend,' says he, very calmly, 'what dost thou mean? Why dost thou not visit thy neighbour in the ship, the door being open for thee?' I understood him immediately, for our guns had so torn their hull, that we had beat two portholes into one, and the bulk-head of their steerage was split to pieces, so that they could not retire to their close quarters; so I gave the word immediately to board them. Our second lieutenant, with about thirty men, entered in an instant over the forecastle, followed by some more with the boatswain, and cutting in pieces about twenty-five men that they found upon the deck, and then throwing some grenadoes into the steerage, they entered there also; upon which the Portuguese cried quarter presently, and we mastered the ship, contrary indeed to our own expectation; for we would have compounded with them if they would have sheered off: but laying them athwart the hawse at first, and following our fire furiously, without giving them any time to get clear of us and work their ship; by this means, though they had six-and-forty guns, they were not able to fight above five or six, as I said above, for we beat them immediately from their guns in the forecastle, and killed them abundance of men between decks, so that when we entered they had hardly found men enough to fight us hand to hand upon their deck.

The surprise of joy to hear the Portuguese cry quarter, and see their ancient struck, was so great to our captain, who, as I have said, was reduced very weak with a high fever, that it gave him new life. Nature conquered the distemper, and the fever abated that very night; so that in two or three days he was sensibly better, his strength began to come, and he was able to give his orders effectually in everything that was material, and in about ten days was entirely well and about the ship.

In the meantime I took possession of the Portuguese man-of-war; and Captain Wilmot made me, or rather I made myself, captain of her for the present. About thirty of their seamen took service with us, some of which were French, some Genoese; and we set the rest on shore the next day on a little island on the coast of Brazil, except some wounded men, who were not in a condition to be removed, and whom we were bound to keep on board; but we had an occasion afterwards to dispose of them at the Cape, where, at their own request, we set them on shore.

Captain Sharkey:

How the Governor of Saint Kitt's Came Home

by

SIR ARTHUR CONAN DOYLE

When the great wars of the Spanish Succession had been brought to an end by the Treaty of Utrecht, the vast number of privateers which had been fitted out by the contending parties found their occupation gone. Some took to the more peaceful but less lucrative ways of ordinary commerce, others were absorbed into the fishing-fleets, and a few of the more reckless hoisted the Jolly Roger at the mizzen and the bloody flag at the main, declaring a private war upon their own account against the whole human race.

With mixed crews, recruited from every nation, they scoured the seas, disappearing occasionally to careen in some lonely inlet, or putting in for a debauch at some outlying port, where they dazzled the inhabitants by their lavishness and horrified them by their brutalities.

On the Coromandel Coast, at Madagascar, in the African waters, and above all in the West Indian and American seas, the pirates were a constant menace. With an insolent luxury they would regulate their depredations by the comfort of the seasons, harrying New England in the summer and dropping south again to the tropical islands in the winter.

They were the more to be dreaded because they had none of that discipline and restraint which made their predecessors, the Buccaneers, both formidable and respectable. These Ishmaels of the sea rendered an account to no man, and treated their prisoners according to the drunken whim of the moment. Flashes of grotesque generosity alternated with longer stretches of inconceivable ferocity, and the skipper who fell into their hands might find himself dismissed with his cargo, after serving as boon companion in some hideous debauch, or might sit at his cabin table with his own nose and his lips served up with pepper and salt in front of him. It took a stout seaman in those days to ply his calling in the Caribbean Gulf.

Such a man was Captain John Scarrow, of the ship *Morning Star*, and yet he breathed a long sigh of relief when he heard the splash of the falling anchor and swung at his moorings within a hundred yards of the guns of the citadel of Basseterre. St Kitt's was his final port of call, and early next morning his bowsprit would be pointed for Old England. He had had enough of those robber-haunted seas. Ever since he had left Maracaibo upon the Main, with his full lading of sugar and red pepper, he had winced at every topsail which glimmered over the violet edge of the tropical sea. He had coasted up the Windward Islands, touching here and there, and assailed continually by stories of villainy and outrage.

Captain Sharkey, of the 20-gun pirate barque, *Happy Delivery*, had passed down the coast, and had littered it with gutted vessels and with murdered men. Dreadful anecdotes were current of his grim pleasantries and of his inflexible ferocity. From the Bahamas to the Main his coal-black barque, with the ambiguous name, had been freighted with death and many things which are worse than death. So nervous was Captain

Scarrow, with his new full-rigged ship and her full and valuable lading, that he struck out to the west as far as Bird's Island to be out of the usual track of commerce. And yet even in those solitary waters he had been unable to shake off sinister traces of Captain Sharkey.

One morning they had raised a single skiff adrift upon the face of the ocean. Its only occupant was a delirious seaman, who yelled hoarsely as they hoisted him aboard, and showed a dried-up tongue like a black and wrinkled fungus at the back of his mouth. Water and nursing soon transformed him into the strongest and smartest sailor on the ship. He was from Marblehead, in New England, it seemed, and was the sole survivor of a schooner which had been scuttled by the dreadful Sharkey.

For a week Hiram Evanson, for that was his name, had been adrift beneath a tropical sun. Sharkey had ordered the man-gled remains of his late captain to be thrown into the boat, 'as provisions for the voyage,' but the seaman had at once committed them to the deep, lest the temptation should be more than he could bear. He had lived upon his own huge frame, until, at the last moment, the *Morning Star* had found him in that madness which is the precursor of such a death. It was no bad find for Captain Scarrow, for, with a short-handed crew, such a seaman as this big New Englander was a prize worth having. He vowed that he was the only man whom Captain Sharkey had ever placed under an oblig-ation.

Now that they lay under the guns of Basseterre, all danger from the pirate was at an end, and yet the thought of him lay heavily upon the seaman's mind as he watched the agent's boat shooting out from the custom-house quay.

'I'll lay you a wager, Morgan,' said he to the first mate, 'that the agent will speak of Sharkey in the first hundred words that pass his lips.'

98

'Well, captain, I'll have you a silver dollar, and chance it,' said the rough old Bristol man beside him.

The negro rowers shot the boat alongside, and the linen-clad steersman sprang up the ladder.

'Welcome, Captain Scarrow!' he cried. 'Have you heard about Sharkey?'

The captain grinned at the mate.

'What devilry has he been up to now?' he asked.

'Devilry! You've not heard, then! Why, we've got him safe under lock and key here at Basseterre. He was tried last Wednesday, and he is to be hanged tomorrow morning.'

Captain and mate gave a shout of joy, which an instant later was taken up by the crew. Discipline was forgotten as they scrambled up through the break of the poop to hear the news. The New Englander was in the front of them with a radiant face turned up to heaven, for he came of the Puritan stock.

'Sharkey to be hanged!' he cried. 'You don't know, Master Agent, if they lack a hangman, do you?'

'Stand back!' cried the mate, whose outraged sense of discipline was even stronger than his interest at the news. 'I'll pay that dollar, Captain Scarrow, with the lightest heart that ever I paid a wager yet. How came the villain to be taken?'

'Why, as to that, he became more than his own comrades could abide, and they took such a horror of him that they would not have him on the ship. So they marooned him upon the Little Mangles to the south of the Mysteriosa Bank, and there he was found by a Portobello trader, who brought him in. There was talk of sending him to Jamaica to be tried, but our good little governor, Sir Charles Ewan, would not hear of it. "He's my meat," said he, "and I claim the cooking of it." If you can stay till tomorrow morning at ten, you'll see the joint swinging.'

'I wish I could,' said the captain, wistfully, 'but I am sadly behind time now. I should start with the evening tide.'

'That you can't do,' said the agent with decision. 'The Governor is going back with you.'

'The Governor!'

'Yes. He's had a dispatch from Government to return without delay. The fly-boat that brought it has gone on to Virginia. So Sir Charles has been waiting for you, as I told him you were due before the rains.'

'Well, well!' cried the captain, in some perplexity, 'I'm a plain seaman, and I don't know much of governors and baronets and their ways. I don't remember that I ever so much as spoke to one. But if it's in King George's service, and he asks a cast in the *Morning Star* as far as London, I'll do what I can for him. There's my own cabin he can have and welcome. As to the cooking, it's lobscouse and salmagundy six days in the week; but he can bring his own cook aboard with him if he thinks our galley too rough for his taste.'

'You need not trouble your mind, Captain Scarrow,' said the agent. 'Sir Charles is in weak health just now, only clear of a quartan ague, and it is likely he will keep his cabin most of the voyage. Dr Larousse said that he would have sunk had the hanging of Sharkey not put fresh life into him. He has a great spirit in him, though, and you must not blame him if he is somewhat short in his speech.'

'He may say what he likes and do what he likes so long as he does not come athwart my hawse when I am working the ship,' said the captain. 'He is Governor of St Kitt's, but I am Governor of the *Morning Star*. And, by his leave, I must weigh with the first tide, for I owe a duty to my employer, just as he does to King George.'

'He can scarce be ready tonight, for he has many things to set in order before he leaves.'

'The early morning tide, then.'

'Very good. I shall send his things aboard tonight, and he will follow them to-morrow early if I can prevail upon him

100

to leave St Kitt's without seeing Sharkey do the rogue's hornpipe. His own orders were instant, so it may be that he will come at once. It is likely that Dr Larousse may attend him upon the journey.'

Left to themselves, the captain and mate made the best preparations which they could for their illustrious passenger. The largest cabin was turned out and adorned in his honour, and orders were given by which barrels of fruit and some cases of wine should be brought off to vary the plain food of an ocean-going trader. In the evening the Governor's baggage began to arrive — great ironbound ant-proof trunks, and official tin packing-cases, with other strange-shaped packages, which suggested the cocked hat or the sword within. And then there came a note, with a heraldic device upon the big red seal, to say that Sir Charles Ewan made his compliments to Captain Scarrow, and that he hoped to be with him in the morning as early as his duties and his infirmities would permit.

He was as good as his word, for the first grey of dawn had hardly begun to deepen into pink when he was brought alongside, and climbed with some difficulty up the ladder. The captain had heard that the Governor was an eccentric, but he was hardly prepared for the curious figure who came limping feebly down his quarterdeck, his steps supported by a thick bamboo cane. He wore a Ramillies wig, all twisted into little tails like a poodle's coat, and cut so low across the brow that the large green glasses which covered his eyes looked as if they were hung from it. A fierce beak of a nose, very long and very thin, cut the air in front of him. His ague had caused him to swathe his throat and chin with a broad linen cravat, and he wore a loose damask powdering-gown secured by a cord round the waist. As he advanced he carried his masterful nose high in the air, but his head turned slowly from side to side in the helpless manner of the purblind, and he called in a high, querulous voice for the captain.

'You have my things?' he asked.

'Yes, Sir Charles,'

'Have you wine aboard?'

'I have ordered five cases, sir?'

'And tobacco?'

'There is a keg of Trinidad.'

'You play a hand at piquet?'

'Passably well, sir.'

'Then up anchor, and to sea!'

There was a fresh westerly wind, so by the time the sun was fairly through the morning haze, the ship was hull down from the islands. The decrepit Governor still limped the deck, with one guiding hand upon the quarter-rail.

'You are on Government service now, captain,' said he. 'They are counting the days till I come to Westminster, I promise you. Have you all that she will carry?'

'Every inch, Sir Charles?'

'Keep her so if you blow the sails out of her. I fear, Captain Scarrow, that you will find a blind and broken man a poor companion for your voyage.'

'I am honoured in enjoying your Excellency's society,' said the captain. 'But I am sorry that your eyes should be so afflicted.'

'Yes, indeed. It is the cursed glare of the sun on the white streets of Basseterre which has gone far to burn them out.'

'I had heard also that you had been plagued by a quartan ague.'

'Yes; I have had a pyrexy, which has reduced me much.'

'We had set aside a cabin for your surgeon.'

'Ah, the rascal! There was no budging him, for he has a snug business amongst the merchants. But hark!'

He raised his ring-covered hand in the air. From far astern there came the low deep thunder of cannon.

'It is from the island!' cried the captain in astonishment. 'Can it be a signal for us to put back?'

The Governor laughed.

'You have heard that Sharkey, the pirate, is to be hanged this morning. I ordered the batteries to salute when the rascal was kicking his last, so that I might know of it out at sea. There's an end of Sharkey!'

'There's an end of Sharkey!' cried the captain; and the crew took up the cry as they gathered in little knots upon the deck and stared back at the low, purple line of the vanishing land.

It was a cheering omen for their start across the Western Ocean, and the invalid Governor found himself a popular man on board, for it was generally understood that but for his insistence upon an immediate trial and sentence, the villain might have played upon some more venal judge and so escaped. At dinner that day Sir Charles gave many anecdotes of the deceased pirate; and so affable was he, and so skilful in adapting his conversation to men of lower degree, that captain, mate, and Governor smoked their long pipes and drank their claret as three good comrades should.

'And what figure did Sharkey cut in the dock?' asked the captain.

'He is a man of some presence,' said the Governor.

'I had always understood that he was an ugly, sneering devil,' remarked the mate.

'Well, I dare say he could look ugly upon occasions,' said the Governor.

'I have heard a New Bedford whaleman say that he could not forget his eyes,' said Captain Scarrow. 'They were of the lightest filmy blue, with red-rimmed lids. Was that not so, Sir Charles?'

'Alas, my own eyes will not permit me to know much of those of others! But I remember now that the Adjutant-General said that he had such an eye as you describe, and added that the jury were so foolish as to be visibly discomposed when it was turned upon them. It is well for them that he is dead, for he was a man who would never forget an injury, and if he had laid hands upon any one of them he would have stuffed him with straw and hung him for a figure-head.'

The idea seemed to amuse the Governor, for he broke suddenly into a high, neighing laugh, and the two seamen laughed also, but not so heartily, for they remembered that Sharkey was not the last pirate who sailed the western seas, and that as grotesque a fate might come to be their own. Another bottle was broached to drink to a pleasant voyage, and the Governor would drink just one other on the top of it, so that the seamen were glad at last to stagger off — the one to his watch and the other to his bunk. But when after his four hours' spell the mate came down again, he was amazed to see the Governor in his Ramillies wig, his glasses, and his powdering-gown still seated sedately at the lonely table with his reeking pipe and six black bottles by his side.

'I have drunk with the Governor of St Kitt's when he was sick,' said he, 'and God forbid that I should ever try to keep pace with him when he is well.'

The voyage of the *Morning Star* was a successful one, and in about three weeks she was at the mouth of the British Channel. From the first day the infirm Governor had begun to recover his strength, and before they were half-way across the Atlantic he was, save only for his eyes, as well as any man upon the ship. Those who uphold the nourishing qualities of wine might point to him in triumph, for never a night passed that he did not repeat the performance of his first one. And yet he would be out upon deck in the early morning as fresh and brisk as the best of them, peering about with his weak eyes, and asking questions about the sails and the rigging, for he was anxious to learn the ways of the sea. And he made up for the deficiency of his eyes by obtaining leave from the captain that the New

104

England seaman — he who had been cast away in the boat — should lead him about, and above all that he should sit beside him when he played cards and count the number of the pips, for unaided he could not tell the king from the knave.

It was natural that this Evanson should do the Governor willing service, since the one was the victim of the vile Sharkey, and the other was his avenger. One could see that it was a pleasure to the big American to lend his arm to the invalid, and at night he would stand with all respect behind his chair in the cabin and lay his great stubnailed forefinger upon the card which he should play. Between them there was little in the pockets either of Captain Scarrow or of Morgan, the first mate, by the time they sighted the Lizard.

And it was not long before they found that all they had heard of the high temper of Sir Charles Ewan fell short of the mark. At a sign of opposition or a word of argument his chin would shoot out from his cravat, his masterful nose would be cocked at a higher and more insolent angle, and his bamboo cane would whistle up over his shoulder. He cracked it once over the head of the carpenter when the man had accidentally jostled him upon the deck. Once, too, when there was some grumbling and talk of a mutiny over the state of the provisions, he was of opinion that they should not wait for the dogs to rise, but that they should march forward and set upon them until they had trounced the devilment out of them.

'Give me a knife and a bucket!' he cried with an oath, and could hardly be withheld from setting forth alone to deal with the spokesman of the seamen.

Captain Scarrow had to remind him that though he might be only answerable to himself at St Kitt's, killing became murder upon the high seas. In politics he was, as became his official position, a stout prop of the House of Hanover, and he swore in his cups that he had never met a Jacobite without pistolling him where he stood. Yet for all his vapouring and his violence he was so good a companion, with such a stream of strange anecdote and reminiscence, that Scarrow and Morgan had never known a voyage pass so pleasantly.

And then at length came the last day, when, after passing the island, they had struck land again at the high white cliffs at Beachy Head. As evening fell the ship lay rolling in an oily calm, a league off from Winchelsea, with the long dark snout of Dungeness jutting out in front of her. Next morning they would pick up their pilot at the Foreland, and Sir Charles might meet the king's ministers at Westminster before the evening. The boatswain had the watch, and the three friends were met for a last turn of cards in the cabin, the faithful American still serving as eyes to the Governor. There was a good stake upon the table, for the sailors had tried on this last night to win their losses back from their passenger. Suddenly he threw his cards down, and swept all the money into the pocket of his long-flapped silken waistcoat.

'The game's mine!' said he.

'Heh, Sir Charles, not so fast!' cried Captain Scarrow; 'you have not played out the hand, and we are not the losers.'

'Sink you for a liar!' said the Governor. 'I tell you that I have played out the hand, and that you are a loser.' He whipped off his wig and his glasses as he spoke, and there was a high, bald forehead, and a pair of shifty blue eyes with the red rims of a bull terrier.

'Good God!' cried the mate. 'It's Sharkey!'

The two sailors sprang from their seats, but the big American castaway had put his huge back against the cabin door, and he held a pistol in each of his hands. The passenger had also laid a pistol upon the scattered cards in front of him, and he burst into his high, neighing laugh.

'Captain Sharkey is the name, gentlemen,' said he, 'and this is Roaring Ned Galloway, the quartermaster of the *Happy Delivery*. We made it hot, and so they marooned us: me on

106

'Heh, Sir Charles, not so fast! You have not played out the hand.'

a dry Tortuga cay, and him in an oarless boat. You dogs — you poor, fond, water-hearted dogs — we hold you at the end of our pistols!'

'You may shoot, or you may not!' cried Scarrow, striking his hand upon the breast of his frieze jacket.

'If it's my last breath, Sharkey, I tell you that you are a bloody rogue and miscreant, with a halter and hell-fire in store for you!'

'There's a man of spirit, and one of my own kidney, and he's going to make a very pretty death of it!' cried Sharkey. 'There's no one aft save the man at the wheel, so you may keep your breath, for you'll need it soon. Is the dinghy astern, Ned?'

'Ay, ay, captain!'

'And the other boats scuttled?'

'I bored them all in three places.'

'Then we shall have to leave you, Captain Scarrow. You look as if you hadn't quite got your bearings yet. Is there anything you'd like to ask me?'

'I believe you're the devil himself!' cried the captain. 'Where is the Governor of St Kitt's?'

'When last I saw him his Excellency was in bed with his throat cut. When I broke prison I learnt from my friends — for Captain Sharkey has those who love him in every port — that the Governor was starting for Europe under a master who had never seen him. I climbed his verandah and I paid him the little debt that I owed him. Then I came aboard you with such of his things as I had need of, and a pair of glasses to hide these tell-tale eyes of mine, and I have ruffled it as a governor should. Now, Ned, you can get to work upon them.'

'Help! Help! Watch ahoy!' yelled the mate; but the butt of the pirate's pistol crashed down on to his head, and he dropped like a pithed ox. Scarrow rushed for the door, but the sentinel clapped his hand over his mouth, and threw his other arm round his waist.

'No use, Master Scarrow,' said Sharkey. 'Let us see you go down on your knees and beg for your life.'

'I'll see you —' cried Scarrow, shaking his mouth clear.

'Twist his arm round, Ned. Now will you?'

'No; not if you twist it off.'

'Put an inch of your knife into him.'

'You may put six inches, and then I won't.'

'Sink me, but I like his spirit!' cried Sharkey.

'Put your knife in your pocket, Ned. You've saved your skin, Scarrow, and it's a pity so stout a man should not take to the only trade where a pretty fellow can pick up a living. You must be born for no common death, Scarrow, since you have lain at my mercy and lived to tell the story. Tie him up, Ned.'

'To the stove, captain?'

'Tut, tut! there's a fire in the stove. None of your rover tricks, Ned Galloway, unless they are called for, or I'll let you know which of us two is captain and which is quarter-master. Make him fast to the table.'

'Nay, I thought you meant to roast him!' said the quarter-master. 'You surely do not mean to let him go?'

'If you and I were marooned on a Bahama cay, Ned Gallo-way, it is still for me to command and for you to obey. Sink you for a villain, do you dare to question my orders?'

'Nay, nay, Captain Sharkey, not so hot, sir!' said the quarter-master, and, lifting Scarrow like a child, he laid him on the table. With the quick dexterity of a seaman, he tied his spreadeagled hands and feet with a rope which was passed underneath, and gagged him securely with the long cravat which used to adorn the chin of the Governor of St Kitt's.

'Now, Captain Scarrow, we must take our leave of you,' said the pirate. 'If I had half a dozen of my brisk boys at my heels I should have had your cargo and your ship, but Roaring Ned could not find a foremast hand with the spirit of a mouse. I see there are some small craft about, and we shall get one of them. When Captain Sharkey has a boat he can get a smack, when he has a smack he can get a brig, when he has a brig he can get a barque, and when he has a barque he'll soon have a full-rigged ship of his own — so make haste into London town, or I may be coming back, after all, for the *Morning Star*.'

Captain Scarrow heard the key turn in the lock as they left the cabin. Then, as he strained at his bonds, he heard their footsteps pass up the companion and along the quarter-deck to where the dinghy hung in the stern. Then, still struggling and writhing, he heard the creak of the falls and the splash of the boat in the water. In a mad fury he tore and dragged at his ropes, until at last, with flayed wrists and ankles, he rolled from the table, sprang over the dead mate, kicked his way through the closed door, and rushed hatless on to the deck.

'Ahoy! Peterson, Armitage, Wilson!' he screamed. 'Cutlasses and pistols! Clear away the long-boat; Clear away the gig! Sharkey, the pirate, is in yonder dinghy. Whistle up the larboard watch, bo'sun, and tumble into the boats all hands.'

Down splashed the long-boat and down splashed the gig, but in an instant the coxswains and crews were swarming up the falls on to the deck once more.

'The boats are scuttled!' they cried. 'They are leaking like a sieve.'

The captain gave a bitter curse. He had been beaten and outwitted at every point. Above was a cloudless, starlit sky, with neither wind nor the promise of it. The sails flapped idly in the moonlight. Far away lay a fishing-smack, with the men clustering over their net.

Close to them was the little dinghy, dipping and lifting over the shining swell.

'They are dead men!' cried the captain. 'A shout all together, boys, to warn them of their danger.'

But it was too late.

At that very moment the dinghy shot into the shadow of the fishing-boat. There were two rapid pistol-shots, a scream, and then another pistol-shot, followed by silence. The clustering fishermen had disappeared. And then, suddenly, as the first puffs of a land-breeze came out from the Sussex shore, the boom swung out, the mainsail filled, and the little craft crept out with her nose to the Atlantic.

The Man With the Belt of Gold

from Kidnapped

by

ROBERT LOUIS STEVENSON

Kidnapped tells the story of David Balfour, whose uncle arranged for him to be kidnapped and shipped aboard the brig Covenant *to prevent him from discovering that he is the rightful heir to the Shaw estate. The year is 1751: the Jacobite rebellion in Scotland has been over for five years, but it is not yet forgotten.*

More than a week went by, in which the ill-luck that had hitherto pursued the *Covenant* upon this voyage grew yet more strongly marked. Some days she made a little way; others, she was driven actually back. As last we were beaten so far to the south that we tossed and tacked to and fro the whole of the ninth day, within sight of Cape Wrath and the wild, rocky coast on either hand of it. There followed on that a council of the officers, and some decision which I did not rightly understand, seeing only the result: that we had made a fair wind of a foul one and were running south.

The tenth afternoon, there was a falling swell and a thick, wet, white fog that hid one end of the brig from the other. All afternoon, when I went on deck, I saw men and officers listening hard over the bulwarks — 'for breakers,' they said; and though I did not so much as understand the word, I felt danger in the air, and was excited.

Maybe about ten at night, I was serving Mr Riach and the captain at their supper, when the ship struck something with a great sound, and we heard voices singing out. My two masters leaped to their feet.

'She's struck,' said Mr Riach.

'No, sir,' said the captain. 'We've only run a boat down.' And they hurried out.

The captain was in the right of it. We had run down a boat in the fog, and she had parted in the midst and gone to the bottom with all her crew, but one. This man (as I heard afterwards) had been sitting in the stern as a passenger, while the rest were on the benches rowing. At the moment of the blow, the stern had been thrown into the air, and the man (having his hands free, and for all he was encumbered with a frieze overcoat that came below his knees) had leaped up and caught hold of the brig's bowsprit. It showed he had luck and much agility and unusual strength, that he should have thus saved himself from such a pass. And yet, when the captain brought him into the round-house, and I set eyes on him for the first time, he looked as cool as I did.

He was smallish in stature, but well set and as nimble as a goat; his face was of a good open expression, but sunburnt very dark, and heavily freckled and pitted with the small-pox; his eyes were unusually light and had a kind of dancing madness in them, that was both engaging and alarming; and when he took off his greatcoat, he laid a pair of fine silver-mounted pistols on the table, and I saw that he was belted with a great sword. His manners, besides, were elegant, and he pledged the captain handsomely. Altogether I thought of him, at the first sight, that here was a man I would rather call my friend than my enemy.

The captain, too, was taking his observations, but rather of the man's clothes than his person. And to be sure, as soon as he had taken off the great coat, he showed forth mighty fine for the round-house of a merchant brig: having a hat with feathers, red waistcoat, breeches of black plush, and a blue coat with silver buttons and handsome silver lace: costly clothes, though somewhat spoiled with the fog and being slept in.

'I'm vexed, sir, about the boat,' says the captain.

'There are some pretty men gone to the bottom,' said the stranger, 'that I would rather see on the dry land again than half a score of boats.'

'Friends of yours?' said Hoseason.

'You have none such friends in your country,' was the reply. 'They would have died for me like dogs.'

'Well, sir,' said the captain, still watching him, 'there are more men in the world than boats to put them in.'

'And that's true too,' cried the other, 'and ye seem to be a gentleman of great penetration.'

'I have been in France, sir,' says the captain, so that it was plain he meant more by the words than showed upon the face of them.

'Well, sir,' says the other, 'and so has many a pretty man, for the matter of that.'

'No doubt, sir,' says the captain; 'and fine coats.'

'Oho!' says the stranger, 'is that how the wind sets?' And he laid his hand quickly on his pistols.

'Don't be hasty,' said the captain. 'Don't do a mischief, before ye see the need for it. Ye've a French soldier's coat upon your back and a Scotch tongue in your head, to be sure; but so has many an honest fellow in these days, and I dare say none the worse of it.'

'So?' said the gentleman in the fine coat: 'are ye of the honest party?' (meaning, Was he a Jacobite? for each side, in these sort of civil broils, takes the name of honesty for its own.)

114

'Why, sir,' replied the captain, 'I am a true-blue Protestant, and I thank God for it.' (It was the first word of any religion I had ever heard from him, but I learnt afterwards he was a great church-goer while on shore.) 'But, for all that,' says he, 'I can be sorry to see another man with his back to the wall.'

'Can ye so, indeed?' asks the Jacobite. 'Well sir, to be quite plain with ye, I am one of those honest gentlemen that were in trouble about the years forty-five and six; and (to be still quite plain with ye) if I got into the hands of any of the red-coated gentry, it's like it would go hard with me. Now, sir, I was for France; and there was a French ship cruising here to pick me up; but she gave us the go-by in the fog — as I wish from the heart ye had done yoursel'! And the best that I can say is this; If ye can set me ashore where I was going, I have that upon me will reward you highly for your trouble.'

'In France?' says the captain. 'No, sir; that I cannot do. But where ye come from — we might talk of that.'

And then, unhappily, he observed me standing in my corner, and packed me off to the galley to get supper for the gentleman. I lost no time I promise you; and when I came back into the round-house, I found the gentleman had taken a money-belt from about his waist, and poured out a guinea or two upon the table. The captain was looking at the guineas, and then at the belt, and then at the gentleman's face; and I thought he seemed excited.

'Half of it,' he cried, 'and I'm your man!'

The other swept back the guineas into the belt, and put it on again under his waistcoat. 'I have told ye, sir,' said he, 'that not one doit of it belongs to me. It belongs to my chieftain' — and here he touched his hat — 'and while I would be but a silly messenger to grudge some of it that the rest might come safe, I should show myself a hound indeed if I bought my own carcase any too dear. Thirty guineas on the seaside, or sixty if ye set me on the Linnhe loch. Take it, if ye will; if not, ye can do your worst.'

'Ay,' said Hoseason. 'And if I give ye over to the soldiers.'

'Ye would make a fool's bargain,' said the other. 'My chief, let me tell you, sir, is forfeited, like every honest man in Scotland. His estate is in the hands of the man they call King George; and it is his officers that collect the rents, or try to collect them. But for the honour of Scotland, the poor tenant bodies take a thought upon their chief lying in exile; and his money is a part of that very rent for which King George is looking. Now, sir, ye seem to me to be a man that understands things: bring this money within the reach of Government, and how much of it'll come to you?'

'Little enough, to be sure,' said Hoseason; and then, 'If they knew,' he added, dryly. 'But I think, if I was to try, that I could hold my tongue about it.'

'Ah, but I'll begowk* ye there,' cried the gentleman. 'Play me false, and I'll play you cunning. If a hand's laid upon me, they shall ken what money it is.'

'Well,' returned the captain, 'what must be must. Sixty guineas, and done. Here's my hand upon it.'

'And here's mine,' said the other.

And thereupon the captain went out (rather hurriedly, I thought), and left me alone in the round-house with the stranger.

At that period (so soon after the forty-five) there were many exiled gentlemen coming back at the peril of their lives, either to see their friends or to collect a little money; and as for the Highland chiefs that had been forfeited, it was a common matter of talk how their tenants would stint themselves to send them money, and their clansmen outface the soldiery to get it in, and run the gauntlet of our great navy to carry it across. All this I had, of course, heard tell of; and now I had a man

116

under my eyes whose life was forfeit on all these counts and upon one more; for he was not only a rebel and a smuggler of rents, but had taken service with King Louis of France. And as if all this were not enough, he had a belt full of golden guineas round his loins. Whatever my opinions, I could not look on such a man without a lively interest.

'And so you're a Jacobite?' said I, as I set meat before him.

'Ay,' said he, beginning to eat. 'And you, by your long face, should be a Whig.'

'Betwixt and between,' said I, not to annoy him; for indeed I was as good a Whig as Mr Campbell could make me.

'And that's naething,' said he. 'But I'm saying, Mr Betwixt-and-Between,' he added, 'this bottle of yours is dry; and it's hard if I'm to pay sixty guineas and be grudged a dram upon the back of it.'

'I'll go and ask for the key,' said I, and stepped on deck.

The fog was as close as ever, but the swell almost down. They had laid the brig too, not knowing precisely where they were, and the wind (what little there was of it) not serving well for their true course. Some of the hands were still hearkening for breakers; but the captain and the two officers were in the waist with their heads together. It struck me, I don't know why, that they were after no good; and the first word I heard, as I drew softly near, more than confirmed me.

It was Mr Riach, crying out as if upon a sudden thought. 'Couldn't we wile him out of the round-house?'

'He's better where he is,' returned Hoseason; 'He hasn't room to use his sword.'

'Well, that's true,' said Riach; 'but he's hard to come at.'

'Hut!' said Hoseason. 'We can get the man in talk, one upon each side, and pin him by the two arms; or if that'll not hold, sir, we can make a run by both the doors and get him under hand before he has the time to draw.'

At this hearing, I was seized with both fear and anger at

these treacherous, greedy, bloody men that I sailed with. My first mind was to run away; my second was bolder.

'Captain,' said I, 'the gentleman is seeking a dram, and the bottle's out. Will you give me the key?'

They all started and turned about.

'Why, here's our chance to get the firearms!' Riach cried; and then to me: 'Hark ye, David,' he said, 'do ye ken where the pistols are?'

'Ay, ay,' put in Hoseason. 'David kens; David's a good lad. Ye see, David my man, yon wild Hielandman is a danger to the ship, besides being a rank foe to King George, God bless him!'

I had never been so be-Davided since I came aboard; but I said yes, as if all I heard were quite natural.

'The trouble is,' resumed the captain, 'that all our firelocks great and little, are in the round-house under this man's nose; likewise the powder. Now, if I, or one of the officers, was to go in and take them, he would fall to thinking. But a lad like you, David, might snap up a horn and a pistol or two without remark. And if ye can do it cleverly, I'll bear it in mind when it'll be good for you to have friends; and that's when we come to Carolina.'

Here Mr Riach whispered him a little.

'Very right, sir,' said the captain; and then to myself: 'And see here, David, yon man has a beltful of gold, and I give you my word that you shall have your fingers in it.'

I told him I would do as he wished, though indeed I had scarce breath to speak with; and upon that he gave me the key of the spirit-locker, and I began to go slowly back to the round-house. What was I to do? They were dogs and thieves; they had stolen me from my own country; they had killed poor Ransome; and was I to hold the candle to another murder? But then, upon the other hand, there was the fear of death very plain before me; for what could a boy and a man, if

118

they were as brave as lions, against a whole ship's company.

I was still arguing it back and forth, and getting no great clearness, when I came into the round-house and saw the Jacobite eating his supper under the lamp; and at that my mind was made up all in a moment. I have no credit by it; it was by no choice of mine, but as if by compulsion, that I walked right up to the table and put my hand on his shoulder.

'Do ye want to be killed?' said I.

He sprang to his feet, and looked a question at me as clear as if he had spoken.

'Oh!' cried I, 'they're all murderers here; it's a ship full of them! They've murdered a boy already. Now it's you.'

'Ay, ay,' said he; 'but they haven't got me yet.' And then looking at me curiously, 'Will ye stand with me?'

'That will I!' said I. 'I am no thief, nor yet murderer. I'll stand by you.'

'Why then,' said he, 'what's your name?'

'David Balfour,' said I; and then thinking that a man with so fine a coat must like fine people, I added for the first time, 'of Shaws.'

It never occurred to him to doubt me, for a Highlander is used to see great gentlefolk in great poverty; but as he had no estate of his own, my words nettled a very childish vanity he had.

'My name is Stewart,' he said, drawing himself up. 'Alan Breck, they call me. A king's name is good enough for me, though I bear it plain and have the name of no farm-midden to clap to the hind-end of it.'

And having administered this rebuke as though it were something of a chief importance, he turned to examine our defences.

The round-house was built very strong, to support the breaching of the seas. Of its five apertures, only the skylight and the two doors were large enough for the passage of a man.

The doors, besides, could be drawn close; they were of stout oak, and ran in grooves, and were fitted with hooks to keep them either shut or open, as the need arose. The one that was already shut, I secured in this fashion; but when I was proceeding to slide to the other, Alan stopped me.

'David,' said he — 'for I cannae bring to mind the name of your landed estate, and so will make so bold as to call you David — that door, being open, is the best part of my defences.'

'It would be better shut,' says I.

'Not so, David,' says he. 'Ye see, I have but one face; but so long as that door is open and my face to it, the best part of my enemies will be in front of me, where I would aye wish to find them.'

Then he gave me from the rack a cutlass (of which there were a few besides the firearms), choosing it with great care, shaking his head and saying he had never in all his life seen poorer weapons; and next he set me down to the table with a powder-horn, a bag of bullets, and all the pistols, which he bade me charge.

'And that will be better work, let me tell you,' said he, 'for a gentleman of decent birth, than scraping plates and raxing drams to a wheen tarry sailors.'

Thereupon he stood up in the midst with his face to the door, and drawing his great sword, made trial of the room he had to wield it in.

'I must stick to the point,' he said, shaking his head; 'And that's a pity, too. It doesn't set my genius, which is all for the upper guard. And now,' said he, 'do you keep on charging the pistols, and give heed to me.'

I told him I would listen closely. My chest was tight, my mouth dry, the light dark to my eyes; the thought of the numbers that were soon to leap in upon us kept my heart in a flutter; and the sea, which I heard washing round the brig, and where I thought my dead body would be cast ere morning, ran in my mind strangely.

'First of all,' said he, 'how many are against us?'

I reckoned them up; and such was the hurry of my mind, I had to cast the numbers twice. 'Fifteen,' said I.

Alan whistled. 'Well,' said he, 'that can't be cured. And now follow me. It is my part to keep this door, where I look for the main battle. In that, ye have no hand. And mind and dinna fire to this side unless they get me down; for I would rather have ten foes in front of me than one friend like you cracking pistols at my back.'

I told him, indeed, I was no great shot.

'And that's very bravely said,' he cried, in a great admiration of my candour. 'There's many a pretty gentleman that wouldnae dare to say it.'

'But then, sir,' said I, 'there is the door behind you, which they may perhap break in.'

'Ay,' said he, 'and that is a part of your work. No sooner the pistols charged, than ye must climb up into yon bed where ye're handy at the window; and if they lift hand against the door, ye're to shoot. But that's not all. Let's make a bit of a soldier of ye, David. What else have ye to guard?'

'There's the skylight,' said I. 'But indeed, Mr Stewart, I would need to have eyes upon both sides to keep the two of them; for when my face is at the one, my back is to the other.'

'And that's very true,' said Alan. 'But have ye no ears to your head?'

'To be sure!' cried I. 'I must hear the bursting of the glass!'

'Ye have some rudiments of sense,' said Alan grimly.

But now our time of truce was come to an end. Those on deck had waited for my coming till they grew impatient; and scarce had Alan spoken, when the captain showed face in the open door.

'Stand!' cried Alan, and pointed his sword at him.

The captain stood, indeed; but he neither winced nor drew back a foot.

'A naked sword?' says he. 'This is a strange return for hospitality.'

'Do ye see me?' said Alan. 'I am come of kings; I bear a king's name. My badge is the oak. Do ye see my sword? It has slashed the heads of mair Whigamores than you have toes upon your feet. Call up your vermin to your back, sir, and fall on! The sooner the clash begins, the sooner ye'll taste this steel throughout your vitals.'

The captain said nothing to Alan, but he looked over at me with an ugly look. 'David,' said he, 'I'll mind this'; and the sound of his voice went through me with a jar.

Next moment he was gone.

'And now,' said Alan, 'let your hand keep your head, for the grip is coming.'

Alan drew a dirk, which he held in his left hand in case they should run in under his sword. I, on my part, clambered up into the berth with an armful of pistols, and something of a heavy heart, and set open the window where I was to watch. It was a small part of the deck that I could overlook, but enough for our purpose. The sea had gone down, and the wind was steady and kept the sails quiet; so that, there was a great stillness in the ship, in which I made sure I heard the sound of muttering voices. A little after, and there came a clash of steel upon the deck, by which I knew they were dealing out the cutlasses and one had been let fall; and after that silence again.

I do not know if I was what you call afraid; but my heart beat like a bird's, both quick and little; and there was a dimness came before my eyes which I continually rubbed away, and which continually returned. As for hope, I had none; but only a darkness of despair and a sort of anger against all the world that made me long to sell my life as dear as I was able. I tried to pray, I remember, but that same hurry of my mind, like a man running, would not suffer me to think upon the words; and my chief wish was to have the thing begin and be done with it.

It came all of a sudden when it did, with a rush of feet and a roar, and then a shout from Alan, and a sound of blows and some one crying out as if hurt. I looked back over my shoulder, and saw Mr Shuan in the doorway, crossing blades with Alan.

'That's him that killed the boy!' I cried.

'Look to your window!' said Alan, and as I turned back to my place, I saw him pass his sword through the mate's body.

It was none too soon for me to look to my own part; for my head was scarce back at the window, before five men carrying a spare yard for a battering-ram, ran past me and took post to drive the door in. I had never fired with a pistol in my life, and not often with a gun; far less against a fellow-creature. But it was now or never; and just as they swung the yard, I cried out, 'Take that!' and shot into their midst.

I must have hit one of them, for he sang out and gave back a step, and the rest stopped as if a little disconcerted. Before they had time to recover, I sent another ball over their heads; and at my third shot (which went as wide as the second) the whole party threw down the yard and ran for it.

Then I looked round again into the deck-house. The whole place was full of the smoke of my own firing, just as my ears seemed to be burst with the noise of the shots. But there was Alan, standing as before; only now his sword was running blood to the hilt, and himself so swelled with triumph and fallen into so fine an attitude, that he looked to be invincible. Right before him on the floor was Mr Shuan, on his hands and knees; the blood was pouring from his mouth, and he was sinking slowly lower, with a terrible, white face; and just as I looked, some of those from behind caught hold of him by the heels and dragged him bodily out of the round-house. I believe he died as they were doing it.

'There's one of your Whigs for ye!' cried Alan; and then turning to me, he asked if I had done much execution.

I told him I had winged one, and thought it was the captain.

'And I've settled two,' says he. 'No, there's not enough blood let; they'll be back again. To your watch, David. This was but a dram before meat.'

I settled back to my place, re-charging the three pistols I had fired, and keeping watch with both eye and ear.

Our enemies were disputing not far off upon the deck, and that so loudly that I could hear a word or two above the washing of the seas.

'It was Shuan bauchled it,' I heard one say.

And another answered him with a 'Wheesht, man! He's paid the piper.'

After that the voices fell again into the same muttering as before. Only now, one person spoke most of the time, as though laying down a plan, and first one and then the other answered him briefly, like men taking orders. By this, I made sure they were coming on again, and told Alan.

'It's what we have to pray for,' said he. 'Unless we can give them a good distaste of us, and done with it, there'll be nae sleep for either you or me. But this time, mind, they'll be in earnest.'

By this, my pistols were ready, and there was nothing to do but listen and wait. While the brush lasted, I had not the time to think if I was frighted; but now, when all was still again, my mind ran upon nothing else. The thought of the sharp swords and the cold steel was strong in me; and presently, when I began to hear stealthy steps and a brushing of men's

The skylight was dashed to pieces, and a man leaped through.

clothes against the roundhouse wall, and knew they were taking their places in the dark, I could have found it in my mind to cry out aloud.

All this was upon Alan's side; and I had begun to think my share of the fight was at an end, when I heard some one drop softly on the roof above me.

Then there came a single call on the sea-pipe, and that was the signal. A knot of them made one rush of it, cutlass in hand, against the door; and at the same moment, the glass of the skylight was dashed in a thousand pieces, and a man leaped through and landed on the floor. Before he got to his feet, I had clapped a pistol to his back, and might have shot him, too; only at the touch of him (and him alive) my whole flesh misgave me, and I could no more pull the trigger than I could have flown.

He had dropped his cutlass, as he jumped, and when he felt the pistol, whipped straight round and laid hold of me, roaring out an oath; and at that either my courage came again, or I grew so much afraid as came to the same thing; for I gave a shriek and shot him in the midst of the body. He gave the most horrible ugly groan and fell to the floor. The foot of a second fellow, whose legs were dangling through the skylight, struck me at the same time upon the head; and at that I snatched another pistol and shot this one through the thigh, so that he slipped through and tumbled in a lump on his companion's body. There was no talk of missing, any more than there was time to aim; I clapped the muzzle to the very place and fired.

I might have stood and stared at them for long, but I heard Alan shout as if for help, and that brought me to my senses.

He had kept the door so long; but one of the seamen, while he was engaged with others, had run in under his guard and caught him about the body. Alan was dirking him with his left hand, but the fellow clung like a leech. Another had broken in and had his cutlass raised. The door was thronged with their faces. I thought we were lost, and catching up my cutlass, fell on them in flank.

But I had not time to be of help. The wrestler dropped at last; and Alan, leaping back to get his distance, ran upon the others like a bull, roaring as he went. They broke before him like water, turning, and running, and falling one against another in their haste. The sword in his hand flashed like quicksilver into the huddle of our fleeing enemies; and at every flash there came the scream of a man hurt. I was still thinking we were lost, when lo! they were all gone, and Alan was driving them along the deck as a sheepdog chases sheep.

Yet he was no sooner out than he was back again, being as cautious as he was brave; and meanwhile the seamen continued running and crying out as if he was still behind them; and we heard them tumble one upon the other into the forecastle, and clap-to the hatch upon the top.

The round-house was like a shambles; three were dead inside, another lay in his death agony across the threshold, and there were Alan and I victorious and unhurt.

He came up to me with open arms. 'Come to my arms!' he cried, and embraced and kissed me hard upon both cheeks. 'David,' said he, 'I love you like a brother. And oh, man,' he cried in a kind of ecstasy, 'am I no a bonny fighter?'

Thereupon he turned to the four enemies, passed his sword clean through each of them, and tumbled them out of doors one after the other. As he did so, he kept humming and sing- ing and whistling to himself, like a man trying to recall an air; only what *he* was trying, was to make one. All the while, the flush was in his face, and his eyes were as bright as a five- year-old child's with a new toy. And presently he sat down upon the table, sword in hand; the air that he was making all the time began to run a little clearer, and then clearer still; and then out he burst with a great voice into a Gaelic song.

I have translated it here, not in verse (of which I have no skill) but at least in the king's English. He sang it often afterwards, and the thing became popular; so that I have heard it, and had it explained to me, many's the time.

> This is the song of the sword of Alan:
> The smith made it,
> The fire set it;
> Now it shines in the hand of Alan Breck.
>
> Their eyes were many and bright,
> Swift were they to behold,
> Many the hands they guided:
> The sword was alone.
>
> The dun deer troop over the hill,
> They are many, the hill is one;
> The dun deer vanish,
> The hill remains.
>
> Come to me from the hills of heather,
> Come from the isles of the sea.
> O far-beholding eagles,
> Here is your meat.

The Gunner's Fight With the Carronade

from Ninety-Three

by

VICTOR HUGO

One of the carronades of the battery, a twenty-pounder, had got loose.

This is perhaps the most formidable of all ocean accidents. Nothing more terrible can happen to a vessel in open sea and under full sail. A gun that breaks its moorings becomes suddenly some indescribable supernatural beast. It is a machine which transforms itself into a monster. This mass turns upon its wheels, has the rapid movements of a billiard ball; rolls with the rolling; pitches with the pitching; goes, comes, pauses, seems to meditate; resumes its course, rushes along the ship from end to end like an arrow, circles about, springs aside, evades, rears, breaks, kills, exterminates. It is a battering ram which assaults a wall at its own caprice. Moreover, the battering ram is of metal, the wall wood. It is the entrance of matter into space. One might say that this eternal slave avenges itself. It seems as if the power of evil hidden in what we call animate objects finds a vent and bursts suddenly out. It has an air of having lost patience, of seeking some fierce, obscure retribution; nothing more inexorable than this rage of the inanimate. The mad mass has the bounds of a panther, the weight of an elephant, the agility of the mouse, the obstinacy of the axe, the unexpectedness of the surge, the rapidity of lightning, the deafness of the tomb. It weighs ten thousand pounds, and it rebounds like a child's ball. Its flight is a wild whirl abruptly cut at right angles. What is to be done? How to end this? A tempest ceases, a cyclone passes, a wind falls, a broken mast is replaced, a leak is stopped, a fire dies out; but how to control this enormous brute of bronze? In what way can one attack it?

You can make a mastiff hear reason, astound a bull, fascinate a boa, frighten a tiger, soften a lion, but there is no resource with that monster, a cannon let loose. You cannot kill it — it is dead; at the same time it lives. It lives with a sinister life bestowed on it by Infinity.

The planks beneath it give it play. It is moved by the ship, which is moved by the sea, which is moved by the wind. This destroyer is a plaything. The ship, the waves, the blasts, all aid it; hence its frightful vitality. How to assail this fury of complication? How to fetter this monstrous mechanism for wrecking a ship? How foresee its comings and goings, its returns, its stops, its shocks? Any one of these blows upon the sides may stave out the vessel. How divine its awful gyrations? One has to deal with a projectile which thinks, seems to possess ideas, and which changes its direction at each instant. How stop the course of something which must be avoided? The horrible cannon flings itself about, advances, recoils, strikes to the right, strikes to the left, flees, passes, disconcerts, ambushes, breaks down obstacles, crushes men like flies. The great danger of the situation is in the mobility of its base. How combat an inclined plane which has caprices? The ship, so to speak, has lightning imprisoned in its womb which seeks to escape; it is like thunder rolling above an earthquake.

In an instant the whole crew were on foot. The fault was the chief gunner's; he had neglected to fix home the screw-nut of the mooring chain, and had so badly shackled the four wheels of the carronade that the play given to the sole and frame had separated the platform and ended by breaking the breeching. The cordage had broken, so that the gun was no longer secure on the carriage. The stationary breeching which prevents recoil was not in use at that period. As a heavy wave struck the port, the carronade, weakly attached, recoiled, burst its chain and began to rush wildly about. Conceive, in order to have an idea of this strange sliding, a drop of water running down a pane of glass.

At the moment when the lashings gave way the gunners were in the battery, some in groups, others standing alone, occupied with such duties as sailors perform in expectation of the command to clear for action. The carronade, hurled forward by the pitching, dashed into this knot of men and crushed four at the first blow; then, flung back and shot out anew by the rolling, it cut in two a fifth poor fellow, glanced off to the larboard side and struck a piece of the battery with such force as to unship it. The men rushed toward the ladder; the gun-deck emptied in the twinkling of an eye. The enormous cannon was left alone. She was given up to herself. She was her own mistress, and mistress of the vessel. She could do what she willed with both. The whole crew, accustomed to laugh in battle, trembled now. To describe the universal terror would be impossible.

Captain Boisberthelot and Lieutenant La Vieuville, although both intrepid men, stopped at the head of the stairs and remained mute, pale, hesitating, looking down on the deck. Someone pushed them aside with his elbow and descended.

It was their passenger — the peasant — the man of whom they had been speaking a moment before.

When he reached the foot of the ladder he stood still.

The cannon came and went along the deck. One might have fancied it the living chariot of the Apocalypse. The marine lantern oscillating from the ceiling added a dizzying whirl of lights and shadows to this vision. The shape of the cannon

131

was indistinguishable from the rapidity of its course; now it looked black in the light, now it cast weird reflections through the gloom.

It kept on its work of destruction. It had already shattered four other pieces, and dug two crevices in the side, fortunately above the water line, though they would leak in case a squall should come on. It dashed itself frantically against the framework. The solid tie-beams resisted, their curved forms giving them great strength; but they creaked ominously under the assaults of this terrible club, which seemed endowed with a sort of appalling ubiquity, striking on every side at once. The strokes of a bullet shaken in a bottle would not be madder or more rapid. The four wheels passed and repassed above the dead men, cut, carved, slashed them till the five corpses were a score of stumps rolling about the deck; the heads seemed to cry out; streams of blood twisted in and out the planks with every pitch of the vessel. The ceiling, damaged in seven places, began to gape. The whole ship was filled with the awful tumult.

The captain promptly recovered his composure, and at his orders the sailors threw down into the deck everything which could deaden or check the mad rush of the gun — mattresses, hammocks, spare sails, coils of rope, extra equipment, and the bales of false assignats of which the corvette carried a whole cargo; an infamous deception which the English considered a fair trick in war.

But what could these rags avail? No one dared descend to arrange them in useful fashion, and in a few instants they were mere heaps of lint. There was just enough sea to render the accident as complete as possible. A tempest would have been desirable; it might have thrown the gun upside down, and the four wheels once in the air, the monster could have been mastered. But the devastation increased. There were gashes and even fractures in the masts, which, embedded in the woodwork of the keel, pierce the decks of ships like great round pillars. The mizzen-mast was cracked, and the mainmast itself was injured under the convulsive blows of the gun. The battery was being destroyed. Ten pieces out of the thirty were disabled; the breaches multiplied in the side, and the corvette began to take in water.

The old passenger who had descended to the gun-deck, looked like a form of stone stationed at the foot of the stairs. He stood motionless, gazing sternly about upon the devastation. Indeed, it seemed impossible to take a single step forward.

Each bound of the liberated carronade menaced the destruction of the vessel. A few minutes more and shipwreck would be inevitable.

They must perish or put a summary end to the disaster — a decision must be made; but how?

What a combatant — this cannon! They must check this mad monster. They must seize this flash of lightning. They must overthrow this thunderbolt.

Boisberthelot said to La Vieuville, 'Do you believe in God, chevalier?'

La Vieuville replied, 'Yes, — no — sometimes.'

'In a tempest?'

'Yes, and in moments like this.'

'Only God can aid us here,' said Boisberthelot.

All were silent — the cannon kept up its horrible fracas.

The waves beat against the ship, their blows from without responded to the strokes of the cannon.

It was like two hammers alternating.

Suddenly into the midst of this sort of inaccessible circus, where the escaped cannon leaped and bounded, there sprang a man with an iron bar in his hand. It was the author of this catastrophe, the gunner whose culpable negligence had caused the accident — the captain of the gun. Having been the means of bringing about the misfortune, he desired to repair it. He

133

The gunner approached to challenge the cannon.

had caught up a handspike in one fist, a tiller-rope with a slipping noose in the other, and jumped down into the gun-deck. Then a strange combat began, a Titanic strife — the struggle of the gun against the gunner; a battle between matter and intelligence; a duel between the inanimate and the human.

The man was posted in an angle, the bar and rope in his two fists; backed against one of the riders, settled firmly on his legs as on two pillars of steel; livid, calm, tragic, rooted as it were in the planks, he waited. He waited for the cannon to pass him.

The gunner knew his piece, and it seemed to him that she must recognise her master. He had lived a long while with her. How many times had he thrust his hand between her jaws! It was his tame monster. He began to address it as he might have done his dog.

'Come!' said he. Perhaps he loved it. He seemed to wish that it would turn towards him. But to come towards him would be to spring upon him. Then he would be lost. How to avoid its crush? There was the question. All stared in terrified silence. Not a breast respired freely, except perchance that of the old man who stood on the deck with the two combatants, a stern second. He himself might be crushed by the piece. He did not stir. Beneath them the blind sea directed the battle.

At the instant when, accepting this awful hand-to-hand contest, the gunner approached to challenge the cannon, some chance fluctuation of the waves kept it for a moment immovable as if suddenly stupified. 'Come on!' the man said to it. It seemed to listen. Suddenly it darted upon him. The gunner avoided the shock.

The struggle began — struggle unheard of — the fragile matching itself against the invulnerable; the thing of flesh attacking the brazen brute; on the one side blind force, on the other a soul. The whole passed in half-light. It was like the indistinct vision of a miracle.

135

A soul — a strange thing; but you would have said that the cannon had one also — a soul filled with rage and hatred. The blindness appeared to have eyes. The monster had an air of watching the man. There was — one might have fancied so at least — cunning in this mass. It also chose its moment. It became some gigantic insect of metal, having, or seeming to have the will of a demon. Sometimes this colossal grasshopper would strike the low ceiling of the gun-deck, then fall back on its four wheels like a tiger upon its four claws, and dart anew on the man. He, supple, agile, adroit, would glide] away like a snake from the reach of these lightning-like movements. He avoided the encounters; but the blows which he escaped fell upon the vessel, and continued the havoc.

An end of broken chain remained attached to the carronade. This chain had twisted itself, one could not tell how, about the screw of the breech-button. One extremity of the chain was fastened to the carriage. The other, hanging loose, whirled madly about the gun, and added to the danger of its blows.

The screw held it like a clenched hand, and the chain, multiplying the strokes of the battering-ram by its strokes of a thong, made a fearful whirlwind about the cannon — a whip of iron in a fist of brass. This chain complicated the battle.

Nevertheless, the man fought. Sometimes, even, it was the man who attacked the cannon. He crept along the side, bar and rope in hand, and the cannon had the air of understand, ing, and fled as if it perceived a snare. The man pursued it, formidable, fearless.

Such a duel could not last long. The gun seemed suddenly to say to itself, 'Come, we must make an end!' and it paused. One felt the approach of the crisis. The cannon, as if in suspense, appeared to have, or had — because it seemed to all a sentient being — a furious premeditation. It sprang unexpectedly upon the gunner. He jumped aside, let it pass, and cried out with a laugh, 'Try again!' The gun, as if in fury, broke a carronade to larboard; then, seized anew by the invisible sling which held it, was flung to starboard towards the man, who escaped.

Three carronades gave way under the blows of the gun; then, as if blind and no longer conscious of what it was doing, it turned its back on the man, rolled from the stern to the bow, bruising the stern and making a breach in the planking of the prow. The gunner had taken refuge at the foot of the stairs, a few steps from the old man, who was watching.

The gunner held his handspike in rest. The cannon seemed to perceive him, and without taking the trouble to turn itself, backed upon him with the quickness of an axe-stroke. The gunner, if driven back against the side, was lost. The crew uttered a simultaneous cry.

But the old passenger, now immovable, made a spring more rapid than all those wild whirls. He seized a bale of the false assignats, and at the risk of being crushed, succeeded in flinging it between the wheels of the carronade. This manoeuvre, decisive and dangerous, could not have been executed with more adroitness and precision by a man trained to all the exercises set down in *Durosel's Manual of Sea Gunnery.*

The bale had the effect of a plug. A pebble may stop a log, a tree branch turn an avalanche. The carronade stumbled. The gunner, in his turn, seizing this terrible chance, plunged his iron bar between the spokes of one of the hind wheels. The cannon was stopped. It staggered. The man, using the bar as a lever, rocked it to and fro. The heavy mass turned over with a clang like a falling bell, and the gunner, dripping with sweat, rushed forward headlong and passed the slipping noose of the tiller-rope about the brazen neck of the overthrown monster.

It was ended. The man had conquered. The ant had subdued the mastodon; the pygmy had taken the thunderbolt prisoner.

The marines and the sailors clapped their hands.

137

The whole crew hurried down with cables and chains, and in an instant the cannon was securely lashed.

The gunner saluted the passenger.

'Sir,' he said to him, 'you have saved my life.'

How Dantès escaped from the Chateau d'If

from The Count of Monte Cristo

by

ALEXANDRE DUMAS

On the bed, at full length, and faintly lighted by the pale ray that penetrated the window, was visible a sack of coarse cloth, under the large folds of which were stretched a long and stiffened form; it was Faria's last winding-sheet — a winding-sheet which, as the turnkey said, costs so little. All, then, was completed. A material separation had taken place between Dantès and his old friend; he could no longer see those eyes which had remained open to look even beyond death; he could no longer clasp that hand of industry which had lifted for him the veil that had concealed hidden and obscure things. Faria, the usual and the good companion, with whom he was accustomed to live so intimately, no longer breathed. He seated himself on the edge of that terrible bed, and fell into a melancholy and gloomy reverie.

Alone! — he was alone again! — again relapsed into silence! he found himself once again in the presence of nothingness! Alone! — no longer to see, no longer to hear the voice of the only human being who attached him to life! Was it not better, like Faria, to seek the presence of his Maker, and learn the

139

enigma of life at the risk of passing through the mournful gate of intense suffering? The idea of suicide, driven away by his friend, and forgotten in his presence whilst living, arose like a phantom before him in the presence of his dead body.

'If I could die,' he said, 'I should go where he goes, and should assuredly find him again. But how to die? It is very easy', he continued, with a smile of bitterness; 'I will remain here, rush on the first person that opens the door, will strangle him, and then they will guillotine me.'

But as it happens that in excessive griefs, as in great tempests, the abyss is found between the tops of the loftiest waves, Dantès recoiled from the idea of his infamous death, and passed suddenly from despair to an ardent desire for life and liberty.

'Die! Oh no!' he exclaimed, 'not die now, after having lived and suffered so long and so much! Die! yes, had I died years since; but now it would be, indeed, to give way to my bitter destiny. No, I desire to live; I desire to struggle to the very last; I wish to reconquer the happiness of which I have been deprived. Before I die I must not forget that I have my executioners to punish, and perhaps too, who knows, some friends to reward. Yet they will forget me here, and I shall die in my dungeon like Faria.'

As he said this, he remained motionless, his eyes fixed like a man struck with a sudden idea, but whom this idea fills with amazement. Suddenly he rose, lifted his hand to his brow as if his brain were giddy, paced twice or thrice round his chamber, and then paused abruptly at the bed.

'Ah, ah!' he muttered, 'who inspires me with this thought? Is it thou, gracious God? Since none but the dead pass freely from this dungeon, let me assume the place of the dead.'

Without giving himself time to reconsider his decision, and, indeed, that he might now allow his thoughts to be distracted from his desperate resolution, he bent over the appalling sack, opened it with the knife which Faria had made, drew the corpse from the sack, and transported it along the gallery to his own chamber, laid it on his couch, passed round its head the rag he wore at night round his own, covered it with his counterpane, once again kissed the ice-cold brow, and tried vainly to close the resisting eyes, which glared horribly; turned the head towards the wall, so that the gaoler might, when he brought his evening meal, believe that he was asleep, as was his frequent custom; returned along the gallery, threw the bed against the wall, returned to the other cell, took from the hiding place the needle and thread, flung off his rags, that they might feel naked flesh only beneath the coarse sackcloth, and getting inside the sack, placed himself in the posture in which the dead body had been laid, and sewed up the mouth of the sack withinside.

The beating of his heart might have been heard, if by any mischance the gaolers had entered at that moment. Dantès might have waited until the evening visit was over, but he was afraid that the governor might change his resolution, and order the dead body to be removed earlier. In that case, his last hope would have been destroyed. Now his project was settled under any circumstances, and he hoped thus to carry it into effect. If, during the time he was being conveyed the grave-diggers should discover they were conveying a live instead of a dead body, Dantès did not intend to give them time to recognise him, but with a sudden cutting of the knife he meant to open the sack from top to bottom, and, profiting by their alarm, escape; if they tried to catch him he would use his knife.

If they conducted him to the cemetery and laid him in the grave, he would allow himself to be covered with earth and then, as it was night, the grave-diggers could scarcely have turned their backs, ere he would have worked his way through the soft soil and escape, hoping that the weight would not be too heavy for him to support. If he was deceived in this, and the earth proved too heavy, he would be stifled, and then, so much the better, all would be over. Dantès had not eaten since the previous evening, but he had not thought of hunger or thirst, nor did he now think of it. His position was too precarious to allow him time to reflect on any thought but one.

The first risk that Dantès ran was that the gaoler, when he brought him his supper at seven o'clock, might perceive the substitution he had effected; fortunately, twenty times at least, from misanthropy or fatigue, Dantès had received his gaoler in bed, and then the man placed his bread and soup on the table and went away without saying a word. This time the gaoler might not be silent as usual, but speak to Dantès, and seeing that he received no reply, go to the bed and discover all.

When seven o'clock came, Dantès' agony really commenced. His hand placed upon his heart was unable to repress its throbbings, whilst, with the other, he wiped the perspiration from his temples. From time to time shudderings ran through his whole frame, and collapsed his heart as if it were frozen. Then he thought he was going to die. Yet the hours passed on without any stir in the *château*, and Dantès felt that he had escaped the first danger: it was a good augury. At length, at the hour the governor had appointed, footsteps were heard on the stair. Edmond felt that the moment had arrived, and summoning up all his courage, held his breath, happy if at the same time he could have repressed in like manner the hasty pulsation of his arteries.

They stopped at the door — there were two steps, and Dantès guessed it was the two grave-diggers who came to seek him — this idea was soon converted into certainty when he heard the noise they made in putting down the hand-bier. The door opened, and a dim light reached Dantès' eyes through the coarse sack that covered him; he saw two shadows approach his bed, a third remaining at the door with a torch in his hands. Each of these two men, approaching the ends of the bed, took the sack by its extremities.

'He's heavy though for an old and thin man,' said one, as he raised the head.

'They say every year adds half a pound to the weight of the bones,' said another, lifting the feet.

'Have you tied the knot?' inquired the first speaker.

'What would be the use of carrying so much more weight?' was the reply; 'I can do that when we get there.'

'What's the knot for?' thought Dantès.

They deposited the supposed corpse on the bier. Edmond stiffened himself in order to play the part of a dead man, and then the party, lighted by the man with the torch, who went first, ascended the stairs. Suddenly he felt the fresh and sharp night air, and Dantès recognised the *Mistral*. It was a sudden sensation, at the same time replete with delight and agony. The bearers advanced twenty paces, then stopped, putting their bier down on the ground. One of them went away, and Dantès heard his shoes on the pavement.

'Where am I then?' he asked himself.

'Really, he is by no means a light load!' said the other bearer, sitting on the edge of the hand-barrow. Dantès first impulse was to escape, but fortunately, he did not attempt it.

'Light me you!' said the other bearer, 'or I shall not find what I am looking for.'

The man with the torch complied, although not asked in the most polite terms.

'What can he be looking for?' thought Edmond. 'The spade?'

An exclamation of satisfaction indicated that the grave-digger had found the object of his search.

'At last,' said the other, 'not without some trouble though.'

'Yes,' was the answer, 'but it has lost nothing by waiting.'

As he said this, the man came towards Edmond, who heard a heavy and sounding substance laid down beside him, and

'One!' said the grave-diggers. 'Two! Three!'

at the same moment a cord was fastened round his feet with sudden and painful violence.

'Well, have you tied the knot?' inquired the grave-digger who was looking on.

'Yes, and pretty tight too, I can tell you,' was the answer.

'Move on, then.' And the bier was lifted once more, and they proceeded.

They advanced fifty paces farther, and then stopped to open a door, then went forward again. The noise of waves dashing against the rocks on which the *château* is built, reached Dantès, ears distinctly as they progressed.

'Bad weather!' observed one of the bearers; 'not a pleasant night for a dip in the sea.'

'Why, yes, the abbé runs a chance of being wet,' said the other; and then there was a burst of brutal laughter.

Dantès did not comprehend the jest, but his hair stood er ec on his head.

'Well, here we are at last,' said one of them.

'A little farther — a little farther,' said the other. 'You know very well that the last was stopped on his way, dashed on the rocks, and the governor told us next day that we were careless fellows.'

They ascended five or six more steps, and then Dantès felt that they took him one by the head and the other by the heels, and swung him to and fro.

'One!' said the grave-diggers. 'Two! Three!'

And at the same instant Dantès felt himself flung into the air like a wounded bird falling, falling with a rapidity that made his blood curdle. Although drawn downwards by a heavy weight which was hastening his rapid descent, it seemed to him as if the time were a century. At last, with a terrific dash, he entered the ice-cold water, and as he did so he uttered a shrill cry, stifled in a moment by his immersion beneath the waves.

Dantès had been flung into the sea, into whose depths he was dragged by a thirty-six pound shot tied to his feet. The sea is the cemetery of the Château d'If.

Dantès, although giddy and almost suffocated, had yet sufficient presence of mind to hold his breath; and as his right hand (prepared as he was for every chance) held his knife open, he rapidly ripped up the sack, extricated his arm, then his head; but in spite of all his efforts to free himself from the shot, he felt it dragging him down still lower. He then bent his body, and by a desperate effort severed the cord that bound his legs, at the moment he was suffocating. With a vigorous spring he rose to the surface of the sea, whilst the shot bore to its depths the sack that had so nearly become his shroud.

Dantès merely paused to breathe, and then dived again, in order to avoid being seen. When he arose a second time he was fifty paces from where he had first sunk. He saw overhead a black and tempestuous sky, over which the wind was driving the fleeting vapours that occasionally suffered a twinkling star to appear; before him was the vast expanse of waters, sombre and terrible, whose waves foamed and roared as if before the approach of a storm. Behind him, blacker than the sea, blacker than the sky, rose like a phantom the giant of granite, whose projecting crags seemed like arms extended to seize their prey; and on the highest rock was a torch that lighted two figures. He fancied these two forms were looking at the sea; doubtless these strange grave-diggers had heard his cry. Dantès dived again, and remained a long time beneath the water. This manoeuvre was already familiar to him, and usually attracted a crowd of spectators in the bay before the lighthouse at Marseilles when he swam there, and who, with one accord, pronounced him the best swimmer in the port. When he reappeared the light had disappeared.

It was necessary to strike out to sea. Ratonneau and Pomègue are the nearest isles of all those that surround the Château d'If; but Ratonneau and Pomègue are inhabited, together with the islet of Daume; Tiboulen or Lemaire were the most secure. The isles of Tiboulen and Lemaire are a league from the Château d'If. Dantès, nevertheless, determined to make for them. But how could he find his way in the darkness of the night? At this moment he saw before him, like a brilliant star, the lighthouse of Planier. By leaving this light on the right, he kept the isle of Tiboulen a little on the left; by turning to the left, therefore, he would find it. But, as we have said, it was at least a league from the Château d'If to this island. Often in prison, Faria had said to him, when he saw him idle and inactive, 'Dantès, you must not give way to this listlessness; you will be drowned if you seek to escape, and your strength has not properly been exercised and prepared for exertion.' These words rang in Dantès' ears, even beneath the waves; he hastened to cleave his way through them to see if he had not lost his strength. He found with pleasure that his captivity had taken away nothing of his power, and that he was still master of that element on whose bosom he had so often sported as a boy.

Fear, that relentless pursuer, clogged Dantès' efforts. He listened if any noise was audible; each time that he rose over the waves his looks scanned the horizon, and strove to penetrate the darkness. Every wave seemed a boat in his pursuit, and he redoubled exertions that increased his distance from the *château*, but the repetition of which weakened his strength. He swam on still, and already the terrible *château* had disappeared in the darkness. He could not see it, but he *felt* its presence. An hour passed, during which Dantès, excited by the feeling of freedom, continued to cleave the waves.

'Let us see,' said he, 'I have swum above an hour, but as the wind is against me, that has retarded my speed; however, if I am not mistaken, I must be close to the isle of Tiboulen.

But what if I were mistaken?' A shudder passed over him. He sought to tread water, in order to rest himself; but the sea was too violent, and he felt that he could not make use of this means of repose. 'Well,' said he, 'I will swim on until I am worn out, or the cramp siezes me, and then I shall sink.' And he struck out with the energy of despair.

Suddenly the sky seemed to him to become still darker and more dense, and compact clouds lowered towards him; at the same time he felt a violent pain in his knee. His imagination told him a ball had struck him, and that in a moment he would hear the report; but he heard nothing. Dantès put out his hand, and felt resistance; he then extended his leg, and felt the land, and in an instant guessed the nature of the object he had taken for a cloud. Before him rose a mass of strangely formed rocks, that resembled nothing so much as a vast fire petrified at the moment of its most fervent combustion. It was the isle of Tiboulen. Dantès rose, advanced a few steps, and, with a fervent prayer of gratitude, stretched himself on the granite, which seemed to him softer than down. Then, in spite of the wind and rain, he fell into the deep, sweet sleep of those worn out by fatigue.

At the expiration of an hour Edmond was awakened by the roar of the thunder. The tempest was unchained and let loose in all its fury; from time to time a flash of lightning stretched across the heavens like a fiery serpent, lighting up the clouds that rolled on like the waves of an immense chaos.

Dantès had not been deceived — he had reached the first of the two isles, which was, in reality, Tiboulen. He knew that it was barren and without shelter; but when the sea became more calm, he resolved to plunge into its waves again, and swim to Lemaire, equally arid, but larger, and consequently better adapted for concealment.

An overhanging rock offered him a temporary shelter, and scarcely had he availed himself of it when the tempest burst forth in all its fury. Edmond felt the rock beneath which he lay, tremble, the waves, dashing themselves against the granite rock, wetted him with their spray. In safety as he was, he felt himself become giddy in the midst of this war of the elements and the dazzling brightness of the lightning. It seemed to him that the island trembled to its base, and that it would, like a vessel at anchor, break her moorings and bear him off into the centre of the storm.

He remembered then that he had not eaten or drunk for four and twenty hours. He extended his hands, and drank greedily of the rain-water that had lodged in a hollow of the rock. As he rose, a flash of lightning that seemed as if the whole of the heavens were opened, illumined the darkness. By its light, between the isle of Lemaire and Cape Croiselle, a quarter of a league distant, Dantès saw, like a spectre, a fishing-boat driven rapidly on by the force of the wind and waves. A second after, he saw it again, approaching nearer. Dantès cried out at the top of his voice to warn them of their danger, but they saw it themselves. Another flash showed him four men clinging to the shattered mast and the rigging, while a fifth clung to the broken rudder. The men he beheld doubtless saw him, for their cries were carried to his ears by the wind. Above the splintered mast a sail rent to tatters was waving; suddenly the ropes that held it gave way, and it disappeared in the darkness of the night like a vast sea-bird.

At the same moment a violent crash was heard, and the cries of distress. Perched on the summit of the rock, Dantès saw, by the lightning, the vessel in pieces; and amongst the fragments were visible the agonised features of the unhappy sailors. Then all became dark again.

Dantès ran down the rocks at the risk of himself being dashed to pieces; he listened, he strove to examine, but he heard and saw nothing — all human cries had ceased and the tempest alone continued to rage. By degrees the wind abated, vast,

149

grey clouds rolled towards the west, and the blue firmament appeared studded with bright stars. Soon a red streak became visible in the horizon, the waves whitened, a light played over them and gilded their foaming crests with gold. It was day.

Dantès stood silent and motionless before this vast spectacle, for since his captivity he had forgotten it. He turned towards the fortress and looked both at the sea and the land. The gloomy building rose from the bosom of the ocean with that imposing majesty of inanimate objects that seems at once to watch and command. It was about five o'clock. The sea continued to grow calmer.

'In two or three hours,' thought Dantès, 'the turnkey will enter my chamber, find the body of my poor friend, recognise it, seek for me in vain, and give the alarm. Then the passage will be discovered; the men who cast me into the sea and who must have heard the cry I uttered will be questioned. Then boats filled with armed soldiers will pursue the wretched fugitive. The cannon will warn everyone to refuse shelter to a man wandering about naked and famished. The police of Marseilles will be on alert by the land, whilst the government pursues me by sea. I am cold. I am hungry. I have lost even the knife that saved me. Oh, my God! I have suffered enough surely. Have pity on me, and do for me now what I am unable to do for myself.'

As Dantès (his eyes turned in the direction of the Château d'If) uttered this prayer, he saw appear at the extremity of the isle of Pomègue like a bird skimming over the sea, a small bark, that the eye of a sailor alone could recognise as a Genoese tartane. She was coming out of Marseilles harbour, and was standing out to sea rapidly, her sharp prow cleaving through the waves.

'Oh!' cried Edmond, 'to think that in half an hour I could join her, did I not fear being questioned, detected, and conveyed back to Marseilles! What can I do? What story can I invent? Under pretext of trading, these men, who are in reality smugglers, will prefer selling me to doing a good action. I must wait. But I cannot — I am starving. In a few hours my strength will be utterly exhausted; besides, perhaps I have not been missed at the fortress. I can pass as one of the sailors wrecked last night. This story will pass current, for there is no one left to contradict me.' As he spoke, Dantès looked towards the spot where the fishing-vessel had been wrecked, and started. The red cap of one of the sailors hung to a point of the rock and some beams that had formed part of the vessel's keep, floated at the foot of the crags.

In an instant Dantès plan was formed. He swam to the cap, placed it on his head, seized one of the beams, and struck out so as to cross the line the vessel was taking. 'I am saved!' murmured he. And this conviction restored his strength.

He soon perceived the vessel, which, having the wind right ahead, was tacking between the Château d'If and the tower of Planier. For an instant he feared less the bark, instead of keeping inshore, should stand out to sea, but he soon saw by her manoeuvres that she wished to pass, like most vessels bound for Italy, between the islands of Jaros and Calaseraigne. However, the vessel and the swimmer insensibly neared one another, and in one of its tacks the bark approached within a quarter of a mile of him. He rose on the waves, making signs of distress; but no one on board perceived him, and the vessel stood on another tack. Dantès would have cried out, but he reflected that the wind would drown his voice.

It was then he rejoiced at his precaution in taking the beam, for without it he would have been unable perhaps, to reach the vessel — certainly to return to shore, should he be unsuccessful in attracting attention.

Dantès, although almost sure as to what course the bark would take, had yet watched it anxiously until it tacked and stood towards him. Then he advanced; before they met however, the vessel again changed her direction.

By a violent effort he rose half out of the water, waving his cap, and uttering a loud shout peculiar to sailors. This time he was both seen and heard, and the tartane instantly steered towards him. At the same time he saw they were about to lower a boat. An instant after, the boat, rowed by two men, advanced rapidly towards him. Dantès abandoned the beam which he now thought useless, and swam vigorously to meet them. But he had reckoned too much upon his strength, and then he felt how serviceable the beam had been to him. His arms grew stiff, his legs had lost their flexibility, and he was almost breathless. He uttered a second cry. The two sailors redoubled their efforts, and one of them cried in Italian, 'Courage'. The word reached his ear as a wave which he no longer had the strength to surmount passed over his head. He rose again to the surface, supporting himself by one of those desperate efforts a drowning man makes, uttered a third cry, and felt himself sink again, as if the fatal shot were again tied to his feet. The water passed over his head, and the sky seemed livid. A violent effort again brought him to the surface. He felt as if something seized him by the hair, but he saw and heard nothing. He had fainted.

When he opened his eyes, Dantès found himself on the deck of the tartane. His first care was to see what direction they were pursuing. They were rapidly leaving the Château d'If behind. Dantès was so exhausted that the exclamation of joy he uttered was mistaken for a sigh.

As we have said, he was lying on the deck. A sailor was rubbing his limbs with a woollen cloth; another, whom he recognised as the one who had cried out 'Courage' held a gourd full of rum to his mouth; while the third, an old sailor, at once the pilot and captain, looked on with that egotistical pity men feel for a misfortune that they have escaped yesterday and which may overtake them tomorrow.

'Who are you?' said the pilot, in bad French.

'I am,' replied Dantès in bad Italian, 'a Maltese sailor. We were coming from Syracuse laden with grain. The storm of last night overtook us at Cape Morgieu, and we were wrecked on these rocks. You have saved my life, and I thank you.'

'Now, what are we to do with you?' said the captain.

'Alas! anything you please. My captain is dead; I have barely escaped; but I am a good sailor. Leave me at the first port you make; I shall be sure to find employment.'

'Do you know the Mediterranean?'

'I have sailed over it since my childhood.'

'You know the best harbours?'

'There are few ports that I could not enter or leave with my eyes shut.'

'I say, Captain,' said the sailor who had cried 'Courage!' to Dantès, 'if what he says is true, what hinders his staying with us?'

'If he says true,' said the captain doubtingly. 'But in his present condition he will promise anything, and take his chance of keeping it afterwards.'

'I will do more than I promise,' said Dantès.

'We shall see,' returned the other, smiling.

'As you will,' said Dantès, getting up. 'Where are you going?'

'To Leghorn.'

'Then why, instead of tacking so frequently, do you not sail nearer the wind?'

'Because we should run straight on to the island of Rion.'

'You shall pass it by twenty fathoms.'

'Take the helm then, and let us see what you know.'

The young man took the helm, ascertaining by a slight pressure if the vessel answered the rudder, and seeing that, without being a first rate sailer, yet she was tolerably obedient:

'To the braces!' said he.

The four seamen who composed the crew, obeyed, whilst the pilot looked on.

'Haul taut!'

They obeyed.

'Belay!'

This order was also executed, and the vessel passed, as Dantès had predicted, twenty fathoms to the right.

'Bravo!' cried the captain.

'Bravo!' repeated the sailors.

And they all regarded with astonishment this man whose eye had recovered an intelligence and his body a vigour they were far from suspecting.

'You see,' said Dantès, quitting the helm, 'I shall be of some use to you at least during the voyage. If you do not want me at Leghorn, you can leave me there, and I will pay you out of the first wages I get, for my food and the clothes you lend me.

'Ah,' said the captain, 'we can agree very well, if you are reasonable.'

'Give me what you give the others,' returned Dantès.

'That's not fair,' said the seaman who had saved Dantès, 'for you know more than we do.'

'What's that to you, Jacopo?' returned the captain. 'Everyone's free to ask what he pleases.'

'That's true,' replied Jacopo, 'I only made a remark.'

'Well, you would do much better to lend him a jacket, and a pair of trousers if you have them.'

'No,' said Jacopo, 'but I have a shirt and a pair of trousers.'

'That is all I want,' interrupted Dantès. 'Thank you, my friend.'

Jacopo dived into the hold and soon returned with what Edmond wanted.

'Now then, do you wish for anything else?' said the captain.

'A piece of bread, and another glass of the capital rum I tasted, for I have not eaten or drunk for a long time.'

He had not in truth, tasted food for forty hours. They brought him a piece of bread, and Jacopo offered him the gourd.

'Larboard your helm!' cried the captain to the helmsman.

Dantès glanced to the same side as he lifted the gourd to his mouth.

'Hulloa! What's the matter at the Château d'If?' said the captain.

A small white cloud, which had attracted Dantès' attention, crowned the summit of the bastion of the Château d'If. A moment later the far off report of a gun was heard. The sailors looked at one another.

'What does it mean?' asked the captain.

'A prisoner has escaped from the Château d'If, and they are firing the alarm gun,' replied Dantès.

The captain glanced at him, but he had lifted the rum to his lips, and was drinking it with so much composure that his suspicions, if he had any, died away.

'At any rate,' murmured he, 'if it be, so much the better, for I have made a rare acquisition.'

Under pretence of being fatigued, Dantès asked to take the helm. The helmsman, enchanted to be relieved, looked at the captain who, by a nod, indicated that he might abandon it to his new comrade. Dantès could thus keep his eye on Marseilles.

'What day of the month?' asked he of Jacopo, who sat down beside him.

'The 28th of February.'

'In what year?' asked Dantès.

'In what year? You ask me what year!'

'Yes,' replied the young man, 'I ask you in what year!'

'You have forgotten?'

'I was so frightened last night,' said Dantès laughing, 'that I have almost lost my memory. I ask you what year it is?'

'1829,' said Jacopo.

It was fourteen years, day for day, since Dantès arrest.

He was nineteen when he entered the Château d'If; he was thirty-three when he escaped. A sorrowful smile passed over his face; he asked himself what had become of Mercédès, who must believe him dead. Then his eyes lighted up with hatred as he thought of the three men who had caused him so long and wretched captivity. He renewed vengeance against, Danglers, Fernand, and Villefort the oath of implacable vengeance he had made in his dungeon. This oath was no longer a vain menace; for the fastest sailor in the Mediterranean would have been unable to overtake the little tartane, that with every stitch of canvas set, was flying before the wind to Leghorn.

Hornblower and the Man Who Felt Queer
from Mr Midshipman Hornblower

by

C. S. FORESTER

This time the wolf was prowling round outside the sheep-fold. H. M. frigate *Indefatigable* had chased the French corvette *Papillon* into the mouth of the Gironde, and was seeking a way of attacking her where she lay anchored in the stream under the protection of the batteries at the mouth. Captain Pellew took his ship into shoal water as far as he dared, until, in fact, the batteries fired warning shots to make him keep his distance, and he stared long and keenly through his glass at the corvette. Then he shut his telescope and turned on his heel to give the order that worked the *Indefatigable* away from the dangerous lee shore — out of sight of land, in fact.

His departure might lull the French into a sense of security which, he hoped, would prove unjustified. For he had no intention of leaving them undisturbed. If the corvette could be captured or sunk, not only would she be unavailable for raids on British commerce but also the French would be forced to increase their coastal defences at this point and lessen the effort that could be put out elsewhere. War is a matter of savage blow and counterblow, and even a forty-gun frigate could strike shrewd blows if shrewdly handled.

Midshipman Hornblower was walking the lee side of the

quarterdeck, as became his lowly station as the junior officer of the watch, in the afternoon, when Midshipman Kennedy approached him. Kennedy took off his hat with a flourish and bowed low, as his dancing master had once taught him, left foot advanced, hat down by the right knee. Hornblower entered into the spirit of the game, laid his hat against his stomach and bent himself in the middle three times in quick succession. Thanks to his physical awkwardness, he could parody ceremonial solemnity almost without trying.

'Most grave and reverend signior,' said Kennedy, 'I bear the compliments of Captain Sir Ed'ard Pellew, who humbly solicits Your Gravity's attendance at dinner at eight bells in the afternoon watch.'

'My respects to Sir Edward,' replied Hornblower, bowing to his knees at the mention of the name, 'and I shall condescend to make a brief appearance.'

'I am sure the captain will be both relieved and delighted,' said Kennedy. 'I will convey him my felicitations along with your most flattering acceptance.'

Both hats flourished with even greater elaboration than before, but at that moment both young men noticed Mr Bolton, the officer of the watch, looking at them from the windward side, and they hurriedly put their hats on and assumed attitudes more consonant with the dignity of officers holding their warrants from King George.

'What's in the captain's mind?' asked Hornblower.

Kennedy laid one finger alongside his nose. 'If I knew that, I should rate a couple of epaulets,' he said. 'Something's brewing, and I suppose one of these days we shall know what it is. Until then, all that we little victims can do is to play, unconscious of our doom. Meanwhile, be careful not to let the ship fall overboard.'

There was no sign of anything brewing while dinner was being eaten in the great cabin of the *Indefatigable*. Pellew was a courtly host at the head of the table. Conversation flowed freely and along indifferent channels among the senior officers present — the two lieutenants, Eccles and Chadd, and the sailing master, Soames. Hornblower and the other junior officer — Mallory, a midshipman of more than two years' seniority — kept silent, as midshipmen should, thereby being able to devote their undivided attention to the food, so vastly superior to what was served in the midshipmen's berth.

'A glass of wine with you, Mr Hornblower,' said Pellew, raising his glass.

Hornblower tried to bow gracefully in his seat while raising his glass. He sipped cautiously, for he had early found that he had a weak head and he disliked feeling drunk.

The table was cleared and there was a brief moment of expectancy as the company awaited Pellew's next move.

'Now, Mr Soames,' said Pellew, 'let us have that chart.'

It was a map of the mouth of the Gironde with the soundings; somebody had pencilled in the positions of the shore batteries.

'The *Papillon*,' said Sir Edward — he did not condescend to pronounce it French-fashion — 'lies just here. Mr Soames took the bearings.' He indicated a pencilled cross on the chart, far up the channel.

'You gentlemen,' went on Pellew, 'are going in with the boats to fetch her out.'

So that was it. A cutting-out expedition.

'Mr Eccles will be in general command. I will ask him to tell you his plan.'

The grey-haired first lieutenant with the surprisingly young blue eyes looked round at the others.

'I shall have the launch,' he said, 'and Mr Soames the cutter. Mr Chadd and Mr Mallory will command the first and second gigs. And Mr Hornblower will command the jolly boat. Each of the boats except Mr Hornblower's will have a junior officer second in command.'

That would not be necessary for the jolly boat with its crew of seven. The launch and cutter would carry from thirty to forty men each, and the gigs twenty each; it was a large force that was being dispatched — nearly half the ship's company.

'She's a ship of war,' explained Eccles, reading their thoughts. 'No merchantman. Ten guns a side, and full of men.'

Nearer two hundred men than a hundred, certainly — plentiful opposition for a hundred and twenty British seamen.

'But we will be attacking her by night and taking her by surprise,' said Eccles, reading their thoughts again.

'Surprise,' put in Pellew, 'is more than half the battle, as you know, gentlemen. Please pardon the interruption, Mr Eccles.'

'At the moment,' went on Eccles, 'we are out of sight of land. We are about to stand in again. We have never hung about this part of the coast, and the Frogs'll think we've gone for good. We'll make the land after nightfall, stand in as far as possible, and then the boats will go in. High water tomorrow morning is at four-fifty; dawn is at five-thirty. The attack will be delivered at four-thirty, so that the watch below will have had time to get to sleep. The launch will attack on the starboard quarter, and the cutter on the larboard quarter. Mr Mallory's gig will attack on the larboard bow, and Mr Chadd's on the starboard bow. Mr Chadd will be responsible for cutting the corvette's cable as soon as he has mastered the forecastle and the other boats' crews have at least reached the quarter-deck.'

Eccles looked round at the three other commanders of the large boats, and they nodded understanding. Then he went on, 'Mr Hornblower with the jolly boat will wait until the attack has gained a foothold on the deck. He will then board at the main chains, either to starboard or larboard, as he sees fit, and he will at once ascend the main rigging, paying no attention to whatever fighting is going on on deck. He will see to it that the main-topsail is loosed, and he will sheet it home on receipt of further orders. I, myself, or Mr Soames in the event of my being killed or wounded, will send two hands to the wheel and will attend to steering the corvette as soon as she is under way. The tide will take us out, and the *Indefatigable* will be awaiting us just out of gunshot from the shore batteries.'

'Any comments, gentlemen?' asked Pellew.

That was the moment when Hornblower should have spoken up — the only moment when he could. Eccles' orders had set in motion sick feelings of apprehension in his stomach. Hornblower was no main-topman, and Hornblower knew it. He hated heights, and he hated going aloft. He knew he had none of the monkey-like agility and self-confidence of the good seaman. He was unsure of himself aloft in the dark even in the *Indefatigable*, and he was utterly appalled at the thought of going aloft in an entirely strange ship and finding his way amid strange rigging. He felt himself quite unfitted for the duty assigned to him, and he should have raised a protest at once, on account of his unfitness. But he let the opportunity pass, for he was overcome by the matter-of-fact way in which the other officers accepted the plan. He looked round at the unmoved faces; nobody was paying any attention to him, and he jibbed at making himself conspicuous. He swallowed; he even got as far as opening his mouth, but still no one looked at him and his protest died.

'Very well, then, gentlemen,' said Pellew. 'I think you had better go into the details, Mr Eccles.'

Then it was too late. Eccles, with the chart before him, was pointing out the course to be taken through the shoals and mudbanks of the Gironde, and expatiating on the position of the shore batteries and on the influence of the lighthouse of Cordouan upon the distance to which the *Indefatigable* could approach in daylight. Hornblower listened, trying to concentrate despite his apprehensions.

Eccles finished his remark and Pellew closed the meeting, 'Since you all know your duties, gentlemen, I think you should start your preparations. The sun is about to set and you will find you have plenty to do.'

The boats' crews had to be told off; it was necessary to see that the men were armed and that the boats were provisioned in case of emergency. Every man had to be instructed in the duties expected of him. And Hornblower had to rehearse himself in ascending the main shrouds and laying out along the main-topsail yard. He did it twice, forcing himself to make the difficult climb up the futtock shrouds, which, projecting outward from the mainmast, made it necessary to climb several feet while hanging back downward, locking fingers and toes into the ratlines.

He could just manage it, moving slowly and carefully, although clumsily. He stood on the foot rope and worked his way out to the yardarm — the foot rope was attached along the yard so as to hang nearly four feet below it. The principle was to set his feet on the rope with his arms over the yard, then, holding the yard in his armpits, to shuffle sideways along the foot rope to cast off the gaskets and loosen the sail.

Twice Hornblower made the whole journey, battling with the disquiet of his stomach at the thought of the hundred-foot drop below him. Finally, gulping with nervousness, he transferred his grip to the brace and forced himself to slide down it to the deck — that would be his best route when the time came to sheet the topsail home. It was a long, perilous descent; Hornblower told himself — as indeed he had said to himself when he had first seen men go aloft — that similar feats in a circus at home would be received with 'Oh's' and 'Ah's' of appreciation.

He was by no means satisfied with himself even when he reached the deck, and at the back of his mind was a vivid picture of his missing his hold, when the time came for him to repeat the performance in the *Papillon*, and falling headlong to the deck — a second or two of frightful fear while rushing through the air, and then a shattering crash. And the success of the attack hinged on him as much as on anyone — if the topsail were not promptly set to give the corvette steerageway, she would run aground on one of the shoals in the river mouth, to be ignominiously recaptured, and half the crew of the *Indefatigable* would be dead or prisoners.

In the waist, the jolly boat's crew was formed up for his inspection. He saw to it that the oars were properly muffled, that each man had pistol and cutlass, and made sure that every pistol was at half cock, so that there was no fear of a premature shot giving warning of the attack. He allocated duties to each man in the loosing of the topsail, laying stress on the possibility that casualties might necessitate unrehearsed changes in the scheme.

'I will mount the rigging first,' said Hornblower.

That had to be the case. He had to lead — it was expected of him. More than that; if he had given any other order, it would have excited comment and contempt.

'Jackson,' went on Hornblower, addressing the coxswain, 'you will quit the boat last and take command if I fall.'

'Aye, aye, sir.'

It was usual to use the poetic expression 'fall' for 'die,' and it was only after Hornblower had uttered the word that he thought about its horrible real meaning in the present circumstances.

'Is that all understood?' asked Hornblower harshly; it was his mental stress that made his voice grate so.

Everyone nodded except one man. 'Begging your pardon, sir,' said Hales, the young man who pulled stroke oar, 'I'm feeling a bit queerlike.'

Hales was a lightly built young fellow of swarthy countenance. He put his hand to his forehead with a vague gesture as he spoke.

'You're not the only one to feel queer,' snapped Hornblower.

The other men chuckled. The thought of running the gauntlet of the shore batteries, of boarding an armed corvette in the teeth of opposition, might well raise apprehension in the breast of any of them. Most of the men detailed for the expedition must have felt qualms to some extent.

'I don't mean that, sir,' said Hales indignantly. 'Course I don't.'

But Hornblower and the others paid him no attention.

'You just keep your mouth shut,' growled Jackson.

There could be nothing but contempt for a man who announced himself sick after being told off on a dangerous duty. Hornblower felt sympathy as well as contempt. He himself had been too much of a coward even to give voice to his apprehension — too much afraid of what people would say about him.

'Dismiss,' said Hornblower. 'I'll pass the word for all of you when you are wanted.'

There were some hours yet to wait while the *Indefatigable* crept inshore, with the lead going steadily and Pellew himself attending to the course of the frigate. Hornblower, despite his nervousness and his miserable apprehensions, yet found time to appreciate the superb seamanship displayed as Pellew brought the big frigate in through these tricky waters on that dark night. His interest was so caught by the procedure that the little tremblings which had been assailing him ceased to manifest themselves; Hornblower was of the type that would continue to observe and to learn on his deathbed.

By the time the *Indefatigable* had reached the point off the mouth of the river where it was desirable to launch the boats, Hornblower had learned a good deal about the practical application of the principle of coastwise navigation and a good deal about the organisation of a cutting-out expedition, and by self-analysis he had learned even more about the psychology of a raiding party before a raid.

He had mastered himself, to all outside appearance, by the time he went down into the jolly boat as she heaved on the inky-black water, and he gave the command to shove off in a quiet, steady voice. Hornblower took the tiller — the feel of that solid bar of wood was reassuring, and it was old habit now to sit in the stern sheets with hand and elbow upon it — and the men began to pull slowly after the dark shapes of the four big boats. There was plenty of time, and the flowing tide would take them up the estuary. That was just as well, for on one side of them lay the batteries of St Dyé, and inside the estuary on the other side was the fortress of Blaye; forty big guns trained to sweep the channel, and none of the five boats could withstand a single shot from one of them.

He kept his eyes attentively on the cutter ahead of him. Soames had the dreadful responsibility of taking the boats up the channel, while all he had to do was to follow in her wake — all, except to loose that main-topsail. Hornblower found himself shivering again.

Hales, the man who had said he felt queer, was pulling stroke oar; Hornblower could just see his dark form moving rhythmically back and forward at each slow stroke. After a single glance, Hornblower paid him no more attention, and was staring after the cutter when a sudden commotion brought his mind back into the boat. Someone had missed his stroke; someone had thrown all six oars into confusion as a result.

'Mind what you're doing, blast you, Hales,' whispered Jackson, the coxswain, with desperate urgency.

For answer there was a sudden cry from Hales, loud, but fortunately not too loud, and Hales pitched forward against Hornblower's and Jackson's legs, kicking and writhing.

'The swine's having a fit,' growled Jackson.

165

The kicking and writhing went on. Across the water through the darkness came a sharp, scornful whisper. 'Mr Hornblower,' said the voice — it was Eccles putting a word of exasperation into his sotto voce question, 'cannot you keep your men quiet?'

Eccles had brought the launch round almost alongside the jolly boat to say this to him, and the desperate need for silence was dramatically demonstrated by the absence of any of the usual blasphemy. Hornblower opened his mouth to make an explanation, but he fortunately realised that raiders in open boats did not make explanations when under the guns of the fortress of Blaye.

'Aye, aye, sir,' was all he whispered back, and the launch continued on its mission of shepherding the flotilla in the tracks of the cutter.

'Take his oar, Jackson,' he whispered furiously to the coxswain, and he stooped and with his own hands dragged the writhing figure toward him and out of Jackson's way.

'You might try pouring water on 'im sir,' suggested Jackson hoarsely as he moved to the after thwart. 'There's the bailer 'andy.'

Sea water was the seaman's cure for every ill, his panacea. But Hornblower let the sick man lie. His struggles were coming to an end, and Hornblower wished to make no noise with the bailer. The lives of more than a hundred men depended on silence. Now that they were well into the actual estuary they were within easy reach of cannon shot from the shore, and a single cannon shot would rouse the crew of the *Papillon*, ready to man the bulwarks to beat off the attack, ready to drop cannon balls into the boats alongside, ready to shatter approaching boats with a tempest of grape.

Silently the boats glided up the estuary; Soames in the cutter was setting a slow pace, with an occasional stroke at the oars to maintain steerageway. Presumably he knew very well what he was doing; the channel he had selected was an obscure one between mudbanks, impracticable for anything except small boats, and he had a twenty-foot pole with him with which to take the soundings — quicker and much more silent than using the lead. Minutes were passing fast, and yet the night was still utterly dark, with no hint of approaching dawn. Strain his eyes as he would, Hornblower could not be sure that he could see the flat shores on either side of him. It would call for sharp eyes on the land to detect the little boats being carried up by the tide.

Hales at his feet stirred and then stirred again. His hand, feeling around in the darkness, found Hornblower's ankle and apparently examined it with curiosity. He muttered something, the words dragging out into a moan.

'Shut up,' whispered Hornblower, trying, like the saint of old, to make a tongue of his whole body, so that he might express the urgency of the occasion without making a sound audible at any distance. Hales set his elbow on Hornblower's knee and levered himself up into a sitting position, swaying with bent knees and supporting himself against Hornblower.

'Sit down, damn you,' whispered Hornblower, shaking with fury and anxiety.

'Where's Mary?' asked Hales in a conversational tone.

'Shut up!'

'Mary!' said Hales, lurching against him. 'Mary!'

Each successive word was louder. Hornblower felt instinctively that Hales would soon be speaking in a loud voice, that he might even soon be shouting. Old recollections of conversations with his doctor further stirred at the back of his mind; he remembered that persons emerging from epileptic fits were not responsible for their actions, and might be, and often were, dangerous.

'Mary!' said Hales again.

Victory and the lives of a hundred men depended on silencing Hales, and silencing him instantly. Hornblower thought of the pistol in his belt, and of using the butt, but there was another weapon more conveniently to his hand. He unshipped the tiller, a three-foot bar of solid oak, and he swung it with all the venom and fury of despair. The tiller crashed down on Hales' head, and Hales, an unuttered word cut short in his throat, fell silent in the bottom of the boat.

There was no sound from the boat's crew, save for something like a sigh from Jackson, whether approving or disapproving, Hornblower neither knew nor cared. He had done his duty, and he was certain of it. He had struck down a helpless idiot, most probably he had killed him, but the surprise upon which the success of the expedition depended had not been imperilled. He reshipped the tiller and resumed the silent task of keeping in the wake of the gigs.

Far away ahead — in the darkness it was impossible to estimate the distance — there was a nucleus of greater darkness, close on the surface of the black water. It might be the corvette. A dozen more silent strokes, and Hornblower was sure of it. Soames had done a magnificent job of pilotage, leading the boats straight to that objective. The cutter and launch were diverging now from the two gigs. The four boats were separating in readiness to launch their simultaneous converging attack.

'Easy,' whispered Hornblower, and the jolly boat's crew ceased to pull.

Hornblower had his orders. He had to wait until the attack had gained a foothold on the deck. His hand clenched convulsively on the tiller; the excitement of dealing with Hales had driven the thought of having to ascend strange rigging in the darkness clear out of his head, and now it recurred with redoubled urgency. Hornblower was afraid.

Although he could see the corvette, the boats had vanished from his sight, had passed out of his field of vision. The corvette rode to her anchor, her spars just visible against the night sky — that was where he had to climb! She seemed to tower up hugely. Close by the corvette he saw a splash in the dark water — the boats were closing in fast and someone's stroke had been a little careless. At that same moment came a shout from the corvette's deck, and when the shout was repeated, it was echoed a hundredfold from the boats rushing alongside. The yelling was lusty and prolonged, of set purpose. A sleeping enemy would be bewildered by the din, and the progress of the shouting would tell each boat's crew of the extent of the success of the others. The British seamen were yelling like madmen. A flash and a bang from the corvette's deck told of the firing of the first shot; soon pistols were popping and muskets banging from several points of the deck.

'Give way!' said Hornblower. He uttered the order as if it had been torn from him by the rack.

The jolly boat moved forward while Hornblower fought down his feelings and tried to make out what was going on on board. He could see no reason for choosing one side of the corvette in preference to the other, and the larboard side was the nearer, and so he steered the boat to the larboard main chains. So interested was he in what he was doing that he remembered only in the nick of time to give the order, 'In oars.' He put the tiller over and the boat swirled round and the bowman hooked on.

From the deck just above came a noise exactly like a tinker hammering on a cooking pot; Hornblower noted the curious noise as he stood up in the stern sheets. He felt the cutlass at his side and the pistol in his belt, and then he sprang for the chains. With a mad leap he reached them and hauled himself up. The shrouds came into his hands, his feet found the ratlines beneath them, and he began to climb. As his head cleared the bulwark and he could see the deck, the flash of a pistol shot illuminated the scene momentarily, fixing the struggle on the deck in a static moment, like a picture. Before and below him a British seaman was fighting a furious cutlass duel with a French officer, and he realised with vague astonishment that the kettle-mending noise he had heard was the sound of cutlass against cutlass — that clash of steel against steel that poets wrote about. So much for romance.

The realisation carried him far up the shrouds. At his elbow he felt the futtock shrouds, and he transferred himself to them, hanging back downward with his toes hooked into the ratlines and his hands clinging like death. That lasted for only two or three desperate seconds, and then he hauled himself onto the topmast shrouds and began the final ascent, his lungs bursting with the effort. Here was the topsail yard, and Hornblower flung himself across it and felt with his feet for the foot rope. Merciful God! There was no foot rope — his feet searching in the darkness met only unresisting air. A hundred feet above the deck he hung, squirming and kicking like a baby held up at arm's length in his father's hands. There was no foot rope; it may have been with this very situation in mind that the Frenchmen had removed it. There was no foot rope, so that he could not make his way out to the yardarm. Yet the gaskets must be cast off and the sail loosed — everything depended on that. Hornblower had seen daredevil seamen run out along the yards, standing upright, as though walking a tight-rope. That was the only way to reach the yardarm now.

For a moment he could not breathe as his weak flesh revolted against the thought of walking along that yard above the black abyss. This was fear, the fear that stripped a man of his manhood, turning his bowels to water and his limbs to paper. Yet his furiously active mind continued to work. He had been resolute enough in dealing with Hales. Where he personally was not involved he had been brave enough; he had not hesitated to strike down the wretched epileptic with all the strength of his arm. That was the poor sort of courage he was capable of displaying. In the simple vulgar matter of physical bravery he was utterly wanting. This was cowardice, the sort of thing that men spoke about behind their hands to other men. He could not bear the thought of that in himself; it was worse — awful though the alternative might be — than the thought of falling through the night to the deck. With a gasp, he brought his knee up onto the yard, heaving himself up until he stood upright. He felt the rounded, canvas-covered timber under his feet, and his instincts told him not to dally there for a moment.

'Come on men!' he yelled, and he dashed out along the yard.

It was twenty feet to the yardarm, and he covered the distance in a few frantic strides. Utterly reckless by now, he put his hands down on the yard, clasped it and laid his body across it again, his hands seeking the gaskets. A thump on the yard told him that Oldroyd, who had been detailed to come after him, had followed him out along the yard — he had six feet less to go. There could be no doubt that the other members of the jolly boat's crew were on the yard, and that Clough had led the way to the starboard yardarm. It was obvious from the rapidity with which the sail came loose. Here was the brace beside him. Without any thought of danger now, for he was delirious with excitement and triumph, he grasped it with both hands and jerked himself off the yard. His waving legs found the rope and twined about it, and he let himself slide down it.

Fool that he was! Would he never learn sense and prudence? Would he never remember that vigilance and precaution must never be relaxed? He had allowed himself to slide so fast that the rope seared his hands, and when he tried to tighten his grip so as to slow down his progress, it caused him such agony that he had to relax it again and slide on down with the rope stripping the skin from his hands as though peeling off a glove. His feet reached the deck and

171

'Come on men!' he yelled, and he dashed out along the yard.

he momentarily forgot the pain as he looked round him.

There was the faintest grey light beginning to show now, and there were no sounds of battle. It had been a well-worked surprise — a hundred men flung suddenly on the deck of the corvette had swept away the anchor watch and mastered the vessel in a single rush before the watch below could come up to offer any resistance.

Chadd's stentorian voice came pealing from the forecastle, 'Cable's cut, sir!'

Then Eccles bellowed from aft, 'Mr Hornblower!'

'Sir!' yelled Hornblower.

'Sheet that topsail home!'

A rush of men came to help — not only his own boat's crew but every man of initiative and spirit. Halyards, sheets and braces; the sail was trimmed round and was drawing full in the light southerly air, and the *Papillon* swung round to go down with the first of the ebb. Dawn was coming up fast, with a trifle of mist on the surface of the water.

Over the starboard quarter came a sullen, bellowing roar, and then the misty air was torn by a series of infernal screams, supernaturally loud. The first cannon balls Hornblower had ever heard were passing him by.

'Mr Chadd! Set the headsails! Loose the fore-tops'l! Get aloft, some of you, and set the mizzen tops'l.'

From the port bow came another salvo — Blaye was firing at them from one side, St Dyé from the other, now that they could guess what had happened on board the *Papillon*. But the corvette was moving fast with wind and tide, and it would be no easy matter to cripple her in the half-light. It had been a very near-run thing; a few seconds' delay could have been fatal. Only one shot from the next salvo passed within hearing, and its passage was marked by a loud snap overhead.

'Mr Mallory, get that forestay spliced!'

'Aye, aye, sir!'

It was light enough to look round the deck now; he could see Eccles at the break of the poop, directing the handling of the corvette, and Soames beside the wheel, conning her down the channel. Two groups of red-coated marines, with bayonets fixed, stood guard over the hatchways. There were four or five men lying on the deck in curiously abandoned attitudes. Dead men; Hornblower could look at them with the callousness of youth. But there was a wounded man, too, crouched groaning over his shattered thigh. Hornblower could not look at him as disinterestedly, and he was glad, maybe only for his own sake, when at that moment a seaman asked for and received permission from Mallory to leave his duties and attend to him.

'Stand by to go about!' shouted Eccles from the poop; the corvette had reached the tip of the middle-ground shoal and was about to make the turn that would carry her into the open sea.

The men came running to the braces, and Hornblower tailed on along with them. But the first contact with the harsh rope gave him such pain that he almost cried out. His hands were like raw meat, and fresh-killed at that, for blood was running from them. Now that his attention was called to them, they smarted unbearably.

The headsail sheets came over, and the corvette went handily about.

'There's the old Indy!' shouted somebody.

The *Indefatigable* was plainly visible now, lying to just out of short from the shore batteries, ready to rendezvous with her prize. Somebody cheered, and the cheering was taken up by everyone, even while the last shots from St Dye, fired at extreme range, pitched sullenly into the water alongside. Hornblower had gingerly extracted his handkerchief from his pocket and was trying to wrap it round his hand.

'Can I help you with that, sir?' asked Jackson.

Jackson shook his head as he looked at the raw surface. 'You was careless, sir. You ought to 'a' gone down 'and over 'and,' he said, when Hornblower explained to him how the injury had been caused. 'Very careless, you was, beggin' your pardon for saying so, sir. But you young gennelmen often is. You don't 'ave no thought for your necks nor your 'ides, sir.'

Hornblower looked up at the main-topsail yard high above his head, and remembered how he had walked along that slender stick of timber out to the yardarm in the dark. At the recollection of it, even here with the solid deck under his feet, he shuddered a little.

'Sorry, sir. Didn't mean to 'urt you,' said Jackson, tying the knot. 'There, that's done, as good as I can do it, sir.'

'Thank you, Jackson,' said Hornblower.

'We got to report the jolly boat as lost, sir,' went on Jackson. 'Lost?'

'She ain't towing alongside, sir. You see, we didn't leave no boat keeper in 'er. Wells, 'e was to be boat keeper, you remember, sir. But I sent 'im up the riggin a'ead o' me, seeing that 'Ales couldn't go. We wasn't too many for the job. So the jolly boat must 'a' come adrift, sir, when the ship went about.'

'What about Hales, then?' asked Hornblower.

''E was still in the boat, sir.'

Hornblower looked back up the estuary of the Gironde. Somewhere up there the jolly boat was drifting about, and lying in it was Hales, probably dead, possibly alive. In either case, the French would find him surely enough, but a cold wave of regret extinguished the warm feeling of triumph in Hornblower's bosom when he thought about Hales back there. If it had not been for Hales, he would never have nerved himself — so, at least, he thought — to run out to the main-topsail yardarm; he would at this moment be ruined and branded as a coward instead of basking in the satisfaction of having capably done his duty.

Jackson saw the bleak look in his face. 'Don't you take on so, sir,' he said. 'They won't 'old the loss of the jolly boat agin you, not the captain and Mr Eccles, they won't.'

'I wasn't thinking about the jolly boat,' said Hornblower. 'I was thinking about Hales.'

'Oh, 'im?' said Jackson. 'Don't you fret about 'im, sir. "E wouldn't never 'ave made no seaman, not no 'ow.'

Jack Easy Aboard the Aurora
from Mr Midshipman Easy
by
CAPTAIN MARRYAT

The first-lieutenant of the *Aurora* was a very good officer in many respects, but, as a midshipman, he had contracted the habit of putting his hands in his pockets, and could never keep them out, even when the ship was in a gale of wind; and hands are of some use in a heavy lurch. He had more than once received serious injury from falling on these occasions, but habit was too powerful; and, although he had once broken his leg by falling down the hatchway, and had moreover a large scar on his forehead, received from being thrown to leeward against one of the guns, he still continued the practice; indeed, it was said that once, when it was necessary for him to go aloft, he had actually taken the two first rounds of the Jacob's ladder without withdrawing them, until, losing his balance, he discovered that it was not quite so easy to go aloft with his hands in his pockets. In fact, there was no getting up his hands, even when all hands were turned up. He had another peculiarity, which was, that he had taken a peculiar fancy to a quack medicine, called Enouy's Universal Medicine for all Mankind; and Mr Pottyfar was convinced in his own mind that the label was no libel, except from the greatness of its truth. In his opinion, it cured everything, and he spent one of his quarterly bills every year in bottles of this stuff; which he not only took himself every time he was unwell, but occasionally when quite well, to prevent his falling sick. He recommended it to everybody in the ship, and nothing pleased him so much as to give a dose of it to everyone who could be persuaded to take it. The officers laughed at him, but it was generally behind his back, for he became very angry if contradicted upon this one point, upon which he certainly might be considered to be a little cracked. He was indefatigable in making proselytes to his creed, and expatiated upon the virtues of the medicine for an hour running, proving the truth of his assertions by a pamphlet which, with his hands, he always carried in his trousers pocket.

Jack reported himself when he came on board, and Mr Pottyfar, who was on the quarter-deck at the time, expressed a hope that Mr Easy would take his share of the duty, now that he had had such a spell on shore; to which Jack very graciously acceded, and then went down below, where he found Gascoigne and his new messmates, with most of whom he was already acquainted.

'Well, Easy,' said Gascoigne, 'have you had enough of the shore?'

'Quite,' replied Jack, recollecting that, after the events of the night before, he was just as well on board; 'I don't intend to ask for any more leave.'

'Perhaps it's quite as well, for Mr Pottyfar is not very liberal on that score, I can tell you; there is but one way of getting leave from him.'

'Indeed,' replied Jack; 'and what is that?'

'You must pretend that you are not well, take some of his quack medicine, and then he will allow you a run on shore to work it off.'

'Oh! that's it, is it? well then, as soon as we anchor in Valetta, I'll go through a regular course, but not till then.'

'It ought to suit you, Jack; it's an equality medicine; cures one disorder just as well as the other.'

'Or kills — which levels all the patients. You're right, Gascoigne, I must patronise that stuff — for more reasons than one. Who was that person on deck in mufti?'

'The mufti, Jack; in other words, the chaplain of the ship; but he's a prime sailor, nevertheless.'

'How's that?'

'Why, he was brought up on the quarter-deck, served his time, was acting-lieutenant for two years, and then, somehow or another, he bore up for the church.'

'Indeed — what were his reasons?'

'No one knows — but they say he has been unhappy since.'

'Why so?'

'Because he did a very foolish thing, which cannot now be remedied. He supposed at the time that he would make a good parson, and now that he has long got over his fit, he finds himself wholly unfit for it — he is still the officer in heart, and is always struggling with his natural bent, which is very contrary to what a parson should feel.'

'Why don't they allow parsons to be broke by a court-martial, and turned out of the service, or to resign their commissions, like other people?'

'It won't do, Jack — they serve Heaven — there's a difference between that and serving his majesty.'

'Well, I don't understand these things. When do we sail?'

'The day after to-morrow.'

'To join the fleet off Toulon?'

'Yes; but I suppose we shall be driven on the Spanish coast going there. I never knew a man-of-war that was not.'

'No; wind always blows from the south, going up the Mediterranean.'

'Perhaps you'll take another prize, Jack — mind you don't go away without the articles of war.'

'I won't go away without Mesty, if I can help it. Oh dear, how abominable a midshipman's berth is after a long run on shore! I positively must go on deck and look at the shore, if I can do nothing else.'

'Why, ten minutes ago you had had enough of it.'

'Yes, but ten minutes here has made me feel quite sick. I shall go to the first-lieutenant for a dose.'

'I say, Easy, we must both be physicked on the same day.'

'To be sure; but stop till we get to Malta.'

Jack went on deck, made acquaintance with the chaplain and some of the officers whom he had not known, then climbed up into the maintop, where he took a seat on the armolest, and, as he looked at the shore, thought over the events that had passed, until Agnes came to his memory, and he thought only of her. When a mid is in love, he always goes aloft to think of the object of his affection; why, I don't know, except that his reverie is not so likely to be disturbed by an order from a superior officer.

The *Aurora* sailed on the second day, and with a fine breeze, stood across, making as much northing as easting; the consequence was, that one fine morning they saw the Spanish coast before they saw the Toulon fleet. Mr Pottyfar took his hands out of his pockets, because he could not examine the coast through a telescope without so doing; but this, it is said, was the first time that he had done so on the quarter-deck from the day that the ship had sailed from Port Mahon. Captain Wilson was also occupied with his telescope, so were many of the officers and midshipmen, and the men at the mastheads used their eyes, but there was nothing but a few small fishing-boats to be seen. So they all went down to breakfast, as the ship was hove-to close in with the land.

'What will Easy bet,' said one of the midshipmen, 'that we don't see a prize to-day?'

'I will not bet that we do not see a vessel — but I'll bet

you what you please, that we do not take one before twelve o'clock at night.'

'No, no, that won't do — just let the teapot travel over this way, for it's my forenoon watch.'

'It's a fine morning,' observed one of the mates, of the name of Martin; 'but I've a notion it won't be a fine evening.'

'Why not?' inquired another.

'I've now been eight years in the Mediterranean, and know something about the weather. There's a watery sky, and the wind is very steady. If we are not under double-reefed topsails to-night, say I'm no conjuror.'

'That you will be, all the same, if we are under bare poles,' said another.

'You're devilish free with your tongue, my youngster. — Easy, pull his ears for me.'

'Pull them easy, Jack, then,' said the boy, laughing.

'All hands make sail!' now resounded at the hatchways.

'There they are, depend upon it,' cried Gascoigne, catching up his hat and bolting out of the berth, followed by all the others except Martin, who had just been relieved, and thought that his presence in the waist might be dispensed with for the short time, at least, which it took him to swallow a cup of tea.

It was very true; a galliot and four lateen vessels had just made their appearance round the easternmost point, and, as soon as they observed the frigate, had hauled their wind. In a minute the *Aurora* was under a press of canvas, and the telescopes were all directed to the vessels.

'All deeply laden, sir,' observed Mr Hawkins, the chaplain; 'how the topsail of the galliot is scored!'

'They have a fresh breeze just now,' observed Captain Wilson to the first-lieutenant.

'Yes, sir, and it's coming down fast.'

'Hands by the royal halyards, there.'

The *Aurora* careened with the canvas to the rapidly increasing breeze.

'Top-gallant sheet and halyards.'

'Luff you may, quarter-master; luff, I tell you. A small pull of that weather maintop-gallant brace — that will do,' said the master.

'Top-men aloft there; — stand by to clew up the royals — and, Captain Wilson, shall we take them in? — I'm afraid of that pole, it bends now like a coach-whip,' said Mr Pottyfar, looking up aloft, with his hands in both pockets.

'In royals — lower away.'

'They are going about, sir,' said the second-lieutenant, Mr Haswell.

'Look out,' observed the chaplain, 'it's coming.'

Again the breeze increases, and the frigate was borne down.

'Hands reef topsails in stays, Mr Pottyfar.'

'Ay, ay, sir — 'bout ship.'

The helm was put down and the topsails lowered and reefed in stays.

'Very well, my lads, very well indeed,' said Captain Wilson.

Again the topsails were hoisted and top-gallant sheets home. It was a strong breeze, although the water was smooth, and the *Aurora* dashed through at the rate of eight miles an hour, with her weather leeches lifting.

'Didn't I tell you so?' said Martin to his messmates on the gangway; 'but there's more yet, my boys.'

'We must take the top-gallant sails off her,' said Captain Wilson, looking aloft — for the frigate now careened to her bearings, and the wind was increasing and squally. 'Try them a little longer'; but another squall came suddenly — the halyards were lowered, and the sails clewed up and furled.

In the meantime the frigate had rapidly gained upon the vessels, which still carried on every stitch of canvas, making short tacks in-shore. The *Aurora* was again put about with her head towards them, and they were not two points on her weather bow. The sky, which had been clear in the morning, was now overcast, the sun was obscured with opaque white clouds, and the sea was rising fast. Another ten minutes, and they then were under double-reefed topsails, and the squalls were accompanied with heavy rain. The frigate now dashed through the waves, foaming in her course and straining under the press of sail. The horizon was so thick that the vessels ahead were no longer to be seen.

'We shall have it, I expect,' said Captain Wilson.

'Didn't I say so?' observed Martin to Gascoigne. 'We take no prizes this day, depend upon it.'

'We must have another hand to the wheel, sir, if you please,' said the quarter-master, who was assisting the helmsman.

Mr Pottyfar, with his hands concealed as usual, stood by the capstern. 'I fear, sir, we cannot carry the mainsail much longer.'

'No,' observed the chaplain, 'I was thinking so.'

'Captain Wilson, if you please, we are very close in,' said the master; 'don't you think we had better go about?'

'Yes, Mr Jones — Hands about ship — and — yes, by heavens, we must! — up mainsail.'

The mainsail was taken off, and the frigate appeared to be immediately relieved. She no longer jerked and plunged as before.

'We're very near the land, Captain Wilson; thick as it is, I think I can make out the loom of it — shall we wear round, sir?' continued the master.

'Yes — hands wear ship — put the helm up.'

It was but just in time, for, as the frigate flew round, describing a circle, as she payed off before the wind, they could perceive the breakers lashing the precipitous coast not two cables' length from them.

'I had no idea we were so near,' observed the captain,

compressing his lips — 'can they see anything of those vessels?'

'I have not seen them this quarter of an hour, sir,' replied the signalman, protecting his glass from the rain under his jacket.

'How's her head now, quarter-master?'

'South-south-east, sir.'

The sky now assumed a different appearance — the white clouds had been exchanged for others dark and murky, the wind roared at intervals, and the rain came down in torrents. Captain Wilson went down into the cabin to examine the barometer.

'The barometer has risen,' said he on his return on deck. 'Is the wind steady?'

'No sir, she's up and off three points.'

'This will end in a south-wester.'

The wet and heavy sails now flapped from the shifting of the wind.

'Up with the helm, quarter-master.'

'Up it is — she's off to south-by-west.'

The wind lulled, the rain came down in a deluge — for a minute it was quite calm, and the frigate was on an even keel.

'Man the braces. We shall be taken aback directly, depend upon it.'

The braces were hardly stretched along before this was the case. The wind flew round to the south-west with a loud roar, and it was fortunate that they were prepared — the yards were braced round, and the master asked the captain what course they were to steer.

'We must give it up,' observed Captain Wilson, holding on by the belaying pin. 'Shape our course for Cape Sicie, Mr Jones.'

And the *Aurora* flew before the gale, under her foresail and topsails close reefed. The weather was now so thick that nothing could be observed twenty yards from the vessel; the thunder pealed, and the lightning darted in every direction over the dark expanse. The watch was called as soon as the sails were trimmed, and all who could went below, wet, uncomfortable, and disappointed.

'What an old Jonah you are, Martin,' said Gascoigne.

'Yes, I am,' replied he; 'but we have the worst to come yet, in my opinion. I recollect, not two hundred miles from where we are now, we had just such a gale in the *Favourite*, and we as nearly went down, when —'

At this moment a tremendous noise was heard above, a shock was felt throughout the whole ship, which trembled fore and aft as if it were about to fall into pieces; loud shrieks were followed by plaintive cries, the lower deck was filled with smoke, and the frigate was down on her beam ends. Without exchanging a word, the whole of the occupants of the berth flew out, and were up the hatchway, not knowing what to think, but convinced that some dreadful accident had taken place.

On their gaining the deck it was at once explained; the foremast of the frigate had been struck by lightning, had been riven into several pieces, and had fallen over the larboard bow, carrying with it the main topmast and jib-boom. The jagged stump of the foremast was in flames, and burnt brightly, notwithstanding the rain fell in torrents. The ship, as soon as the foremast and main topmast had gone overboard, then broached-to furiously, throwing the men over the wheel and dashing them senseless against the carronades; the forecastle, the fore part of the main deck, and even the lower deck, were spread with men, either killed or seriously wounded, or insensible from the electric shock. The frigate was on her beam ends, and the sea broke furiously over her; all was dark as pitch, except the light from the blazing stump of the foremast, appearing like a torch, held up by the wild demons of the

The ship was on her beam ends, and the sea broke furiously over her.

storm, or when occasionally the gleaming lightning cast a momentary glare, threatening every moment to repeat its attack upon the vessel, while the deafening thunder burst almost on their devoted heads. All was dismay and confusion for a minute or two: at last Captain Wilson, who had himself lost his sight for a short time, called for the carpenter and axes — they climbed up, that is, two or three of them, and he pointed to the mizen-mast; the master was also there, and he cut loose the axes for the seamen to use; in a few minutes the mizen-mast fell over the quarter, and the helm being put hard up, the frigate payed off and slowly righted. But the horror of the scene was not yet over. The boatswain, who had been on the forecastle, had been led below, for his vision was gone for ever. The men who lay scattered about had been examined, and they were assisting them down to the care of the surgeon, when the cry of 'Fire!' issued from the lower deck. The ship had taken fire at the coal-hole and carpenter's store-room, and the smoke that now ascended was intense.

'Call the drummer,' said Captain Wilson, 'and let him beat to quarters — all hands to their stations — let the pumps be rigged and the buckets passed along. Mr Martin, see that the wounded men are taken down below. Where's Mr Haswell? Mr Pottyfar, station the men to pass the water on by hand on the lower deck. I will go there myself. Mr Jones, take charge of the ship.'

Pottyfar, who actually had taken his hands out of his pockets, hastened down to comply with the captain's orders on the main deck, as Captain Wilson descended to the deck below.

'I say, Jack, this is very different from this morning,' observed Gascoigne.

'Yes,' replied Jack, 'so it is; but I say, Gascoigne, what's the best thing to do? — when the chimney's on fire on shore, they put a wet blanket over it.'

'Yes,' replied Gascoigne; 'but when the coal-hole's on fire on board, they will not find that sufficient.'

'At all events, wet blankets must be a good thing, Ned, so let us pull out the hammocks; cut the lanyards and get some out — we can but offer them, you know, and if they do no good, at least it will show our zeal.'

'Yes, Jack, and I think when they turn in again, those whose blankets you take will agree with you, that zeal makes the service very uncomfortable. However, I think you are right.'

The two midshipmen collected three or four hands, and in a very short time they had more blankets than they could carry — there was no trouble in wetting them, for the main deck was afloat — and followed by the men they had collected, Easy and Gascoigne went down with large bundles in their arms to where Captain Wilson was giving directions to the men.

'Excellent, Mr Easy! Excellent, Mr Gascoigne!' said Captain Wilson. Come, my lads, throw them over now, and stamp upon them well; the men's jackets and the captain's coats had already been sacrificed to the same object.

Easy called the other midshipmen, and they went up for a further supply; but there was no occasion, the fire had been smothered: still the danger had been so great that the fore magazine had been floated. During all this, which lasted perhaps a quarter of an hour, the frigate had rolled gunwale under, and many were the accidents which occurred. At last all danger from fire had ceased, and the men were ordered to return to their quarters, when three officers and forty-seven men were found absent — seven of them were dead — most of them were already under the care of the surgeon, but some were still lying in the scuppers.

No one had been more active or more brave during this time of danger than Mr Hawkins the chaplain. He was everywhere, and when Captain Wilson went down to put out the fire he was there, encouraging the men and exerting himself most gallantly. He and Mesty came aft when all was over, one just as black as the other. The chaplain sat down and wrung his hands — 'God forgive me!' said he, 'God forgive me!'

'Why so sir?' said Easy, who stood near. 'I am sure you need not be ashamed of what you have done.'

'No, no, not ashamed of what I've done; but, Mr Easy, I have sworn so, sworn such oaths at the men in my haste — I, the chaplain! God forgive me! — I meant nothing.' It was very true that Mr Hawkins had sworn a great deal during his exertions, but he was at that time the quarter-deck officer and not the chaplain; the example to the men and his gallantry had been most serviceable.

'Indeed, sir,' said Easy, who saw that the chaplain was in great tribulation, and hoped to pacify him, 'I was certainly not there all the time, but I only heard you say, "God bless you, my men! be smart," and so on; surely, that is not swearing.'

'Was it that I said, Mr Easy, are you sure? I really had an idea that I had d----d them all in heaps, as some of them deserved — no, no, not deserved. Did I really bless them — nothing but bless them?'

'Yes, sir,' said Mesty, who perceived what Jack wanted; 'it was nothing, I assure you, but "God bless you Captain Wilson! — Bless your heart, my good men! — Bless the king!" and so on. You do nothing but shower down blessing and wet blanket.'

'I told you so,' said Jack.

'Well, Mr Easy, you've made me very happy,' replied the chaplain: 'I was afraid it was otherwise.'

So indeed it was, for the chaplain had sworn like a boatswain; but as Jack and Mesty had turned all his curses into blessings, the poor man gave himself absolution, and shaking hands with Jack, hoped he would come down into the gunroom and take a glass of grog (nor did he forget Mesty, who received a good allowance at the gunroom door), to which Jack gladly consented, as the rum in the middy's berth had all been exhausted after the rainy morning — but Jack was interrupted in his third glass by somebody telling him the captain wanted to speak with Mr Hawkins and with him.

Jack went up and found the captain on the quarter-deck with the officers.

'Mr Easy,' said Captain Wilson, 'I have sent for you, Mr Hawkins, and Mr Gascoigne to thank you on the quarter-deck for your exertions and presence of mind on this trying occasion.' Mr Hawkins made a bow. Gascoigne said nothing, but he thought of having extra leave when they arrived at Malta. Jack felt inclined to make a speech, and began something about when there was danger that it levelled every one to an equality even on board of a man-of-war.

'By no means, Mr Easy,' replied Captain Wilson, 'it does the very contrary, for it proves which is the best man, and those who are the best raise themselves at once above the rest.'

Jack was very much inclined to argue the point, but he took the compliment and held his tongue, which was the wisest thing he could have done; so he made his bow, and was about to go down into the midshipmen's berth when the frigate was pooped by a tremendous sea, which washed all those who did not hold on down into the waist. Jack was among the number, and naturally catching at the first object which touched him, he caught hold of the chaplain by the leg, who commenced swearing most terribly; but before he could finish the oath, the water which had burst into the cabin through the windows — for the dead lights, in the confusion, had not yet been shipped — burst out the cross bulkheads, sweeping like a torrent the marine, the cabin-door, and everything else in its force, and floating Jack and the chaplain with several others down the main hatchway on to the lower deck. The lower deck being also full of water, men and chests were rolling and tossing about, and Jack was sometimes in company with the chaplain, and at other times separated; at last they both recovered their legs, and gained the midshipmen's berth, which, although afloat, was still a haven of security. Mr Hawkins spluttered and spat, and so did Jack, until he began to laugh.

'This is very trying, Mr Easy,' said the chaplain; 'very trying indeed to the temper. I hope I have not sworn — I hope not.'

'Not a word,' said Jack — 'I was close to you all the time — you onlys aid, "God preserve us!" '

'Only that? I was afraid that I said "God d--n it!" '

'Quite a mistake, Mr Hawkins. Let's go into the gunroom, and try to wash this salt water out of our mouths, and then I will tell you all you said, as far as I could hear it, word for word.'

So Jack by this means got another glass of grog, which was very acceptable in his wet condition, and made himself very comfortable, while those on deck were putting on the dead lights, and very busy setting the goose-wings of the mainsail, to prevent the frigate from being pooped a second time.

The White Whale
from Moby Dick

by
HERMAN MELVILLE

Soon after Ishmael boarded the whaler Pequod, he realised that he was involved in no ordinary whaling cruise. Captain Ahab, obsessed with his purpose to hunt down the white whale Moby Dick, leads his entire crew to fantastic adventure and horrible destruction. Only Ishmael lives to tell the tale.

Sing Out for the Whale

One morning shortly after breakfast, Ahab, as was his wont, ascended the cabin gangway to the deck. There most sea-captains usually walk at that hour, as country gentlemen, after the same meal, take a few turns in the garden.

Soon his steady, ivory stride was heard, as to and fro he paced his old round, upon planks so familiar to his tread, that they were all over dented, like geological stones, with the peculiar marks of his walk. Did you fixedly gaze, too, upon that ribbed and dented brow; there also, you would see still stranger footprints — the footprints of his one unsleeping ever pacing thought.

But on the occasion in question, these dents looked deeper, even as his nervous step that morning left a deeper mark. And, so full of his thought was Ahab, that at every uniform turn that he made, now at the mainmast and now at the binnacle, you could almost see that thought turn in him, indeed, that it all but seemed the inward mould of every outer movement.

'D'ye mark him, Flask?' whispered Stubb; 'the chick that's in him pecks the shell. 'Twill soon be out.'

The hours wore on; — Ahab now shut up within his cabin; anon, pacing the deck, with the same intense bigotry of purpose in his aspect. It drew nearer to the close of day. Suddenly he came to a halt by the bulwarks, and inserting his bone leg into the auger-hole there, and with one hand grasping a shroud, he ordered Starbuck to send everybody aft.

'Sir!' said the mate, astonished at an order seldom or never given on shipboard except in some extraordinary case.

'Send everybody aft', repeated Ahab. 'Mastheads, there! come down!'

When the entire ship's company were assembled, and with curious and not wholly unapprehensive faces, were eyeing him, for he looked not unlike the weather horizon when a storm is coming up, Ahab, after rapidly glancing over the bulwarks, and then darting his eyes among the crew, started from his standpoint; and as though not a soul were nigh him resumed his heavy turns upon the deck. With bent head and half-slouched hat he continued to pace, unmindful of the wondering whispering among the men; till Stubb whispered to Flask, that Ahab must have summoned them there for the purpose of witnessing a pedestrian feat. But this did not last long. Vehemently pausing he cried: —

'What do ye do when ye see a whale, men?'

'Sing out for him!' was the impulsive rejoinder from a score of clubbed voices.

'Good!' cried Ahab, with a wild approval in his tones; observing the hearty animation into which his unexpected question had so magnetically thrown them.

'And what do ye do next, men?'

'Lower away, and after him!'

'And what tune is it ye pull to, men?'

'A dead whale or a stove boat!'

More and more strangely and fiercely glad and approving grew the countenance of the old man at every shout; while the mariners began to gaze curiously at each other, as if marvelling how it was that they themselves became so excited at such seemingly purposeless questions.

But they were all eagerness again, as Ahab, now half revolving in his pivot-hole, with one hand reaching high up a shroud, and tightly, almost convulsively grasping it, addressed them thus —

'All ye mastheaders have before now heard me give orders about a white whale. Look ye! d'ye see this Spanish ounce of gold?' — holding up a broad bright coin to the sun — 'it is a sixteen dollar piece, men. D'ye see it? Mr Starbuck, hand me yon top-maul.'

While the mate was getting the hammer, Ahab, without speaking, was slowly rubbing the gold piece against the skirts of his jacket, as if to heighten its lustre, and without using any words was meanwhile lowly humming to himself, producing a sound so strangely muffled and inarticulate that it seemed the mechanical humming of the wheels of his vitality in him.

Receiving the top-maul from Starbuck, he advanced towards the mainmast with the hammer uplifted in one hand, exhibiting the gold with the other, and with a high-raised voice exclaiming: 'Whosoever of ye raises me a white-headed whale with a wrinkled brow and a crooked jaw; whosoever of ye raises me that white-headed whale, with three holes punctured in his starboard fluke — look ye, whosoever of ye raises me that same white whale, he shall have this gold ounce, my boys!'

'Huzza! huzza!' cried the seamen, as with swinging tarpaulins they hailed the act of nailing the gold to the mast.

'It's a white whale, I say,' resumed Ahab, as he threw down the top-maul; 'a white whale. Skin your eyes for him, men; look sharp for white water; if ye see but a bubble, sing out.'

All this while Tashtego, Daggoo, and Queequeg had looked on with even more intense interest and surprise than the rest, and at the mention of the wrinkled brow and crooked jaw, they had started as if each was separately touched by some specific recollection.

'Captain Ahab,' said Tashtego, 'that white whale must be the same that some call Moby Dick.'

'Moby Dick?' shouted Ahab. 'Do ye know the white whale then, Tash?'

'Does he fan-tail a little curious, sir, before he goes down?' said the Gay-Header deliberately.

'And he has a curious spout too,' said Daggoo, 'very bushy, even for a parmacetty, and mighty quick, Captain Ahab?'

'And he have one, two, tree — oh! good many iron in him hide, too, Captain,' cried Queequeg disjointedly. 'All twisketee be-twisk, like him — him —' faltering hard for a word, and screwing his hand round and round as though uncorking a bottle — 'like him — him —'

'Corkscrew!' cried Ahab; 'ay, Queequeg, the harpoons lie all twisted and wrenched in him; ay, Daggoo, his spout is a big one, like a whole shock of wheat, and white as a pile of our Nantucket wool after the great annual sheep-shearing; aye, Tashtego, and he fan-tails like a split jib in a squall. Death and devils! Men, it is Moby Dick ye have seen — Moby Dick — Moby Dick!'

'Captain Ahab,' said Starbuck, who with Stubb and Flask, had thus far been eyeing his superior with increasing surprise, but at last seemed struck with a thought which somewhat explained all the wonder. 'Captain Ahab, I have heard of Moby Dick — was it not Moby Dick that took off thy leg'?

'Who told thee that?' cried Ahab; then pausing. 'Aye, Starbuck; aye, my hearties all round; it was Moby Dick that dismasted me; Moby Dick that brought me to this dead stump I stand on now. Aye, Aye,' he shouted with a terrific, loud, animal sob, like that of a heart-stricken moose; 'Aye, aye! it was that accursèd white whale that razed me; made a poor pegging lubber of me for ever and a day!' Then tossing both arms, with measureless imprecations, he shouted out: 'Aye, Aye! and I'll chase him round Good Hope, and round the Horn, and round the Norway Maelstrom, and round perdition's flames before I give him up. And this is what ye have shipped for, men! to chase that white whale on both sides of land, and over all sides of earth, till he spouts black blood and rolls fin out. What say ye, men, will ye splice hands on it, now? I think ye do look brave.'

'Aye, aye!' shouted the harpooners and seamen, running closer to the excited old man; 'A sharp eye for the White Whale; a sharp lance for Moby Dick!'

'God bless ye,' he seemed to half sob and half shout, 'God bless ye, men. Steward! go draw the great measure of grog. Death to Moby Dick! God hunt us all, if we do not hunt Moby Dick to his death!'

The White Whale

I, Ishmael, was one of that crew; my shouts had gone up with the rest; my oath had been welded with theirs; and stronger I shouted, and more did I hammer and clinch my oath, because of the dread in my soul. A wild, mystical sympathetical feeling was in me; Ahab's quenchless feud seemed mine. With greedy ear I learned the history of that murderous monster against whom I and all the others had taken our oaths of violence and revenge.

For some time past, though at intervals only, the unaccompanied, secluded White Whale had haunted those uncivilised seas most frequented by the Sperm Whale fishermen. But not all of them knew of his existence; only a few of them, comparatively, had knowingly seen him; while the number who as yet had actually and knowingly given battle to him was small indeed. For, owing to the large number of whale cruisers; the disorderly way they were sprinkled over the entire watery circumference, many of them adventurously pushing their quest along solitary latitudes, so as seldom or never for a whole twelvemonth or more on a stretch, to encounter a single news-telling sail of any sort; the inordinate length of each separate voyage; the irregularity of the times of sailing from home; all these, with other circumstances, direct and indirect, long obstructed the spread through the whole world-wide whaling fleet, of the special individualising tidings concerning Moby Dick. It was hardly to be doubted, that several vessels reported to have encountered, at such and such a time, or on such a meridian, a sperm whale of uncommon magnitude and malignity, which whale, after doing great mischief to his assailants, had completely escaped them; to some minds it was not an unfair presumption. I say, that the whale in question must have been no other than Moby Dick. Yet as of late, the sperm whale fishery had been marked by various and not unfrequent instances of great ferocity, cunning and malice in the monster attacked; therefore it was, that those who by accident ignorantly gave battle to Moby Dick; such hunters, perhaps, for the most part, were content to ascribe the peculiar terror he bred, more, as it were, to the perils of the Sperm Whale fishery at large, than to the individual cause. In that way, mostly, the disastrous encounter between

Ahab and the whale had hitherto been popularly regarded.

As for those who, previously hearing of the White Whale, by chance caught sight of him; in the beginning of the thing they had every one of them, almost, as boldly and fearlessly lowered for him, as for any other whale of that species. But at length, such calamities did ensue in these assaults — not restricted to sprained wrists and ankles, broken limbs or devouring amputations — but fatal to the last degree of fatality; those repeated disastrous repulses, all accumulating and piling their terrors upon Moby Dick; those things had gone far to shake the fortitude of many brave hunters, to whom the story of the White Whale had eventually come.

Nor did wild rumours of all sorts fail to exaggerate, and still the more horrify, the true histories of these deadly encounters. For not only do fabulous rumours naturally grow out of the very body of all surprising terrible events — as the smitten tree gives birth to its fungi; but, in maritime life, far more than in that of *terra firma*, wild rumours abound, wherever there is any adequate reality for them to cling to. And as the sea surpasses the land in this matter, so the whale fishery surpasses every other sort of maritime life, in the wonderfulness and fearfulness of the rumours which sometimes circulate there.

No wonder, then, that ever gathering volume from the mere transit over the widest watery spaces, the outblown rumours of the White Whale did in the end incorporate with themselves all manner of morbid hints, the half-formed foetal suggestions of supernatural agencies, which eventually invested Moby Dick with new terrors unborrowed from anything that visibly appears. So that in many cases, such a panic did he finally strike, that few who by those rumours, at least, had heard of the White Whale, few of those hunters were willing to encounter the perils of his jaws.

One of the wild suggestions referred to, as at last coming to be linked with the White Whale in the minds of the super-

198

stitiously inclined, was the unearthly conceit that Moby Dick was ubiquitous; that he had actually been encountered in opposite latitudes at one and the same instant of time.

Nor, credulous as such minds must have been, was this conceit altogether without some faint show of superstitious probability. For as the secrets of the currents in the seas have never yet been divulged even to the most erudite research, so the hidden ways of the Sperm Whale when beneath the surface remain, in great part, unaccountable to his pursuers; and from time to time have originated the most curious and contradictory speculations regarding them, especially concerning the mystic modes whereby, after sounding to a great depth, he transports himself with such vast swiftness to the most widely distant points.

It is a thing well known to both American and English whaleships, and as well a thing placed upon authoritative record years ago by Scoresby, that some whales have been captured far north in the Pacific in whose bodies have been found the barbs of harpoons darted in the Greenland seas. Nor is it to be gainsaid, that in some of these instances it has been declared that the interval of time between the two assaults could not have exceeded very many days. Hence, by inference, it has been believed by some whalemen, that the Nor'-West Passage, so long a problem to man, was never a problem to the whale. So that here, in the real living experience of living men, the prodigies related in old times of the inland Strello mountain in Portugal (near whose top there was said to be a lake in which the wrecks of ships floated up to the surface); and that still more wonderful story of the Arethusa fountain near Syracuse (whose waters were believed to come from the Holy Land by an underground passage); these fabulous narrations are almost fully equalled by the realities of the whaleman.

Forced into familiarity, then, with such prodigies as these, and knowing that after repeated, intrepid assaults, the White Whale had escaped alive, it cannot be much matter of surprise that some whalemen should go still further in their superstitions; declaring Moby Dick not only ubiquitous, but immortal. (For immortality is but ubiquity in time); and though groves of spears should be planted in his flanks, he would still swim away unharmed; or if indeed he should ever be made to spout thick blood, such a sight would be but a ghastly deception; for again in unensanguined billows hundreds of leagues away, his unsullied jet would once more be seen.

But even stripped of these supernatural surmisings, there was enough in the earthly make and incontestable character of the monster to strike the imagination with unwonted power. For, it was not so much his uncommon bulk that so much distinguished him from other sperm whales, but, as was elsewhere thrown out — a peculiar snow-white wrinkled forehead, and a high, pyramidal white hump. These were his prominent features; the tokens whereby, even in the limitless, uncharted seas, he revealed his identity, at a long distance, to those who knew him.

The rest of his body was so streaked, and spotted, and marbled with the same shrouded hue, that, in the end, he had gained his distinctive appelation of the White Whale; a name indeed, literally justified by his vivid aspect, when seen gliding at high noon through a dark blue sea, leaving a milky-way wake of creamy foam, all spangled with golden gleamings. Nor was it his unwonted magnitude, nor his remarkable hue, nor yet his deformed lower jaw, that so much invested the whale with natural terror, as that unexampled, intelligent malignity which, according to specific accounts, he had over and over again evinced in his assaults. More than all, his treacherous retreats struck more of dismay than perhaps else. For, when swimming before his exulting pursuers, with every symptom of alarm, he had several times been known to turn round suddenly, and, bearing down upon them, either stave their boats to splinters, or drive them back in consternation to their ship.

Already several fatalities had attended his chase. But though similar disasters however little bruited ashore, were by no means unusual in the fishery; yet, in most instances, such seemed the White Whale's internal forethought of ferocity, that every dismembering or death he caused, was not wholly regarded as having been inflicted by an unintelligent agent.

Judge, then, to what pitches of inflamed, distracted fury the minds of his more desperate hunters were impelled, when amid the chips of chewed boats, and the sinking limbs of torn comrades, they swam out of the white curds of the whale's direful wrath into the serene, exasperating sunlight, that smiled on, as if at a birth or a bridal.

His three boats stove around him, and oars and men both, whirling in the eddies; one captain, seizing the line-knife from his broken prow, had dashed at the whale, as an Arkansas duellist at his foe, blindly seeking with a six-inch blade, to reach the fathom-deep life of the whale. That captain was Ahab. And then it was, that suddenly sweeping his sickle-shaped lower jaw beneath him, Moby Dick had reaped away Ahab's leg, as a mower a blade of grass in the field. No turbaned Turk, no hired Venetian or Malay, could have smote him with more seeming malice. Small reason was there, to doubt then, that ever since that almost fatal encounter, Ahab had cherished a wild vindictiveness against the whale, all the more fell, that for his frantic morbidness he at last came to identify with him, not only all his bodily woes, but all his intellectual and spiritual exasperations. The White Whale swam before him as the monomaniac incarnation of all those malicious agencies which some deep men feel eating in them, till they are left living on with half a heart and half a lung. That intangible malignity which has been found from the beginning; which the ancient Ophites of the east reverenced in their statue devil; — Ahab did not fall down and worship it like them; but deliriously transferring its idea to the abhorred white whale, he pitted himself, all mutilated, against it. All that most maddens and torments; all that stirs up the lees of things; all truth with malice in it; all that cracks the sinews and cakes the brain; the subtle demonisms of life and thought; all evil, to crazy Ahab, were visibly personified, and made practically assailable in Moby Dick. He piled upon the whale's white hump the sum of all the general rage and hate felt by his whole race from Adam down.

Moby Dick's Last Fight

That night, in the mid-watch, when the old man- as his wont at intervals — stepped forth from the scuttle in which he leaned, and went to his pivot-hole, he suddenly thrust out his face fiercely, snuffing up the sea air as a sagacious ship's dog will, in drawing nigh to some barbarous isle. He declared that a whale must be near. Soon that peculiar odour, sometimes to a great distance given forth by the living Sperm Whale, was palpable to all the watch; nor was any mariner surprised when, after inspecting the compass, and then the dog-vane, and then ascertaining the precise bearing of the odour as nearly as possible, Ahab rapidly ordered the ship's course to be slightly altered, and the sail to be shortened. The acute policy dictating these movements was sufficiently vindicated at daybreak by the sight of a long sleek on the sea directly and lengthwise ahead, smooth as oil, and resembling in the pleated watery wrinkles bordering it, the polished metallic-like marks of some swift tide-rip, at the mouth of a deep, rapid stream.

'Man the mastheads! Call all hands!'

Thundering with the butts of three clubbed handspikes on the forecastle deck, Daggoo roused the sleepers with such judgement claps that they seemed to exhale from the scuttle, so instantaneously did they appear with their clothes in their hands.

'What d'ye see?' cried Ahab, flattening his face to the sky.

'Nothing, nothing, sir!' was the sound hailing down in reply.

'T'gallant-sails! stunsails alow and aloft on both sides!'

All sail being set, he now cast loose the life-line, reserved for swaying him to the mainroyal masthead; and in a few moments they were hoisting him thither, when, while but two-thirds of the way aloft, and while peering ahead through the horizontal vacancy between the maintopsail and top-gallant sail, he raised a gull-like cry in the air, 'There she blows! — there she blows! A hump like a snow-hill! It is Moby Dick!'

Fired by the cry which seemed simultaneously taken up by the three look-outs, the men on deck rushed to the rigging to behold the famous whale they had so long been pursuing. Ahab, now had gained his final perch, some feet above the other look-outs, Tashtego, standing just beneath him on the cap of the top-gallant mast, so that the Indian's head was almost on a level with Ahab's heel. From this height the whale was seen some mile or so ahead, at every roll of the sea revealing his high sparkling hump, and regularly jetting his silent spout into the air. To the credulous mariners, it seemed the same silent spout they had so long ago beheld in the moonlit Atlantic and Indian Oceans.

'And did none of yet see it before?' cried Ahab, hailing the perched men all around him.

'I saw him almost the same instant, sir, that Captain Ahab did, and I cried out,' said Tashtego.

'Not the same instant; not the same — no, the doubloon is mine, Fate reserved the doubloon for me. I only; none of ye could have raised the White Whale first. There she blows! there she blows! There she blows! There again! — there again!' he cried, in long-drawn lingering methodic tones, attuned to the gradual prolongings of the whale's visible jets. 'He's going to sound! In stunsails! Down top-gallant sails! Stand by the three boats. Mr Starbuck, remember, stay on board, and keep the ship. Helm there! Luff, luff a point! So; steady, man, steady! There go flukes. No, no; only black water! All ready the boats there? Stand by, stand by! Lower me, Mr Starbuck; lower, lower, — quick, quicker!' and he slid through the air to the deck.

'He is heading straight to leeward, sir,' cried Stubb; 'right away from us; cannot have seen the ship yet.'

'Be dumb, man! Stand by the braces! Hard down the helm! — brace up! Shiver her! — shiver her! So; well that! Boats, boats!'

Soon all the boats but Starbuck's were dropped; the boat-sails set; all the paddles plying; with rippling swiftness, shooting to leeward; and Ahab heading the onset. A pale, death-glimmer lit up Fedallah's sunken eyes; a hideous motion gnawed his mouth.

Like noiseless nautilus shells, their light prows sped through the sea; but only slowly they neared the foe. As they neared him, the ocean grew still more smooth; seemed drawing a carpet over its waves; seemed a noon-meadow, so serenely it spread. At length, the breathless hunter came so nigh his seemingly unsuspecting prey, that his entire dazzling hump was distinctly visible, sliding along the sea as if an isolated thing, and continually set in a revolving ring of finest, fleecy, greenish foam. He saw the vast involved wrinkles of the slightly projecting head beyond. Before it, far out on the soft Turkish-rugged waters, went the glistening white shadows from his broad milky forehead, a musical rippling playfully accompanying the shade; and behind, the blue waters interchangeably flowed over into the moving valley of his steady wake; and on either hand bright bubbles arose and danced by his side. But these were broken again by the light toes of hundreds of gay fowl softly feathering the sea, alternate with their fitful flight; and like to some flagstaff rising from the painted hull of an argosy, the tall but shattered pole of a recent lance projected from the white whale's back; and at intervals one of the cloud of soft-toed fowls hovering, and to and fro skimming like a canopy over the fish, silently perched and rocked on this pole, the long tail feathers streaming like pennons.

A gentle joyousness — a mighty mildness of repose in swiftness, invested the gliding whale. Not the white bull Jupiter swimming away with ravished Europa clinging to his graceful horns; his lovely leering eyes sideways intent upon the maid; with smooth bewitching fleetness rippling straight for the nuptual bower in Crete; not Jove did surpass the glorified White Whale as he so divinely swam.

On each soft side — coincident with the parted swell, that but once leaving him, then flowed so wide away — on each bright side, the whale shed off enticings. No wonder there had been some among the hunters who namelessly transported and allured by all this serenity had ventured to assail it; but had fatally found that quietude but the vesture of tornadoes. Yet, calm, enticing calm, oh whale; thou glidest on, to all who for the first time eye thee, no matter how many in that same way thou may'st have bejuggled and destroyed before.

And thus, through the serene tranquillities of the tropical sea, among waves whose hand-clappings were suspended by exceeding rapture, Moby Dick moved on, still withholding from sight the full terrors of his submerged trunk, entirely hiding the wretched hideousness of his jaws. But soon the fore part of him slowly rose from the water; for an instant his whole marbleised body formed a high arch, like Virginia's Natural Bridge, and warningly waving his bannered flukes in the air. The grand god revealed himself, sounded and went out of sight. Hoveringly halting, and dipping on the wing, the white sea-fowls longingly lingered over the agitated pool that he left.

With oars apeak, and paddles down, the sheets of their sails adrift, the three boats now stilly floated, awaiting Moby Dick's appearance.

'An hour,' said Ahab, standing rooted in his boat's stern, and he gazed beyond the whale's place, towards the dim blue spaces and wide wooing vacancies to leeward. It was only an instant, for again his eyes seemed whirling in his head as he swept the watery circle. The breeze now freshened; the sea began to swell.

'The birds! — the birds!' cried Tashtego.

In long Indian file, as when herons take wing, the white birds were now all flying towards Ahab's boat; and when within a few yards began fluttering over the water there, wheeling round and round, with joyous expectant cries. Their vision was keener than man's; Ahab could discover no sign in the sea. But suddenly as he peered down and into its depths, he profoundly saw a white living spot no bigger than a white weasel, with a wonderful celerity uprising and magnifying as it rose, till it turned and then there were plainly revealed two long crooked rows of white, glistening teeth, floating up from the undiscoverable bottom. It was Moby Dick's open mouth and scrolled jaw; his vast shadowed bulk but still half blending with the blue of the sea. The glittering mouth yawned beneath the boat like an open-doored marble tomb; and giving one sidelong sweep with his steering oar, Ahab whirled the craft aside from this tremendous apparition. Then, calling upon Fedellah to change placeds with him, went forward to the bows, and seizing Perth's harpoon, commanded his crew to grasp their oars and stand by to stern.

Both jaws like an enormous shears bit the craft completely in twain.

Now, by reason of this timely spinning round the boat upon its axis, its bow, by anticipation, was made to face the whale's head while yet under water. But as if perceiving this stratagem, Moby Dick with that malicious intelligence ascribed to him, sidelingly transplanted himself, as it were, in an instant, shooting his plaited head lengthwise beneath the boat.

Through and through; through every plank and each rib, it thrilled for an instant, the whale obliquely lying on his back, in the manner of a biting shark, slowly and feelingly taking its bows full within his mouth, so that the long, narrow, scrolled lower jaw curled high up into the open air, and one of the teeth caught in a rowlock. The bluish pearl-white of the inside of the jaw was within six inches of Ahab's head, and reached higher than that. In this altitude the White Whale now shook the slight cedar as a mildly cruel cat her mouse. With unastonished eyes Fedallah gazed, and crossed his arms; but the tiger-yellow crew were tumbling over each other's heads to gain the uttermost stern.

And now, while both elastic gunwales were springing in and out, as the whale dallied with the doomed craft in this devilish way; and from his body being submerged beneath the boat, he could not be darted at from the bows, for the bows were almost inside of him, as it were; and while the other boats involuntarily paused, as before a quick crisis impossible to withstand, then it was that monomaniac Ahab, furious with this tantalising vicinity of his foe, which placed him all alive and helpless in the very jaws he hated; frenzied with all this, he seized the long bone with his naked hands, and wildly strove to wrench it from its grip. As he now thus vainly strove, the jaw slipped from him; the frail gunwales bent in, collapsed and snapped, as both jaws like an enormous shears, sliding further aft, bit the craft completely in twain, and locked themselves fast again in the sea, midway between the two floating wrecks. These floated aside, the broken ends drooping, the crew at the sternwreck clinging to the gunwales, and striving to hold fast to the oars to lash them across.

At that preluding moment, ere the boat was yet snapped, Ahab, the first to perceive the whale's intent, by the crafty upraising of his head, a movement that loosed his hold for the first time; at that moment his hand had made one final attempt to push the boat out of the bite. But only slipping further into the whale's mouth, and tilting over sideways as it slipped, the boat had shaken off his hold on the jaw; spilled him out of it, as he leaned to the push, and so he fell flat-faced upon the sea.

Ripplingly withdrawing from his prey, Moby Dick now lay at a little distance, vertically thrusting his oblong white head up and down in the billows; and at the same time slowly revolving his whole splendid body; so that when his vast wrinkled forehead rose — some twenty or more feet out of the water — the now rising swells, with all their confluent waves, dazzling broke against it; vindictively tossing their shivered spray still higher into the air. So, in a gale, the but half baffled Channel billows only recoil from the base of Eddystone, triumphantly to overlap its summit with their scud.

But soon resuming his horizontal attitude, Moby Dick swam swiftly round and round the wrecked crew; sideways churning up the water in his vengeful wake, as if lashing himself up to still another and more deadly assault. The sight of the splintered boat seemed to madden him, as the blood of grapes and mulberries cast before Antiochus's elephant in the book of Maccabees. Meanwhile Ahab half smothered in the foam of the whale's insolent tail, and too much of a cripple to swim, — though he could still keep afloat, even in the heart of such a whirlpool as that; helpless Ahab's head was seen, like a tossed bubble which the least chance shock might burst. From the boat's fragmentary stern, Fedallah incuriously and mildly eyed him; the clinging crew, at the other drifting end, could

209

not succour him; more than enough it was for them to look to themselves. For so revolvingly appalling was the White Whale's aspect, and so planetarily swift the ever-contracting circles he made, that he seemed horizontally swooping upon them. And though the other boats, unharmed, still hovered hard by, still they dared not pull into the eddy to strike, lest that should be the signal for the instant destruction of the jeopardised castaways, Ahab, and all; nor in that case could they themselves hope to escape. With straining eyes, then, they remained on the outer edge of the direful zone, whose centre had now become the old man's head.

Meantime, from the beginning all this had been descried from the ship's mastheads; and squaring her yards, she had borne down upon the scene; and was now so nigh, that Ahab, in the water hailed her; — 'Sail on the' — but that moment a breaking sea dashed on him from Moby Dick, and whelmed him for the time. But struggling out of it again, and chancing to rise on a towering crest, he shouted, — 'Sail on the whale! — Drive him off!'

The *Pequod's* prows were pointed; and breaking up the charmed circle, she effectually parted the White Whale from his victim. As he sullenly swam off, the boats flew to the rescue.

Dragged into Stubb's boat with bloodshot blinding eyes, the white brine caking in his wrinkles; the long tension of Ahab's bodily strength did crack, and helplessly he yielded to his body's doom: for a time, lying all crushed in the bottom of Stubb's boat, like one trodden under foot of a herd of elephants. Far inland, nameless wails came from him, as desolate sounds from our ravines.

But the intensity of his physical prostration did but so much the more abbreviate it. In an instant's compass, great hearts sometimes condense to one deep pang, the sum-total of those shallow pains kindly diffused through feebler men's whole lives. And so, such hearts, though summary in each one suffering; still, if the gods decree it, in their lifetime aggregate a whole age of woe, wholly made up of instantaneous intensities; for even in their pointless centres those noble natures contain the entire circumferences of inferior souls.

'The harpoon,' said Ahab, half-way rising and draggingly leaning on one bended arm — 'is it safe?'

'Aye, sir, for it was not darted; this is it,' said Stubb, showing t.

'Say it before me; — any missing men?'

'One, two, three, four, five; — there were five oars, sir, and here are five men.'

'That's good. — Help me, man; I wish to stand. So, so I see him! there! there! going to leeward still; what a leaping spout! — Hands off from me! The eternal sap runs in Ahab's bones again! Set the sail; out oars; the helm!'

It is often the case that when a boat is stove, its crew, being picked up by another boat, help to work that second boat; and the chase is thus continued with what is called double-banked oars. It was thus now. But the added power of the boat did not equal the added power of the whale, for he seemed to have treble-banked his every fin; swimming with a velocity which plainly showed that, if now, under these circumstances, pushed on, the chase would prove an indefinitely prolonged, if not a hopeless one; nor could any crew endure for so long a period, such an unintermitted, intense, straining at the oar; a thing barely tolerable only in some one brief vicissitude. The ship itself, then, as it sometimes happens, offered the most promising intermediate means of overtaking the chase. Accordingly, the boats now made for her, and were soon swayed up to their cranes — the two parts of the wrecked boat having been previously secured by her — and then hoisting everything to her side, and stacking the canvas high up, and sideways outstretching it with stunsails, like the double-jointed wings of an albatross; the *Pequod* bore down in the leeward wake of Moby Dick. At the well-known, methodical intervals, the whale's glittering spout was regularly announced from the manned mastheads; and when he would be reported as just gone down, Ahab would take the time, and then pacing the deck, binnacle-watch in hand, so soon as the last sound of the allotted hour expire, his voice was heard — 'Whose is the doubloon now? D'ye see him?' and if the reply was 'No, sir!' straightway he commanded them to lift him to his perch. In this way the day wore on; Ahab, now aloft and motionless; anon, unrestingly pacing the planks.

As he was thus walking, uttering no sound, except to hail the men aloft, or to bid them hoist a sail still higher, or to spread one to a still greater breadth — thus to and fro pacing, beneath his slouched hat, at every turn he passed his own wrecked boat, which had been dropped upon the quarter-deck, and lay there reversed, broken bow to shattered stern. At last, he paused before it; and as in an already over-clouded sky fresh troops of clouds will sometimes sail across, so over the old man's face there now stole some such added gloom as this.

Stubb saw him pause; and perhaps intending, not vainly, though, to evince his own unabated fortitude, and thus keep up a valiant place in his Captain's mind, he advanced, and eyeing the wreck exclaimed — 'The thistle the ass refused — it pricked his mouth too keenly, sir; ha! ha!'

'What soulless thing is this that laughs before a wreck? Man, man! did I not know thee brave as fearless fire (and as mechanical) I could swear thou wert a poltroon. Groan nor laugh should be heard before a wreck.'

'Aye, sir,' said Starbuck, drawing near, ''tis a solemn sight; an omen, and an ill one.'

'Omen? omen? — the dictionary! If the gods think to speak outright to a man, they will honourably speak outright; not shake their heads and give an old wife's darkling hint. —

Begone! Ye two are the opposite poles of one thing; Starbuck is Stubb reversed, and Stubb is Starbuck; and ye two are all mankind; and Ahab stands alone among the millions of the peopled earth, nor gods nor men his neighbours! Cold, cold — I shiver! — How now? Aloft there? D'ye see him? Sing out for every spout, though he spout ten times a second!'

The day was nearly done; only the hem of his golden robe was rustling. Soon, it was almost dark, but the look-out men still remained unset.

'Can't see the spout now, sir; — too dark' — cried a voice from the air.

'How heading when last seen?'

'As before, sir — straight to leeward'

'Good! he will travel slower now 'tis night. Down royals and top—gallant stunsails, Mr Starbuck. We must not run over him before morn. He's making a passage now, and may heave-to a while. Helm there! — keep her full before the wind! — Aloft! come down! — Mr Stubb, send a fresh hand to the foremast head, and see it manned till morning.' — Then advancing towards the doubloon in the mainmast — 'Men, this gold is mine, for I earned it; but I shall let it abide here till the White Whale is dead; and then, whosoever of ye first raises him, upon the day he shall be killed, this gold is that man's; and if on that day I shall again raise him, then, ten times its sum shall be divided among all of ye! Away now! — the deck is thine, Sir.'

And so saying, he placed himself half-way within the scuttle, and slouching his hat, stood there till dawn, except when at intervals rousing himself to see how the night wore on.

At daybreak the three mastheads were punctually manned afresh.

'D'ye see him?' cried Ahab after allowing a little space for the light to spread.

213

'See nothing, sir.'

'Turn up all hands and make sail! he travels faster than I thought for — the top-gallant sails! — aye, they should have been kept on her all night. But no matter — 'tis but resting for the rush.'

The ship tore on, leaving such a furrow in the sea as when a cannon-ball, missent, becomes a ploughshare and turns up the level field.

'By salt and hemp!' cried Stubb, 'but this swift motion of the deck creeps up one's legs and tingles at the heart. This ship and I are two grave fellows! Ha! ha! Some one take me up, and launch me, spine-wise, on the sea, for by live-oaks! my spine's a keel. Ha, ha! we go the gait that leaves no dust behind!'

'There she blows — she blows! — she blows! — right ahead!' was now the masthead cry.

'Aye, aye!' cried Stubb, 'I knew it — ye can't escape — blow on and split your spout, O Whale! the mad fiend himself is after ye! Blow your trump — blister your lungs! Ahab will dam off your blood, as a miller shuts his gater-gate upon the stream.'

And Stubb did but speak out for well-nigh all that crew. The frenzies of the chase had by this time worked them bubblingly up, like old wine worked anew. Whatever pale fears and forebodings some of them might have felt before; these were not only now kept out of sight through the growing awe of Ahab, but they were broken up, and on all sides routed, as timid prairie hares that scatter before the bounding bison. The hand of Fate had snatched all their souls; and, by the stirring perils of the previous day; the rack of the past night's suspense; the fixed unfearing, blind, reckless way in which their wild craft went plunging towards its flying mark; by all these things, their hearts were bowled along. The wind that made great bellies of their sails, and rushed the vessel on by arms invisible as irresistible; this seemed the symbol of that unseen agency which so enslaved them to the race.

There were one man, not thirty. For as the one ship that held them all, though it was put together of all contrasting things — oak, and maple, and pine wood; iron and pitch, and hemp — yet all these ran into each other in the one concrete hull, which shot on its way, both balanced and directed by the long central keel; even so, all the individualities of the crew. This man's valour, that man's fear; guilt and guiltiness, all varieties were welded into oneness, and were all directed to that fatal goal which Ahab their one lord and keel did point to.

The rigging lived. The mastheads, like the tops of tall palms, were out-spreadingly tufted with arms and legs. Clinging to a spar with one hand, some reached forth the other with impatient wavings; others, shading their eyes from the vivid sunlight, sat far out on the rocking yards; all the spars in full bearing of mortals, ready and ripe for their fate. Ah! how they still strove through that infinite blueness to seek out the thing that might destroy them!

'Why sing ye not out for him, if ye see him?' cried Ahab, when, after the lapse of some minutes since the first cry, no more had been heard. 'Sway me up, men; ye have been deceived; not Moby Dick casts one odd jet that way, and then disappears.'

It was even so; in their headlong eagerness, the men had mistaken some other thing for the whale-spout, as the event itself soon proved; for hardly had Ahab reached his perch; hardly was the rope belayed to its pin on deck, when he struck the key-note to an orchestra, that made the air vibrate as with the combined discharges of rifles. The triumphant halloo of thirty buckskin lungs was heard, as — much nearer to the ship than the place of the imaginary jet, less than a mile ahead — Moby Dick bodily burst into view. For not by any calm and indolent spoutings; not by the peaceable gush of that mystic fountain in his head, did the White Whale now reveal his vicinity; but by the far more wondrous phenomenon of breaching. Rising with his utmost velocity from the furthest depths, the Sperm Whale thus booms his entire bulk into the pure element of air, and piling up a mountain of dazzling foam, shows his place to the distance of seven miles and more. In those moments, the torn, enraged waves he shakes off seem his mane; in some cases this breaching is his act of defiance.

'There she breaches! there she breaches!' was the cry, as in his immeasurable bravadoes the White Whale tossed himself salmon-like to Heaven. So suddenly seen in the blue plain of the sea, and relieved against the still bluer margin of the sky, the spray that he raised, for the moment, intolerably glittered and glared like a glacier; and stood there gradually fading away from its first sparkling intensity, to the dim and fading mistiness of an advancing shower in a vale.

'Aye, breach your last to the sun, Moby Dick!' cried Ahab, 'thy hour and thy harpoon are at hand! Down! down all of ye, but one man at the fore. The boats! — stand by!'

Undmindful of the tedious rope-ladders of the shrouds, the men, like shooting stars, slid to the deck, by the isolated backstays and halyards; while Ahab, less dartingly but still rapidly, was dropped from his perch.

'Lower away,' he cried, so soon as he had reached his boat — a spare one, rigged the afternoon previous. 'Mr Starbuck, the ship is thine — keep away from the boats, but keep near them. Lower all!'

As if to strike a quick terror into them, by this time being the first assailant himself, Moby Dick had turned, and was now coming for the three crews. Ahab's boat was central; and cheering his men, he told them he would take the whale head-and-head — that is, pull straight up to his forehead — not an uncommon thing; for when within a certain limit, such a course excludes the coming onset from the whale's sidelong vision. But ere that close limit was gained, and while yet all three boats were plain as the ship's three masts to his eye; the White Whale, churning himself into furious speed, almost in an instant as it were, rushing among the boats with open jaws, and lashing tail, offered appalling battle on every side; and heedless of the irons darted at him from every boat, seemed only intent on annihilating each separate plank of which those boats were made. But skilfully manoeuvred, incessantly wheeling like trained chargers in the field; the boats for a while eluded him; though, at times, but by a plank's breadth; while all the time, Ahab's unearthly slogan tore every other cry but his to shreds.

But at last in his untraceable volutions, the White Whale so crossed and recrossed, and in a thousand ways entangled the slack of the three lines now fast to him, that they foreshortened, and, of themselves, warped the devoted boats towards the planted irons in him; though now for a moment the whale drew aside a little, as if to rally for a more tremendous charge. Seizing that opportunity, Ahab first paid out more line; and then was rapidly hauling and jerking in upon it again — hoping that way to disencumber it of some snarls — when lo! — a sight more savage than the embattled teeth of sharks!

Caught and twisted — corkscrewed in the mazes of the line — loose harpoons and lances, with all their bristling barbs and points, came flashing and dripping up to the chocks in the bows of Ahab's boat. Only one thing could be done. Seizing the boat-knife, he critically reached within — through — and then, without — the rays of steel; dragged in the line beyond, passed it, inboard, to the bowsman, and then, twice sundering the rope near the chocks — dropped the intercepted fagot of steel into the sea; and was all fast again. That instant, the White Whale made a sudden rush among the remaining tangles of the other lines; by doing so, irresistibly dragged the more involved boats of Stubb and Flask towards his flukes; dashed them together like two rolling husks on a surf-beaten beach, and then, diving down into the sea, disappeared in a coiling maelstrom, in which, for a space, the odorous cedar chips of the wrecks danced round and round, like the grated nutmeg in a swiftly stirred bowl of punch.

While the two crews were yet circling in the waters, reaching out after the revolving line-tubs, oars, and other floating furniture, while aslope little Flask bobbed up and down like an empty vial, twitching his legs upwards to escape the dreaded jaws of sharks; and Stubb was lustily singing out for some one to ladle him up; and while the old man's line — now parting — admitted of his pulling into the creamy pool to rescue whom he could — in that wild simultaneousness of a thousand concreted perils — Ahab's yet unstricken boat seemed drawn up towards Heaven by invisible wires — as, arrow-like, shooting perpendicularly from the sea, the White Whale dashed his broad forehead against its bottom, and sent it, turning over and over, into the air; till it fell again — gunwale downwards — and Ahab and his men struggled out from under it, like seals from a seaside cave.

The first uprising momentum of the whale — modifying its direction as he struck the surface — involuntarily launched him along it, to a little distance from the centre of the destruction he had made; and with his back to it, he now lay for a moment slowly feeling with his flukes from side to side; and whenever a stray oar, bit of plank, the least chip or crumb of the boats touched his skin, his tail swiftly drew back, and came sideways, smiting the sea. But soon, as if satisfied that his work for that time was done, he pushed his plaited forehead through the ocean, and trailing after him the intertangled lines, continued his leeward way at a traveller's methodic pace.

As before, the attentive ship having descried the whole fight, again came bearing down to the rescue, and dropping a boat,

'Aye, aye, Starbuck, 'tis sweet to lean sometimes.'

picked up the floating mariners, tubs, oars, and whatever else could be caught at, and safely landed them upon her decks. Some sprained shoulders, wrists and ankles; livid contusions; wrenched harpoons and lances; inextricable intricacies of rope, shattered oars and planks; all these were there; but no fatal or even serious ill seemed to have befallen anyone. As with Fedallah the day before, so Ahab was now found grimly clinging to his boat's broken half, which offered a comparatively easy float; nor did it exhaust him as the previous day's mishap.

But when he was helped to the deck, all eyes were fastened upon him; as instead of standing by himself he still half-hung upon the shoulder of Starbuck, who had thus far been the foremost to assist him. His ivory leg had been snapped off, leaving but one short sharp splinter.

'Aye, aye, Starbuck, 'tis sweet to lean sometimes, be the leaner who he will; and would old Ahab had leaned oftener than he has.'

'The ferrule has not stood, sir,' said the carpenter, now coming up; 'I put good work into that leg.'

'But no bones broken, sir, I hope,' said Stubb with true concern.

'Aye! and all splintered to pieces, Stubb! d'ye see it? But even with a broken bone, old Ahab is untouched; and I account no living bone of mine one jot more me than this dead one that's lost. Nor white whale, nor man, nor fiend, can so much as graze old Ahab in his own proper and inaccessible being. Can any lead touch yonder floor, any mast scrape yonder roof? Aloft there! which way?

'Dead to leeward, sir.'

'Up helm, then; pile on the sail again, shipkeepers; down the rest of the spare boats and rig them — Mr Starbuck, away, and muster the boats and crews.'

'Let me first help thee towards the bulwarks, sir.'

220

'Oh, oh, oh! how this splinter gores me now! Accursed fate! that the unconquerable captain in the soul should have had such a craven mate!'

'Sir?'

'My body, man, not thee. Give me something for a cane — there, that shivered lance will do. Muster the men. Surely I have not seen him yet. By heaven, it cannot be! — missing? quick! call them all.'

The old man's hinted thought was true. Upon mustering the company, the Parsee was not there.

'The Parsee!' cried Stubb, 'he must have been caught in —'

'The black vomit wrench thee! Run all of ye above, alow cabin, forecastle — find him — not gone — not gone!'

But they returned to him with the tidings that the Parsee was nowhere to be found.

'Aye, sir,' said Stubb — 'caught among the tangles of your line. I thought I saw him dragged under.'

'*My* line? *My* line? Gone? Gone? What means that little word? What death-knell rings in it, that old Ahab shakes as if he were the belfry. The harpoon, too! Toss over the litter there, d'ye see it? — the forged iron, men, the white whale's — no, no, no, blistered fool! this hand did dart it! 'Tis in the fish! Aloft there! Keep him nailed. Quick! all hands to the rigging of the boats — collect the oars — harpooners! the irons, the irons! Hoist the royals higher — a pull on all the sheets! Helm there! steady, steady, for your life! I'll ten times girdle the unmeasured globe; yea and dive straight through it, but I'll slay him yet!'

'Great God! but for one single instant show thyself,' cried Starbuck. 'Never, never wilt thou capture him, old man. In Jesus' name, no more of this, that's worse than devil's madness. Two days chased; twice stove to splinters; thy very leg once more snatched from under thee; thy evil shadow gone — all good angels mobbing thee with warnings; what more wouldst thou have? Shall we be dragged by him to the bottom of the sea? Shall we be towed by him to the infernal world? Oh, oh! Impiety and blasphemy to hunt him more!'

'Starbuck, of late I've felt strangely moved to thee; ever since that hour we both saw — thou know'st what, in one another's eyes. But in this matter of the whale, be the front of thy face to me as the palm of this hand — a lipless, unfeatured blank. Ahab is for ever Ahab, man. This whole act's immutably decreed. 'Twas rehearsed by thee and me a billion years before this ocean rolled. Fool! I am the Fates' lieutenant; I act under orders. Look thou, underling! that thou obeyest mine. Stand round me, men. Ye see an old man cut down to the stump; leaning on a shivered lance; propped up on a lonely foot. 'Tis Ahab — his body's part; but Ahab's soul's a centipede, that moves upon a hundred legs. I feel strained, half stranded, as ropes that tow dismasted frigates in a gale; and I may look so. But ere I break, ye'll hear me crack; and till ye hear *that*, know that Ahab's hawser tows his purpose yet. Believe ye, men, in the things called omens? Then laugh aloud, and cry encore! For ere they drown, drowning things will twice rise to the surface; then rise again, to sink for evermore. So with Moby Dick — two days he's floated — tomorrow will be the third. Aye, men, he'll rise once more — but only to spout his last.'

The morning of the third day dawned fair and fresh, and once more the solitary night-man at the fore-masthead was relieved by crowds of the daylight look-outs, who dotted every mast and almost every spar.

'D'ye see him?' cried Ahab. 'Aloft there. What d'ye see?'

'Nothing, sir.'

'Nothing! The doubloon goes a-begging! See the sun! Aye, aye, it must be so. I've over-sailed him. How, got the start? Aye, he's chasing *me*, now; not I, *him* — that's bad. I might have known it, too. Fool! the lines — the harpoons

222

he's towing. Aye, aye, I have run him by last night. About! About! Come down, all of ye, but the regular look-outs! Man the braces!'

Steering as she had done, the wind had been somewhat on the *Pequod's* quarter, so that now being pointed in the reverse direction, the braced ship sailed hard upon the breeze as she rechurned the cream in her own white wake.

'Against the wind he now steers for the open jaw,' murmured Starbuck to himself, as he coiled the new-hauled main-brace upon the rail. 'God keep us, but already my bones feel damp within me, and from the inside wet my flesh. I misdoubt me that I disobeyed my God in obeying him!'

'Stand by to sway me up!' cried Ahab, advancing to the hempen basket. 'We should meet him soon.'

'Aye, aye, sir,' and straightway Starbuck did Ahab's bidding, and once more Ahab swung on high.

A whole hour now passed; golden-beaten out to ages. Time itself now held long breaths with keen suspense. But at last, some three points off the weather-bow, Ahab descried the spout again, and instantly from the three mastheads three shrieks went up as if the tongues of fire had voiced it.

'Forehead to forehead I meet thee, this third time, Moby Dick! On deck there! Brace sharper up; crowd her into the wind's eye. He's too far off to lower yet, Mr Starbuck. The sails shake! Stand over that helmsman with a topmaul! So, so he travels fast, and I must down.'

He gave the word, and still gazing round him, was steadily lowered through the cloven blue air to the deck.

In due time the boats were lowered; but as standing in his shallop's stern, Ahab just hovered upon the point of the descent, he waved to the mate, who held one of the tackle-ropes on deck, and bade him pause.

'Starbuck!'

'Sir?'

'For the third time my soul's ship starts upon this voyage, Starbuck.'

'Aye, sir, thou wilt have it so.'

'Some ships sail from their ports, and ever afterwards are missing, Starbuck! Some men die at ebb tide; some at low water; some at the full of the flood; and I feel now like a billow that's all one crested comb, Starbuck. Lower away! Stand by the crew!'

In an instant the boat was pulling round close under the stern.

'The sharks! the sharks!' cried a voice from the low cabin-window there. 'O master, my master, come back!'

But Ahab heard nothing; for his own voice was high-lifted then; and the boat leaped on.

Yet the voice spake true; for scarce had he pushed from the ship, when numbers of sharks, seemingly rising from out of the dark waters, beneath the hull, maliciously snapped at the blades of the oars, every time they dipped in the water; and in this way accompanied the boat with their bites. It is a thing not uncommonly happening to the whale-boats in those swarming seas; the sharks at times apparently following them in the same prescient way that vultures hover over the banners of marching regiments in the east. But these were the first sharks that had been observed by the *Pequod* since the White Whale had been first descried; and whether it was that Ahab's crew were all such tiger-yellow barbarians, and therefore their flesh more musky to the senses of sharks — a matter sometimes well known to affect them — however it was, they seemed to follow that one boat without molesting the others.

'Heart of wrought steel,' murmured Starbuck, gazing over the side, and following with his eyes the receding boat, 'canst thou yet ring boldly to that sight? lowering thy keel among ravening sharks, and followed by them, open-mouthed, to the chase; and this the critical third day? For when three days

224

flow together in one continuous intense pursuit, be sure the first in the morning, the second the noon, and the third the evening and the end of that thing — be that the end what it may.'

The boats had not gone very far, when by a signal from the mastheads — a downward pointed arm, Ahab knew that the whale had sounded; but intending to be near him at the next rising, he held on his way a little sideways from the vessel; the becharmed crew maintaining the profoundest silence, as the head-beat waves hammered and hammered against the opposing bow.

Suddenly the waters around them slowly swelled in broad circles, then quickly upheaved, as if sideways sliding from a submerged berg of ice, swiftly rising to the surface. A low rumbling sound was heard; a subterraneous hum; and then all held their breaths; as bedraggled with trailing ropes, and harpoons, and lances, a vast form shot lengthwise, but obliquely from the sea. Shrouded in a thin drooping veil of mist, it hovered for a moment in the rainbowed air; and then fell swamping back into the deep. Crushed thirty feet upwards, the waters flashed for an instant like heaps of fountains, then brokenly sank in a shower of lakes, leaving the circling surface creamed like new milk round the marble trunk of the whale.

'Give way!' cried Ahab to the oarsmen and the boats darted forward to the attack; but maddened by yesterdays fresh irons that corroded in him, Moby Dick seemed combinedly possessed by all the angels that fell from heaven. The wide tiers of welded tendons overspreading his broad white forehead, beneath the transparent skin, looked knitted together; as head on, he came churning his tail among the boats; and once more flailed them apart; spilling out the irons and lances from the two mates' boats, and dashing in one side of the upper part of their bows, but leaving Ahab's almost without a scar.

While Daggoo and Queequeg were stopping the strained

planks; and as the whale swimming out from them, turned, and showed one entire flank as he shot by them again; at that moment a quick cry went up. Lashed round and round to the fish's back; pinioned in the turns upon turns in which, during the past night, the whale had reeled the involutions of the lines around him, the half-torn body of the Parsee was seen; his sable raiment frayed to shreds, his distended eyes turned full upon old Ahab.

The harpoon dropped from his hand.

'Befooled, befooled!' — drawing in a long lean breath — 'Aye, Parsee! I see thee again. Aye, and thou goest before; and this, *this* then is the hearse that thou didst promise. But I hold thee to the last letter of thy word. Where is the second hearse? Away, mates, to the ship! Those boats are useless now; repair them if ye can in time, and return to me; if not, Ahab is enough to die. Down, men! The first thing that but offers to jump from this boat I stand in, that thing I harpoon. Ye are not other men, but my arms and legs; so obey me. Where's the whale? gone down again?'

But he looked too nigh the boat; for as if bent upon escaping with the corpse he bore, and as if the particular place of the last encounter had been but a stage in his leeward voyage, Moby Dick was now again steadily swimming forward; and had almost passed the ship, which thus far had been sailing in the contrary direction to him, though for the present her headway had been stopped. He seemed swimming with his utmost velocity, and now only intent upon pursuing his own straight path in the sea.

'Oh! Ahab,' cried Starbuck, 'not too late is it even now, the third day, to desist. See! Moby Dick seeks thee not. It is thou, thou, that madly seekest him!'

Setting sail to the rising wind, the lonely boat was swiftly impelled to leeward by both oars and canvas. And at last when Ahab was sliding by the vessel, so near as plainly to distinguish Starbuck's face as he leaned over the rail, he hailed him to turn the vessel about, and follow him, not too swiftly, at a judicious interval. Glancing upwards, he saw Tashtego, Queequeg, and Daggoo, eagerly mounting to the three mastheads; while the oarsmen were rocking in the two staved boats which had just been hoisted to the side, and were busily at work in repairing them. One after the other, through the port holes, as he sped, he also caught flying glimpses of Stubb and Flask, busying themselves on deck among bundles of new irons and lances. As he saw all this; as he heard the hammers in the broken boats; far other hammers seemed driving a nail into his heart. But he rallied. And now marking that the vane of flag was gone from the main masthead, he shouted to Tashtego, who had just gained that perch, to descend again for another flag, and a hammer and nails, and so nail it to the mast.

Whether fagged by the three days' running chase, and the resistance to his swimming in the knotted hamper he bore; or whether it was some latent deceitfulness and malice in him; whichever was true, the White Whale's way now began to abate, as it seemed, from the boat so rapidly nearing him once more; though indeed the whale's last start had not been so long a one as before. And still as Ahab glided over the waves the unpitying sharks accompanied him; and so pertinaciously stuck to the boat; and so continually bit at the plying oars, that the blades became jagged and crunched, and left small splinters in the sea, at almost every dip.

'Heed them not! those teeth but give new rowlocks to your oars. Pull on! 'tis the better rest, the shark's jaws than the yielding water.'

'But at every bite, sir, the thin blades grow smaller and smaller!'

'They will last long enough! Pull on! But who can tell' — he muttered — 'whether these sharks swim to feast on a whale or on Ahab? But pull on! Aye, all alive now — we near him. The helm! take the helm; let me pass,' — and so saying, two of the oarsmen helped him forward to the bows of the still flying boat.

At length as the craft was cast to one side, and ran ranging along with the White Whale's flank, he seemed strangely oblivious of its advance — as the whale sometimes will — and Ahab was fairly within the smoky mountain mist, which, thrown off from the whale's spout, curled round his great Monadnock hump. He was even thus close to him; when, with body arched back, and both arms lengthwise high-lifted to the poise, he darted his fierce iron, and his far fiercer curse into the hated whale. As both steel and curse sank to the socket, as if sucked into a morass, Moby Dick sideways writhed; spasmodically rolled his nigh flank against the bow, and, without staving a hole in it, so suddenly canted the boat over, that had it not been for the elevated part of the gunwale to which he then clung, Ahab would have once more been tossed into the sea. As it was, three of the oarsmen — who foreknew not the precise instant of the dart, and were therefore unprepared for its effects — these were flung out; but so fell, that, in an instant two of them clutched the gunwale again, and rising to its level on a combing wave, hurled themselves bodily inboard again; the third man helplessly drooping astern, but still afloat and swimming.

Almost simultaneously, with a mighty volition of ungraduated instantaneous swiftness, the White Whale darted through the weltering sea. But when Ahab cried out to the steersman to take new turns with the line, and hold it so; and commanded the crew to turn round on their seats, and tow the boat up to the mark; the moment the treacherous line felt that double strain and tug, it snapped in the empty air!

'What breaks in me? Some sinew cracks! — 'tis whole again; oars! oars! Burst in upon him!'

Hearing the tremendous rush of the sea-crashing boat, the whale wheeled round to present his blank forehead at bay; but in that evolution, catching sight of the nearing black hull of the ship; seemingly seeing in it the source of all his persecutions; bethinking it — it may be — a larger and nobler foe; of a sudden he bore down upon its advancing prow, smiting his jaws amid fiery showers of foam.

Ahab staggered; his hand smote his forehead. 'I grow blind; hands! stretch out before me that I may yet grope my way. Is't night?'

'The whale! The ship!' cried the clinging oarsmen.

'Oars! oars! Slope downwards to thy depths, O sea, that ere it be for ever too late, Ahab may slide this last, last time upon his mark! I see: the ship! the ship! Dash on, my men! Will ye not save my ship?'

But as the oarsmen violently forced their boat through the sledge-hammering seas, the before whale-smitten bow-ends of two planks burst through, and in an instant almost, the temporarily disabled boat lay nearly level with the waves; its half-wading, splashing crew, trying hard to stop the gap and bale out the pouring water.

Meantime, for that one holding instant, Tashtego's mast-head hammer remained suspended in his hand; and the red flag, half-wrapping him as with a plaid, then streamed itself straight out from him, as his own forward-flowing heart; while Starbuck and Stubb, standing upon the bowsprit beneath, caught sight of the downcoming monster just as soon as he.

'The whale! the whale! Up helm, up helm! Oh, all ye sweet powers of air, now hug me close! Let not Starbuck die, if die he must, in a woman's fainting fit. Up helm, I say — ye fools, the jaw! the jaw! Is this the end of all my bursting prayers? all my life-long fidelities? Oh, Ahab, Ahab, lo, thy work. Steady! helmsman, steady! Nay, nay! Up helm again!

He turns to meet us! Oh, his unappeasable brow drives on towards one, whose duty tells him he cannot depart. My God, stand by me now!'

'Stand not by me, but stand under me, whoever you are that will now help Stubb; for Stubb, too, sticks here. I grin at thee, thou grinning whale! Whoever helped Stubb, or kept Stubb awake, but Stubb's own unwinking eye? And now poor Stubb goes to bed upon a mattress that is all too soft; would it were stuffed with brushwood. I grin at thee, thou grinning whale! Look ye, moon and stars! I call ye assassins of as good a fellow as ever spouted up his ghost. For all that, I would yet ring glasses with ye, would ye but hand the cup! Oh, oh, oh, oh! thou grinning whale, but there'll be plenty of gulping soon! Why fly ye not, O Ahab? For me, off shoes and jacket to it; let Stubb die in his drawers! A most mouldy and over-salted death, though; — cherries! cherries! Oh, Flask, for one red cherry ere we die!'

'Cherries? I only wish that we were where they grow. Oh, Stubb, I hope my poor mother's drawn my part-pay ere this; if not, few coppers will come to her now, for the voyage is up.'

From the ship's bows, nearly all the seamen now hung inactive, hammers, bits of plank, lances, and harpoons, mechanically retained in their hands, just as they had darted from their various employments; all their enchanted eyes intent upon the whale, which from side to side strangely vibrating his predestinating head, sent a broad band of overspreading semi-circular foam before him as he rushed. Retribution, swift vengeance, eternal malice were in his whole aspect, and spite of all that mortal man could do, the solid white buttress of his forehead smote the ship's starboard bow, till men and timbers reeled. Some fell flat upon their faces. Like dislodged trucks, the heads of the harpooners aloft shook on their hull-like necks. Through the breach, they heard the waters pour, as mountain torrents down a flume.

'The ship! The hearse! — the second hearse!' cried Ahab from the boat; 'its wood could only be American!'

Diving beneath the settling ship, the Whale ran quivering along its keel, but turning under water, swiftly shot to the surface again, far off the other bow, but within a few yards of Ahab's boat, where, for a time, he lay quiescent.

'I turn my body from the sun. What ho, Tashtego! let me hear thy hammer. Oh! ye three unsurrendered spires of mine; thou uncracked keel; and only god-bullied hull; thou firm deck, and haughty helm, and Pole-pointed prow — death-glorious ship! must ye then perish, and without me? Am I cut off from the last fond pride of meanest shipwrecked captains? Oh, lonely death on lonely life! Oh, now I feel my topmost greatness lies in my topmost grief. Ho, ho! from all your furthest bounds, pour ye now in, ye bold billows of my whole foregone life, and top this one piled comber of my death! Towards thee I roll, thou all-destroying but unconquering whale; to the last I grapple with thee; from hell's heart I stab at thee; for hate's sake I spit my last breath at thee. Sink all coffins and all hearses to one common pool! and since neither can be mine let me then tow to pieces, while still chasing thee, though tied to thee, thou damned whale! *Thus*, I give up the spear.'

The harpoon was darted; the stricken whale flew forward; with igniting velocity the line ran through the groove; ran foul. Ahab stooped to clear it, he did clear it; but the flying turn caught him round the neck, and voicelessly as Turkish mutes bow-string their victims, he was shot out of the boat, ere the crew knew he was gone. Next instant, the heavy eye-splice in the rope's final end flew out of the stark-empty tub, knocked down an oarsman, and smoting the sea, disappeared in its depth.

For an instant, the tranced boat's crew stood still then turned.

'The ship! Great God, where is the ship?'

Soon they through dim, bewildering mediums saw her sidelong fading phantom, as in the gaseous Fata Morgana; only the uppermost masts out of water; while fixed by infatuation or fidelity, or fate, to their once lofty perches, the pagan harpooners still maintained their sinking lookouts on the sea. And now concentric circles seized the lone boat itself, and all its crew, and each floating oar, and every lance-pole and spinning, animate and inanimate, all round and round in one vortex, carried the smallest chip of the *Pequod* out of sight.

But as the last whelmings intermixingly poured themselves over the sunken head of the Indian at the mainmast, leaving a few inches of the erect spar yet visible, together with long streaming yards of the flag, which calmly undulated, with ironical coincidings, over the destroying billows they almost touched; — at that instant, a red arm and a hammer hovered backwardly uplifted in the open air, in the act of nailing the flag faster and yet faster to the subsiding spar. A sky-hawk that tauntingly had followed the main-truck downwards from its natural home among the stars, pecking at the flag, and incommoding Tashtego there; this bird now chanced to intercept its broad fluttering wing between the hammer and the wood; and simultaneously feeling that ethereal thrill, the submerged savage beneath, in his death-grasp, kept his hammer frozen there; and so the bird of heaven, with unearthly shrieks, and his imperial beak thrust upwards, and his whole captive form folded in the flag of Ahab, went down with his ship, which, like Satan, would not sink to hell till she had dragged a living part of heaven along with her, and helmeted herself with it.

Now small fowls flew screaming over the yet yawning gulf; a sullen white surf beat against its steep sides; then all collapsed, and the great shroud of the sea rolled on as it rolled five thousand years ago.

Two Adventures
of Baron Munchhausen
from Gulliver Revived

by
RUDOLF ERICH RASPE

I

I embarked at Portsmouth in a first-rate English man-of-war, of one hundred guns, and fourteen hundred men, for North America; nothing worth relating happened till we arrived within three hundred leagues of the river Saint Lawrence, when the ship struck with amazing force against (as we supposed) a rock; however, upon heaving the lead, we could find no bottom, even with three hundred fathom. What made this circumstance the more wonderful, and indeed beyond all comprehension, was, that the violence of the shock was such that we lost our rudder, broke our bowsprit in the middle, and split all our masts from top to bottom, two of which went by the board; a poor fellow, who was aloft, furling the main-sheet, was flung at least three leagues from the ship; but he fortunately saved his life, by laying hold of the tail of a very large sea-gull, who brought him back, and lodged him on the very spot whence he was thrown. Another proof of the violence of the shock was the force with which the people between decks were driven against the floors above them; my head particularly was pressed into my stomach, where it continued for some months, before it recovered its natural situation. Whilst we were all in a state of astonishment at the general and unaccountable confusion in which we were involved, the whole was suddenly explained by the appearance of a large whale, who had been basking asleep within sixteen feet of the surface of the water. This animal was so much displeased with the disturbance which our ship had given him (for in our passage we had with our rudder scratched his nose), that he beat in all the gallery and part of the quarter-deck with his tail, and almost at the same instant, took the main sheet-anchor, which was suspended, as it usually is, from the head, between his teeth, and ran away with the ship, for at least sixty leagues, at the rate of twelve leagues an hour, when fortunately the cable broke, and we lost both the whale and the anchor. However, upon our return to Europe some months after, we found the same whale, within a few leagues of the same spot, floating dead upon the water; it measured above half-a-mile in length. As we could but take a small quantity of such a monstrous animal on board, we got our boats out, and, with much difficulty, cut off his head, where, to our great joy, we found the anchor, and above 40 fathoms of the cable concealed on the left side of his mouth, just under his tongue. Perhaps this was the cause of his death, as that side of his tongue was much swelled, with a great degree of inflammation. This was the only extraordinary circumstance that happened on this voyage.

II

In a voyage which I made to the East Indies with Captain Hamilton I took a favourite pointer with me; he was, to use a common phrase, worth his weight in gold, for he never deceived me. One day, when we were by the best observations we could make, at least three hundred leagues from the land, my dog pointed; I observed him for near an hour with astonishment, and mentioned the circumstance to the Captain,

I bet one hundred guineas that we should find game within half an
hour.

and every officer on board, asserting that we must be near land, for my dog smelt game; this occasioned a general laugh; but that did not alter in the least the good opinion I had of my dog. After much conversation pro and con, I boldly told the Captain, I placed more confidence in Tray's nose, than I did in the eyes of every seaman on board, and therefore boldly proposed laying the sum I had agreed to pay for my passage (viz., one hundred guineas) that we should find game within half an hour; the Captain (a good hearty fellow) laughed again, desired Mr Crawford, the surgeon who was present, to feel my pulse; he did so, reported me in good health; the following dialogue between them took place; I overheard it, though spoken low and at some distance.

CAPTAIN His brain is turned; I cannot with honour accept his wager.

SURGEON I am of a different opinion; he is quite sane, and depends more upon the scent of his dog, than he will upon the judgment of all the officers on board; he will certainly lose, and he richly merits it.

CAPTAIN Such a wager cannot be fair on my side; but I'll take him up, if I can return his money later.

During the above conversation, Tray continued in the same situation, and confirmed me still more in my former opinion. I proposed the wager a second time; it was then accepted.

Done and Done were scarcely said on both sides, when some sailors who were fishing in the long-boat, which was made fast to the stern of the ship, harpooned an exceedingly large shark, which they brought on board, and began to cut up for the purposes of barrelling the oil, when behold, they found no less than *six brace of live partridges* in this animal's stomach! They had been so long in that situation, that one of the hens was sitting upon four eggs, and a fifth was hatching when the shark was opened!!!

236

This young bird we brought up, by placing it with a litter of kittens that came into the world a few minutes before! The old cat was as fond of it as any of her own four-legged progeny, and made herself very unhappy when it flew out of her reach till it returned again; as to the other partridges, there were four hens amongst them; one or more were, during the voyage, constantly sitting, and consequently we had plenty of game at the Captain's table; and in gratitude to poor Tray (for being the means of winning one hundred guineas) I ordered him the bones daily, and sometimes a whole bird.

A Descent
into the Maelstrom

by
EDGAR ALLAN POE

We had now reached the summit of the loftiest crag. For some minutes the old man seemed too much exhausted to speak.

'Not long ago,' said he at length, 'and I could have guided you on this route as well as the youngest of my sons; but, about three years past, there happened to me an event such as never before happened to mortal man — or at least such as no man ever survived to tell of — and the six hours of deadly terror which I then endured have broken me up body and soul. You suppose me a *very* old man — but I am not. It took less than a single day to change these hairs from a jetty black to white, to weaken my limbs, and to unstring my nerves, so that I tremble at the least exertion, and am frightened at a shadow. Do you know that I can scarcely look over this little cliff without getting giddy?'

The 'little cliff' upon whose edge he had so carelessly thrown himself down to rest that the weightier portion of his body hung over it, while he was only kept from falling by the tenure of his elbow on its extreme and slippery edge — this 'little cliff' arose, a sheer unobstructed precipice of black shining rock, some fifteen or sixteen hundred feet from the world of crags beneath us. Nothing would have tempted me within half a dozen yards of its brink. In truth so deeply was I excited by the perilous position of my companion, that I fell at full length on the ground, clung to the shrubs around me, and dared not even glance upward at the sky — while I struggled in vain to divest myself of the idea that the very foundations of the mountain were in danger from the fury of the winds. It was long before I could reason myself into sufficient courage to sit up and look out into the distance.

'You must get over these fancies,' said the guide, for 'I have brought you here that you might have the best possible view of the scene of that event I mentioned — and to tell you the whole story with the spot just under your eye.'

'We are now,' he continued, in that particularising manner which distinguished him — 'we are now close upon the Norwegian coast — in the sixty-eighth degree of latitude — in the great province of Nordland — and in the dreary district of Lofoden. The mountain upon whose top we sit is Helseggen, the Cloudy. Now raise yourself up a little higher — hold on to the grass if you feel giddy — so — look out, beyond the belt of vapour beneath us, into the sea.'

I looked dizzily, and beheld a wide expanse of ocean, whose waters were so inky a hue as to bring at once to my mind the Nubian geographer's account of the *Mare Tenebrarum*. A panorama more deplorably desolate no human imagination can conceive. To the right and left, as far as the eye could reach, there lay outstretched, like ramparts of the world, lines of horridly black and beetling cliff, whose character of gloom was but the more forcibly illustrated by the surf which reared high up against it, its white and ghastly crest, howling and shrieking for ever. Just opposite the promontory upon whose apex we were placed, and at a distance of some five or six miles out at sea, there was visible a small, bleak-looking island; or, more properly, its position was discernible through the wilderness of surge in which it was enveloped. About two miles nearer the land, arose another of smaller size, hideously craggy and barren, and encompassed at various intervals by a cluster of dark rocks.

239

The appearance of the ocean, in the space between the more distant island and the shore, had something very unusual about it. Although, at the time, so strong a gale was blowing landward that a brig in the remote offing lay-to under a double-reefed trysail, and constantly plunged her whole hull out of sight, still there was here nothing like a regular swell, but only a short, quick, angry cross dashing of water in every direction — as well in the teeth of the wind as otherwise. Of foam there was little except in the immediate vicinity of the rocks.

'The island in the distance,' resumed the old man, 'is Moskoe. That a mile to the northward is Ambaaren. Yonder are Islesen, Hotholm, Keildhelm, Suarven, and Buckholm. Farther off — between Moskoe and Vurrgh — are Otterholm, Flimen, Sandflesen, and Stockholm. These are the true names of the places — but why it has been thought necessary to name them at all, is more than either you or I can understand. Do you hear anything? Do you see any change in the water?'

We had now been about ten minutes upon the top of Helseggen, to which we had ascended from the interior of Lofoden, so that we had caught no glimpse of the sea until it had burst upon us from the summit. As the old man spoke I became aware of a loud and gradually increasing sound, like the moaning of a vast herd of buffaloes upon an American prairie; and at the same moment I perceived that what seamen term the 'chopping' character of the ocean beneath us, was rapidly changing into a current which set to the eastward. Even while I gazed, this current acquired a monstrous velocity. Each moment added to its speed — to its headlong impetuosity. In five minutes the whole sea, as far as Vurrgh, was lashed into ungovernable fury; but it was between Moskoe and the coast that the main uproar held its sway. Here the vast bed of the waters, seamed and scarred into a thousand conflicting channels, burst suddenly into frenzied convulsion — heaving, boiling, hissing — gyrating in gigantic and innumerable vortices, and all whirling and plunging on to the eastward with a rapidity which water never elsewhere assumes, except in precipitous descents.

In a few minutes more, there came over the scene another radical alteration. The general surface grew somewhat more smooth, and the whirlpools, one by one, disappeared, while prodigious streaks of foam became apparent where none had been seen before. These streaks, at length, spreading out to a great distance, and entering into combination, took unto themselves the gyratory motion of the subsided vortices, and seemed to form the germ of another more vast. Suddenly — very suddenly — this assumed a distinct and definite existence, in a circle of more than a mile in diameter. The edge of the whirl was represented by a broad belt of gleaming spray; but no particle of this slipped into the mouth of the terrific funnel, whose interior, as far as the eye could fathom it, was a smooth, shining, and jet-black wall of water, inclined to the horizon at an angle of some forty-five degrees, speeding dizzily round and round with a swaying and sweltering motion, and sending forth to the winds an appalling voice, half shriek, half roar, such as not even the mighty cataract of Niagara ever lifts up in its agony to Heaven.

The mountain trembled to its very base, and the rock rocked. I threw myself upon my face, and clung to the scant herbage in an excess of nervous agitation.

'This,' said I at length, to the old man — 'this *can* be nothing else but the great whirlpool of the Maelstrom.'

'So it is sometimes termed,' said he. 'We Norwegians call it the Moskoe-strom, from the island of Moskoe in the midway.

The ordinary account of this vortex had by no means prepared me for what I saw. That of Jonas Ramus, which is perhaps the most circumstantial of any, cannot impart the faintest conception either of the magnificence or of the horror of the scene — or of the wild bewildering sense of *the novel* which confounds the beholder. I am not sure from what point of view the writer in question surveyed it, nor at what time, but it could neither have been from the summit of Helseggen, nor during a storm. There are some passages of his description nevertheless, which may be quoted for their details, although their effect is exceedingly feeble in conveying an impression of the spectacle.

'Between Lofoden and Moskoe,' he says, 'the depth of the water is between thirty-six and forty fathoms; but on the other side, toward Ver (Vurrgh) this depth decreases so as not to afford a convenient passage for a vessel, without the risk of splitting on the rocks, which happens even in the calmest weather. When it is flood, the stream runs up the country between Lofoden and Moskoe with a boisterous rapidity; but the roar of its impetuous ebb to the sea is scarce equalled by the loudest and most dreadful cataracts; the noise being heard several leagues off, and the vortices or pits are of such an extent and depth, that if a ship comes within its attraction, it is inevitably absorbed and carried down to the bottom, and there beat to pieces against the rocks; and when the water relaxes, the fragments thereof are thrown up again. But these intervals of tranquillity are only at the turn of the ebb and flood, and in calm weather, and last but a quarter of an hour, its violence gradually returning. When the stream is most boisterous, and its fury heightened by a storm, it is dangerous to come within a Norway mile of it. Boats, yachts, and ships have been carried away by not guarding against it before they were carried within its reach. It likewise happens frequently, that whales come too near the stream, and are overpowered by its violence; and then it is impossible to describe their howlings and bellowings in their fruitless struggles to disengage themselves. A bear once, in attempting to swim from Lofoden to Moskoe, was caught by the stream and borne down, while he roared terribly, so as to be heard on shore. Large stocks of firs and pine-trees, after being absorbed by the current, rise again broken and torn to such a degree as if bristles grew upon them. This plainly shows the bottom to consist of craggy rocks, among which they are whirled to and fro. This stream is regulated by the flux and reflux of the sea — it being constantly high and low water every six hours. In the year 1645, early in the morning of Sexagesima Sunday, it raged with such a noise and impetuosity that the very stones of the houses on the coast fell to the ground.'

In regard to the depth of the water, I could not see how this could have been ascertained at all in the immediate vicinity of the vortex. The 'forty fathoms' must have reference only to portions of the channel close upon the shore of either Moskoe or Lofoden. The depth in the middle of the Moskoe-strom must be immeasurably greater; and no better proof of this fact is necessary than can be obtained from even the sidelong glance into the abyss of the whirl which may be had from the highest crag of Helseggen. Looking down from this pinnacle upon the howling Phlegethon below, I could not help smiling at the simplicity with which the honest Jonas Ramus records, as a matter difficult of belief, the anecdotes of the whales and the bears, for it appeared to me, in fact, a self-evident thing, that the largest ships of the line in existence, coming within the influence of that deadly attraction, could resist it as little as a feather the hurricane, and must disappear bodily at once.

The attempts to account for the phenomenon — some of which I remember, seemed to me sufficiently plausible on perusal — now wore a very different and unsatisfactory aspect. The idea generally received is that this, as well as three smaller vortices among the Ferroe Islands, 'have no other cause than the collision of waves rising and falling, at flux and reflux, against a ridge of rocks and shelves, which confines the water so that it precipitates itself like a cataract; and thus the higher the flood rises, the deeper the fall must be, and the natural result of all is a whirlpool or vortex, the prodigious suction of which is sufficiently known by lesser experiments. —'

These are the words of the *Encyclopaedia Britannica.* Kircher and others imagine that in the centre of the channel of the Maelstrom is an abyss penetrating the globe, and issuing in some very remote part — the Gulf of Bothnia being somewhat decidedly named in one instance. This opinion, idle in itself, was the one to which, as I gazed, my imagination most readily assented; and, mentioning it to the guide, I was rather surprised to hear him say that, although it was the view almost universally entertained of the subject by the Norwegians, it nevertheless was not his own. As to the former notion, he confessed his inability to comprehend it; and here I agreed with him — for, however conclusive on paper, it becomes altogether unintelligible, and even absurd, amid the thunder of the abyss.

'You have had a good look at the whirl now,' said the old man, 'and if you will creep round this crag, so as to get in its lee, and deaden the roar of the water, I will tell you a story that will convince you I ought to know something of the Moskoe-strom.'

I placed myself as desired, and he proceeded.

'Myself and my two brothers once owned a schooner-rigged smack of about seventy tons burthen, with which we were in the habit of fishing among the islands beyond Moskoe, nearly to Vurrgh. In all violent eddies at sea there is good fishing at proper opportunities, if one has only the courage to attempt it; but among the whole of the Lofoden coastmen, we three were the only ones who made a regular business of going out to the islands, as I tell you. The usual grounds are a great way down to the southward. There fish can be got at all hours, without much risk, and therefore these places were preferred. The choice spots over here among the rocks, however, not only yield the finest variety, but in greater abundance; so that we often got in a single day, what the more timid of the craft could not scrape together in a week. In fact, we made it a matter of desperate speculation — the risk of life standing instead of labour, and courage answering for capital.'

'We kept the smack in a cove about five miles higher up the coast than this; and it was our practice, in fine weather, to take advantage of the fifteen minutes' slack to push across the main channel of the Moskoe-strom, far above the pool, and then drop down upon anchorage somewhere near Otterholm, or Sandflesen, where the eddies are not so violent as elsewhere. Here we used to remain until nearly time for slack-water again, when we weighed and made for home. We never set out upon this expedition without a steady side wind for coming and going, one that we felt sure would not fail us before our return, and we seldom made a miscalculation upon this point. Twice, during six years, we were forced to stay all night at anchor on account of a dead calm, which is a rare thing indeed just about here; and once we had to remain on the grounds nearly a week, starving to death, owing to a gale which blew up shortly after our arrival, and made the channel too boisterous to be thought of. Upon this occasion we should have been driven out to sea in spite of everything (for the whirlpools threw us round and round so violently, that, at length, we fouled our anchor and dragged it), if it had not been that we drifted into one of the innumerable cross-currents — here to-day and gone to-morrow — which drove us under the lee of Flimen, where, by good luck, we brought up.

'I could not tell you the twentieth part of the difficulties we encountered "on the ground" — it is a bad spot to be in even in good weather — but we made shift always to run the gauntlet of the Moskoe-strom itself without accident; although at times my heart has been in my mouth when we happened to be a minute or so behind or before the slack. The wind sometimes was not as strong as we thought it at starting, and then we made rather less way than we could wish, while the current rendered the smack unmanageable. My eldest brother had a son eighteen years old, and I had two stout boys of my own. These would have been of great assistance at such times, in using the sweeps as well as afterward in fishing — but, somehow, although we ran the risk ourselves, we had not the heart to let the young ones get into danger — for, after all said and done, it *was* a horrible danger, and that is the truth.

'It is now within a few days of three years since what I am going to tell you occurred. It was on the 10th July, 18 —, a day which the people of this part of the world will never forget — for it was one in which blew the most terrible hurricane that ever came out of the heavens. And yet all the morning, and indeed until late in the afternoon, there was a gentle and steady breeze from the south-west, while the sun shone brightly, so that the oldest seaman among us could not have foreseen what was to follow.

'The three of us — my two brothers and myself — had crossed over to the islands, about two o'clock p. m., and soon nearly loaded the smack with fine fish, which we all remarked were more plenty that day than we had ever known them. It was just seven, *by my watch*, when we weighed and started for home, so as to make the worst of the Strom at slack water, which we knew would be at eight.

'We set out with a fresh wind on our starboard quarter, and for some time spanked along at a great rate, never dreaming of danger, for indeed we saw not the slightest reason to apprehend it. All at once we were taken aback by a breeze from over Helseggen. This was most unusual — something that had never happened to us before — and I began to feel a little uneasy, without exactly knowing why. We put the boat on the wind, but could make no headway at all for the eddies, and I was upon the point of proposing to return to the anchorage when, looking astern, we saw the whole horizon covered with a singular copper-coloured cloud that rose with the most amazing velocity.

'In the meantime the breeze that had headed us off fell away and we were dead becalmed, drifting about in every direction. This state of things, however, did not last long enough to give us time to think about it. In less than a minute the storm was upon us — in less than two the sky was entirely overcast — and what with this and the driving spray, it became suddenly so dark that we could not see each other in the smack.

'Such a hurricane as then blew it is folly to attempt describing. The oldest seaman in Norway never experienced anything like it. We had to let our sails go by the run before it cleverly took us; but, at the first puff, both our masts went by the board as if they had been sawed off — the mainmast taking with it my youngest brother who had lashed himself to it for safety.

'Our boat was the lightest feather of a thing that ever sat upon water. It had a complete flush deck, with only a small hatch near the bow, and this hatch it had always been our custom to batten down when about to cross the Strom, by way of precaution against the chopping seas. But for this circumstance we should have foundered at once — for we lay entirely buried for some moments. How my eldest brother escaped destruction I cannot say, for I never had an opportunity of ascertaining. For my part, as soon as I had let the foresail run, I threw myself flat on deck, with my feet against the narrow gunwale of the bow, and with my hands grasping a ring-bolt near the foot of the foremast. It was mere instinct that prompted me to do this — which was undoubtedly the best thing I could have done — for I was much too flurried to think.

'For some moments we were completely deluged, as I say, and all this time I held my breath, and clung to the bolt. When I could stand it no longer, I raised myself upon my knees, still keeping hold with my hands and thus got my head clear. Presently our little boat gave herself a shake just as a dog does in coming out of the water, and thus rid herself, in some measure, of the seas. I was now trying to get the better of the stupor that had come over me, and to collect my senses so as to see what was to be done, when I felt somebody grasp my arm. It was my eldest brother, and my heart leaped for joy, for I had made sure that he was overboard — but the next moment all this joy was turned to horror — for he put his mouth close to my ear, and screamed out the word *"Moskoe-strom!"*

'No one will ever know what my feelings were at that moment. I shook from head to foot as if I had had the most violent fit of ague. I knew what he meant by that one word well enough — I knew what he wished to make me understand. With the wind that now drove us on, we were bound for the whirl of the Strom, and nothing could save us.

'You perceive that in crossing the Strom *channel*, we always went a long way up above the whirl, even in the calmest weather, and then had to wait and watch carefully for the slack — but now we were driving right upon the pool itself, and in such a hurricane as this! "To be sure," I thought, "we shall get there just about the slack — there is some little hope in that" — but in the next moment I cursed myself for being so great a fool as to dream of hope at all. I knew very well that we were doomed, had we been ten times a ninety-gun ship.

'By this time the first fury of the tempest had spent itself, or perhaps we did not feel it so much, as we scudded before it, but at all events the seas, which at first had been kept down by the wind, and lay flat and frothing, now got up into absolute mountains. A singular change, too, had come over the heavens. Around in every direction it was still as black as pitch, but nearly overhead there burst out, all at once, a circular rift of clear sky — as clear as I ever saw — and of a deep bright blue — and through it there blazed forth the full moon with a lustre that I never before knew her to wear. She lit up everything about us with the greatest distinctness — but oh God, what a scene it was to light up!

'I now made one or two attempts to speak to my brother — but in some manner which I could not understand, the din had so increased that I could not make him hear a single word, although I screamed at the top of my voice in his ear. Presently he shook his head, looking as pale as death, and held up one of his fingers, as if to say "*listen!*"

'At first I could not make out what he meant — but soon a hideous thought flashed upon me. I dragged my watch from its fob. It was not going. I glanced at its face in the moonlight and then burst into tears as I flung it far away into the ocean. *It had run down at seven o'clock! We were behind the time of the slack and the whirl of the Strom was in full fury!*

'When a boat is well built, properly trimmed, and not deep laden, the waves in a strong gale, when she is going large, seem always to slip from beneath her — which appears strange to a landsman, and this is what is called "*riding*", in sea phrase.

'Well, so far we had ridden the waves very cleverly; but presently a gigantic sea happened to take us right under the counter, and bore us with it as it rose — up — up — as if into the sky. I would not have believed that any wave could rise so high. And then down we came with a sweep, a slide, and a plunge that made me feel sick and dizzy, as if I was falling from some lofty mountain-top in a dream. But while we were up I had thrown a quick glance around — and that one glance was all-sufficient. I saw our exact position in an instant. The Moskoe-strom whirlpool was about a quarter of a mile dead ahead — but no more like the every-day Moskoe-strom than the whirl, as you now see it, is like a mill race. If I had now known where we were, and what we had to expect, I should not have recognised the place at all. As it was, I involuntarily closed my eyes in horror. The lids clenched themselves together as if in a spasm.

It could not have been more than two minutes afterwards until we suddenly felt the waves subside, and were enveloped in foam. The boat made a sharp half-turn to larboard, and then shot off in its new direction like a thunderbolt. At the same moment the roaring noise of the water was completely drowned in a kind of shrill shriek — such a sound as you might imagine given out by the water-pipes of many thousand steam-vessels letting off their steam all together. We were now in the belt of surf that always surrounds the whirl; and I thought, of course, that another moment would plunge us into the abyss, down which we could only see indistinctly on account of the amazing velocity with which we were borne along. The boat did not seem to sink into the water at all, but to skim like an air-bubble upon the surface of the surge. Her starboard side was next the whirl, and on the larboard arose the world of ocean we had left. It stood like a huge writhing wall between us and the horizon.

'It may appear strange, but now, when we were in the very jaws of the gulf, I felt more composed than when we were only approaching it. Having made up my mind to hope no more, I got rid of a great deal of that terror which unmanned me at first. I suppose it was despair that strung my nerves.

'It may look like boasting — but what I tell you is the truth — I began to reflect how magnificent a thing it was to die in such a manner, and how foolish it was in me to think of so paltry a consideration as my own individual life, in view of so wonderful a manifestation of God's power. I do believe that I blushed with shame when this idea crossed my mind. After a little while I became possessed with the keenest curiosity about the whirl itself. I positively felt a *wish* to explore its depths, even at the sacrifice I was going to make; and my

250

principal grief was that I should never be able to tell my old companions on shore about the mysteries I should see. These, no doubt, were singular fancies to occupy a man's mind in such extremity — and I have often thought since, that the revolutions of the boat around the pool might have rendered me a little light-headed.

'There was another circumstance which tended to restore my self-possession; and this was the cessation of the wind, which could not reach us in our present position — for, as you saw for yourself, the belt of the surf is considerably lower than the general bed of the ocean, and this latter now towered above us, a high, black, mountainous ridge. If you have never been at sea in a heavy gale, you can form no idea of the confusion of mind occasioned by the wind and spray together. They blind, deafen, and strangle you, and take away all power of action or reflection. But we were now, in a great measure, rid of these annoyances — just as death-condemned felons in prison are allowed petty indulgences, forbidden them while their doom is yet uncertain.

'How often we made the circuit of the belt it is impossible to say. We careered round and round for perhaps an hour, flying rather than floating, getting gradually more and more into the middle of the surge, and then nearer and nearer to its horrible inner edge. All this time I had never let go of the ring-bolt. My brother was at the stern, holding on to a small empty water-cask which had been securely lashed under the coop of the counter, and was the only thing on deck that had not been swept overboard when the gale first took us. As we approached the brink of the pit he let go his hold upon this, and made for the ring, from which, in the agony of his terror, he endeavoured to force my hands, as it was not large enough to afford us both a secure grasp. I never felt deeper grief than when I saw him attempt this act — although I knew he was a madman when he did it — a raving maniac through sheer fright. I did not care, however, to contest the point with him. I knew it could make no difference whether either of us held on at all; so I let him have the bolt, and went astern to the cask. This there was no great difficulty in doing; for the smack flew round steadily enough, and upon an even keel — only swaying to and fro with the immense sweeps and swelters of the whirl. Scarcely had I secured myself in my new position, when we gave a wild lurch to starboard, and rushed headlong into the abyss. I muttered a hurried prayer to God and thought all was over.

'As I felt the sickening sweep of the descent, I had instinctively tightened my hold upon the barrel, and closed my eyes. For some seconds I dared not open them — while I expected instant destruction, and wondered that I was not already in my death-struggles with the water. But moment after moment elapsed. I still lived. The sense of falling had ceased; and the motion of the vessel seemed much as it had been before, while in the belt of foam, with the exception that she now lay more along. I took courage and looked once again upon the scene.

'Never shall I forget the sensation of awe, horror and admiration with which I gazed about me. The boat appeared to be hanging, as if by magic, midway down, upon the interior surface of a funnel vast in circumference, prodigious in depth, and whose perfectly smooth sides might have been mistaken for ebony, but for the bewildering rapidity with which they spun round, and for the gleaming and ghastly radiance they shot forth, as the rays of the full moon, from that circular rift amid the clouds which I have already described, streamed in a flood of golden glory along the black walls, and far away down into the inmost recesses of the abyss.

At first I was too much confused to observe anything accurately. The general burst of terrific grandeur was all that I beheld. When I recovered myself a little, however, my gaze

The boat appeared to be hanging upon the interior surface of a vast
funnel.

fell instinctively downward. In this direction I was able to obtain an unobstructed view, from the manner in which the smack hung on the inclined surface of the pool. She was quite upon an even keel — that is to say, her deck lay in a plane parallel with that of the water — but this latter sloped at an angle of more than forty-five degrees, so that we seemed to be lying upon our beam-ends. I could not help observing, nevertheless, that I had scarcely more difficulty in maintaining my hold and footing in this situation, than if we had been upon a dead level; and this I suppose was owing to the speed at which we revolved.

'The rays of the moon seemed to search to the very bottom of the profound gulf; but still I could make out nothing distinctly on account of a thick mist in which everything there was enveloped, and over which there hung a magnificent rainbow, like that narrow and tottering bridge which Mussulmans say is the only pathway between Time and Eternity. This mist, or spray, was no doubt occasioned by the clashing of the great walls of the funnel, as they all met together at the bottom — but the yell that went up to the Heavens from out of that mist I dare not attempt to describe.'

'Our first slide into the abyss itself, from the belt of foam above, had carried us a great distance down the slope; but our further descent was by no means proportionate. Round and round we swept — not with any uniform movement — but in dizzying swings and jerks, that sent us sometimes only a few hundred yards — sometimes nearly the complete circuit of the whirl. Our progress downward, at each revolution, was slow, but very perceptible!'

'Looking about me upon the wide waste of liquid ebony on which we were thus born, I perceived that our boat was not the only object in the embrace of the whirl. Both above and below us were visible fragments of vessels, large masses of building-timber and trunks of trees, with many smaller

254

articles, such as pieces of house furniture, broken boxes, barrels and staves. I have already described the unnatural curiosity which had taken the place of my original terrors. It appeared to grow upon me as I drew nearer and nearer to my dreadful doom. I now began to watch, with a strange interest, the numerous things that floated in our company. I *must* have been delirious, for I even sought *amusement* speculating upon the relative velocities of their several descents toward the foam below. "This fir-tree", I found myself at one time saying, "will certainly be the next thing that takes the awful plunge and disappears," — and then I was disappointed to find that the wreck of a Dutch merchant ship overtook it and went down before. At length, after making several guesses of this nature, and being deceived in all — this fact — the fact of my invariable miscalculation, set me upon a train of reflection that made my limbs again tremble, and my heart beat heavily once more.'

'It was not a new terror that thus affected me, but the dawn of a more exciting *hope*. This hope arose partly from memory, and partly from present observation. I called to mind the great variety of buoyant matter that strewd the coast of Lofoden, having been absorbed and then thrown forth by the Moskoe-strom. By far the great number of the articles were shattered in the most extraordinary way — so chafed and roughened as to have the appearance of being stuck full of splinters — but then I distinctly recollected that there were *some* of them which were not disfigured at all. Now I could not account for this difference except by supposing that the roughened fragments were the only ones which had been *completely absorbed* — that the others had entered into the whirl at so late a period of the tide, or, from some reason, had descended so slowly after entering, that they did not reach the bottom before the turn of the flood came, or of the ebb, as the case might be. I conceived it possible, in either instance, that they might thus be whirled up again to the level of the ocean, without undergoing the fate of those which had been drawn in more early or absorbed more rapidly. I made, also, three important observations. The first was, that as a general rule, the larger the bodies were, the more rapid their descent — the second, that, between two masses of equal extent, the one spherical, and the other *of any other shape* the superiority in speed of descent was with the sphere — the third, that, between two masses of equal size, the one cylindrical, and the other of any other shape, the cylinder was absorbed more slowly. Since my escape, I have had several conversations on this subject with an old schoolmaster in the district; and it was from him that I learned the use of the words "cylinder" and "sphere". He explained to me — although I have forgotten the explanation — how what I observed was, in fact, the natural consequence of the forms of the floating fragments — and showed me how it happened that a cylinder, swimming in a vortex, offered more resistance to its suction, and was drawn in with greater difficulty than an equally bulky body, of any form whatever.'

'There was one startling circumstance which went a great way in enforcing these observations, and rendering me anxious to turn them to account, and this was that, at every revolution we passed something like a barrel, or else the yard or the mast of a vessel, while many of these things, which had been on our level when I first opened my eyes upon the wonders of the whirlpool, were now high up above us, and seemed to have moved but little from their original station.

'I no longer hesitated what to do. I resolved to lash myself securely to the water-cask upon which I now held, to cut it loose from the counter, and to throw myself with it into the water. I attracted my brother's attention by signs, pointed to the floating barrels that came near us, and did everything in my power to make him understand what I was about to do. I thought at length that he comprehended my design — but, whether this was the case or not, he shook his head despairingly, and refused to move from his station by the ring-bolt. It was impossible to reach him; the emergency admitted of no delay; and so, with a bitter struggle, I resigned him to his fate, fastened myself upon the cask by means of the lashings which secured it to the counter, and precipitated myself with it into the sea, without another moment's hesitation.'

'The result was precisely what I had hoped it might be. As it is myself who now tells you this tale — and you see that I *did* escape — and as you are already in possession of the mode in which this escape was effected, and must therefore anticipate all that I have further to say — I will bring my story quickly to conclusion. It might have been an hour, or thereabout, after my quitting the smack, when, having des-cended to a vast distance beneath me, it made three or four wild gyrations in rapid succession, and, bearing my beloved brother with it, plunged headlong, at once and forever, into the chaos of foam below. The barrel to which I was attached sunk very little farther than half the distance between the bottom of the gulf and the spot at which I leaped overboard, before a great change took place in the character of the whirlpool. The slope of the sides of the vast funnel became momently less and less steep. The gyrations of the whirl grew, gradually, less and less violent. By degrees, the froth and the rainbow disappeared, and the bottom of the gulf seemed slowly to uprise. The sky was clear, the winds had gone down and the full moon was setting radiantly in the west, when I found myself on the surface of the ocean, in full view of the shores of Lofoden, and above the spot where the pool of the Moskoe-strom *had been*. It was the hour of the slack — but the sea still heaved in mountainous waves from the effects of the hurricane. I was borne violently into the channel of the Strom, and in a few minutes was hurried down the coast into the "grounds" of the fishermen. A boat picked me up — exhausted from fatigue — and (now that the danger was removed) speechless from the memory of its horror. Those who drew me on board were my old mates and daily companions — but they knew me no more than they would have known a traveller from the spirit-land. My hair which had been raven black the day before, was white as you see it now. They say too that the whole expression of my countenance had changed. I told them my story — they did not believe it. I now tell it to *you* — and I can scarcely expect you to put more faith in it than did the merry fishermen of Lofoden.'

The Bottom of the Sea

From 20,000 Leagues
Under the Sea

by
JULES VERNE

The submarine made an appearance in science fiction long before it became a reality. P. Arronax, the narrator of 20,000 Leagues Under the Sea *(written in 1869) is a scientist who joins an expedition in search of a mysterious sea monster which has been reported to roam the seas. The 'monster' is discovered to be the electrically-propelled subma-rine* Nautilus. *Its captain, Nemo, takes Arronax, his servant Conseil and the harpooner Ned Land as prisoners. They are treated as honoured guests, however, and Captain Nemo shows them the wonders of his underwater world.*

This cell was, to speak correctly, the arsenal and wardrobe of the Nautilus. A dozen diving apparatuses hung from the partition waiting our use.

Ned Land, on seeing them, showed evident repugnance to dress himself in one.

'But, my worthy Ned, the forests of the Island of Crespo are nothing but submarine forests.'

'Good!' said the disappointed harpooner, who saw his dreams of fresh meat fade away. 'And you, M. Arronax, are you going to dress yourself in those clothes?'

'There is no alternative, Master Ned.'

'As you please, sir,' replied the harpooner, shrugging his shoulders; 'but as for me, unless I am forced, I will never get into one.'

259

'No one will force you, Master Ned,' said Captain Nemo.

'Is Conseil going to risk it?' asked Ned.

'I follow my master wherever he goes,' replied Conseil.

At the Captain's call two of the ship's crew came to help us to dress in these heavy and impervious clothes, made of india-rubber without seam, and constructed expressly to resist considerable pressure. One would have thought it a suit of armour, both supple and resisting. This suit formed trousers and waistcoat. The trousers were finished off with thick boots, weighted with heavy leaden soles. The texture of the waistcoat was held together by bands of copper, which crossed the chest, protecting it from the great pressure of the water, and leaving the lungs free to act; the sleeves ended in gloves, which in no way restrained the movement of the hands. There was a vast difference noticeable between these consummate apparatuses and the old cork breastplates, jackets, and other contrivances in vogue during the eighteenth century.

Captain Nemo and one of his companions (a sort of Hercules, who must have possessed great strength), Conseil, and myself, were soon enveloped in the dresses. There remained nothing more to be done but to enclose our heads in the metal box. But before proceeding to this operation, I asked the Captain's permission to examine the guns we were to carry.

One of the Nautilus men gave me a simple gun, the butt end of which, made of steel, hollow in the centre, was rather large. It served as a reservoir for compressed air, which a valve, worked by a spring, allowed to escape into a metal tube. A box of projectiles, in a groove in the thickness of the butt end, contained about twenty of these electric balls, which, by means of a spring, were forced into the barrel of the gun. As soon as one shot was fired, another was ready.

'Captain Nemo,' said I, 'this arm is perfect, and easily handled; I only ask to be allowed to try it. But how shall we gain the bottom of the sea?'

260

'At this moment, Professor, the Nautilus is stranded in five fathoms, and we have nothing to do but to start.'

'But how shall we get off?'

'You shall see.'

Captain Nemo thrust his head into the helmet, Conseil and I did the same, not without hearing an ironical 'Good sport!' from the Canadian. The upper part of our dress terminated in a copper collar, upon which was screwed the metal helmet. Three holes, protected by thick glass, allowed us to see in all directions, by simply turning our head in the interior of the headdress. As soon as it was in position, the Rouquayrol apparatus on our backs began to act; and, for my part, I could breathe with ease.

With the Ruhmkorff lamp hanging from my belt, and the gun in my hand, I was ready to set out. But to speak the truth, imprisoned in these heavy garments, and glued to the deck by my leaden soles, it was impossible for me to take a step.

But this state of things was provided for. I felt myself being pushed into a little room contiguous to the wardrobe-room. My companions followed, towed along in the same way. I heard a water-tight door, furnished with stopper-plates, close upon us, and we were wrapped in profound darkness.

After some minutes, a loud hissing was heard. I felt the cold mount from my feet to my chest. Evidently from some part of the vessel they had, by means of a tap, given entrance to the water, which was invading us, and with which the room was soon filled. A second door cut in the side of the Nautilus then opened. We saw a faint light. In another instant our feet trod the bottom of the sea.

And now, how can I retrace the impression left upon me by that walk under the waters? Words are impotent to relate such wonders! Captain Nemo walked in front, his companion followed some steps behind. Conseil and I remained near each other, as if an exchange of words had been possible through our metallic cases. I no longer felt the weight of my clothing, or of my shoes, of my reservoir of air, or my thick helmet, in the midst of which my head rattled like an almond in its shell.

The light, which lit the soil thirty feet below the surface of the ocean, astonished me by its power. The solar rays shone through the watery mass easily, and dissipated all colour, and I clearly distinguished objects at a distance of a hundred and fifty yards. Beyond that the tints darkened into fine gradations of ultramarine, and faded into vague obscurity. Truly this water which surrounded me was but another air denser than the terrestrial atmosphere, but almost as transparent. Above me was the calm surface of the sea. We were walking on fine even sand, not wrinkled, as on a flat shore, which retains the impression of the billows. This dazzling carpet, really a reflector, repelled the rays of the sun with wonderful intensity, which accounted for the vibration which penetrated every atom of liquid. Shall I be believed when I say that, at the depth of thirty feet, I could see as if I was in broad daylight?

For a quarter of an hour I trod on this sand, sown with the impalpable dust of shells. The hull of the Nautilus, resembling a long shoal, disappeared by degrees; but its lantern, when darkness should overtake us in the waters, would help to guide us on board by its distinct rays.

Soon forms of objects outlined in the distance were discernible. I recognised magnificent rocks, hung with a tapestry of zoophites of the most beautiful kind, and I was at first struck by the peculiar effect of this medium.

It was then ten in the morning; the rays of the sun struck the surface of the waves at rather an oblique angle, and at the touch of their light, decomposed by refraction as through a prism, flowers, rocks, plants, shells, and polypi were shaded at the edges by the seven solar colours. It was marvellous, a feast for the eyes, this complication of coloured tints, a perfect kaleidoscope of green, yellow, orange, violet, indigo, and blue; in one word, the whole palette of an enthusiastic colourist! Why could I not communicate to Conseil the lively sensations which were mounting to my brain, and rival him in expressions of admiration? For aught I knew, Captain Nemo and his companion might be able to exchange thoughts by means of signs previously agreed upon. So, for want of better, I talked to myself; I declaimed in the copper box which covered my head, thereby expending more air in vain words than was perhaps expedient.

Various kinds of isis, clusters of pure tuft-coral, prickly fungi, and anemones, formed a brilliant garden of flowers, enamelled with porphitae, decked with their collarettes of blue tentacles, sea-stars studding the sandy bottom, together with asterophytons like fine lace embroidered by the hands of naiads, whose festoons were waved by the gentle undulations caused by our walk. It was a real grief to me to crush under my feet the brilliant specimens of molluscs which strewed the ground by thousands, of hammerheads, donaciae (veritable bounding shells), of staircases, and red helmet shells, angel-wings, and many others produced by this inexhaustible ocean. But we were bound to walk, so we went on, whilst above our heads waved shoals of physalides leaving their tentacles to float in their train, medusae whose umbrellas of opal or rose-pink, escalloped with a band of blue, sheltered us from the rays of the sun and fiery pelagiae, which, in the darkness, would have strewn our path with phosphorescent light.

All these wonders I saw in the space of a quarter of a mile, scarcely stopping, and following Captain Nemo, who beckoned me on by signs. Soon the nature of the soil changed; to the sandy plain succeeded an extent of slimy mud, which the Americans call 'ooze,' composed of equal parts of silicious and calcareous shells. We then travelled over a plain of sea-weed of wild and luxuriant vegetation. This sward was of close texture, and soft to the feet, and rivalled the softest carpet woven by the hand of man. But whilst verdure was spread at our feet, it did not abandon our heads. A light network of marine plants, of that inexhaustible family of sea-weeds of which more than two thousand kinds are known, grew on the surface of the water. I saw long ribbons of fucus floating, some globular, others tuberous; laurenciae and cladostephi of most delicate foliage, and some rhodomeniae palmatae, resembling the fan of a cactus. I noticed that the green plants kept nearer the top of the sea, whilst the red were at a greater depth, leaving to the black or brown hydrophytes the care of forming gardens and parterres in the remote beds of the ocean.

We had quitted the Nautilus about an hour and a half. It was near noon; I knew by the perpendicularity of the sun's rays, which were no longer refracted. The magical colours disappeared by degrees, and the shades of emerald and sapphire were effaced. We walked with a regular step, which rang upon the ground with astonishing intensity; the slightest noise was transmitted with a quickness to which the ear is unaccustomed on the earth; indeed, water is a better conductor of sound than air, in the ratio of four to one. At this period the earth sloped downwards; the light took a uniform tint. We were at a depth of a hundred and five yards and twenty inches, undergoing a pressure of six atmospheres.

At this depth I could still see the rays of the sun, though feebly; to their intense brilliancy had succeeded a reddish twilight, the lowest state between day and night; but we could still see well enough; it was not necessary to resort to the Ruhmkorff apparatus as yet. At this moment Captain Nemo stopped; he waited till I joined him, and then pointed to an obscure mass, looming in the shadow, at a short distance.

'It is the forest of the Island of Crespo,' thought I — and I was not mistaken.

A Submarine Forest

We had at last arrived on the borders of this forest, doubtless one of the finest of Captain Nemo's immense domains. He looked upon it as his own, and considered he had the same right over it that the first men had in the first days of the world. And, indeed, who would have disputed with him the possession of this submarine property? What other hardier pioneer would come, hatchet in hand, to cut down the dark copses?

This forest was composed of large tree-plants; and the moment we penetrated under its vast arcades, I was struck by the singular position of their branches — a position I had not yet observed.

Not a herb which carpeted the ground, not a branch which clothed the trees, was either broken or bent, nor did they extend horizontally; all stretched up to the surface of the ocean. Not a filament, not a ribbon, however thin they might be, but kept as straight as a rod of iron. The fuci and llianas grew in rigid perpendicular lines, due to the density of the element which had produced them. Motionless, yet, when bent to one side by the hand, they directly resumed their former position. Truly it was the region of perpendicularity!

I soon accustomed myself to this fantastic position, as well as to the comparative darkness which surrounded us. The soil of the forest seemed covered with sharp blocks, difficult to avoid. The submarine flora struck me as being very perfect, and richer even than it would have been in the arctic or tropical zones, where these productions are not so plentiful. But for some minutes I involuntarily confounded the genera, taking zoophytes for hydrophytes, animals for plants; and who would not have been mistaken? The fauna and the flora are too closely allied in this submarine world.

These plants are self-propagated, and the principle of their existence is in the water, which upholds and nourishes them. The greater number, instead of leaves, shoot forth blades of capricious shapes, comprised within a scale of colours — pink, carmine, green, olive, fawn, and brown. I saw there (but not dried up, as our specimens of the Nautilus are) pavonari spread like a fan, as if to catch the breeze; scarlet ceramies, whose laminaries extended their edible shoots of fern-shaped nereocysti, which grow to a height of fifteen feet; clusters of acetabuli, whose stems increase in size upwards; and numbers of other marine plants, all devoid of flowers!

'Curious anomaly, fantastic element!' said an ingenious naturalist, 'in which the animal kingdom blossoms, and the vegetable does not!'

Under these numerous shrubs (as large as trees of the temperate zone), and under their damp shadow, were massed together real bushes of living flowers, hedges of zoophytes, on which blossomed some zebrameandrines, with crooked grooves, some yellow caryophylliae; and, to complete the illusion, the fish-flies flew from branch to branch like a swarm of humming-birds, whilst yellow lepisacomthi, with bristling jaws, dactyl-opteri, and monocentrides rose at our feet like a flight of snipes.

In about an hour Captain Nemo gave the signal to halt. I, for my part, was not sorry, and we stretched ourselves under an arbour of alariae, the long thin blades of which stood up like arrows.

This short rest seemed delicious to me; there was nothing wanting but the charm of conversation; but, impossible to speak, impossible to answer, I only put my great copper head to Conseil's. I saw the worthy fellow's eyes glistening with delight, and to show his satisfaction, he shook himself in his breastplate of air, in the most comical way in the world.

After four hours of this walking I was surprised not to find myself dreadfully hungry. How to account for this state of the stomach I could not tell. But instead I felt an insurmountable desire to sleep, which happens to all divers. And my eyes soon closed behind the thick glasses, and I fell into a heavy slumber, which the movement alone had prevented before. Captain Nemo and his robust companion, stretched in the clear crystal, set us the example.

How long I remained buried in this drowsiness, I cannot judge; but when I woke, the sun seemed sinking towards the horizon. Captain Nemo had already risen, and I was beginning to stretch my limbs, when an unexpected apparition brought me briskly to my feet.

A few steps off, a monstrous sea-spider, about thirty-eight inches high, was watching me with squinting eyes, ready to spring upon me. Though my diver's dress was thick enough to defend me from the bite of this animal, I could not help shuddering with horror. Conseil and the sailor of the Nautilus awoke at this moment. Captain Nemo pointed out the hideous crustacean, which a blow from the butt end of the gun knocked over, and I saw the horrible claws of the monster writhe in terrible convulsions. This accident reminded me that other animals more to be feared might haunt these obscure depths, against whose attacks my diving-dress would not protect me. I had never thought of it before, but I now resolved to be upon my guard. Indeed, I thought that this halt would mark the termination of our walk; but I was mistaken, for, instead of returning to the Nautilus, Captain Nemo continued his bold excursion. The ground was still on the incline, its declivity seemed to be getting greater, and to be leading us to greater depths. It must have been about three o'clock when we reached a narrow valley, between high perpendicular walls, situated about seventy-five fathoms deep. Thanks to the perfection of our apparatus, we were forty-five fathoms below the limit which nature seems to have imposed on man as to his submarine excursions.

I say seventy-five fathoms, though I had no instrument by which to judge the distance. But I knew that even in the clearest waters the solar rays could not penetrate further. And accordingly the darkness deepened. At ten paces not an object was visible. I was groping my way, when I suddenly saw a brilliant white light. Captain Nemo had just put his electric apparatus into use; his companion did the same, and Conseil and I followed their example. By turning a screw I established a communication between the wire and the spiral glass, and the sea, lit by our four lanterns, was illuminated for a circle of thirty-six yards.

Captain Nemo was still plunging into the dark depths of the forest, whose trees were getting scarcer at every step. I noticed that vegetable life disappeared sooner than animal life. The medusae had already abandoned the arid soil, from which a great number of animals, zoophytes, articulata, molluscs, and fishes, still obtained sustenance.

As we walked, I thought the light of our Ruhmkorff apparatus could not fail to draw some inhabitant from its dark couch. But if they did approach us, they at least kept at a respectful distance from the hunters. Several times I saw Captain Nemo stop, put his gun to his shoulder, and after some moments drop it and walk on. At last, after about four hours, this marvellous excursion came to an end. A wall of superb rocks, in an imposing mass, rose before us, a heap of gigantic blocks, an enormous steep granite shore, forming dark grottos, but which presented no practicable slope; it was the prop of the Island of Crespo. It was the earth! Captain Nemo stopped suddenly. A gesture of his brought us all to a halt; and however desirous I might be to scale the wall, I was obliged to stop. Here ended Captain Nemo's domains.

And he would not go beyond them. Further on was a portion of the globe he might not trample upon.

The return began. Captain Nemo hed returned to the head of his little band, directing their course without hesitation. I thought we were not following the same road to return to the Nautilus. The new road was very steep, and consequently very painful. We approached the surface of the sea rapidly. But this return to the upper strata was not so sudden as to cause relief from the pressure too rapidly, which might have produced serious disorder in our organisation, and brought on internal lesions, so fatal to divers. Very soon light reappeared and grew, and the sun being low on the horizon, the refraction edged the different objects with a spectral ring. At ten yards and a half deep, we walked amidst a shoal of little fishes of all kinds, more numerous than the birds of the air, and also more agile; but no aquatic game worthy of a shot had as yet met our gaze, when at that moment I saw the Captain shoulder his gun quickly, and follow a moving object into the shrubs. He fired; — I heard a slight hissing, and a creature fell stunned at some distance from us. It was a magnificent sea-otter, an enhydrus, the only exclusively marine quadruped. This otter was five feet long, and must have been very valuable. Its skin, chestnut-brown above, and silvery underneath, would have made one of those beautiful furs so sought after in the Russian and Chinese markets; the fineness and the lustre of its coat would certainly fetch £ 80. I admired this curious mammal, with its rounded head ornamented with short ears, its round eyes, and white whiskers like those of a cat, with webbed feet and nails, and tufted tail. This precious animal, hunted and tracked by fishermen, has now become very rare, and taken refuge chiefly in the northern parts of the Pacific, or probably its race would soon become extinct.

Captain Nemo's companion took the beast, threw it over his shoulder, and we continued our journey. For one hour a plain of sand lay stretched before us. Sometimes it rose to within two yards and some inches of the surface of the water. I then saw our image clearly reflected, drawn inversely, and above us appeared an identical group reflecting our movements and our actions; in a word, like us in every point, except that they walked with their heads downward and their feet in the air.

Another effect I noticed, which was the passage of thick clouds which formed and vanished rapidly; but on reflection I understood that these seeming clouds were due to the varying thickness of the reeds at the bottom, and I could even see the fleecy foam which their broken tops multiplied on the water, and the shadows of large birds passing above our heads, whose rapid flight I could discern on the surface of the sea.

On this occasion, I was witness to one of the finest gunshots which ever made the nerves of a hunter thrill. A large bird of great breadth of wing, clearly visible, approached, hovering over us. Captain Nemo's companion shouldered his gun and fired, when it was only a few yards above the waves. The creature fell stunned, and the force of its fall brought it within the reach of the dexterous hunter's grasp. It was an albatross of the finest kind.

Our march had not been interrupted by this incident. For two hours we followed these sandy plains, then fields of algae very disagreeable to cross. Candidly, I could do no more when I saw a glimmer of light, which, for a half mile, broke the darkness of the waters. It was the lantern of the Nautilus. Before twenty minutes were over we should be on board, and I should be able to breathe with ease, for it seemed that my reservoir supplied air very deficient in oxygen. But I did not reckon on an accidental meeting, which delayed our arrival for some time.

I had remained some steps behind, when I presently saw Captain Nemo coming hurriedly towards me. With his strong hand he bent me to the ground, his companion doing the same to Conseil. At first I knew not what to think of this sudden attack, but I was soon reassured by seeing the Captain lie down beside me, and remain immovable.

I was stretched on the ground, just under shelter of a bush of algae, when raising my head, I saw some enormous mass, casting phosphorescent gleams, pass blusteringly by.

My blood froze in my veins as I recognised two formidable sharks which threatened us. It was a couple of tintoreas, terrible creatures, with enormous tails and a dull glassy stare, the phosphorescent matter ejected from holes pierced around the muzzle. Monstrous brutes! which would crush a whole man in their iron jaws. I did not know whether Conseil stopped to classify them; for my part, I noticed their silver bellies, and their huge mouths bristling with teeth, from a very unscientific point of view, and more as a possible victim than as a naturalist.

Happily the voracious creatures do not see well. They passed without seeing us, brushing us with their brownish fins, and we escaped by a miracle from a danger certainly greater than meeting a tiger full-face in the forest. Half an hour after, guided by the electric light, we reached the *Nautilus*. The outside door had been left open, and Captain Nemo closed it as soon as we had entered the first cell. He then pressed a knob. I heard the pumps working in the midst of the vessel, I felt the water sinking from around me, and in a few moments the cell was entirely empty. The inside door then opened, and we entered the vestry.

There our diving-dress was taken off, not without some trouble; and, fairly worn out from want of food and sleep, I returned to my room, in great wonder at this surprising excursion at the bottom of the sea.

A Vanished Continent

That night, about eleven o'clock, I received a most unexpected visit from Captain Nemo. He asked me very graciously if I felt fatigued from my watch of the preceding night. I answered in the negative.

'Then, M. Aronnax, I propose a curious excursion.'

'Propose, Captain?'

'You have hitherto only visited the submarine depths by daylight, under the brightness of the sun. Would it suit you to see them in the darkness of the night?'

'Most willingly.'

'I warn you, the way will be tiring. We shall have far to walk, and must climb a mountain. The roads are not well kept.'

'What you say, Captain, only heightens my curiosity; I am ready to follow you.'

'Come then, sir, we will put on our diving dresses.'

Arrived at the robing-room, I saw that neither of my companions nor any of the ship's crew were to follow us on this excursion. Captain Nemo had not even proposed my taking with me either Ned or Conseil.

In a few moments we had put on our diving dresses; they placed on our backs the reservoirs, abundantly filled with air, but no electric lamps were prepared. I called the Captain's attention to the fact.

'They will be useless,' he replied.

I thought I had not heard aright, but I could not repeat my observation, for the Captain's head had already disappeared in its metal case. I finished harnessing myself, I felt them put an ironpointed stick into my hand, and some minutes later, after going through the usual form, we set foot on the bottom of the Atlantic, at a depth of 150 fathoms. Midnight was near. The waters were profoundly dark, but Captain Nemo pointed out in the distance a reddish spot, a sort of large light shining brilliantly, about two miles from the *Nautilus*. What this fire might be, what could feed it, why and how it lit up the liquid mass, I could not say. In any case, it did light our way, vaguely, it is true, but I soon accustomed myself to the peculiar darkness, and I understood, under such circumstances, the uselessness of the Ruhmkorff apparatus.

As we advanced, I heard a kind of pattering above my head. The noise redoubling, sometimes producing a continual shower, I soon understood the cause. It was rain falling violently, and crisping the surface of the waves. Instinctively the thought flashed across my mind that I should be wet through! By the water! in the midst of the water! I could not help laughing at the odd idea. But indeed, in the thick diving dress, the liquid element is no longer felt, and one only seems to be in an atmosphere somewhat denser than the terrestrial atmosphere. Nothing more.

After half an hour's walk the soil became stony. Medusae, microscopic crustacea, and pennatules lit it slightly with their phosphorescent gleam. I caught a glimpse of pieces of stone covered with millions of zoophytes, and masses of sea-weed. My feet often slipped upon this viscous carpet of seaweed, and without my iron-tipped stick I should have fallen more than once. In turning round, I could still see the whitish lantern of the *Nautilus* beginning to pale in the distance.

But the rosy light which guided us increased and lit up the horizon. The presence of this fire under water puzzled me in the highest degree. Was it some electric effulgence? Was I going towards a natural phenomenon as yet unknown to the savants of the earth? Or even (for this thought crossed my brain) had the hand of man aught to do with this conflagration? Had he fanned this flame? Was I to meet in these depths companions and friends of Captain Nemo whom he was going to visit, and who, like him, led this strange existence? Should I find down there a whole colony of exiles, who, weary of the miseries of this earth, had sought and found independence in the deep ocean? All these foolish and unreasonable ideas pursued me. And in this condition of mind, over-excited by the succession of wonders continually passing before my eyes, I should not have been surprised to meet at the bottom of the sea one of those submarine towns of which Captain Nemo dreamed.

Our road grew lighter and lighter. The white glimmer came in rays from the summit of a mountain about 800 feet high. But what I saw was simply a reflection, developed by the clearness of the waters. The source of this inexplicable light was a fire on the opposite side of the mountain.

In the midst of this stony maze, furrowing the bottom of the Atlantic, Captain Nemo advanced without hesitation. He knew this dreary road. Doubtless he had often travelled over it, and could not lose himself. I followed him with unshaken confidence. He seemed to me like a genie of the sea; and, as he walked before me, I could not help admiring his stature, which was outlined in black on the luminous horizon.

It was one in the morning when we arrived at the first slopes of the mountain; but to gain access to them we must venture through the difficult paths of a vast copse.

Yes; a copse of dead trees, without leaves, without sap, trees petrified by the action of the water, and here and there overtopped by gigantic pines. It was like a coal pit, still standing, holding by the roots to the broken soil, and whose branches, like fine black paper cuttings, showed distinctly on the watery ceiling. Picture to yourself a forest in the Hartz, hanging on to the sides of the mountain, but a forest swallowed up. The paths were encumbered with seaweed and fucus, between which grovelled a whole world of crustacea. I went along, climbing the rocks, striding over extended trunks, breaking the sea bind-weed, which hung from one tree to the other; and frightening the fishes, which flew from branch to branch. Pressing onward, I felt no fatigue. I followed my guide, who was never tired. What a spectacle! how can I express it? how paint the aspect of those woods and rocks in this medium, — their under parts dark and wild, the upper coloured with red tints, by that light which the reflecting powers of the waters doubled? We climbed rocks, which fell directly after with gigantic bounds, and the low growling of an avalanche. To right and left ran long, dark galleries, where sight was lost. Here opened vast glades which the hand of man seemed to have worked; and I sometimes asked myself if some inhabitant of these submarine regions would not suddenly appear to me.

But Captain Nemo was still mounting. I could not stay behind. I followed boldly. My stick gave me good help. A false step would have been dangerous on the narrow passes sloping down to the sides of the gulfs; but I walked with firm step, without feeling any giddiness. Now I jumped a crevice the depth of which would have made me hesitate had it been among the glaciers on the land; now I ventured on the unsteady trunk of a tree, thrown across from one abyss to the other, without looking under my feet, having only eyes to admire the wild sights of this region.

There, monumental rocks, leaning on their regularly cut bases, seemed to defy all laws of equilibrium. From between their stony knees, trees sprang, like a jet under heavy pressure, and upheld others which upheld them. Natural towers, large scarps, cut perpendicularly, like a 'curtain,' inclined at an angle which the laws of gravitation could never have tolerated in terrestrial regions.

Two hours after quitting the Nautilus, we had crossed the line of trees, and a hundred feet above our heads rose the top of the mountain, which cast a shadow on the brilliant irradiation of the opposite slope. Some petrified shrubs ran fantastically here and there. Fishes got up under our feet like birds in the long grass. The massive rocks were rent with impenetrable fractures, deep grottos, and unfathomable holes, at the bottom of which formidable creatures might be heard moving. My blood curdled when I saw enormous antennae blocking my road, or some frightful claw closing with a noise in the shadow of some cavity. Millions of luminous spots shone brightly in the midst of the darkness. They were the eyes of giant crustacea crouched in their holes; giant lobsters setting themselves up like halberdiers, and moving their claws with the clicking sound of pincers; titanic crabs, pointed like a gun on its carriage; and frightful looking poulps, interweaving their tentacles like a living nest of serpents.

We had now arrived on the first platform, where other surprises awaited me. Before us lay some picturesque ruins, which betrayed the hand of man, and not that of the Creator. There were vast heaps of stone, amongst which might be traced the vague and shadowy forms of castles and temples, clothed with a world of blossoming zoophytes, and over which, instead of ivy, seaweed and fucus threw a thick vegetable mantle. But what was this portion of the globe which had been swallowed by cataclysms? Who had placed those rocks and stones like cromlechs of pre-historic times? Where was I? Whither had Captain Nemo's fancy hurried me?

I would fain have asked him; not being able to, I stopped him — I seized his arm. But shaking his head, and pointing to the highest point of the mountain, he seemed to say —

'Come, come along; come higher!'

I followed, and in a few minutes I had climbed to the top, which for a circle of ten yards commanded the whole mass of rock.

I looked down the side we had just climbed. The mountain did not rise more than seven or eight hundred feet above the level of the plain; but on the opposite side it commanded from twice that height the depths of this part of the Atlantic. My eyes ranged far over a large space lit by a violent fulguration. In fact, the mountain was a volcano.

At fifty feet above the peak, in the midst of a rain of stones and scoriae, a large crater was vomiting forth torrents of lava which fell in a cascade of fire into the bosom of the liquid mass. Thus situated, this volcano lit the lower plain like an immense torch, even to the extreme limits of the horizon. I said that the submarine crater threw up lava, but no flames. Flames require the oxygen of the air to feed upon, and cannot be developed under water; but streams of lava, having in themselves the principles of their incandescence, can attain a white heat, fight vigorously against the liquid element, and turn it to vapour by contact.

Rapid currents bearing all these gases in diffusion, and torrents of lava, slid to the bottom of the mountain like an eruption of Vesuvius on another Terra del Greco.

There, indeed, under my eyes, ruined, destroyed, lay a town — its roofs open to the sky, its temples fallen, its arches dislocated, its columns lying on the ground, from which one could still recognise the massive character of Tuscan architecture. Further on, some remains of a gigantic aqueduct; here the high base of an Acropolis, with the floating outline of a Parthenon; there traces of a quay, as if an ancient port had formerly abutted on the borders of the ocean, and disappeared with its merchant vessels and its war-galleys. Further on again, long lines of sunken walls and broad deserted streets — a perfect Pompeii escaped beneath the waters. Such was the sight that Captain Nemo brought before my eyes!

Where was I? Where was I? I must know, at any cost. I tried to speak, but Captain Nemo stopped me by a gesture, and picking up a piece of chalk stone, advanced to a rock of black basalt, and traced the one word — ATLANTIS.

There, under my eyes, ruined, destroyed, lay a town...

What a light shot through my mind! Atlantis, the ancient Meropis of Theopompus, the Atlantis of Plato, that continent denied by Origen, Jamblichus, D'Anville, Malte-Brun, and Humboldt, who placed its disappearance amongst the legendary tales admitted by Posidonius, Pliny, Ammianus Marcellinus, Tertullian, Engel, Buffon, and D'Avezac. I had it there now before my eyes, bearing upon it the unexceptionable testimony of its catastrophe. The region thus engulfed was beyond Europe, Asia, and Lybia, beyond the columns of Hercules, where those powerful people, the Atlantides, lived, against whom the first wars of ancient Greece were waged.

Thus, led by the strangest destiny, I was treading under foot the mountains of this continent, touching with my hand those ruins a thousand generations old, and contemporary with the geological epochs. I was walking on the very spot where the contemporaries of the first man had walked.

Whilst I was trying to fix in my mind every detail of this grand landscape, Captain Nemo remained motionless, as if petrified in mute ecstasy, leaning on a mossy stone. Was he dreaming of those generations long since disappeared? Was he asking them the secret of human destiny? Was it here this strange man came to steep himself in historical recollections, and live again this ancient life, — he who wanted no modern one? What would I not have given to know his thoughts, to share them, to understand them! We remained for an hour at this place, contemplating the vast plain under the brightness of the lava, which was sometimes wonderfully intense. Rapid tremblings ran along the mountain caused by internal bubblings, deep noises distinctly transmitted through the liquid medium were echoed with majestic grandeur. At this moment the moon appeared through the mass of waters, and threw her pale rays on the buried continent. It was but a gleam, but what an indescribable effect! The Captain rose, cast one last look on the immense plain, and then bade me follow him.

We descended the mountain rapidly, and the mineral forest once passed, I saw the lantern of the *Nautilus* shining like a star. The Captain walked straight to it, and we got on board as the first rays of light whitened the surface of the ocean.

The Ghost Ship

by
RICHARD MIDDLETON

Fairfield is a little village lying near the Portsmouth Road about halfway between London and the sea. Strangers who find it by accident now and then, call it a pretty, old-fashioned place; we, who live in it and call it home, don't find anything very pretty about it, but we should be sorry to live anywhere else. Our minds have taken the shape of the inn and the church and the green, I suppose. At all events we never feel comfortable out of Fairfield.

Of course the Cockneys, with their vast houses and their noise-ridden streets, can call us rustics if they choose, but for all that Fairfield is a better place to live in than London. Doctor says that when he goes to London his mind is bruised with the weight of the houses, and he was a Cockney born. He had to live there himself when he was a little chap, but he knows better now. You gentlemen may laugh — perhaps some of you come from London way — but it seems to me that a witness like that is worth a gallon of arguments.

Dull? Well, you might find it dull, but I assure you that I've listened to all the London yarns you have spun tonight, and they're absolutely nothing to the things that happen at Fairfield. It's because of our way of thinking and minding our own business. If one of your Londoners were set down on the green of a Saturday night when the ghosts of the lads who died in the war keep tryst with the lasses who lie in the churchyard, he couldn't help being curious and interfering, and then the ghosts would go somewhere where it was quieter. But we just let them come and go and don't make any fuss, and in consequence Fairfield is the ghostiest place in all England. Why, I've seen a headless man sitting on the edge of the well in broad daylight, and the children playing about his feet as if he were their father. Take my word for it, spirits know when they are well off as much as human beings.

Still, I must admit that the thing I'm going to tell you about was queer even for our part of the world, where three packs of ghost-hounds hunt regularly during the season, and blacksmith's great-grandfather is busy all night shoeing the dead gentlemen's horses. Now that's a thing that wouldn't happen in London, because of their interfering ways, but blacksmith he lies up aloft and sleeps as quiet as a lamb. Once when he had a bad head he shouted down to them not to make so much noise, and in the morning he found an old guinea left on the anvil as an apology. He wears it on his watch-chain now. But I must get on with my story; if I start telling you about the queer happenings at Fairfield I'll never stop.

It all came of the great storm in the spring of '97, the year that we had two great storms. This was the first one, and I remember it very well, because I found in the morning that it had lifted the thatch of my pigsty into the widow's garden as clean as a boy's kite. When I looked over the hedge, widow — Tom Lamport's widow that was — was prodding for her nasturtiums with a daisy-grubber. After I had watched her for a little I went down to the Fox and Grapes to tell landlord what she had said to me. Landlord he laughed, being a married man and at ease with the sex. 'Come to that,' he said, 'the tempest has blowed something into my field. A kind of ship I think it would be.'

I was surprised at that until he explained that it was only a ghost-ship and would do no hurt to the turnips. We argued that it had been blown up from the sea at Portsmouth, and then we talked of something else. There were two slates down at the parsonage and a big tree in Lumley's meadow. It was a rare storm.

I reckon the wind had blown our ghosts all over England. They were coming back for days afterwards with foundered horses and as footsore as possible, and they were so glad to get back to Fairfield that some of them walked up the street crying like little children. Squire said that his great-grandfather's great-grandfather hadn't looked so dead-beat since the battle of Naseby, and he's an educated man.

What with one thing and another, I should think it was a week before we got straight again, and then one afternoon I met the landlord on the green and he had a worried face. 'I wish you'd come and have a look at that ship in my field,' he said to me; it seems to me it's leaning real hard on the turnips. I can't bear thinking what the missus will say when she sees it.'

I walked down the lane with him, and sure enough there was a ship, in the middle of his field, but such a ship as no man had seen on the water for three hundred years, let alone in the middle of a turnip-field. It was all painted black and covered with carvings, and there was a great bay window in the stern for all the world like the Squire's drawing-room. There was a crowd of little black cannon on the deck and looking out of her port-holes, and she was anchored at each end to the hard ground. I have seen the wonders of the world on picture-postcards, but I have never seen anything to equal that.

'She seems very solid for a ghost-ship,' I said, seeing the landlord was bothered.

'I should say it's a betwixt and between,' he answered, puzzling it over, 'but it's going to spoil a matter of fifty turnips, and missus she'll want it moved.' We went up to her and touched the side, and it was as hard as a real ship. 'Now there's folks in England would call that very curious,' he said.

Sure enough, there was a ship in the middle of his field.

Now I don't know much about ships, but I should think that that ghost-ship weighed a solid two hundred tons, and it seemed to me that she had come to stay, so that I felt sorry for Landlord, who was a married man. 'All the horses in Fairfield won't move her out of my turnips,' he said frowning at her.

Just then we heard a noise on her deck, and we looked up and saw that a man had come out of her front cabin and was looking down at us very peaceably. He was dressed in a black uniform set out with rusy gold lace, and he had a great cutlass by his side in a brass sheath. 'I'm Captain Bartholomew Roberts,' he said, in a gentleman's voice, 'put in for recruits. I seem to have brought her rather far up the harbour.'

'Harbour!' cried landlord; 'why, you're fifty miles from the sea.'

Captain Roberts didn't turn a hair. 'So much as that, is it?' he said coolly. 'Well, it's of no consequence.'

Landlord was a bit upset at this. 'I don't want to be un-neighbourly,' he said, 'but I wish you hadn't brought your ship into my field. You see, my wife sets great store on these turnips.

The captain took a pinch of snuff out of a fine gold box that he pulled out of his pocket, and dusted his fingers with a silk handkerchief in a very genteel fashion. 'I'm only here for a few months,' he said; 'but if a testimony of my esteem would pacify your good lady I would be content,' and with the words he loosed a great gold brooch from the neck of his coat and tossed it down to landlord.

Landlord blushed as red as a strawberry. 'I'm not denying she's fond of jewellery,' he said, 'but it's too much for half a sackful of turnips.' And indeed it was a handsome brooch.

The captain laughed. 'Tut, man,' he said, 'it's a forced sale, and you deserve a good price. Say no more about it,' and nodding good-day to us, he turned on his heel and went into the cabin. Landlord walked back up the lane like a man with a weight off his mind. 'That tempest has blowed me a bit of luck,' he said; 'The missus will be main pleased with that brooch. It's better than the blacksmith's guinea any day.'

Ninety-seven was Jubilee year, the year of the second Jubilee, you remember, and we had great doings at Fairfield, so that we hadn't much time to bother about the ghost-ship, though anyhow it isn't our way to meddle in things that don't concern us. Landlord, he saw his tenant once or twice when he was hoeing his turnips and passed the time of day, and landlord's wife wore her new brooch to church every Sunday. But we didn't mix much with the ghosts at any time, all except an idiot lad there was in the village, and he didn't know the difference between a man and a ghost, poor innocent! On Jubilee Day, however, somebody told Captain Roberts why the church bells were ringing, and he hoisted a flag and fired off his guns like a royal Englishman. 'Tis true the guns were shotted, and one of the round shot knocked a hole in Farmer Johnstone's barn, but nobody thought much of that in such a season of rejoicing.

It wasn't till our celebrations were over that we noticed that anything was wrong in Fairfield. 'Twas shoemaker who told me first about it one morning at the Fox and Grapes. 'You know my great great-uncle?' he said to me.

'You mean Joshua, the quiet lad,' I answered, knowing him well.

'Quiet!' said shoemaker indignantly. 'Quiet you call him, coming home at three o' clock every morning as drunk as a magistrate and waking up the whole house with his noise.'

'Why, it can't be Joshua!' I said, for I knew him for one of the most respectable young ghosts in the village.

'Joshua it is,' said shoemaker; 'and one of these nights he'll find himself out in the street if he isn't careful.'

This kind of talk shocked me, I can tell you, for I don't

like to hear a man abusing his own family, and I could hardly believe that a steady youngster like Joshua had taken to drink. But just then in came butcher Aylwin in such a temper that he could hardly drink his beer. 'The young puppy! the young puppy!' he kept on saying; and it was some time before shoemaker and I found out that he was talking about his ancestor that fell at Senlac.

'Drink?' said shoemaker hopefully, for we all like company in our misfortunes, and butcher nodded grimly.

'The young noodle,' he said, emptying his tankard.

Well, after that I kept my ears open, and it was the same story all over the village. There was hardly a young man among all the ghosts of Fairfield who didn't roll home in the small hours of the morning the worse for liquor. I used to wake up in the night and hear them stumble past my house, singing outrageous songs. The worst of it was that we couldn't keep the scandal to ourselves, and the folk at Greenhill began to talk of 'sodden Fairfield' and taught their children to sing a song about us:

Sodden Fairfield, sodden Fairfield has no use for
bread-and-butter,
Rum for breakfast, rum for dinner, rum for tea, and
rum for supper!

We are easy-going in our village, but we didn't like that.

Of course we soon found out where the young fellows went to get the drink, and landlord was terribly cut up that his tenant should have turned out so badly, but his wife wouldn't hear of parting with the brooch, so that he couldn't give the Captain notice to quit. But as time went on, things grew from bad to worse, and at all hours of the day you would see those young reprobates sleeping it off on the village green. Nearly every afternoon a ghost-wagon used to jolt down to the ship with a lading of rum, and though the older ghosts seemed inclined to give the Captain's hospitality the go-by, the youngsters were neither to hold nor to bind.

So one afternoon when I was taking my nap I heard a knock at the door, and there was parson looking very serious, like a man with a job before him that he didn't altogether relish. 'I'm going down to talk to the Captain about all this drunkenness in the village, and I want you to come with me,' he said straight out.

I can't say that I fancied the visit much myself, and I tried to hint to the parson that as, after all, they were only a lot of ghosts, it didn't very much matter.

'Dead or alive, I'm responsible for their good conduct,' he said, 'and I'm going to do my duty and put a stop to this continued disorder. And you are coming with me, John Simmons.' So I went, parson being a persuasive kind of man.

We went down to the ship, and as we approached her I could see the Captain tasting the air on deck. When he saw parson he took off his hat very politely, and I can tell you that I was relieved to find that he had a proper respect for the cloth. Parson acknowledged his salute and spoke out stoutly enough. 'Sir, I should be glad to have a word with you.'

'Come on board, sir, come on board,' said the Captain, and I could tell by his voice that he knew why we were there. Parson and I climbed up an uneasy kind of ladder, and the Captain took us into the great cabin at the back of the ship, where the bay-window was. It was the most wonderful place you ever saw in your life, all full of gold and silver plate, swords with jewelled scabbards, carved oak chairs, and great chests that looked as though they were bursting with guineas. Even parson was surprised, and he did not shake his head very hard when the Captain took down some silver cups and poured us out a drink of rum. I tasted mine, and I don't mind saying that it changed my view of things entirely. There was nothing betwixt and between about that rum, and I felt that it was ridiculous to blame the lads for drinking too much of stuff like that. It seemed to fill my veins with honey and fire.

Parson put the case squarely to the Captain, but I didn't listen much to what he said; I was busy sipping my drink and looking through the window at the fishes swimming to and fro over landlord's turnips. Just then it seemed the most natural thing in the world that they should be there, though afterwards, of course, I could see that proved it was a ghost-ship.

But even then I thought it was queer when I saw a drowned sailor float by in the thin air with his hair and beard all full of bubbles. It was the first time I had seen anything quite like that at Fairfield.

All the time I was regarding the wonders of the deep, parson was telling Captain Roberts how there was no peace or rest in the village owing to the curse of drunkenness, and what a bad example the youngsters were setting to the older ghosts. The Captain listened very attentively, and only put in a word now and then about boys being boys and young men sowing their wild oats. But when parson had finished his speech he filled up our silver cups and said to parson, with a flourish, 'I should be sorry to cause trouble anywhere where I have been made welcome, and you will be glad to hear that I put to sea tomorrow night. And now you must drink me a prosperous voyage.' So we all stood up and drank the toast with honour, and that noble rum was like hot oil in my veins.

After that Captain showed us some of the curiosities he had brought back from foreign parts, and we were greatly amazed, though afterwards I couldn't clearly remember what they were. And then I found myself walking across the turnips with parson, and I was telling him of the glories of the deep that I had seen through the window of the ship. He turned on me severely. 'If I were you, John Simmons,' he said, 'I should go straight home to bed.' He has a way of putting things that wouldn't occur to an ordinary man, has parson, and I did as he told me.

Well, next day it came on to blow, and it blew harder and harder, till about eight o'clock at night I heard a noise and looked out into the garden. I dare say you won't believe me, it seems a bit tall even to me, but the wind had lifted the thatch of my pigsty into the widow's garden a second time. I thought I wouldn't wait to hear what widow had to say about it, so I went across the green to the Fox and Grapes, and the wind was so strong that I danced along on tip-toe like a girl at the fair. When I got to the inn landlord had to help me shut the door; it seemed as though a dozen goats were pushing against it to come in out of the storm.

'It's a powerful tempest,' he said, drawing the beer. 'I hear there's a chimney down at Dickory End.'

'It's a funny thing how these sailors know about the weather,' I answered. 'When Captain said he was going tonight, I was thinking it would take a capful of wind to carry the ship back to sea, but now here's more than a capful.'

'Ah, yes,' said landlord, 'it's tonight he goes true enough, and, mind you, though he treated me handsome over the rent, I'm not sure it's a loss to the village. I don't hold with gentrice who fetch their drink from London instead of helping local traders to get their living.'

'But you haven't got any rum like his,' I said to draw him out.

His neck grew red above his collar, and I was afraid I'd gone too far; but after a while he got his breath with a grunt.

'John Simmons,' he said, 'if you've come down here this windy night to talk a lot of fool's talk, you've wasted a journey.'

Well, of course, then I had to smooth him down with praising his rum and Heaven forgive me for swearing it was better than Captain's. For the like of that rum no living lips have

290

tasted save mine and parson's. But somehow or other I brought landlord round, and presently we must have a glass of his best to prove its quality.

'Beat that if you can!' he cried, and we both raised our glasses to our mouths, only to stop halfway and look at each other in amaze. For the wind that had been howling outside like an outrageous dog had all of a sudden turned as melodious as the carol-boys of a Christmas Eve.

'Surely that's not my Martha,' whispered landlord; Martha being his great-aunt that lived in the loft overhead.

We went to the door, and the wind burst it open so that the handle was driven clean into the plaster of the wall. But we didn't think about that at the time; for over our heads, sailing very comfortably through the windy stars, was the ship that had passed the summer in landlord's field. Her portholes and her bay-window were blazing with lights, and there was a noise of singing and fiddling on her decks. 'He's gone,' shouted the landlord above the storm, 'and he's taken half the village with him!' I could only nod in answer, not having lungs like bellows of leather.

In the morning we were able to measure the strength of the storm, and over and above my pigsty there was damage enough wrought in the village to keep us busy. True it is that the children had to break down no branches for the firing that autumn, since the wind had strewn the woods with more than they could carry away. Many of our ghosts were scattered abroad, but this time very few came back, all the young men having sailed with Captain; and not only ghosts, for a poor half-witted lad was missing, and we reckoned that he had stowed himself away or perhaps shipped as cabin-boy, not knowing any better.

What with the lamentations of the ghost-girls and the grumblings of families who had lost an ancestor, the village was upset for a while, and the funny thing was that it was the folk who had complained most of the carryings-on of the youngsters, who made most noise now that they were gone. I hadn't any sympathy with shoemaker or butcher, who ran about saying how much they missed their lads, but it made me grieve to hear the poor bereaved girls calling their lovers by name on the village green at nightfall. It didn't seem fair to me that they should have lost their men a second time, after giving up life in order to join them, as like as not. Still, not even a spirit can be sorry for ever, and after a few months we made up our mind that the folk who had sailed in the ship were never coming back, and we didn't talk about it any more.

And then one day, I dare say it would be a couple of years after, when the whole business was quite forgotten, who should come trapesing along the road from Portsmouth but the daft lad who had gone away with the ship, without waiting till he was dead to become a ghost. You never saw such a boy as that in all your life. He had a great rusty cutlass hanging to a string at his waist, and he was tattooed all over in fine colours, so that even his face looked like a girl's sampler. He had a hand-kerchief in his hand full of foreign shells and old-fashioned pieces of small money, very curious, and walked up to the well outside his mother's house and drew himself a drink as if he had been nowhere in particular.

The worst of it was that he had come back as soft-headed as he went, and try as we might we couldn't get anything reasonable out of him. He talked a lot of gibberish about keel-hauling and walking the plank and crimson murders — things which a decent sailor should know nothing about, so that it seemed to me that for all his manners Captain had been more of a pirate than a gentleman mariner. But to draw sense out of that boy was as hard as picking cherries off a crab-tree. One silly tale he had that he kept on drifting back to, and to hear him you would have thought that it was the only thing that happened to him in his life. 'We was at anchor,' he would say, 'off an island called the Basket of Flowers, and the sailors had caught a lot of parrots and we were teaching them to swear. Up and down the decks, up and down the decks, and the language they used was dreadful. Then we looked up and saw the masts of the Spanish ship outside the harbour. Outside the harbour they were, so we threw the parrots into the sea and sailed out to fight. And all the parrots were drowned in the sea and the language they used was dreadful.' That's the sort of boy he was, nothing but silly talk of parrots when we asked him about the fighting. And we never had a chance of teaching him better, for two days after he ran away again, and hasn't been seen since.

That's my story, and I assure you that things like that are happening at Fairfield all the time. The ship has never come back, but somehow as people grow older they seem to think that one of these windy nights, she'll come sailing in over the hedges with all the lost ghosts on board. Well, when she comes, she'll be welcome. There's one ghost-lass that has never grown tired of waiting for her lad to return. Every night you'll see her out on the green, straining her poor eyes with looking for the mast-lights among the stars. A faithful lass you'd call her, and I'm thinking you'd be right.

Landlord's field wasn't a penny the worse for the visit, but they do say that since then the turnips that have been grown in it have tasted of rum.

In the Abyss

by

H. G. WELLS

The lieutenant stood in front of the steel sphere and gnawed a piece of pine splinter. 'What do you think of it, Steevens?' he asked.

'It's an idea,' said Steevens, in the tone of one who keeps an open mind.

'I believe it will smash — flat,' said the lieutenant.

'He seems to have calculated it all out pretty well,' said Steevens, still impartial.

'But think of the pressure,' said the lieutenant. 'At the surface of the water it's fourteen pounds to the inch, thirty feet down it's double that; sixty, treble; ninety, four times; nine hundred, forty times; five thousand, three hundred — that's a mile — it's two hundred and forty times fourteen pounds; that's — let's see — thirty hundredweight — a ton and a half, Steevens; *a ton and a half* to the square inch. And the ocean where he's going is five miles deep. That's seven and a half —'

'Sounds a lot,' said Steevens, 'but it's jolly thick steel.'

The lieutenant made no answer, but resumed his pine splinter. The object of their conversation was a huge ball of steel, having an exterior diameter of perhaps nine feet. It looked like the shot for some Titanic piece of artillery. It was elaborately nested in a monstrous scaffolding built into the framework of the vessel, and the gigantic spars that were presently to sling it overboard gave the stern of the ship an appearance that had raised the curiosity of every decent sailor who had sighted it, from the Pool of London to the Tropic of Capricorn. In two places, one above the other, the steel gave place to a couple of circular windows of enormously thick glass, and one of these, set in a steel frame of great solidity, was now partially unscrewed. Both the men had seen the interior of this globe for the first time that morning. It was elaborately padded with air cushions, with little studs sunk between bulging pillows to work the simple mechanism of the affair. Everything was elaborately padded, even the Myers apparatus which was to absorb carbonic acid and replace the oxygen inspired by its tenant, when he had crept in by the glass manhole, and had been screwed in. It was so elaborately padded that a man might have been fired from a gun in it with perfect safety. And it had need to be, for presently a man was to crawl in through that glass manhole, to be screwed up tightly, and to be flung overboard, and to sink down — down — down, for five miles, even as the lieutenant said. It had taken the strongest hold of his imagination; it made him a bore at mess; and he found Steevens, the new arrival aboard, a godsend to talk to about it, over and over again.

'It's my opinion,' said the lieutenant, 'that that glass will simply bend in and bulge and smash, under a pressure of that sort. Daubree has made rocks run like water under big pressures — and, you mark my words —'

'If the glass did break in,' said Steevens, 'what then?'

'The water would shoot in like a jet of iron. Have you ever felt a straight jet of high pressure water? It would hit as hard as a bullet. It would simply smash him and flatten him. It would tear down his throat, and into his lungs; it would blow in his eyes —'

'What a detailed imagination you have!' protested Steevens, who saw things vividly.

'It's a simple statement of the inevitable,' said the lieutenant.

'And the globe?'

'Would just give out a few little bubbles, and it would settle down comfortably against the day of judgment, among the oozes and the bottom clay — with poor Elstead apread over his own smashed cushions like butter over bread.'

He repeated this sentence as though he liked it very much. 'Like butter over bread,' he said.

'Having a look at the jigger?' said a voice, and Elstead stood behind them, spick and span in white, with a cigarette between his teeth, and his eyes smiling out of the shadow of his ample hat-brim. 'What's that about bread and butter, Weybridge? Grumbling as usual about the insufficient pay of naval officers? It won't be more than a day now before I start. We are to get the slings ready today. This clean sky and gentle swell is just the kind of thing for swinging off a dozen tons of lead and iron, isn't it?'

'It won't affect you much,' said Weybridge.

'No. Seventy or eighty feet down, and I shall be there in a dozen seconds, there's not a particle moving, though the wind shriek itself hoarse up above, and the water lifts halfway to the clouds. No. Down there' — He moved to the side of the ship and the other two followed him. All three leant forward on their elbows and stared down into the yellow-green water.

'*Peace*,' said Elstead, finishing his thought aloud.

'Are you dead certain that clockwork will act?' asked Weybridge presently.

'It has worked thirty-five times,' said Elstead. 'It's bound to work.'

'But if it doesn't.'

'Why shouldn't it?'

'I wouldn't go down in that confounding thing,' said Weybridge, 'for twenty thousands pounds.'

'Cheerful chap you are,' said Elstead, and spat sociably at a bubble below.

'I don't understand yet how you mean to work the thing,' said Steevens.

'In the first place, I'm screwed into the sphere,' said Elstead, 'and when I've turned the electric light off and on three times to show I'm cheerful, I'm swung out over the stern by that crane, with all those big lead sinkers slung below me. The top lead weight has a roller carrying a hundred fathoms of strong cord rolled up, and that's all that joins the sinkers to the sphere, except the slings that will be cut when the affair is dropped. We use cord rather than wire rope because it's easier to cut and more buoyant — necessary points, as you will see.

'Through each of these lead weights you notice there is a hole, and an iron rod will be run through that and will project six feet on the lower side. If that rod is rammed up from below, it knocks up a lever and sets the clockwork in motion at the side of the cylinder on which the cord winds.

'Very well. The whole affair is lowered gently into the water, and the slings are cut. The sphere floats — with the air in it, it's lighter than water — but the lead weights go down straight and the cord runs out. When the cord is all paid out, the sphere will go down too, pulled down by the cord.'

'But why the cord?' asked Steevens. 'Why not fasten the weights directly to the sphere?'

'Because of the smash down below. The whole affair will go rushing down, mile after mile, at a headlong pace at last. It would be knocked to pieces on the bottom if it wasn't for that cord. But the weights will hit the bottom, and directly they do, the buoyancy of the sphere will come into play. It will go on sinking slower and slower; come to a stop at last, and then begin to float upward again.

'That's where the clockwork comes in. Directly the weights smash against the sea bottom, the rod will be knocked through and will kick up the clockwork, and the cord will be rewound on the reel. I shall be lugged down to the sea bottom. There I shall stay for half an hour, with the electric light on, looking about me. Then the clockwork will release a spring knife, the cord will be cut, and up I shall rush again, like a soda-water bubble. The cord itself will help the flotation.'

'And if you should chance to hit a ship?' said Weybridge.

'I should come up at such a pace, I should go clean through it,' said Elstead, 'like a cannon ball. You needn't worry about that.'

'And suppose some nimble crustacean should wriggle into your clockwork —'

'It would be a pressing sort of invitation for me to stop,' said Elstead, turning his back on the water and staring at the sphere.

They had swung Elstead overboard by eleven o'clock. The day was serenely bright and calm, with the horizon lost in haze. The electric glare in the little upper compartment beamed cheerfully three times. Then they let him down slowly to the surface of the water, and a sailor in the stern chains hung ready to cut the tackle that held the lead weights and the sphere together. The globe, which had looked so large in deck, looked the smallest thing conceivable under the stern of the ship. It rolled a little, and its two dark windows, which floated uppermost, seemed like eyes turned up in round wonderment at the people who crowded the rail. A voice wondered how Elstead liked the rolling. 'Are you ready?' sang out the commander. 'Ay, ay, sir!' 'Then let her go!'

The rope of the tackle tightened against the blade and was cut, and an eddy rolled over the globe in a grotesquely helpless fashion. Someone waved a handkerchief, someone else tried an ineffectual cheer, a middy was counting slowly, 'Eight, nine, ten!' Another roll, then with a jerk and a splash the thing righted itself.

It seemed to be stationary for a moment, to grow rapidly smaller, and then the water closed over it, and it became visible, enlarged by refraction and dimmer, below the surface.

Before one could count three it had disappeared. There was a flicker of white light far down in the water, that diminished to a speck and vanished. Then there was nothing but a depth of water going down into blackness, through which a shark was swimming.

Then suddenly the screw of the cruiser began to rotate, the water was crickled, the shark disappeared in a wrinkled confusion, and a torrent of foam rushed across the crystalline clearness that had swallowed up Elstead. 'What's the idea?' said one A. B. to another.

'We're going to lay off about a couple of miles, 'fear he should hit us when he comes up,' said his mate.

The ship steamed slowly to her new position. Aboard her almost everyone who was unoccupied remained watching the breathing swell into which the sphere had sunk. For the next half-hour it is doubtful if a word was spoken that did not bear directly or indirectly on Elstead. The December sun was now high in the sky, and the heat very considerable.

'He'll be cold enough down there,' said Weybridge. 'They say that below a certain depth sea-water's always just about freezing.'

'Where'll he come up?' asked Steevens. 'I've lost my bearings.'

'That's the spot,' said the commander, who prided himself on his omniscience. He extended a precise finger southeastward. 'And this, I reckon, is pretty nearly the moment,' he said. 'He's been thirty-five minutes.'

'How long does it take to reach the bottom of the ocean?' asked Steevens.

'For a depth of five miles, and reckoning — as we did — an acceleration of two feet per second, both ways, is just about three-quarters of a minute.'

'Then he's overdue,' said Weybridge.

'Pretty nearly,' said the commander. 'I suppose it takes a few minutes for that cord of his to wind in.'

'I forgot that,' said Weybridge, evidently relieved.

And then began the suspense. A minute slowly dragged itself out, and no sphere shot out of the water. Another followed, and nothing broke the low oily swell. The sailors explained to one another that little point about the winding-in of the cord. The rigging was dotted with expectant faces. 'Come up, Elstead!' called one hairy-chested salt impatiently, and the others caught it up, and shouted as though they were waiting for the curtain of a theatre to rise.

The commander glanced irritably at them.

'Of course, if the acceleration is less than two,' he said, 'he'll be all the longer. We aren't absolutely certain that was the proper figure. I'm no slavish believer in calculations.'

Steevens agreed concisely. No one on the quarterdeck spoke for a couple of minutes. Then Steevens' watchcase clicked.

When, twenty-one minutes after, the sun reached the zenith, they were still waiting for the globe to reappear, and not a man aboard had dared to whisper that hope was dead. It was Weybridge who first gave expression to that realisation. He spoke while the sound of eight bells still hung in the air. 'I always distrusted that window,' he said quite suddenly to Steevens.

'Good God!' said Steevens; 'you don't think — ?'

'Well!' said Weybridge, and left the rest to his imagination.

'I'm no great believer in calculations myself,' said the commander dubiously, 'so that I'm not altogether hopeless yet.' And at midnight the gunboat was steaming slowly in a spiral round the spot where the globe had sunk, and the white beam of the electric light fled and halted and swept discontentedly onward again over the waste of phosphorescent waters under the little stars.

'If his window hasn't burst and smashed him,' said Weybridge, 'then it's a cursed sight worse, for his clockwork has gone wrong, and he's alive now, five miles under our feet, down there in the cold and dark, anchored in that little bubble of his, where never a ray of light has shone or a human being lived, since the waters were gathered together. He's there without food, feeling hungry and thirsty and scared, wondering whether he'll starve or stifle. Which will it be? The Myers apparatus is running out, I suppose. How long do they last?'

'Good heavens!' he exclaimed; 'what little things we are! What daring little devils! Down there, miles and miles of water — all water, and all this empty water about us and this sky. Gulfs!' He threw his hands out, and as he did so, a little white streak swept noiselessly up the sky, travelled more slowly, stopped, became a motionless dog, as though a new star had fallen up into the sky. Then it went sliding back again and lost itself amidst the reflections of the stars and the white haze of the sea's phosphorescence.

At the sight he stopped, arm extended and mouth open. He shut his mouth, opened it again, and waved his arms with an impatient gesture. Then he turned, shouted 'El-stead ahoy!' to the first watch, and went at a run to Lindley and the searchlight. 'I saw him,' he said. 'Starboard there! His light's on, and he's just shot out of the water. Bring the light round. We ought to see him drifting, when he lifts on the swell.'

But they never picked up the explorer until dawn. Then they almost ran him down. The crane was swung out and a boat's crew hooked the chain to the sphere. When they had shipped the sphere, they unscrewed the manhole and peered into the darkness of the interior (for the electric light chamber was intended to illuminate the water about the sphere, and was shut off entirely from its general cavity).

The air was very hot within the cavity, and the india-rubber at the lip of the manhole was soft. There was no answer to their eager questions and no sound of movement within.

Elstead seemed to be lying motionless, crumpled up in the bottom of the globe. The ship's doctor crawled in and lifted him out to the men outside. For a moment or so they did not know whether Elstead was alive or dead. His face, in the yellow light of the ship's lamps, glistened with perspiration. They carried him down to his own cabin.

He was not dead, they found, but in a state of absolute nervous collapse, and besides cruelly bruised. For some days he had to lie perfectly still. It was a week before he could tell his experiences.

Almost his first words were that he was going down again. The sphere would have to be altered, he said, in order to allow him to throw off the cord if need be, and that was all. He had had the most marvellous experience. 'You thought I should find nothing but ooze,' he said. 'You laughed at my explorations, and I've discovered a new world!' He told his story in disconnected fragments, and chiefly from the wrong end, so that it is impossible to re-tell it in his words. But what follows is the narrative of his experience.

It began atrociously, he said. Before the cord ran out the thing kept rolling over. He felt like a frog in a football. He could see nothing but the crane and the sky overhead, with an occasional glimpse of the people on the ship's rail. He couldn't tell a bit which way the thing would roll next. Suddenly he would find his feet going up, and try to step, and over he went rolling, head over heels, and just anyhow, on the padding. Any other shape would have been more comfortable, but no other shape was to be relied upon under the huge pressure of the nethermost abyss.

Suddenly the swaying ceased; the globe righted, and when he had picked himself up, he saw the water all about him greeny-blue, with an attenuated light filtering down from above, and a shoal of little floating things went rushing up past him, as it seemed to him, towards the light. And even

302

as he looked, it grew darker and darker, until the water above was as dark as the midnight sky, albeit of a greener shake, and the water below black. And little transparent things in the water developed a faint tint of luminosity, and shot past him in faint greenish streaks.

And the feeling of falling! It was just like the start of a lift, he said, only it kept on. One has to imagine what that means, that keeping on. It was then of all times that Elstead repented his adventure. He saw the chances against him in an altogether new light. He thought of the big cuttle-fish people knew to exist in the middle waters, the kind of things they find half digested in whales at times, or floating dead and rotten and half eaten by fish. Suppose one caught hold and wouldn't let go. And had the clockwork really been sufficiently tested? But whether he wanted to go on or to go back mattered not the slightest now.

In fifty seconds everything was as black as night outside, except where the beam from his light struck through the waters, and picked out every now and then some fish or scrap of sinking matter. They flashed by too fast for him to see what they were. Once he thinks he passed a shark. And then the sphere began to get hot by friction against the water. They had under-estimated this, it seems.

The first thing he noticed was that he was perspiring, and then he heard a hissing growing louder under his feet, and saw a lot of little bubbles — very little bubbles they were — rushing upward like a fan through the water outside. Steam! He felt the window and it was hot. He turned on the minute glow-lamp that lit his own cavity, looked at the padded watch by the studs, and saw he had been travelling now for two minutes. It came into his head that the window would crack through the conflict of temperatures, for he knew the bottom water is very near freezing.

Then suddenly the floor of the sphere seemed to press

against his feet, the rush of bubbles outside grew slower and slower, and the hissing diminished. The sphere rolled a little. The window had not cracked, nothing had given, and he knew that the dangers of sinking, at any rate, were over.

In another minute or so he would be on the floor of the abyss. He thought, he said, of Steevens and Weybridge and the rest of them five miles overhead, higher to him than the very highest clouds that ever floated over land are to us, steaming slowly and staring down and wondering what had happened to him.

He peered out of the window. There were no more bubbles now, and the hissing had stopped. Outside there was a heavy blackness — as black as black velvet — except where the electric light pierced the empty water and showed the colour of it — a yellow-green. Then three things like shapes of fire swam into sight, following each other through the water. Whether they were little and near or big and far off he could not tell.

Each was outlined in a bluish light almost as bright as the lights of a fishing smack, a light which seemed to be smoking greatly, and all along the sides of them were specks of this, like the lighter portholes of a ship. Their phosphorescence seemed to go out as they came within the radiance of his lamp, and he saw then that they were little fish of some strange sort, with huge heads, vast eyes, and dwindling bodies and tails. Their eyes were turned towards him, and he judged they were following him down. He supposed they were attracted by his glare.

Presently others of the same sort joined them. As he went on down, he noticed that the water became of a pallid colour, and that little specks twinkled in his ray like motes in a sunbeam. This was probably due to the clouds of ooze and mud that the impact of his leaden sinkers had disturbed.

By the time he was drawn down to the lead weights he was

304

in a dense fog of white that his electric light failed altogether to pierce for more than a few yards, and many minutes elapsed before the hanging sheets of sediment subsided to any extent. Then, lit by his light and by the transient phosphorescence of a distant shoal of fishes, he was able to see under the huge blackness of the superincumbent water an undulating expanse of greyish-white ooze, broken here and there by tangled thickets of a growth of sea lilies, waving hungry tentacles in the air.

Farther away were the graceful, translucent outlines of a group of gigantic sponges. About this floor there were scattered a number of bristling flattish tufts of rich purple and black, which he decided must be some sort of sea-urchin, and small, large-eyed or blind things having a curious resemblance, some to wood-lice, and others to lobsters, crawled sluggishly across the track of the light and vanished into the obscurity again, leaving furrowed trails behind them.

Then suddenly the hovering swarm of little fishes veered about and came towards him as a flight of starlings might do. They passed over him like a phosphorescent snow, and then he saw behind them some larger creature advancing towards the sphere.

At first he could see it only dimly, a faintly moving figure remotely suggestive of a walking man, and then it came into the spray of light that the lamp shot out. As the glare struck it, it shut its eyes, dazzled. He stared in rigid astonishment.

It was a strange vertebrated animal. Its dark purple head was dimly suggestive of a chameleon, but it had such a high forehead and such a braincase as no reptile ever displayed before; the vertical pitch of its face gave it a most extraordinary resemblance to a human being.

Two large and protruding eyes projected from sockets in chameleon fashion, and it had a broad reptilian mouth with hoary lips beneath its little nostrils. In the position of the ears were two huge gill-covers, and out of these floated a branching tree of coralline filaments, almost like the tree-like gills that very young rays and sharks possess.

But the humanity of the face was not the most extraordinary thing about the creature. It was a biped; its almost globular body was poised on a tripod of two frog-like legs and a long thick tail, and its fore limbs, which grotesquely caricatured the human hand, much as a frog's do, carried a long shaft of bone, tipped with copper. The colour of the creature was variegated; its head, hands, and legs were purple; but its skin, which hung loosely upon it, even as clothes might do, was a phosphorescent grey. And it stood there blinded by the light.

At last this unknown creature of the abyss blinked its eyes open, and, shading them with its disengaged hand, opened its mouth and gave vent to a shouting noise, articulate almost as speech might be, that penetrated even the steel case and padded jacket of the sphere. How a shouting may be accomplished without lungs Elstead does not profess to explain. It then moved sideways out of the glare into the mystery of shadow that bordered it on either side, and Elstead felt rather than saw it was coming towards him. Fancying the light had attracted it, he turned the switch that cut off the current. In another moment something soft dabbed upon the steel, and the globe swayed.

Then the shouting was repeated, and it seemed to him that a distant echo answered it. The dabbing recurred, and the globe swayed and ground against the spindle over which the wire was rolled. He stood in the blackness and peered out into the everlasting night of the abyss. And presently he saw, very faint and remote, other phosphorescent quasi-human forms hurrying towards him.

Hardly knowing what he did, he felt about in his swaying prison for the stud of the exterior electric light, and came by accident against his own small glow-lamp in its padded recess.

The sphere twisted, and then threw him down; he heard shouts like shouts of surprise, and when he rose to his feet, he saw two pairs of stalked eyes peering into the lower window and reflecting his light.

In another moment hands were dabbing vigorously at his steel casing, and there was a sound, horrible enough in his position, of the metal protection of the clockwork being vigorously hammered. That, indeed, sent his heart into his mouth, for if these strange creatures succeeded in stopping that, his release would never occur. Scarcely had he thought as much when he felt the sphere sway violently, and the floor of it press had against his feet. He turned off the small glow-lamp that lit the interior, and set the ray of the large light in the separate compartment out into the water. The sea-floor and the man-like creatures had disappeared, and a couple of fish chasing each other dropped suddenly by the window.

He thought at once that these strange denizens of the deep sea had broken the rope, and that he had escaped. He drove up faster and faster, and then stopped with a jerk that sent him flying against the padded roof of his prison. For half a minute, perhaps he was too astonished to think.

Then he felt that the sphere was spinning slowly, and rocking, and it seemed to him that it was also being drawn through the water. By crouching close to the window, he managed to make his weight effective and roll that part of the sphere downward, but he could see nothing save the pale ray of his light striking down ineffectively into the darkness. It occurred to him that he would see more if he turned the lamp off, and allowed his eyes to grow accustomed to the profound obscurity.

In this he was wise. After some minutes the velvety blackness became a translucent blackness, and then, far away, and as faint as the zodiacal light of an English summer evening, he saw shapes moving below. He judged these creatures had detached his cable, and were towing him along the sea bottom.

And then he saw something faint and remote across the undulations of the submarine plain, a broad horizon of pale luminosity that extended this way and that way as far as the range of his little window permitted him to see. To this he was being towed, as a balloon might be towed by men out of the open country into a town. He approached it very slowly, and very slowly the dim irradiation was gathered together into more definite shapes.

It was nearly five o'clock before he came over this luminous area, and by that time he could make out an arrangement suggestive of streets and houses grouped about a vast roofless erection that was grotesquely suggestive of a ruined abbey. It was spread out like a map below him. The houses were all roofless enclosures of walls, and their substance being, as he afterwards saw, of phosphorescent bones, gave the place an appearance as if it were built of drowned moonshine.

Among the inner caves of the place waving trees of crinoid stretched their tentacles, and tall, slender, glassy sponges shot like shining minarets and lilies of filmy light out of the general glow of the city. In the open spaces of the place he could see a stirring movement as of crowds of people, but he was too many fathoms above them to distinguish the individuals in those crowds.

Then slowly they pulled him down, and as they did so, the details of the place crept slowly upon his apprehension. He saw that the courses of the cloudy buildings were marked out with beaded lines of round objects, and then he perceived that at several points below him, in broad open spaces, were forms like the encrusted shapes of ships.

Slowly and surely he was drawn down, and the forms below him became brighter, clearer, more distinct. He was being pulled down, he perceived, towards the large building in the centre of the town, and he could catch a glimpse ever and again of the multitudinous forms that were lugging at his cord.

Slowly and surely they pulled him down into their world.

He was astonished to see that the rigging of one of the ships, which formed such a prominent feature of the place, was crowded with a host of gesticulating figures regarding him, and then the walls of the great building rose about him silently, and hid the city from his eyes.

And such walls they were, of water-logged wood, and twisted wire-rope, and iron spars, and copper, and the bones and skulls of dead men. The skulls ran in zigzag lines and spirals and fantastic curves over the building; and in and out of their eye-sockets, and over the whole surface of the place, lurked and played a multitude of silvery little fishes.

Suddenly his ears were filled with a low shouting and a noise like the violent blowing of horns, and this gave place to a fantastic chant. Down the sphere sank, past the huge pointed windows, through which he saw vaguely a great number of these strange, ghostlike people regarding him, and at last he came to rest, as it seemed, on a kind of altar that stood in the centre of the place.

And now he was at such a level that he could see these strange people of the abyss plainly once more. To his astonishment, he perceived that they were prostrating themselves before him, all save one, dressed as it seemed in a robe of placoid scales, and crowned with a luminous diadem, who stood with his reptilian mouth opening and shutting, as though he led the chanting of the worshippers.

A curious impulse made Elstead turn on his small globe-lamp again, so that he became visible to these creatures of the abyss, albeit the glare made them disappear forthwith into night. At this sudden sight of him, the chanting gave place to a tumult of exultant shouts; and Elstead, being anxious to watch them, turned his light off again, and vanished from before their eyes. But for a time he was too blind to make out what they were doing, and when at last he could distinguish them, they were kneeling again. And thus they continued worshipping him, without rest or intermission, for a space of three hours.

Most circumstantial was Elstead's account of this astounding city and its people, these people of perpetual night, who have never seen sun or moon or stars, green vegetation, nor any living, air-breathing creatures who know nothing of fire, nor any light but the phosphorescent light of living things.

Startling as is his story, it is yet more startling to find that scientific men, of such eminence as Adams and Jenkins, find nothing incredible in it. They tell me they see no reason why intelligent, water-breathing, vertebrated creatures, inured to a low temperature and enormous pressure, and of such a heavy structure, that neither alive nor dead would they float, might not live upon the bottom of the deep sea, and quite unsuspected by us, descendants like ourselves of the great Theriomorpha of the New Red Sandstone age.

We should be known to them, however, as strange meteoric creatures, wont to fall catastrophically dead out of the mysterious blackness of their watery sky. And not only we ourselves, but our ships, our metals, our appliances, would come raining down out of the night. Sometimes sinking things would smite down and crush them, as if it were the judgment of some unseen power above, and sometimes would come things of the utmost rarity or utility, or shapes of inspiring suggestion. One can understand, perhaps, something of their behaviour at the descent of a living man, if one thinks what a barbaric people might do, to whom an enhaloed, shining creature came suddenly out of the sky.

At one time or another Elstead probably told the officers of the *Ptarmigan* every detail of his strange twelve hours in the abyss. That he also intended to write them down is certain, but he never did, and so we have to piece together the discrepant fragments of his story from the reminiscences of Commander Simmons, Weybridge, Steevens, Lindley and the others.

We see the thing darkly in fragmentary glimpses — the huge ghostly building, the bowing, chanting people, with their dark chameleon-like heads and faintly luminous clothing, and Elstead, with his light turned on again, vainly trying to convey to their minds that the cord by which the sphere was held was to be severed. Minute after minute slipped away, and Elstead looking at his watch, was horrified to find that he had oxygen only for four hours more. But the chant in his honour kept on as remorselessly as if it was the marching song of his approaching death.

The manner of his release he does not understand, but to judge by the end of cord that hung from the sphere, it had been cut through by rubbing against the edge of the altar. Abruptly the sphere rolled over, and he swept up, out of their world, as an ethereal creature clothed in a vacuum would sweep through our own atmosphere back to its native ether again. He must have torn out of their sight as a hydrogen bubble hastens upward from our air. A strange ascension it must have seemed to them.

The sphere rushed up with even greater velocity than, when weighted with the lead sinkers, it had rushed down. It became exceedingly hot. It drove up with the windows uppermost, and he remembers the torrent of bubbles frothing against the glass. Every moment he expected this to fly. Then suddenly something like a huge wheel seemed to be released in his head, the padded compartment began spinning about him, and he fainted. His next recollection was of his cabin, and of the doctor's voice.

But that is the substance of the extraordinary story that Elstead related in fragments to the officers of the *Ptarmigan*. He promised to write it all down at a later date. His mind was chiefly occupied with the improvement of his apparatus, which was effected at Rio.

It remains only to tell that on February 2, 1896, he made his second descent into the ocean abyss, with the improvements his first experience suggested. What happened we shall probably never know. He never returned. The *Ptarmigan* beat about over the point of his submersion, seeking him in vain for thirteen days. Then she returned to Rio, and the news was telegraphed to his friends. So the matter remains for the present. But it is hardly probable that no further attempt will be made to verify his strange story of these hitherto unsuspected cities of the deep sea.

Laffey *and the Kamikazes*

by
COMMANDER JOHN KERANS D. S. O., R. N.

When the radar operator's urgent voice called out: 'Kamikazes — too many to count — coming in fast!' Commander Frederick Becton of the destroyer U. S. S. *Laffey* knew he and his men were in for a tough time.

The date was 16 April, 1945, and the place fifty miles north of the Japanese fortress island of Okinawa. Since 1 April the 10th U. S. Army, with massive fleet support, had been engaged in a desperate assault on Okinawa. From the bitterness of the Japs' resistance it was obvious this was going to be the most murderous battle of all the Pacific islands' campaign. The enemy were fully aware once Okinawa was captured the Americans would have a base only 325 miles from the Japanese mainland.

That the fanaticism already widespread among the Japanese fighting men flamed even more ferociously when their homeland was threatened with invasion, was already terribly apparent. The cult of the Kamikaze — the young men who gloried in sacrificing themselves in suicide attacks — was at its peak. Kamikaze pilots were diving their bomb-loaded planes squarely on to warships, supply ships and troop transports; suicide swimmers and boatmen were ramming contact-detonated high-explosive against ships; shore soldiers crouched in fox holes, clutching big bombs which they detonated when tanks or armoured carriers passed over them. At Okinawa

314

there were more Jap suicide attacks made by land, sea and air than any other battlefield.

The reason why the U. S. S. *Laffey* was where she was, at station Roger Peter One, on this calm sunny April morning, was because she was operating as a radar picket ship to give warning of approaching Kamikazes. She was in fact, the forward picket ship, nearly one hundred miles closer to Japan than the main force attacking Okinawa. Inevitably she would be the first of the hated enemy the Japs would see as they flew out on their desperate one-way missions. And now the first wave was approaching: 'Range 17,000 — still coming fast and impossible to count!' called the breathless voice of the radar operator.

Commander Becton, a quietly-spoken, intense man who became suddenly dynamic when action was required, sounded the general alarm. Down the voice pipe to the Chief Engineer he called for speed: 'Henke we want every turn you've got!' Although the *Laffey* had not been attacked or in action yet, her men had a good idea what happened when the Kamikazes came. In the Hagushi anchorage of Okinawa, seized in the opening assault and now thronged with the multitude of vessels of the invading force, there had been many victims of the power-diving suicide planes. Contorted metal, gaping holes in decks, smouldering wreckage, gruesome remains of what had been men and already ashore a cemetery which daily expanded... All was grim testimony to the fact that many a Jap pilot had taken far more than one enemy with him when he died. While the *Laffey* was briefly in that graveyard anchorage being equipped with the complicated radar installation of an early-warning ship, they had been tersely advised by a gun captain from a battle-scarred destroyer: 'You guys will have a fighting chance — you'll knock a lot of them down and you'll think you're doing fine but they'll just keep on coming until one of them gets you!'

The *Laffey*, a powerfully-gunned destroyer of 2,200 tons, had been on extreme forward duty exactly twenty-four hours when the scanning radar first registered the swarming cluster of blips. The seas were calm, so that she gently rocked as she cruised beneath a sky smiling and blue by day and soft star-spangled velvet by night. Pacific seemed the right name for this ocean and there was nothing to indicate it would be different until the threshing propellers churned up the bloated body of a Jap pilot and the charred wreckage of his plane.

Now the lean, grey destroyer was a-shudder with the pulse of her engines as the men below responded to the orders for full speed. Still the wide blue heavens were innocent of anything at all that could be deemed hostile. High-powered glasses on the bridge intently scanning the sky to the north, searched for something that at first would look like a swarm of gnats. Although still invisible to the naked eye, the approaching Kamikazes were coming up bigger and bigger on the radar screen. Then: 'Seem to be opening out — but they're still coming on!' came the operator's report.

That Jap suicide planes were heading her way did not necessarily mean the *Laffey* was their target. It was more likely they had been ordered to crash with their bomb-loads on to the decks of the huge American aircraft carriers which were playing such a great part in the island-hopping advance on Japan. Other priority targets would be the battleships, cruisers and big transports whose destruction must bring death to large numbers of Americans. 'Most likely they'll go over us,' suggested one of the *Laffey's* officers. 'Maybe they will get shot down by our combat air patrols before they can do any damage.' But Lieutenant Challen McCune, the Executive Officer, reported that the American fighter patrol was at the moment being relieved; it would be some little time before the relieving fighters could get to the area.

Suddenly Captain Becton's binoculars picked out the Jap

The planes dived to certain death for the destruction of their enemies.

planes! 'Bogies ahead — coming fast!' a sailor shouted from the look-out platform at that moment. The Kamikazes were coming! (Afterwards the survivors learned there were no fewer than 165 Jap suicide planes in that approaching cloud!) 'Lieutenant Smith requests permission to fire;' came in excited tones from the forward five-inch guns. 'Fire when ready!' rapped the Captain. The murmur of the approaching enemy could now be heard; with each second it swelled until it was an angry hornet-like drone. Suddenly the forward guns belched fire and smoke. The whole ship shuddered. 'Hard left rudder! All guns commence fire!' roared Captain Becton. And the azure morning erupted into one vast bellowing, flaming inferno.

The roar of the *Laffey*'s big guns was joined by insistent throbbing from forty millimetre guns and pulsing whip-cracks from twenty millimetre cannons. The sky ahead was full of Jap planes. Crackling smoke puffs of the destroyer's first salvo were planted blackly in their path. Then four Aichi Ninety-nine dive bombers peeled off and power-dived at the *Laffey*. Engines bellowing they hurtled down, down, down like thunderbolts, two at the bows and two at the stern. Their fanatical pilots were giving every atom of engine power, every taut, strained fibre of their own dedicated beings. They dived to certain death for the destruction of their enemies.

A stream of smoke whirled back from one of the bombers forward. Suddenly it was a fire-streaked comet plunging straight into the sea. The five-inch guns had claimed their first victim. The water still frothed where it had vanished when the other bomber diving at the bows lurched, cartwheeled dramatically, shattered into fragments as it struck the sea. All around and above her now the *Laffey* was surrounded by the black smoke of her bursting shells. Then the red and white tracer streams of her close-range automatic weapons leaped out and up. Abruptly a billow of smoke and flame aft told the

318

ending of another of the attackers: shells from No. 3 turret had destroyed it. The tail of the fourth was spectacularly whipped away by a cannon-shell stream; it disintegrated in mid-air and was gone. Momentarily man looked at man in speechless wonderment at what they had done — then the next attack was coming in.

Two Kamikaze bombers streaked in headlong, then parted and peeled off left and right for flank attacks. Boiling the sea into foam behind her, flinging out great spumes of white water forward, the *Laffey* heeled to port and then to starboard as she dodged and weaved. One Jap plane tearing in at 2,000 yards range was suddenly the centre of shell bursts and criss-cross tracer streams. It had its wings torn off in mid-air, and a great water spout climbed up where it vanished into the sea. The Kamikaze on the other side twisted frantically, got within fifty yards, then was caught by a salvo of the destroyer's big guns which blew it apart. Although the pilot was dead the big bomb he had intended to take with him to his death on the *Laffey's* deck tumbled from the smoke cloud and burst alongside. The ship lurched violently at the concussion, her nearest escape yet, but although men were flung down none was wounded.

'God! How long can our luck hold!' gasped a gunner. The men of the Laffey were well aware that most of the savagely-torn ships they had seen in Hagushi Bay had each been victim of no more than one Kamikaze. Yet already the *Laffey* had survived six separate attacks and destroyed the attackers. The roar above them now was deafening; the Kamikaze swarm seemed to be milling round waiting to take it in turns to dive bomb. Surely there could be no hope of surviving if the Kamikazes did not press on to other targets?

'Hard right!' By both voice and gesture Commander Becton gave the order urgently. Another Jap bomber was coming, skimming the sea on the port bow. The destroyer keeled over,

319

steeper and steeper, until the frothing sea surged along her slanting deck, until she was round with the Kamikaze howling over her stern instead of attacking her broadside. The pilot missed his death crash but barely clipped the top of one of the five-inch guns and killed one of the crew instantly. The *Laffey* had suffered her first casualty. The ensuing lull was just long enough for the dead man to be dragged away, and hasty repairs to be made to the broken signal wires, then the eighth Kamikaze was coming at them.

This Jap torpedo bomber also dodged in at sea level, on the starboard beam. But a deadly concentration of tracer fastened on to it, its fuel tank exploded and it was a funeral pyre rushing toward them. Then the whole thing disintegrated and vanished, leaving only a sinister patch on the sea. Without any respite the ninth attacker screamed down. Down, down, down it plunged then zoomed in a short shattering climb, levelled out, and was at them. Every gun that the twisting, turning *Laffey* could bring to bear thundered and cracked and rattled, but to no avail. As he hurtled towards the thunderous death he had chosen the Kamikaze pilot bore a charmed life. Some men who glimpsed his face in the last split seconds swore it had a set, dedicated look, as though he were already not of this world; which he wasn't an instant later, when the plane smashed into the destroyer amongst a nest of guns amidship. With a horrible 'whoof' a great tower of smoke and flame boiled up from the destroyer. 'Fire amidships!' the dread call went out. 'Damage control and fire fighting parties needed topside on the double!'

With this pillar of smoke and fire standing up from the ocean to make the *Laffey* a target that could be seen for miles, the Jap suicide pilots were spurred to an absolute frenzy. Despite all the variety of targets beyond at Okinawa, all the great warships and transport whose destruction was so vital to the Japanese soldiers fanatically defending the island, the Kami-

320

kaze pilots seemed obsessed with a desire to obliterate this one American destroyer. Perhaps it was because this warship was the closest enemy to their homeland, perhaps it was the unreasoning inflexibility which so often caused the Japs to squander fighting men on comparatively unimportant outposts which they should have by-passed. Whatever it was, the blind, furious persistance with which the Kamikazes kept attacking the *Laffey* undoubtedly saved countless American lives at Okinawa.

Weaving and writhing through the sea like a living thing in extreme pain, the destroyer was now amidst a swarm of plunging Japanese warplanes piloted by fanatics seeking death and glory. Fortunately there were still sufficient guns working, and men to serve them, to put up a formidable curtain of exploding steel. But the tenth Kamikaze also got home, and even more devastatingly than the previous one. Wave-hopping and jinking it burst through the fire curtain and crashed terrifyingly on to the after five-inch gun mounting. Almost immediately an eleventh, hot on its heels, shattered down on to almost exactly the same place. A huge billow of flame, like sudden engulfment by a prairie fire, enveloped the destroyer from end to end. One complete side of the turret had been blown out, great holes gaped in the main deck, and flaming fuel spewed through into the living space below. The *Laffey* shuddered as though in her death throes as the forty millimetre ammunition magazine took fire and shells began to explode deep down within her, blowing men there to bits.

As though that were not enough yet another attacker, the twelfth, glided in silently on the portside, masked by the billowing smoke. He dropped a bomb near the stern and it tore through the ship's side, exploded in a machine gun magazine and jammed the rudder. Listing, blazing, crippled, the *Laffey* could now only circle on the one course. She was an absolute-sitting target. In the inferno below a damage control party

321

worked heroically. Dr Mathew Darnell, Jnr, the ship's M.O., plucked live ammunition from amidst red hot metal and tossed it overboard. Commander Becton, still in complete control of an almost indescribably desperate situation, kept the destroyer flat out on its jammed circular course.

The thirteenth Kamikaze plunged down with the fourteenth hot on its tail. They crashed on to the after deckhouse almost simultaneously. The terrifying impact coupled with the shattering explosion of the bombs nearly power-punched the *Laffey* beneath the sea. But she rode up again, with yet another terrible fire adding to her shroud of black smoke and leaping flames. High-octane fuel released by the smashing of watertight hatches added to the roaring conflagration.

A brave attempt was now made by Lieutenant Ted Runk and three enlisted men to repair the damaged steering. They fought their way through smoke and flame without breathing masks and struggled to clear the rudder. But the flames were licking closer all the time and they were forced back. On their way out they walked straight into an unexploded Japanese bomb ringed by flames and quickly rolled it overboard. Meanwhile, on a wrecked forty millimetre gun aft with flames leaping around him, Lieutenant Joe Youngquist tossed live hot ammunition into the sea.

The attacking Jap bombers could now only be glimpsed through rifts in the pall of smoke that enveloped the destroyer. Suddenly the fifteenth Kamikaze was plunging down upon them, but as they saw it they saw also there was a Corsair fighter of the U. S. Navy tearing after it with guns blazing. The *Laffey's* forward machine guns opened up on the Jap and at the last minute its nose lifted and it howled over the ship instead of on to it, just clipping the radar mast. Seconds later it disintegrated, struck by a concentration of fire. The Corsair could not pull out and also hit the radar mast, rolled over as it zoomed, and the pilot bailed out.

Yet another Kamikaze roared in, this time to port, again with a Corsair hammering away on its tail. It burst into flames before reaching the destroyer but dropped a bomb which burst so close that splinters struck down some of the gunners still tirelessly serving the now nearly red hot forty-millimetre and twenty-millimetre guns. It also destroyed the communications to the two five-inch guns still in action. The fate of the seventeenth Kamikaze proved that the destruction of communications had not put these guns out of action. One of them, now manually trained, blasted the Jap suicide plane out of the sky as it came in head on.

The next two Kamikazes to attack were just too easy to be true. They were two Nakajima army fighters fitted out with bombs. The destroyer's remaining big guns just blasted them out of the sky — one — two — at long range. But the twentieth suicide bomber was far more formidable. Dropping down from a steep glide out of the sun, it twisted and turned to present the most difficult target possible, then opened up its engine and howled down upon the ship. But yet again a Corsair came swooping in with all guns blazing, braving the curtain of fire put up by the destroyer's guns. Shots ripped the Jap plane from above and below as it thundered over, so close as to clip off the one remaining yardarm. It plummeted into the water just beyond the *Laffey's* stern. Still the Kamikazes came! And still the half-sunken destroyer fought back! The twenty-first Jap bomber was blasted out of the sky by the forward five-inch guns and the last remaining forty-millimetre gun. The twenty-second howled in through a hail of shell-fire and machine-gun bullets, then abruptly reeled, spun and disintegrated in a great puff of smoke.

Then suddenly all the brave men aboard the *Laffey* who still could listen stood stock still. Their eyes and ears strained out and upwards towards a new sound that was filling the sky. It was a crescendo of engine song of a great number of diving warplanes, pitched in a key they recognised as American. At last the combat air patrol had arrived! Squadrons of Marine-piloted Corsair fighters hurtled upon the milling Kamikazes. Now the *Laffey* plunged clear of her smoke shroud — and high above her could be seen the downrush of the attacking fighters and the twisting flaming downfall of their victims. It was as though a band of shining angels had suddenly rescued them from the hell that enveloped them. For a moment the men stood in bewilderment, as though they could hardly comprehend that they were going to live after all. Then cheer after cheer rose from the destroyer and the bloodstained, sweat-stained, smoke-blackened men shouted exultingly: 'Get the bastards! — Rip 'em up! — Give 'em hell!'

A great silence descended upon the Pacific Ocean fifty miles north of Okinawa. The crippled, heroic *Laffey* wallowed there amidst the wreckage of the unbelievable battle through which she had just fought. For seventy-nine minutes non-stop she had been subjected to relentless Kamikaze attacks, no fewer than twenty-two of them pressed right home. Yet still she was afloat, still prepared to fight on. She had lost thirty-one killed, seventy-two wounded and was a mass of tortured, smoking wreckage, but she was still indomitable.

Early that afternoon another warship steamed up, warned of the *Laffey's* condition by the figher pilots who had terminated the battle. She took the gallant destroyer in tow, back to Hagushi Bay. In that harbour of Kamikaze victims the *Laffey* caused wonderment and admiration, for the minds of men who had experienced the terror of suicide bombers boggled at the thought of the *Laffey's* twenty-two attacks and could not imagine how she had still fought on and lived to tell the tale.

In due course the destroyer was patched up at Pearl Harbor, then moved back to be rebuilt in the great Todd shipyards at San Francisco. While there she was for five days put on display so that the American people could appreciate what their sailors had to face from the Kamikaze suicide attacks. Commander Frederick Becton — who is now Rear Admiral Becton — was awarded the Navy Cross for his great heroism and devotion to duty. Many said he should have received America's highest award for valour, the Congressional Medal.

It is of interest to record that Captain Frank Manson, one of the *Laffey's* surviving officers, is now known the world over as the man who thought up the idea of the Great White Fleet. This project envisages a 'mercy task force' of obsolete warships and other vessels not in use to take aid anywhere in the world that disease, hunger and disaster requires it. Britain's own bomber hero Group Captain Leonard Cheshire, V. C., is associated with Manson in this. The American officer was obsessed with the idea after becoming convinced of the futility of the slaughter he had witnessed. He determined that warships 'in their retirement' should be used to alleviate some of the world's misery, particularly in South-east Asia, of which he had experience.

You'll Never Make a Sailor

by

ROBERT BATEMAN

This was the best moment of the day, Bill Jory thought as he scrambled up the ladder to the bridge of the 'Tahiti Star', hanging on with one hand while with the other he carried three steaming hot mugs of coffee. His fingers were jammed tightly through the handles of the thick mugs, and he held them out beyond the rail of the ladder, so that if the 'Tahiti Star' gave a sudden lurch in a high sea there was no risk of being half-drowned in hot coffee.

It was the best moment because up high on the bridge he could watch the bows rise up on the huge Atlantic waves and then drop down, down, down into the troughs that followed. Salt spray whipped up as the bows crashed into the seas cascading over the foredeck.

'Hello, Bill, there you are! Is that my coffee? Good lad.'

The Second Mate, Harry Rawston, was broad as a barn door, red-faced, and at least a foot taller than Bill. Ever since the start of the trip he had been leg-pulling about Bill's small size. But at least it *was* leg-pulling. Even though it was his first voyage, even though for a week he had been too seasick to work, everybody from Captain Fallon downwards had told him, 'Never mind. You'll make a good sailor.'

Bill opened the wheelhouse door and fought his way inside as the 'Tahiti Star' rolled and made the deck into a steep hill.

'Brought my coffee?' Captain Fallon grinned at him.

'Thanks, Bill. You haven't spilled it. That's pretty good — it's blowing up rough.' As he spoke, the 'Tahiti Star' plunged between two waves, and Bill had to grab a stanchion in order not to be flung straight at him.

'Better give the helmsman his coffee before you drop it,' the Captain laughed.

Still hanging on to the stanchion, Bill reached out and handed over the coffee.

Suddenly the door in the back of the wheelhouse swung open. Captain Fallon turned his head. 'Hello, Sparks, what's the matter?'

The Radio Officer held out a scrap of paper. 'Ship in distress, sir. I've just picked up this S. O. S. message. She's about thirty miles ahead of us, I reckon, just off the Irish coast.'

The Captain glanced at the piece of paper. 'Bill, ask the Second Mate to come in here, will you?'

'Aye, aye, sir.' Bill opened the wheelhouse door, chose his moment when the ship was on an even keel, and went out to the wing of the bridge. Harry Rawston was crouching behind the canvas weatherscreen with his sextant raised to his eyes, trying to take a bearing to work out the ship's position. Bill clutched the bridge rail and hung on tight, waiting for him to finish. Then he said, 'There's a ship in trouble, Mr Rawston. Captain Fallon wants you in the wheelhouse.'

He hoped to be able to go in again and hear what was said, but the Second Mate shook his head. 'Sorry, Bill, you'd be in the way. And you've got your own work to do, haven't you?'

That made Bill jump to the ladder. He had forgotten about the six other mugs of coffee on the tray in the steward's pantry. Dodging as a heavy sea smashed its way up on to the boat deck, he went down below and took coffee to the First and Third Mates and the Engineers.

327

Then he was free for an hour. He stood on deck, braced against the 'midships cargo hatch, and looked at the rough sea to starboard.

'You'll never make a sailor.'

That was what he had heard at home ever since he was eight years old. His father, tough and leathery after twenty years as bo'sun of the old *Corymer*, would come home on leave and look at him scornfully. 'What's up with the boy, mother? Looks like a midget to me. Better get him a good safe shore job. He'll *never* make a sailor.'

But here he was, on the way home after his first Atlantic crossing. All right — so he was small. But he'd show his father — he'd make his father admit that he, too, could be tough enough for a lifetime on cargo ships in the rough north Atlantic.

'Bill!'

He looked up towards the bridge. The Second Mate was beckoning to him, so he raced up the ladders, halting only once when the *Tahiti Star* rolled so far to starboard that if he had not clung on rightly with both hands he would have been swept over the side. Below him, on the midships deck he had just left, a giant wave crashed through the rails, roared over the hatchtop with a welter of white foam, and caught the Steward, soaking him to the waist.

Bill reached the top of the ladder. 'Yes, sir?'

'Bill, tell the Steward to get out extra bedding. Get the galley to make up a big pan of hot soup. We may have two boatloads of cold and hungry survivors.'

'What ship is she, sir?'

'Oh just another old tramp ship like this one. Her name's the *Corymer*.'

Bill froze at the head of the ladder.

'What's the matter, boy?'

'That's my father's ship, sir.'

Harry Rawston looked at him sharply. 'You're sure of that?' Bill nodded. 'Dead sure, sir. He's been bo'sun on the *Corymer* for years.' He swallowed. 'Sir, what's happened to the '*Corymer*'? Is she sinking?'

The Second Mate braced himself against the bridge rail as the *Tahiti Star* nose-dived between waves. Bill looked down as water seemed for a moment to be clmbing the ladder below him. He stared at it, thinking differently about it now. Up to now the gale and the huge white-crested waves had been exciting; now he saw them as a menace. He glanced across to the boat deck. The lifeboats looked small and frail. He tried to imagine them packed with men, battling to keep afloat, struggling not to be swamped by every wave. He thought of his father, and shivered.

'We don't know whether she's sinking,' said the Second Mate. 'She hit an underwater wreck.'

Bill looked at him wildly. 'Don't we know any more than that?'

He saw that the Second Mate was looking at him, as if weighing him up. 'I suppose you'd better know the truth,' said Harry Rawston. 'We've only had one message from the *Corymer*.'

'But why haven't they gone on sending signals?'

The Second Mate drew in his breath. 'She's carrying iron ore.'

'I don't understand, sir.'

'Iron ore's one of the heaviest cargoes a ship ever carries, Bill. When an ore-ship gets a hole in her, she goes down... well, pretty fast.'

Bill felt cold panic inside him. 'How long?'

'It could be only two or three minutes. Just long enough to get the boats away.' He paused for a moment. 'When we pick them up they'll need that hot soup and the warm bunks. Better get on your way and see the Steward.

'Aye, aye, sir.'

Bill went down to the 'midships deck in a daze.

If it had been any other ship it would have been different. But the very idea of the *Corymer* going down seemed impossible. For as long as he could remember, his father had been crossing the Atlantic aboard her. 'Tough old tub,' his father had said. 'They really knew *how* to build ships in the old days when she came out of the yards. An iceberg couldn't sink her.'

Suddenly the steady throb of the *Tahiti Star's* engines speeded up. The whole ship vibrated as she hurled herself at the seas, breaking a passage through them, but pitching fore and aft so steeply that Bill went slithering along the deck to fetch up with a crash against the galley door, making the steel plating ring like a gong.

The door opened, and the Steward put his head out. Bill gave him the message.

Then he went back to the bridge ladder. Up aloft, the First Mate had now joined Captain Fallon and Harry Rawston. He was wedged tightly in the starboard wing of the bridge, peering out across the crests of the giant waves.

It was now three hours since the S. O. S. message. If the *Tahiti Star* had been doing her usual eight knots, then by now she must be only a few miles from the *Corymer* — if the *Corymer* was still afloat. But remembering what Rawston had said, Bill realised the First Mate wasn't searching for the ship.

He was searching for tiny black specks rising high on each mountainous wave, then dropping with sickening force into the trough while the drenched, half frozen men aboard struggled to bale out the water.

He was searching for lifeboats.

Bill had an excuse to go back on the bridge. He went up the ladders, and into the chartroom behind the wheelhouse, where the Second Mate was bending over a chart with a ruler and pencil.

'Sir, the Steward said to tell you there's enough hot soup for forty men, and solid food to follow.'

Harry Rawston did not look up. 'Good lad, What about bedding?'

'He can't manage enough for forty, sir, but he's found enough blankets for twenty.'

The Second Mate straightened himself up. 'Then the rest of them will have to use our bunks. They'll need 'em more than we shall.' He glanced through the porthole. 'We should be sighting something any time now. Don't worry, Bill — we'll have your father safe aboard in an hour or two.'

Bill swallowed hard.

It was funny, he thought. His father was tough. They'd had rows — plenty of them. He still felt angry whenever he thought of those sarcastic words, 'You'll never make a sailor.' It was only now, when there was danger, that he realised how much he cared about his father.

The shout from outside on the bridge came suddenly. 'Boat on the port quarter!'

Before Bill could move, Harry Rawston had leaped past him, throwing the cartroom door opened. The wind screamed in, lifting charts from the table and scattering them across the floor. Bill dashed out after the Second Mate, and joined him on the port wing of the bridge.

At first he could see nothing. The gale was now so fierce that stinging spray slammed into his face like a rainstorm the moment he raised it above the weathershield. Ahead, the sea was a vast boiling mass of white foam.

His heart sank. Surely lifeboats could not stay afloat in that wilderness?

Shielding his eyes with his hands, he strained to pick out the dark outlines of boats against the background of churning water.

The Second Mate shouted to the helmsman, and down below, near the engine room, the steering engine clanked busily, swinging the bows of the *Tahiti Star* to port.

Immediately, with the seas no longer dead ahead, the ship lurched violently as a giant wave hit her starboard flank. Hundreds of tons of water swept across the decks, tearing away tarpaulin hatch covers. Just forward of the bridge one of the off-duty sailors, darting to his tea in the forecastle, was caught and thrown against the rail. He stood, holding on, pinned to it by the terrific force of rushing water, with only his head visible. Then, as the sea fell away, he clambered to safety.

The Second Mate was beside Bill. 'Quick, boy, get below and warn the Steward and the Engineers. Secure everything. This is going to be rough!'

Bill was half way down the ladder when the next wave struck. He saw it climb towards him at tremendous speed as the whole port side of the *Tahiti Star* disappeared beneath it. Then, icy cold, it was on him like an avalanche, sweeping his legs from under him so that he hung outwards from the ladder with only the ocean below him, and his hands taking his full weight.

For what seemed hours the *Tahiti Star* lay on her beam ends. Bill's wrists ached with the agony of holding on. Then, terribly slowly and with a groan of strained metal, she righted herself, and he swung back to regain a foothold on the ladder.

Water was streaming off him, but Bill grinned. 'Huh!' he said softly to himself. 'So you'll never make a sailor?'

And then, only a few hundred yards away, he saw the boats. Only they were not boats — just rafts, each with black dots of heads around them, the heads of men clinging desperately to the safety ropes as they struggled not to be torn away by each wave. As he looked, a raft rose high on the crest of a wave, then dropped like a stone into what seemed like a bottomless trough beyond. Before he could see what happened to it, another great sea struck the *Tahiti Star*, and once again he had to cling on as she was flung over on her side by a thundering torrent of water. This time his head went under, for he was lower down the ladder. He held his breath to keep his lungs from filling with water, then, as the wave fell away, he scrambled down to the deck and raced along the rail. No use now to pass on the Second Mate's orders — if they hadn't been carried out already, it was too late. Everything that could move would have moved. That giant pan of hot soup would have raced the full length of the galley stove, then raced back again, with the cook darting out of the way as it chased him. Every loose cup and saucer aboard would have been smashed.

No, he knew what he was doing. There was only one way of saving the men on the rafts, and that was by managing to lower the port lifeboat in one of the gaps between the great seas.

And when they did that, he intended to be aboard.

He looked over his shoulder as he reached the narrow iron ladder to the boat deck, but nobody was watching him. Nobody had any time at a moment like this except for the job of keeping the *Tahiti Star* from turning turtle in the next big sea.

He was up the ladder just in time to miss another battle with a giant wave. From behind him came a crash; looking back he saw the galley door fly open and the cook come racing out, grabbing at the door handle just in time to avoid being swept over the rail into the water.

Then Bill was beside the lifeboat, heaving at the lines holding the tarpaulin cover. He loosened them just enough to be able to wriggle over the gunwale into the boat, and then, as he heard shouts and the tramp of feet on the boat deck, he scrambled under the loose cover of the engine.

There was more shouting, then bangs like pistol shots when men pulled off the tarpaulin cover and the wind caught it, beating it out of their hands with savage force.

The boat jerked upwards as it was swung out on the davits. Somebody crashed into the side of the engine cover only inches away from Bill. The boat rocked wildly as the *Tahiti Star* lurched in another big wave, and then, when once again she was on her beam ends, there was a shout from the Second Mate and a rattle of pulleys. Down went the lifeboat, so fast that Bill's stomach seemed to come up into his throat.

Men piled into the boat. 'Cast off!' yelled the Second Mate.

And then the engine cover was ripped away.

Bill straightened up.

The Second Mate stared at him in astonishment. 'What are you doing here, Bill? Get back aboard.'

But as they looked up at the rusty, heaving flank of the *Tahiti Star* they both knew it was impossible. The Second Mate looked angry for a moment, then he smiled grimly. 'All right, Bill. I understand. Get in the stern and keep down low.'

The petrol engine burst into life. The Second Mate swung the tiller, bringing the lifeboat round in a tight curve as the *Tahiti Star* came back from her steep roll. For a horrible moment, perched high on a wave the lifeboat seemed to hang above the ship, threatening to slide down and crash on the midships hatch, then the pull of the little engine dragged her away from the brink and out of danger.

'There they are!' somebody shouted, pointing to a spot dead ahead.

The raft at which he was pointing was very low in the water, weighed down by at least twenty men clinging to the safety ropes. One of them raised his arm and waved it feebly.

'Engine dead slow,' shouted the Second Mate.

The fast roar of the petrol engine slowed to a grumbling

murmur, speeding up only as each wave lifted the lifeboat and took the propeller high out of the water. A wave carried them up and up, until they towered above the raft, then, with superb steering, the Second Mate brought the boat sliding down the flank of the wave, with her gunwale just above the water, to a point only six feet from the raft.

Now, as Bill could see, was the most dangerous moment. The exhausted men had to cross the six feet of heaving water to the safety ropes of the lifeboat before the next wave slammed their heavy raft into the wooden sides of the boat.

Six of them made it, grabbing frantically at the safety ropes, then gasping with relief as the boat's crew reached down and hauled them aboard.

That left fourteen — and no chance for any of them to make another move. From the direction of the *Tahiti Star* another giant wave began to life the lifeboat once again. Bill hung on beside the Second Mate as the lifeboat rose higher and higher, canting over steeply until her crew flung themselves like yachtsmen to the other side. Even their combined weight had hardly any effect. The Second Mate reached down, wrenched open a locker door, and flung out three bailing tins. Bill grabbed one of them and began scooping water out of the bottom of the boat. As he did so he could see the raft down at the bottom of what looked like an immense pit, but rising rapidly to meet them.

It came up only three feet away, and stayed there, just long enough for the remaining men to leap across to the safety ropes. Then, as the raft began drifting away, they were dragged aboard. Anxiously Bill looked at every face, but there was none with that familiar quarter inch of stubble, none with the heavy eyebrows and the huge square chin.

His father must be on the second raft.

The lifeboat's engine picked up speed again, and the bows slammed hard into a heavy sea. Harry Rawston brought her round full circle, judging his turn cleverly to avoid being caught broadside on by the next wave.

The second raft was no more than a hundred yards away, but to Bill it seemed like ten miles as the boat crept up towards it, changing course every few seconds to dodge being swamped. The Second Mate squatted at the tiller, his eyes on every movement of the seas, watching for treacherous waves that could catch them on the flank.

Bill caught only one glimpse of the raft until they were almost alongside. Then, without warning, it rose up ahead of them on a wave, and tobogganed down at them — half a ton of timber and metal buoyancy tanks. Yelling, men let go of the safety ropes and flung themselves clear to avoid being crushed as the raft hit the boat.

The crash came with a rending, tearing shock that sent Bill flying over the stern, hanging on by one hand while he fought to keep his feet from being hit by the spinning propeller. He heaved himself back aboard, and grabbed the tiller from the Second Mate, who was crouched forward with his hands half covering a wound on his face. In the bows, water was pouring in through a ragged hole torn by the raft, and men came stumbling into the stern of the boat to weigh it down and lift the hole above water level.

Two men flung from the raft thrust their hands up over the gunwale close to Bill. Locking one leg over the tiller bar to keep it in check, Bill grabbed one pair of hands and pulled. He felt his muscles crack with the strain, then the man below managed to get his elbows over the gunwale.

Bill looked round, and shouted for help, but every man in sight was busy on the same task. He shook the Second Mate by the shoulder, but Harry Rawston was too dazed to do more than shake his head.

He looked back at the exhausted man clinging to the gunwale. Somehow he would have to manage the weight alone.

Bill thrust both hands under the man's shoulders.

The man's eyes were closing; Bill seized his hair and pulled it. The sudden tug was painful enough to jerk the man back into consciousness; when Bill took his hands he summoned up a last reserve of strength, hauled his body upwards, and toppled forward into the boat.

Bill glanced hurriedly towards the bows as he heard the engine cough, splutter, and then unexpectedly pick up speed again. He almost let out a cheer when he saw that the raft had remained wedged in the hole, keeping the bows afloat. He swung the tiller slightly, heading the boat back towards the heaving flank of the *Tahiti Star*, then once again locked the tiller under his leg, and reached out for the second pair of hands of the gunwale.

This time it took a greater heave than before. The man below was a heavyweight. He seemed to be too far gone to do anything to help himself. Agonisingly slowly, inch by inch, he came up, then feebly hooked his forearms over the gunwale.

Bill stretched out as far as he dared, and thrust both hands under the man's shoulders. With an effort, the man looked up. Water was streaming down his face, which was pinched and white with exposure. His eyes were only half open.

In a frenzy Bill heaved again. He released his leg from the tiller, planted both feet firmly in the bottom boards, stood up, and wrenched himself backwards as the next wave tipped the boat. A huge figure in oilskins came up out of the water like a cork from a bottle and crashed down on top of him, knocking him flat in the bottom of the boat.

Dazed, Bill sat up. They were on the crest of the wave now; he looked down what seemed a sheer wall of water, then as the lifeboat and the raft, locked together, slid down into the trough, he saw the *Tahiti Star's* other lifeboat coming in a wide circle towards them.

It looked as though it would be only just in time. With nearly fifty men crowded aboard, their own boat was wallowing,

338

shipping gallons of water every second — far faster than the men with baling tins could hurl it back. He jumped for the tiller, to put the boat head on into the seas again.

But the giant in oilskins was already there, heaving the tiller with strong, skilled hands, placing the wrecked boat so that the other lifeboat could come safely alongside.

Bill let out a gasp of exhaustion and relief.

Forgetting they were balanced on the crest of a wave, he stood up again, and cheered.

The man in the oilskins caught him just in time, as a sudden violent lurch sent him flying towards the gunwale. Only then did Bill recognise him.

A great horny hand came out from an oilskin-covered sleeve. It shook his. For a moment Bill thought his father was going to say thanks — thanks for a strong haul up out of the sea.

What his father did was to shake his head, and look at the gunwale over which Bill had nearly plunged. 'You'll never make a sailor!' he said.

But he said it differently now.

He said it with a grin!

The Stranger from the Sea

by

JOHN DAVIES

The fog had come down suddenly, in the middle of the afternoon. Through the clammy greyness glided a trim little sailing dinghy with two boys in it. The slim, dark, quiet-looking one sitting amidships handling the jib-sheets was Jeremy Hamilton. The stockier, red-haired boy at the tiller was Simon Ward, and the dinghy belonged to him. Its name was *Seaspray*.

'Lost at sea!' Jeremy said. 'What fun!'

Simon grinned. 'We aren't really.'

'You mean you can find your way through this stuff?'

'I reckon so. We've just passed the West Shoal Buoy, so the harbour's only a mile ahead.'

Seaspray sailed slowly on. Jeremy couldn't help being excited by this latest development in a day of excitements. He was a Londoner and not used to boats or the sea. His cousin Simon, on the other hand, had been born in the little Cornish village of Towan, and had been sailing nearly all his life.

Jeremy was spending a holiday with Simon, and, though they were very different in temperament, the two boys had quickly become the best of friends.

'The only thing we've got to look out for is the oil-rig platform,' Simon said. He peered out over the bows. 'Hullo — what's this?'

Jeremy stared into the fog. He said, 'It's a boat.'

The dinghy sailed nearer the vague, pale shape ahead.

'A motor-cruiser,' Simon said. A biggish job too.' He kept his eyes on the boat as *Seaspray* glided nearer. 'I don't recognise her. She doesn't belong to Towan.'

'Is she moving?'

'If she is, she's going dead slow.' Simon was puzzled. 'I wonder if the people aboard her know where they are? On that course she'll end up on West Bay rocks.'

'Perhaps they're lost, if they're strangers?'

'They could be. We'd better give them a hail and find out.' Simon raised his voice and shouted, 'Motor cruiser ahoy!'

The call drifted away into the greyness. There was no response from the motor cruiser. In fact there was no sign of life aboard her at all.

Jeremy said, 'She's at anchor — I can see the chain. Maybe they're waiting for the fog to clear?'

'Maybe,' Simon said. 'But why don't they answer?' He called again. 'Motor cruiser ahoy! Are you in trouble?'

No reply. Simon frowned, and altered course directly towards the other boat.

Jeremy looked back at him quickly. 'What are you going to do?'

'There's something funny about this,' Simon said, I'm going alongside to check up. There may be somebody ill or something.'

A minute or so later he brought the dinghy gently alongside the cruiser. She was a big, white, powerful-looking craft. Standing up and hanging on to her well-coaming, he called again, 'Anybody aboard?'

No answer.

Jeremy said, 'There must be somebody.'

'I don't believe there is,' Simon said. 'I think she's deserted.' He took a firm grip on the coaming. Hang on to her a moment while I have a look.'

'O. K.'

Simon stepped up on to *Seaspray's* transom. Then, with a jump and a heave, he hauled himself over the motor-cruiser's side. Jeremy saw him stand there for a moment, then move forward and disappear.

He felt a little shiver run down his spine.

What would Simon find? Somebody ill, he had said. Supposing it was somebody dead? A body?

A little while passed, then Simon reappeared. He was looking more puzzled than ever.

'I was right,' he said. 'This is a very funny business indeed. Chuck me up the painter — you'd better come aboard too.'

While Simon tied *Seaspray* up astern, Jeremy climbed aboard the motor cruiser. Then Simon led the way through the wheelhouse and into the saloon.

There was nobody there, but Jeremy at once noticed signs of very recent occupation. On the table were the remains of a meal, and on one of the settees a shirt, sweater and a pair of jeans lay in an untidy heap, as though they had recently been thrown down there.

Simon nodded towards the table. 'Feel the teapot.'

Jeremy did so, then stared at his friend. 'It's still warm!

'Exactly,' Simon said.

They stood there in the cruiser's saloon, trying to work it out.

Jeremy said, 'Perhaps she's broken down and they've gone ashore in their dinghy to get help?'

'The dinghy's still in its chocks on the foredeck,' Simon said. 'I noticed it as we came alongside.'

'Then I don't know,' Jeremy said. 'I . . .'

He broke off as Simon gripped his arm. The motor-cruiser had just given a little lurch to starboard, as though a weight had been put on that side.

'Someone coming aboard!' Simon hissed.

The two boys stood stock still, watching the entrance to the saloon. Who was it? And where had he come from? There had been no sound of a boat approaching.

The lurch was followed by a commotion in the water somewhere alongside the cruiser. Then they heard someone moving about in the well aft... someone coming forward through the wheelhouse... someone — or something — moving with a slithering flapping sound...

A figure appeared in the entrance to the saloon, a tall, weird figure, clothed from head to foot in glistening black. As he caught sight of the boys, he stopped, blocking the doorway. His face was pale, and he stared at them expressionlessly. He looked like a visitant from another world.

The man in black said, 'What are you doing here?'

Simon almost laughed. The 'apparition' wasn't in fact anything more frightening than a frogman. He was wearing a frogman's black rubber suit, with a compass on his wrist, and was carrying his mask in his hand.

'I'm sorry,' he said. 'We didn't get any reply when we hailed, so we wondered if you were in trouble.'

The man grunted. 'Good of you to bother.' He didn't sound very friendly.

Jeremy said, 'We thought that, with the fog...'

'That's why I anchored,' the man in the rubber suit said. 'And I thought that while I was stuck here I might as well try for a fish for my supper.' He paused. 'No luck, though, I'm afraid.'

There was an awkward silence. Then Simon said, 'Well, I suppose we'd better be on our way...'

The man didn't try to stop them. He followed them out into the well.

'It seems to be thinning a bit,' he said. 'So I think I'll be on my way too.'

Simon glanced quickly round the well of the cruiser, but he

343

couldn't see what he was looking for. He felt the frogman's eyes on him and said, as casually as he could, 'Where are you heading for?'

'Paenporth. If I can get there, I'll have my supper ashore instead'.

Five minutes later the two boys were back in *Seaspray* again, heading for Towan harbour. The motor-cruiser had disappeared in the fog astern.

Jeremy said, 'So it wasn't such a mystery after all.'

'Wasn't it?' Simon retorted.

Jeremy gave him a quick, surprised look. 'What do you mean?'

'I mean I think it was all very fishy.' Simon paused. 'Talking of that, he said he'd been trying to get a fish for his supper, didn't he? But he hadn't a spear gun when he came into the saloon — and he didn't leave it outside. I looked.'

'You could have missed it.'

'All right. Perhaps I did. But he was lying about something else too.'

'What?'

'He said if he could get to Paenporth, he'd go ashore for supper. He couldn't do that because the harbour at Paenporth is dry at low tide, and with the tide the way it is today, he won't be able to get in until about three o'clock tomorrow morning.'

'Perhaps he doesn't know that,' Jeremy said. But he too was now convinced that there had been something suspicious about the frogman.

They were silent for a while. Then Simon said, 'I was a silly fool. I ought to have noticed the cruiser's name.'

'I did,' Jeremy said. 'It was *Amaryllis*.'

'Good for you,' Simon said. 'Was there anything to say where she belonged to — any yacht club initials or anything?'

'I don't think so,' Jeremy said. 'I didn't notice any.'

344

A little later they passed the oil-rig platform. It was as yet only half completed, and rose like a gaunt skeleton out of the sea. Simon had already told Jeremy that a big drilling operation was planned for this area. Then the breakwater of Towan harbour appeared ahead. They sailed in, and half an hour later they were ashore and heading for home.

That night Simon lay in bed listening to the grunt of the Outer Bank foghorn, which meant there was still fog out at sea. He kept thinking about the strange incident of the frogman and the motor cruiser. Before he finally dropped off to sleep he resolved to find out a bit more about that boat, if he could...

In the morning the weather was clear and sunny again. Before he and Jeremy left the house, Simon phoned the harbour-master at Paenporth, who told him there was no motor-cruiser named *Amaryllis* based there.

It was a perfect day for sailing, but they couldn't go out that morning because *Seaspray* was due to have her rigging tuned up for the weekend's racing. They went along to the yacht yard where a weatherbeaten old man known as Rigger was busily at work on the dinghy. No one knew whether that was really his name or just his job.

They watched for a while. Then Simon said, 'Rigger — do you know a motor-cruiser named *Amaryllis?*'

Rigger knew most of the boats along that bit of coast, but he shook his head. 'Never heard of her.' Then he thought again. 'Wait a minute — there's that charter firm along at Polwen. They've got a lot of boats, all beginning with A. Might be one of them.'

'Thanks,' Simon said. 'Thanks, Rigger.'

He and Jeremy wandered along to the end of the harbour wall and stood there looking out to sea.

'Where's Polwen?' Jeremy asked.

'About twenty miles along the coast to the westward,'

Simon said. The opposite way from Paenporth, where that chap said he was going.' He paused thoughtfully. 'I could ring up the charter firm and ask them about the *Amaryllis*, I suppose.' Suddenly his face lightened. 'Or we could sail over there. We could take sleeping bags and a primus and make a short cruise of it. What do you think?'

Jeremy said, 'I think it's a smashing idea!'

They were both excited now, and couldn't wait to get cracking. They decided to start off as soon as the dinghy was ready.

The first thing was to ask permission from Simon's parents and then get the necessary gear together. They dashed home. Simon's mother said she thought it would be all right, but that he ought to ask his father. So Simon got on the phone to Dad at his office in Plymouth — and Dad, as usual turned up trumps. The weather forecast was good, and he didn't believe in boys being mollycoddles. The only thing he asked was that Simon should look after Jeremy, and Simon said he would; thought he felt, privately, that Jeremy was quite capable of looking after himself.

Simon's mother turned up trumps too. She put on an early lunch for them, and drove them down to the harbour with their gear. The dinghy was ready, and by two o'clock they were under way.

They had a marvellous sail. The dinghy sped along before a fresh breeze, over a sparkling sea. Simon was prepared to drop anchor for the night, if necessary, in Mawn Creek, which was half way between Towan and Polwen, but by the time they got there they were making such good progress that he decided to press on to Polwen.

An hour later their progress was almost too good. In spite of the forecast of fair weather, the wind had strengthened, and a great bank of black cloud was climbing up in the sky behind them. The dinghy was roaring along, her rigging humming.

'It looks as though we're in for a blow,' Simon said. 'It's a good job we've got the wind behind us.'

Jeremy did not answer. This was his first experience of rough weather, and the thrill of it took his breath away.

They made one of the fastest passages even Simon had ever known. Just before seven that evening they charged in past the small lighthouse on the Polwen harbour breakwater.

They spotted the motor-cruiser almost at once. Neither of them could believe it at first, for up till then she had seemed so mysterious and elusive. She was lying alongside the harbour wall, near its outer end, some distance away from any other craft. They thought they recognised her as they approached and when they passed her and looked back, there was proof positive — the name *Amaryllis* plainly visible on her stern. There was no sign of life aboard.

'We'd better take a closer look at her as soon as we can,' Simon said. 'In case she puts to sea and we lose her.'

'She wouldn't go out in this, would she?' Jeremy asked.

'She might,' Simon said. 'Bad weather can be useful cover, if you're up to no good.'

They sailed on across the harbour, and Simon brought *Seaspray* expertly alongside the Town Quay. In a matter of minutes the little boat was securely moored to the quay with her sails lowered.

'She'll be all right there until we get back,' Simon said.

He didn't, of course, know just how long it would be before they got back. Neither did Jeremy...

An iron ladder led up to the top of the quay. Jeremy followed Simon up it. The *Amaryllis* was lying about a couple of hundred yards away round the curve of the harbour wall. With their hands in the pockets of their jeans they strolled casually towards her.

It was an easy enough stalk. The motor cruiser was lying well below the level of the harbour wall, and they had only to stay back from the edge to keep out of sight. On the wall a few yards short of the *Amaryllis* there was a large red buoy which had been brought in from sea for servicing and this made a first-rate observation point. If anyone came out from below decks on the motor cruiser, they had only to move back into the shelter of the buoy.

They watched from the lee of the buoy. For a long time nothing happened. Then a short, fat man came out into the well with a plastic bowl in his hand. As they drew back they heard him tip the contents over the side. A moment later some potato parings floated into the boy's range of vision.

'He's been peeling spuds,' Simon whispered. 'Seems harmless enough.'

A voice said, 'I wouldn't be too sure about that.'

Both the boys had been so intent on watching the motor cruiser that they were taken completely by surprise. Their heads jerked round. Behind them, not more than three yards away, stood a tall man. He was wearing a white roll-necked sweater and khaki drill trousers today, but they recognised him at once.

It was the frogman.

'You two seem very interested in my boat,' the tall man said. 'A little too interested, shall we say?'

Both Simon and Jeremy could only stare, speechlessly.

They were staring at the thing the man was holding in his hand. It was a snub-nosed, wicked-looking little gun.

'Perhaps you'd like to come on board again?' the man said. 'In fact, you're going to, whether you like it or not.' The gun jerked in his hand and his voice sharpened. 'All right — down that ladder! Get moving — and no nonsense!

Mechanically, the boys obeyed. To both of them this seemed like a dream — or a nightmare. They couldn't really believe that they were at the wrong end of a gun, but they were. They couldn't believe the man would use it; and yet that wouldn't have been any more incredible than the rest of the situation.

His head in a whirl, Simon climbed down the iron ladder abreast of the motor-cruiser. Jeremy followed. The man already aboard heard them and came out from below. When he saw the boys, his face was almost comical with surprise.

'Peters!' he exclaimed. 'What. . . ?' His voice was guttural and he spoke with a foreign accent.

Peters followed Jeremy down the ladder into the motor-cruiser's well.

'These are the two nosey little devils I told you about,' he said. The gun jerked at Simon and Jeremy again. 'Get below — and be quick about it!'

In a daze, the two boys stumbled through the wheelhouse into the saloon. Peters was hard at their heels. The little fat man was saying something, protesting, but Peters took no notice. He drove the boys right forward, into the forepeak. Then, almost before they knew what was happening, the forepeak door was slammed and they heard the grating of the key in the lock. They were prisoners, in a cramped, dark little compartment right up in the bows of the boat.

They were still stunned.

'Simon,' Jeremy said. He tried to keep his voice steady, but didn't quite succeed. 'What are they going to. . . ?'

'Shut up a minute,' Simon said. There were raised voices in the saloon. 'Let's see if we can hear what they are saying.'

The two men — they heard Peters call the other one Margolis — were quarrelling.

'Why did you bring them aboard?' Margolis demanded.

'I told you,' Peters said. 'They're the two I found on the boat yesterday. They must have got wind of something, or they wouldn't have turned up here the way they did. And I'm not going to risk my neck for a couple of kids.'

'But they couldn't have done anything!'

'I'm not so sure they couldn't,' Peters retorted. 'Anyway,

they're coming with us now. We're not taking any chances,'

'But' — Margolis repeated the question Jeremy had started to ask — 'what are we going to do with them?'

'I don't know,' Peters said. 'We'll see about that later.'

The tone of his voice was ominous.

Margolis seemed to accept the situation then, and the quarrel died away into ordinary talk. It was harder to hear what the men were saying, and they weren't talking about the boys any more, but what little Simon could make out made him almost as alarmed as if they had been. He heard Peters say something about 'the charge on the rig,' and then Margolis asked anxiously about the 'cable to the plunger.'

In the gloom of the forepeak Simon turned urgently to Jeremy.

'You know what?' he whispered hoarsely. 'They're going to blow up the oil platform!'

The men's voices droned on.

'We've got to get out of here!' Jeremy said. 'We must warn somebody!'

But how?

'Perhaps if we shouted?' Simon said. 'Someone ashore might hear us and...'

But it was already too late. At that moment the motor-cruiser's engine roared into life. There were footsteps on the deck overhead as one of the men cast off. The engine sound settled to a steady throb, and they could hear the rush of water past the boat's bows. They were under way.

In a few minutes the boys' prison began to lift and fall. They were out of the harbour. The motion became more violent, and soon the cruiser's bows were soaring sickeningly and crashing down again into the sea.

'It's a gale, isn't it?' Jeremy said. Where they had previously been whispering, he now had to raise his voice against the noise outside.

350

'It's a gale all right,' Simon said. He added bitterly. 'If they don't know what they're doing, we may all go to the bottom together!'

Jeremy didn't say any more. The idea of being shut up in that horrible little compartment when the *Amaryllis* sank was not very pleasant.

Neither of them spoke again for a long while after that. The motor-cruiser soared and plunged on. Then at last her motion seemed to get easier. Some time later she was in comparatively smooth water.

Later still they heard footsteps overhead again. The anchor chain rattled out, the cruiser's engine was cut, and all was silence except for the sound of the wind and the gentle wash of the sea.

Simon looked at the luminous dial of his watch and was amazed to see that the time was nearly midnight. He and Jeremy had been shut up there in the forepeak for five hours. Where were they now? Were they back in Towan? He realised at once that they couldn't be since Towan harbour was very small and they had been in fairly calm water for some time. His guess was that they had run into one of the lonely creeks somewhere along that stretch of coast.

He and Jeremy listened intently, trying to hear what the two men were doing. They heard muffled movements, a faint creaking, and then a sudden throaty whine which Simon recognised immediately.

'An outboard!' he exclaimed. 'They've gone off in the dinghy!'

The knowledge that the two men had gone gave a great lift to the boys' spirits.

Jeremy said, 'Now we've got to get out of her! Fast!'

The question remained — how? The door was still locked and there was nothing in the forepeak to batter it down with. Simon had already explored and found nothing except a couple of coils of rope and one or two tins of paint.

Then he had an inspiration and began to pull at the floor-boards. They should be loose, so that you could get at the bilges. They were. He pulled the centre one up, and underneath it he found what he had been desperately hoping would be there: a heavy chunk or 'pig' of cast iron which was part of the cruiser's ballast.

He told Jeremy excitedly about his find and hauled the pig out. It was all he could do to lift it.

He was about to attack the door with it when Jeremy stopped him.

'Wait,' he said. It'll make a devil of a noise, so let them get well clear first.'

They waited impatiently until the sound of the outboard had faded right away, and for five minutes after that. Then Simon went to work on the door. The lock gave as he crashed the pig against it the second time. They were free!

They rushed out through the saloon into the well of the cruiser. Simon stared around him, trying to get his bearings. As it happened, it was easy. The night, though rough, was not really dark. A full moon was racing through ragged clouds, and by its light he saw a great black headland which he recognised immediately. It was the Barrow. On the other side of it was Towan harbour.

He told Jeremy where they were.

'We're about five miles from the oil rig,' he said. 'We've got to get there before anything happens!'

Jeremy said blankly, 'How?'

'In this boat, of course! How else? If I start the engine, can you get the anchor up?'

'Yes.'

Simon was already groping around the controls. He wasn't used to motor-cruisers, but he did know a bit about engines. He found the starter, and the engine roared into life. Jeremy

352

was already up on the bows, hauling on the anchor chain. He shouted as the anchor came free... Simon shoved the engine in gear and took the wheel. They were under way!

A quarter of an hour later they were out in the open sea again. The night was as wild as ever, and the motor cruiser surged and rolled crazily, dashing great sheets of spray up over her bows.

Hanging on beside Simon, Jeremy said, 'Why do you think those two went ashore?'

Simon said, 'From that talk about a cable and plunger, I reckon they're planning to blow up the rig from somewhere on land — and the other side of the Barrow would be the nearest point. But they must have known they couldn't land on that side in this weather, so they ran in behind. My guess is they're making their way over the headland on foot.' He laughed shortly. 'They've got a rough walk.'

'How long will it take them?'

'A good hour. It must be three miles, and there's a lot of marshland first.

'Oughtn't we to have gone after them — to try to stop them?'

Simon said, 'I thought about that, but we couldn't risk it. We might not have been able to catch them up, or even find them, in the dark. And there may be someone on the rig. Sometimes they work all night, and there's always a watchman.' His tone became suddenly more urgent. 'We've got to get there before the whole thing goes sky-high!'

The motor-cruiser plunged on. Jeremy marvelled that anyone could navigate in that wild waste of waters, but Simon had the fleeting light of the moon and the dim glow of the compass in front of him to help him...

A gaunt black skeleton tower appeared ahead, in the middle of a great smother of breaking seas.

'The rig!' Jeremy yelled. 'And there's someone on it! I can see a light!'

Simon took the cruiser round to the leeward side of the rig, where the sea was a little calmer and there was an embarkation ladder. There were several lights on the rig, and one of them came bobbing down the ladder. Simon brought the cruiser in as close as he dared, and the man clinging to the ladder shone a torch on his face.

'Young Simon!'

The voice was deep, with a strong Scottish accent. The man on the ladder was the rig boss, Bob Mclean, whom Simon had got to know well during the time the oil platform had been under construction.

'Bob?' Simon yelled. 'How many of you on there?'

'Six,' Bob shouted back. 'We got cut off by the storm!'

'You've got to come off now — quick!' Simon shouted. 'The rig may go any moment!'

'But what...'

'Don't waste time!' Simon yelled desperately. 'It's sabotage!'

On the way to the rig he had been terribly afraid that, even if he raised the alarm, no one would believe him. He need not have worried. The rig boss climbed quickly back up the ladder, and a few moments later the two boys saw a line of men descending it. Simon nudged the cruiser in until, one by one, they had all jumped aboard.

Bob McLean came last. He grabbed the well-coaming beside Simon.

'Now, then,' he said sharply, 'what's all the fuss?'

Simon told him. He added, 'It's my guess they're planning to blow her from the nearest point on the Barrow' — he pointed — 'somewhere over there.'

'O. K.' Bob said grimly. 'We've got to get there.' He hesitated. 'But how?'

'There's only one way,' Simon said. 'We haven't got time to muck about. We'll have to run the boat on the beach.'

Bob still hesitated. The whole weight of the storm was

The cruiser rolled over on her beam ends, spilling everyone out.

pounding on the long beach on this side of the Barrow. There was no telling what might happen to the cruiser if she was deliberately run ashore there.

But as Simon had said, it was the only way...

'Verra gude,' Bob said. He looked around him at the other dark figures crowded into the cruiser's well. 'You know what we're after!' he told them and divided them into two parties, one to search the beach in each direction. 'And,' he added, 'when she grounds, it's every man for himself!'

Now, with the storm behind her, the *Amaryllis* was rushing towards the beach, surging and slewing dizzily. There were breakers ahead...

The cruiser struck and swung broadside on. A great sea lifted her and flung her shorewards. She struck again, with a cracking splintering sound and rolled over on her beam ends, spilling everyone out of her.

The sea closed over Jeremy's head. He held his breath and tried to swim. Then there was sand underfoot. He stumbled, gasping. Another wave picked him up and flung him shoreward. He was in the shallows. He floundered out on to the beach.

There were dark figures running, spreading out. He thought he saw Simon and was about to follow him when he spotted something else; something up near the flat coarse grass of the dunes which might have been a small rock, except that it moved, or seemed to.

He dashed towards the 'rock'. It moved again. The moon shone suddenly out and he saw two men crouching over a sort of box. One of them saw him and shouted a warning. Jeremy flung himself forward. He fell on the box in a flurry of sand and hugged it to him. Hands grabbed at him and someone was cursing. Then someone else rushed up. He heard a sharp Scots voice exclaim, 'No ye don't, ye devil!' Then there was a dull thumping sound, and a yell of pain.

356

It was Saturday morning two days after the storm, and the weather was sparkling again. Simon and Jeremy had sailed the dinghy home, arriving back the previous evening. This morning they had come out to the oil platform, at Bob Mc-Lean's invitation, to have a look round.

Peters and Margolis were safe under lock and key, and Bob had explained what they had been up to. If oil was found off the coast of Britain, less would have to be brought in from abroad, and one of the foreign companies most likely to suffer had bribed the two men to try and sabotage the rig. They had failed.

Thanks to Simon and Jeremy.

This morning the rig was swarming with men and everyone was in high spirits. Since the sabotage bid had been foiled, everyone felt sure they must strike oil soon.

Simon and Jeremy spent an hour on the rig. Then Simon said 'I'm afraid we must be off.'

'Racing this afternoon?' Bob asked.

'Yes'.

Bob turned to Jeremy. 'Well — at least you've had a lively holiday so far.'

Jeremy grinned. And Simon said. 'He's sailing with me in the race this afternoon. He'll get a bit of *real* excitement then!'

ACKNOWLEDGMENTS

The publishers wish to express their thanks to authors and publishers for permission to include the following stories.

'Famous Ships' from *Stories of Famous Ships* (Oliver & Boyd) © copyright Frank Knight 1962.

'Strange Tales of the Coast' by George Goldsmith-Carter © copyright Odhams Periodicals 1960-61.

'Jackdaw Baits the Trap' © copyright John E. Edwards 1965.

'*Laffey* and the Kamikazes' from *The World's Greatest Sea Adventures* (Odhams) © copyright Commander John Kerans 1964.

'Hornblower and the Man who felt Queer' from *Mr Midshipman Hornblower* © copyright C. S. Forester 1950. Reprinted by permission of A. D. Peters & Co.

'Captain Sharkey: How the Governor Of Saint Kitt's Came Home' from *The Conan Doyle Stories*. Reprinted by permission of John Murray (Publishers) Ltd and the Estate of Sir Arthur Conan Doyle.

'In the Abyss' from *The Short Stories of H. G. Wells*. Reprinted by permission of the Executors of H. G. Wells.

SWORD OF EMPIRE

SWORD OF EMPIRE

CHRISTOPHER NICOLE

C

CENTURY

LONDON SYDNEY AUCKLAND JOHANNESBURG

The right of Christopher Nicole to be identified as the author
of this work has been asserted by him in accordance with the
Copyright, Designs and Patents Act 1988.

First published in Great Britain in 1991 by
Random Century Group
20 Vauxhall Bridge Road, London SW1V 2SA

Century Hutchinson South Africa (Pty) Ltd
PO Box 337, Bergvlei 2012, South Africa

Random Century Australia Pty Ltd
20 Alfred Street, Milsons Point, Sydney, NSW 2061
Australia

Random Century New Zealand Ltd
PO Box 40–086, Glenfield, Auckland 10
New Zealand

British Library Cataloguing in Publication Data

Sword of Empire
Nicole, Christopher
I. Title   II Series
ISBN 0–7126–4759–7

Photoset by Deltatype Ltd, Ellesmere Port, Cheshire
Printed in Great Britain

This is a novel. Except where they can be historically identified, the characters are invented, and are not intended to depict real persons, living or dead.

Contents

Bombay, 2 February, 1825

Since my life as an officer in the Honourable East India Company's Army will, I hope, be a tremendous adventure, I have decided to keep a journal. I should, I suppose, have started to write it on leaving England, but the voyage proved so damnably tedious that there was precious little to tell. It lasted three months with but two stops, at St Helena and Cape Town. St Helena has fresh water, and that is all that can be said for it. I suspect Boney died of boredom. The Cape is magnificently beautiful, but the Boers gaze at one with frank dislike, and I did not care for them.

We had several storms, which were at least exciting, and several periods of flat calm, which were desperately boring. I was dreadfully seasick. How happy I am that I chose the Army instead of the Navy. I would willingly never put to sea again.

It is popularly supposed that a young man aboard ship, particularly if he is a handsome subaltern, twenty-three years old, in all the glory of crimson tunic and yellow sidewhiskers, is surrounded by marriageable females on their way to seek husbands among the lovelorn soldiery. Oh, that it had been so! While there was one female on board not *quite* old enough to be my mother, she was on her way to Bombay to marry a major in the artillery. Subalterns were not her line of country at all. I might have pressed the matter had she been in the least attractive. But she was not.

Now, to write of Bombay. The place is an island, although connected to the mainland by a causeway. It is small, and must be the most crowded place on earth. Most of the inhabitants are Indians, as one would expect. They are a small people, dark of skin and hair and eye, but in many cases very handsome,

3

especially the women, who go about very scantily covered, except for gold ornaments, which they wear in profusion, even in their noses, and which I am told constitute their entire wealth. The Colonel has warned me about the women, that they are diseased and deceitful, and really hate the sahibs.

Well, if Colonel Partridge is correct and they are diseased, I am undoubtedly most confoundedly clapped, although as yet there is no manifestation of it. My brother junior officers considered it necessary that I be initiated into the regiment, and thus on my second night here while my friends stood around laughing I discovered myself bound hand and foot to my bed, and stripped naked besides, and introduced into the midst of a dusky charmer. I use the words advisedly. Within an hour I was sucked dry – and again the words are not mere figures of speech.

I will confess I enjoyed it, at the time. Since then I have been racked with a variety of emotions: alarm, that I may at any moment discover myself incapable; lust, to repeat the performance with my hands free to investigate her as she investigated me; and most of all shame, that I should have coupled with a native and surely therefore left myself unfit for proper intercourse . . . and at such a moment! For I have just met the most heavenly creature on earth!

Her name is Laura Dean, and she is perfectly beautiful. I am not alone in this opinion; she is much talked of in the Presidency, particularly among the young officers. Her hair is as yellow as mine – what a pair we would make, arm in arm – and she is tall for a woman, and statuesque. She makes one think of a Greek goddess, and moves like one too, back as straight as an infantryman's, head held high; this posture shows off both her swanlike neck and her splendid bosom. I have no doubt at all that the rest of her is equally desirable.

In short, I am besotted. You will say, gentle reader, but this young lady is the toast of the Presidency and the young gentleman is but a junior subaltern. Is he not preparing to tilt against windmills? But this is not necessarily so. Miss Dean is eighteen years of age, has lived in Bombay the better part of her life, and is unmarried! Not even betrothed! Ah, you will say, there must be some mystery here, one perhaps better not investigated. But it is really very simple.

4

Miss Dean's father is a humble clerk. True, his brother, Harrison Dean, is the Presidency's leading factor, and as such is a man to be noted. But Carmichael Dean is merely in his brother's employ and, as Harrison Dean is a miser, is kept in very short funds. Thus Miss Dean, save for her beauty, is not the catch she immediately appears. Most of the young men are desperately anxious to marry money, or at least advancement. Miss Dean promises neither. But she smiled most graciously upon me on the occasion of our first meeting. Thus . . . who knows?

Should not I also be considering marrying money, having none of my own, or advancement? No doubt I should. But when I regard so ravishing a creature, surely crying out to be ravished, even if marriage lies at the end of it, I feel it better to remain a penniless subaltern all my life than let such an opportunity go by. Oh, a fellow needs to dream!

For the rest, I am well settled here. The regiment consists entirely of Indians, who are called sepoys. This appears to be a corruption of the Turkish word sipahi. In the Turkish army, as I understand it, a sipahi is a mounted soldier, whereas our sepoys are infantry. They have their own corporals, or naiks, and their own sergeants, or havildars. They are splendid fellows, who wear red jackets and white trousers but prefer to go barefoot. Instead of shakos they wrap their heads in yards of white cloth, which they call a turban. Colonel Partridge is quite a good fellow, so is Major Hargreaves. My captain is called Smythe, and is not so good-natured. But I do not doubt we shall get along as I am determined to do my duty. My sole wish – after obtaining a closer acquaintance with Miss Dean – is to get to the mainland and see something of the country. But for the time being it is drill and whisky and cards, day in and day out.

The food is mostly meat served in a sauce known as kari. The Hindus and the old India hands consider this a great delicacy. But the first time I tasted it, I supposed I had been poisoned with sulphuric acid. It is the hottest thing I have ever tasted. However, one can get used to anything, especially when there is little else. And the stuff is, apparently, very necessary. The mixture – I shall not describe what it looks like – contains certain spices which enable food to be kept for more than a few hours after cooking – otherwise it would go off in the heat.

And I drink spirits. There is no wine here, and to attempt to send any from England would be disastrous.

I think I shall get myself a dog. There are a great number of them about. I already have a servant, a jovial rascal named Ramjohn. Of course, that is not his real name, but that is what he is called in the regiment.

So here I am, broiling in the sun, drilling my dusky soldiers, dining in the mess – a very drunken affair – playing at cards, and dreaming of Miss Dean.

Prologue

'We will stop for tiffin in an hour, Partaj,' announced Harrison Dean, peering down from his elephant.

'I am thinking we should not stop for tiffin today, Harrison Sahib,' replied the Indian who walked beside the huge beast. 'Maybe we should keep on going.'

'Not stop for tiffin?' Dean was astounded. He was also quite hungry. 'I never heard of such a thing.'

'Ramdas has told me, sahib, that he has seen a man, and then another, looking at us from the trees.' Partaj himself looked around at the jungle with some apprehension. The little caravan was following a well-trodden pathway between looming trees and concealing undergrowth, but it was only eight feet wide, and the elephants were strung out over nearly a mile.

'What is so alarming in a man, or even two men, looking at us from the trees?' Harrison Dean inquired.

'Why, sahib, a man may look at us as much as he likes, but is it not strange that he does not step out and look at us openly? Or even speak with us?'

'I am sure he has his reasons,' Dean said equably. 'We will stop for tiffin . . .' he looked at his watch, '. . . in forty-five minutes.'

He leaned back comfortably in the howdah, and allowed his ample body to sway in time to the slow movement of the elephant. Above his head the wide umbrella also swayed gently, keeping the sun from his face. Harrison Dean was at peace with the world.

The annual jaunt to Madras was the highlight of his year. He had first made the journey, from Bombay to Madras and back, as a young writer soon after arriving in India forty years before. Those had been exciting times. In 1785, the East India

7

Company's hold on the Deccan had been slight indeed; apart from the Marathas, who were at war with everyone, the army of Tippoo Sahib in Mysore waged war specifically on the British. French renegades had been everywhere, and British too. The entire sub-continent had been in a state of endemic warfare.

In those days no caravan would have dreamed of attempting to cross the peninsula without a large armed escort.

But such men as the Duke of Wellington and his politician brother Lord Mornington had turned the tide irrevocably in favour of the Company. Now, not only almost all the southern half of the peninsula, but the huge eastern territories of Bengal and Bihar, as well as the rump of the Sultanate of Delhi, the heartland of the once-great Mughal empire, were under direct British control, the Emperor himself a helpless puppet. Even powerful native states like Hyderabad and Rajputana took care to remain on friendly terms with the Governor-General.

It had been a time for growing rich and living well. It had not taken Harrison Dean long to grow rich. He had always been a hard worker; he drank little and gambled less; and he had no time for women – he had never married. His contemporaries, in fact, had always considered him rather a bore.

But where were they all now? Most were dead of fever or venereal disease, or had died of drink. The rest had returned to England, their health shattered, with no more than a modest portion to see out their old age. Only some half dozen had found true wealth.

Dean alone remained living in Bombay, enjoying the lifestyle of a monarch with none of the responsibilities. Many people wondered why Harrison Dean did not retire and go home. The truth was that he had nothing to go home for. He dearly loved his sister, but knew that he and she would remain the more fond of each other when separated by several thousand miles. He did not love his brother Carmichael, an indolent rascal who had got a woman into trouble and then been stupid enough to marry her, though she had had neither money nor prospects. Yet he considered it important to remain in Bombay and keep an eye on the scoundrel, lest he bring more disgrace on the family name.

As a young man, Carmichael Dean's peccadilloes had

caused him to fall upon hard times, and to escape the debtors' prison he had fled England with his pregnant wife, to throw himself upon the generosity of his successful brother. Their daughter had actually been born at sea.

That had been eighteen years ago. Harrison had been scandalised at the appearance of the ne'er-do-well on his doorstep – but Carmichael was his brother. He could not be allowed to starve or rot in gaol. Of course, Harrison could, with the greatest of ease, have paid Carmichael's debts and put him and his family on a ship back to England, but that was not Harrison Dean's way. Men worked their way through life, in his opinion. Given the opportunity, Carmichael would only return to the dissolute existence from which he had been forced to flee.

Harrison had given his brother a job as a writer in his factory, and told him to earn his keep.

Carmichael had grumbled, but had had no option other than to obey. Thus he had lived and worked in Bombay for eighteen years, and was still a humble writer. The dolt had not the slightest spark of ambition to rise in the world.

Harrison Dean felt no pity for his brother, only contempt, and he heartily disliked Marjorie Dean. While prepared to admit that their daughter Laura was a remarkably pretty girl, Dean was quite convinced that she was no better than she should be, just like her mother.

He chose to see little of them socially, yet insisted that they remain in Bombay. Employing Carmichael was an act of charity sufficient to make all others unnecessary; and he took a malicious pleasure in the all-too visible difference between his brother's modest life and his own success.

Thus he pursued his own life with its simple pleasures, among them this annual pilgrimage to Madras. He had first gone as a boy, now he travelled in considerably more comfort. His determination to play the part of a junior clerk once a year caused gossip in both the Presidencies, he knew. But he could afford to ignore gossip, and relive in his mind those glorious years so long ago.

Besides, the journey also allowed him to indulge his interest in botany. No sooner had the elephants been brought to a halt

9

and the ladder erected so that he could climb down, than he got out his magnifying glass and basket, and set off into the bushes. It would be half an hour before Partaj had lunch on the table; in that time he might well find an interesting specimen.

Partaj watched his master disappear into the trees with a quizzical expression. He knew that the British nabobs considered themselves the rulers of all the earth. Their confidence and arrogance were quite frightening. They had conquered most of India, and the certainty that they would mete out the most severe punishment to anyone who challenged their rule had turned it into a land of peace. Certainly, Partaj was sure, Dean Sahib could conceive of no change in that satisfactory situation.

But why had those men stared at the caravan from behind the trees? Had they been afraid? Or were they to be feared?

Harrison Dean exclaimed in delight, and knelt beside a wild orchid. The purple and white flower was larger than usual, and beckoned him with an almost sensuous beauty. He opened his basket, reached for his shears, and slipped his hand down the stem, seeking to cut the flower as far down as possible, the better to preserve it until he regained Bombay. And discovered, on parting the bush from which the orchid emerged, that he was gazing at a pair of feet, brown, bare and mud-stained.

Harrison reared back on his haunches in surprise. There were several men, all naked save for dhotis and turbans. This was not at all unusual among lower caste Indians; it was the faces of these men that disconcerted Harrison. There was a wildness in their eyes he had not seen before, except when an Indian had been chewing bhang, the intoxicating drug taken from the hemp plant.

'That is Dean Sahib,' one of the men said.

The leader smiled. The man had a handsome face, with bold features and deep black eyes, and yet it was quite the most evil smile Harrison had ever seen. The face was vaguely familiar, but Harrison Dean was in no mood for remembering faces.

Equally, he was not going to be browbeaten by a handful of

coolies. He made to stand, but his shoulders were grasped to push him back to his knees. A hand whipped away his hat.

'Now, look here,' he protested.

'Christians pray on their knees,' the man said. 'And you should pray.'

'Pray?' Harrison demanded. 'If the slightest harm is done to me or my people, you will be hanged!'

The man grinned again, his teeth white against his dark skin. 'Pray, Dean Sahib,' he said. 'Pray to the Great Goddess Kali, Mother of Death. Pray to her, before she folds you in her embrace.'

'Kali? Of all the . . .' Harrison Dean's mouth sagged as he saw the knotted silk cord. He had of course heard of Kali, and of her devotees who murdered as a way of life to feed her insatiable lust for death. But Kali ruled in the north, beyond the reach of the Company. That such a thing should be happening, here, in British India!

'Now look here,' he blustered. 'If . . .'

But the cord was thrown round his neck and drawn tight, the knots already eating into his flesh.

'Pray,' the man said again. 'Pray to Kali. Or she will throw your soul to the dogs.'

Part One

THE BEGUM

Bombay, 4 April, 1825

There has been the most frightful to-do. A murder, no less! Or an act of rebellion. A most horrendous event, in any case. Harrison Dean, our leading factor, has been killed. Together with every man of his caravan!

When he failed to return from a visit to Madras, an excursion he apparently takes with great regularity once a year, a company was sent out to look for him. Naturally I volunteered; it was my opportunity to see something of the country.

The country is unbelievable. I shall have to write of it at a later date. Suffice it to say that I have seen tigers as big as a carriage, and crocodiles as long as a small ship. And snakes . . .

It took some days to discover Dean's caravan, but for the last twelve hours we were guided by our nostrils. Most of the bodies had been picked clean by the ants and the buzzards, but there was enough lying around . . . my God, it was like nothing I have ever seen.

To explain the impact this event has had on the Presidency, and no doubt on Madras as well, I should record that for the last dozen years this has been the most peaceful country in the world. The Company has made it so, and the massacre of an entire caravan, not to mention the Presidency's most wealthy resident, is therefore as shocking here as it would be had it happened between Epsom and London. It is also an affront to the army.

To make matters worse, it is feared that this was the work of no mere band of robbers. Captain Smythe, who is apparently experienced in these matters, found some oddly knotted lengths of silk at the scene of the crime, and has declared the deed to be the work of Thugs. These Thugs are the worshippers of a heathen goddess named Kali, the Goddess of

Death in the Hindu pantheon, and they believe that by murdering sufficient victims they will gain access to their paradise. One shudders to think what sort of a paradise it will be. However, the murders are carried out in a ritual known as Thuggee, in which the victims are strangled with these lengths of knotted silk, or rumals, which are said to represent the hem of Kali's garment.

The Presidency is in an uproar.

We are now living under virtual martial law. The guards have been doubled, and every Hindu wishing to enter the Presidency must submit to being stripped and searched. We let our sepoys search the men, while we officers search the women. Well, we do not wish to hear any accusations of rape against our people, and a fellow must occupy himself.

Meanwhile strong patrols are constantly sent out into the bush. I have been on two of these so far, and damned uncomfortable they are too. It is as hot as hell and the jungle plays havoc with one's uniform. It is also filled with unpleasant creatures; one of my men had an encounter with a scorpion of enormous size, and all but died, so severe was his fever. All this without seeing a single bandit.

Fortunately, I am told that all this activity will be forced to cease with the arrival of the monsoon, which should be in another month or so.

The murdered factor was the uncle of my fair Laura. She and her mother have retired into the most stringent privacy; I have not seen her since my return. Her period of mourning will of course come to an end soon enough, and I shall resume my advances then, although now I fear she may be beyond my reach. Harrison Dean was a wealthy fellow, and Carmichael is his only brother, I understand. Fair Laura is now most definitely an heiress.

I have got my dog. His name is Rufus, and he has a very interesting ancestry. He is a large, handsome fellow, ludicrously fierce. He has already bitten Ramjohn and the water carrier, who now refuses to approach my bungalow. Yesterday I persuaded him, with difficulty, not to savage Colonel Partridge. Such an occurrence would have ended my glorious military career before it has even begun.

16

1

The Rajah

Carmichael Dean stamped up the front steps of his bungalow and threw his hat on to a cane chair on the verandah. Servants hurried forward, but he waved them away.

They were used to his ill temper; they saw it often enough. Disappointment and irritation were etched on his face, evidenced by the turned-down mouth, the dull eyes; his love of drink was to be seen in the puffy jowls, the over-red cheeks.

He went into the small sitting room, and his wife jumped to her feet, fingers twined together as she gazed at him in expectation.

'Well?'

His daughter sat on the sofa, hands on her lap, back as straight as ever. Laura always seemed to be on parade, he thought. But no doubt she was as anxious as her mother to discover what Lawyer Wilkins had had to say.

He poured himself a liberal measure of whisky.

'We are to receive five hundred pounds.'

There was a moment's silence, then Marjorie Dean stammered, 'Five hundred pounds? But . . .'

'Oh, and a most generous recommendation, that the new factor continue to employ me.'

'Do you mean Uncle Harry was not wealthy, after all?' Laura inquired quietly.

'Oh, he was even more wealthy than we thought. But it has all gone to Ella.'

'Your sister?' Marjorie's voice rose an octave.

Carmichael finished his drink and poured another.

'Surely Aunt Ella will recognise the inequity of such a Will, Papa,' Laura said. 'All you need to do is approach her.'

'That woman?' Marjorie sneered. 'We approached her once

17

before, when our need was greater, and she showed us the door. Or rather, she showed *me* the door. Said I was a . . . a *harlot*!'

Carmichael sighed. 'Nevertheless, I do intend to approach her . . .'

'Shall we be going home?' For the first time Laura looked animated.

'No, no. We cannot afford to do that without far more money than five hundred pounds. There is still a warrant out for my arrest. I will write to Ella, and put the situation to her, and . . . well, we must hope for the best.'

'It will take not less than six months for a letter to reach England and for the answer to return,' Marjorie pointed out. 'That is, if she bothers to reply.'

'It's the best I can do,' Carmichael snapped. He looked from one woman to the other. 'But we'll keep this private. Wilkins will not blab it about. We'll let people think what they wish; they'll assume Harrison left me a considerable legacy. However, there'll be no silks or jewellery for a while yet, my dears.'

Laura raised her parasol and walked past the bazaar to one of the paths leading across the island to the beaches that faced the Arabian Sea. Indians bowed to her and greeted her; white men touched their hats. It was the first time in several weeks she had taken a promenade.

White women mostly ignored her. But she was used to that.

How she hated them all! How she dreamed of escaping this over-heated prison, of returning to England while she was still young, and before malaria and disappointment had ruined her complexion.

She took great care of her skin, shielding it from the sun, and keeping it soft with creams and lotions. Her beauty was all she possessed, all she would *ever* possess now.

The bitterness of her uncle's disposition of his wealth was just beginning to sink in. She had been born poor, she had lived all of her life poor, and now she would undoubtedly die poor.

And unmarried. Laura Dean, spinster of this parish. So much beauty, left on a shelf to rot.

There had been gentlemen callers enough, ever since her sixteenth birthday. Few had remained interested for very long. They would all have liked to get their hands beneath her skirts or inside her bodice, that was obvious, but marriage to the penniless daughter of a writer had been an unattractive prospect.

Sometimes she wondered why she did not give in to one of them and have done with it. If she were to become pregnant he might have to marry her.

But then she would be repeating her mother's life over again, and her mother's life had been one long disaster, entirely because of Papa's inadequacy. Was she really going to tread the same path?

Had she any choice?

She left the houses and the bustle behind, and made her way through the trees, listening for the ripple of surf on the sand. She had taken this walk more times than she could count, and felt not the least concerned about the sundry rustles in the bushes. They were almost certainly caused by lizards; the last snake in Bombay had been killed some years ago.

Yet she could not help but wonder if Uncle Harrison had felt as secure as this in the moments before he was murdered.

She felt no sympathy for the old miser. His contempt for his brother had condemned her to a life of futureless penury. She knew that she could not continue to live in Bombay, in her circumstances.

The beach was secluded because all the fishing boats were kept on the eastern, sheltered side of the island. It was a trysting place, too. Laura had been invited here often enough, usually at dawn or dusk, but she had never come. She had been saving herself. But for what?

She wondered how many lovers had met here, how much adultery had been committed on these very sands, the men who had invited her to meet them here had all been married.

Then she heard the barking of a dog, and turned to see a very large hound of indeterminate breed bounding towards her.

Instinctively she closed her parasol and thrust it out like a sword to ward the beast off, and saw a red-coated soldier, running along the sand behind it.

'Down, Rufus!' he was shouting. 'Down, sir! Down!'

19

Rufus lolloped up to Laura, who stood absolutely still, her parasol still held in front of her. She was not afraid, she was more interested in what might happen next.

The dog stopped within six feet of her, barking ferociously, but jumping up and down like a puppy at the same time.

'Rufus! Down, sir! Damnable cur! I do beg your pardon, Miss Dean.'

Laura recognised Guy Bartlett, the latest subaltern to arrive for service in the Bombay Regiment. He was quite an attractive young man, with good features and a splendid physique well displayed by his tight-fitting red tunic, now sadly sweat-stained. Although she did not care for very fair men, she had been able to tell at their first meeting that he was most certainly attracted to her. But he had not done any more than look, thus far; he seemed, in fact, to be painfully shy.

'Is this creature yours?' Laura inquired.

'I'm afraid he is. He really is a splendid fellow, when you get to know him.'

'I'm sure he is. May I take my walk now, or is he going to tear my dress?'

'He will do no such thing,' Guy declared. 'Ah . . . may I accompany you, Miss Dean?'

'Why not?' Laura raised her parasol again, and commenced strolling along the beach.

'Now, behave yourself, Rufus,' Guy commanded, and fell into step beside her. 'May I say what a pleasure it is to see you out and about again?'

'One cannot remain in mourning forever,' Laura said. 'Even for such a dear old soul as Uncle Harry.'

'Oh, quite.' They walked in silence for some moments, the dog panting at their heels, then Guy said, 'I suppose you will be leaving Bombay?'

'I really cannot say, Mr Bartlett. I don't think we shall be leaving for a while, certainly. There is so much to be sorted out, and Papa has to decide what is to be done with the factory.'

'Will he not take it over himself?'

'I don't think he wishes to do that. I imagine he will suggest to the Directors that they send out a new man. But he will undoubtedly wish to remain to break him in.'

20

What an accomplished liar she was becoming, she thought. And how this nice young man would despise her when the truth came out, as it undoubtedly would.

'Of course. Well, if I may say so, Miss Dean, from my point of view . . . well, I am very pleased that you will be remaining in Bombay for a while longer.'

Laura stopped, and turned to him. 'Will you, Mr Bartlett?'

Rufus started to bark and went bounding off after a bird which had been incautious enough to alight on the sand.

'Stupid dog,' Guy commented. 'Oh, indeed. I . . . well, I am speaking entirely out of turn, and now more so than ever, of course, but as we have encountered each other for tuitously . . .'

'Mr Bartlett,' Laura smiled. 'You are losing the thread.'

'Oh, ah . . . yes. I do apologise.'

'And you could stop apologising,' she suggested sweetly.

She gazed at him as disarmingly as she knew how. Really, he was *very* good looking, and she found his artlessness strangely charming. After all, he was a soldier, and a promising one, she had been told. His awkwardness might only be caused by adoration of her. She was in the mood for, at least, a flirtation. When the truth came out she would be damned anyway. She might as well have a little fun first.

'I don't suppose you would consider . . .'

'Yes,' she said. 'But we do not have to consider. We are here now, perfectly alone.' She looked along the beach. 'Except for your dog.' She selected a smooth area of sand, and sat down, straightening her skirts, her legs carefully arranged in front of her, her parasol, still extended, resting on the sand, to shelter them from one direction, at any rate. 'Will you not sit beside me?' she invited.

Guy sat down, carefully leaving some space between them.

'You were going to ask me for an assignation?' she prompted. 'Well, here we are. What is it you would like to say to me?'

Rufus came bounding back in a flurry of scattered sand, having abandoned the fruitless chase.

'Oh, Rufus!' Guy said. 'Do lie down, there's a good fellow.'

Rufus lay down, panting, and staring at them. He was

somewhat disconcerting. But Laura was feeling willful; she would carry this absurd event through to its logical conclusion, whatever that might be.

'Yes, Mr Bartlett?' she pressed.

'Well . . .' he was obviously steeling himself. 'I know I have not been in Bombay very long, Miss Dean. And I also know that this is a most unfortunate time for you. But I fear that, now you are your uncle's heiress, you will surely soon fly entirely beyond my reach, if I do not, well . . .'

'Snare me now?' she suggested wickedly.

'Well, I hope you will not think of it as a snare.'

'I do not know what "it" is, Mr Barlett.' She opened her cobalt blue eyes as innocently wide as they would go.

He licked his lips. 'I would like to marry you.'

Laura's mouth opened in surprise. She had anticipated some kind of a proposition. But . . . '*Marry* me?'

'I have insulted you.'

'You have flattered me, sir. May I ask . . . would you have made such a proposal were I not my uncle's heiress?'

'I would have made such a proposal were you a beggar in rags. I have thought of nothing else since my arrival here, Miss Dean. I fell in love with you at first sight.'

'That was an unworthy thought of mine,' she confessed. 'But marriage . . .'

'I can offer you very little, at the moment, save my love. But as time goes by, and I rise in the service . . .'

'I think I would settle for love, Mr Bartlett. But you must give me a little time. As you say, we hardly know each other.' She turned to gaze out to sea, and to hide an unavoidable glint of calculation in her eyes. 'That is something that should be remedied before we can consider marriage, do you not suppose?'

It seemed to take him a few moments to realise that she had not actually said no, rather that she was actually inviting him to take advantage of his situation. By then she was already leaning towards him. Their lips touched, and then she was in his arms, falling over backwards on to the sand so that he was lying half on top of her. For a few moments, they both indulged the wildest passion, mouths working together, tongues caressing,

22

her hands tight on his back while his swept up and down from her hips to her breasts, afraid to linger for more than a passing second.

For how long had she wanted to lie in the arms of a man? But with the thought came a recognition of her danger. Mr Bartlett's hand had now settled on her bodice, very lightly – but she was enjoying the sensation too much.

She got her mouth free, 'Mr Bartlett!' she gasped. 'You are so vehement.'

Instantly he released her and sat up, face flushed, with some difficulty adjusting his breeches. 'Forgive me. I apologise. But I do adore you so, Laura.'

'Do not apologise,' she told him. 'Promise me that you will never apologise again. To anyone.'

'I promise. Laura . . .'

She sat up in turn. Her bonnet had fallen off, and hung around her neck by its ribbon. Undoubtedly there would be sand in her hair.

'I must be going home.'

She stood up, and dusted herself down.

He stood also, and took her into his arms again. She did not resist. Would she settle for being Mrs Guy Bartlett, a subaltern's wife? It would mean remaining in Bombay. But at least she would be married. However, she must not appear over eager.

'Will you marry me? I shall have to obtain permission from Colonel Partridge, of course, and we may have to wait a couple of years, but in all the circumstances . . .'

'Give me time, Guy dearest. Give me time.'

'Well . . . can we meet again?'

'Certainly. Tomorrow?'

'I am on duty tomorrow. And the day after. Damnation! I will be free on Sunday.'

'Sunday,' she said. 'I will take a walk on Sunday morning at dawn.' That would guarantee privacy.

'May I walk back with you, now?'

'I think not,' she said. Rufus was also on his feet, panting with impatience. 'Perhaps you should finish your walk. Otherwise people will talk.'

23

'I don't care about that.'

'But it would not do, would it?' She smiled, and kissed his cheek. 'Till Sunday.'

Would she do it? On the beach, in his arms, she had felt there was nothing she would rather do. But as she walked back through the trees, although she still burned where he had touched her, could still taste him, she realised that she had no idea whether she actually loved him. Indeed, she had no idea what love was.

She felt attracted to him, as he clearly did to her. In fact, she doubted he had ever thought of her in any other terms. But then, had she not always known that she would be married simply for her face and body?

Was sexual attraction enough, when it meant remaining in Bombay, and being poor, for the rest of her life?

And they could not even get married for years; no colonel would allow a penniless twenty-three year old subaltern to take on a wife.

But if she was going to say yes, it must be on Sunday, before he could change his mind. Or, if she were to be totally honest with herself, before he found out she was not an heiress after all.

She entered the house on tiptoe. She wanted to go upstairs and take off her clothes and shake out the sand before encountering her mother.

'Laura! Is that you?'

Laura sighed. 'Yes, Mama.'

'Come in here. The most remarkable thing has happened.'

Laura hesitated, then went into her mother's bedroom. She could not imagine what could have happened that would be more remarkable than the other two events of today, unless news had come that Aunt Ella had also died, making them rich after all.

And what would she think of Guy Bartlett then?

Marjorie Dean was waving a piece of pasteboard at her. 'We have been invited to the ball at Government House!'

Laura frowned as she took the invitation. They had never been invited to Government House before; it was not an honour usually extended to mere writers.

But there it was: His Excellency The Honourable

Mountstuart Elphinstone had indeed invited Mr and Mrs Carmichael Dean and Miss Dean to a ball at Government House on Saturday 4 June 1825, in honour of His Highness Rajah Scindhia Sitraj of Sittapore.

Laura's excitement was only dimmed by the knowledge that everyone else had received their invitation some weeks before.

She raised her head. 'Is that the man who arrived last week with such a lot of noise and elephants?'

'The very man.'

'I wish we'd gone out to look.'

Everyone else had, but they had still been in mourning.

'Why? He's just some fat little Hindu, I imagine.'

'He seems to be a friend of the Governor. But why have we been invited now, at the last minute?'

'Isn't it obvious? Everyone thinks we have inherited a fortune from your uncle.'

'Are we going to go?'

'Well, of course we are.'

'But . . . when they all find out . . . they'll think . . .'

'We'll still have been to a ball at Government House,' Marjorie declared. 'And they will look like fools. *We* have made no representations. Are we to refuse an invitation on the grounds that we are not as rich as they imagine us to be? No, indeed! Now, we must decide what we are going to wear.'

'Oh, heavens!' Laura sat down, and sand scattered out of her skirt and on to the floor, but both women were too excited to notice. 'What *are* we going to wear?'

Saturday, Laura thought, was the night before Sunday. Would that make any difference? Mr Bartlett had made no mention of attending the ball at Government House. Presumably if he was on duty he would be unable to do so. Besides, subalterns were seldom invited by the Governor. But he certainly could not object if she went. Mama had found some lovely silks in the bazaar, and she and Laura worked from dawn to dusk for the next few days. Papa even allowed them to employ one of the Indian women to help them. Now they were finished and Laura's, in pale green taffeta, she thought exquisite; it showed up her fair colouring to perfection.

25

Indeed, she thought she had never been so excited in her life. It was not merely the fact of going to a ball, it was that they were parading under false colours, even if, as Mama claimed, they were doing it innocently. How people would talk, afterwards! But afterwards she would be Mrs Guy Bartlett, and they could say what they liked!

Papa also hired a landaulet for the occasion, and they arrived at Government House promptly at nine, in the midst of a large crowd of people, all of whom seemed to know each other. They also obviously knew who the Deans were, and greeted them courteously.

'Money has a smell to it,' Carmichael Dean said cynically.

Then they were in the line, waiting to be presented to the Governor. As he was a bachelor, he usually asked the wife of a senior factor or army officer to act as his hostess, and tonight it was Mrs Partridge, wife of the Colonel of the Regiment. The sight of her, the thought that she would have a part to play in her husband's decision as whether or not to allow Guy to marry, made Laura nervous as, following her father, she made a curtsey and all but overbalanced. She was raised by the Governor himself.

'Miss Dean,' he said kindly. 'How very charming you look.'

'Thank you, Your Excellency,' she said.

'Now, I would have you meet Rajah Scindhia Sitraj of Sittapore.'

Mama and Papa had already shaken hands with the Rajah and Mrs Partridge and had gone on their way into the thronged ball room. Laura lowered herself into the necessary curtsey, hardly looking at the Rajah, only raising her eyes when she had her balance under control. Then she gave a little gasp.

Rajah Sitraj was a young man, certainly not over thirty. Although he was no taller than Laura he was well-muscled and trim. His clothes were of the best, a blue silk tunic over white breeches and black boots; his belt was red velvet. Round his neck hung a dazzling necklace of rubies, emeralds and diamonds, and in his blue silk turban, there was a huge ruby.

His cleanshaven face was handsomely aquiline, his teeth gleamingly white. As he smiled at her, his black eyes seemed to catch fire.

'It is my great privilege, Miss Dean,' he said in perfect English.

Laura could think of nothing to say in reply. She had never seen such an attractive man in her life. And Mama had thought he would be a fat little Hindu!

She realised the Rajah was still holding her hand, but did not know how she could free herself; presumably one did not do that sort of thing with a rajah. Then to her consternation he raised her hand and kissed the back of her glove.

'You must dance with me,' he said, very softly.

Laura didn't know if Mountstuart Elphinstone had heard him or not, but everyone in the room would have seen the gesture. She managed a smile, and as he released her, gave a quick curtsey to Mrs Partridge, and hurried to find her mother, aware of the flutter of fans in her wake.

'Well!' Marjorie commented. 'Of all the effrontery!'

'I thought he was perfectly charming,' Laura said, feeling the heat in her cheeks.

'An Indian,' her mother said disparagingly.

'But a Rajah, my dear. And he must be wearing ten thousand pounds worth of jewellery,' Carmichael Dean remarked. 'My word, who's this fellow?'

They had been approached by another Indian, who wore uniform, a yellow tunic over blue breeches, and black boots; a sword hung at his side. He gave a stiff bow. 'Miss Dean,' he said, his English not quite as good as the Rajah's. 'His Highness has asked me to fill in your card for him. I am Colonel Mujhabi, His Highness' aide-de-camp.'

Laura gave him her card without a word, and he took out a pencil and began to write. She wasn't really aware of what he was doing, until he returned the card. Then she saw that every dance had been taken by *HH The Rajah of S*. The Colonel merely smiled, and bowed, and withdrew.

'But . . .' Laura looked at her mother, and the regimental band struck up a waltz.

'He's coming over,' Marjorie hissed.

Laura felt as if her knees were going to give way. She turned to the Rajah as he came towards them, again aware that everyone in the room was staring at her.

27

'Sir,' Sitraj said with the utmost courtesy. 'Would you permit me to dance with your daughter?'

Carmichael Dean's mouth opened and closed soundlessly.

'Of course, Your Highness,' Marjorie said, performing a quick volte-face with her most charming smile.

Sitraj extended his hand, and Laura laid hers on top of it. She felt like a queen as he walked her to the centre of the room and began to waltz quite perfectly.

'This is my first visit to Bombay,' he explained. 'I would have come sooner had I realised how much beauty there is in the Presidency.'

'You are a flatterer, Your Highness,' she protested.

'I prefer to think that I am a connoisseur of beautiful things. May I ask how old you are?'

She was taken aback. One did not ask such a thing in polite society. But he was an Indian rajah.

'I am eighteen,' she said.

'Ah! But unmarried, of course.'

'Yes, Your Highness.'

'You must forgive my directness. I know little of drawing rooms.'

'You speak English so perfectly,' Laura ventured. 'And you dance divinely.'

'Why, thank you. I am very flattered. I was fortunate as a boy. Unlike most of my family, my father had a great admiration for the English. So he imported an English tutor for me.'

'How interesting.'

'It was for me, certainly. Mr Humphries taught me English, and he taught me how to eat as an Englishman, and how to dance. I would dance with my sisters by the hour.' Sitraj smiled. 'Without any music. Mr Humphries would whistle. But he insisted I learn. He said every gentleman must be able to dance well.'

'Absolutely,' she said. 'Is Mr Humphries still in . . .' she hesitated. Where *was* he Rajah of?

'Sittapore? No. Sadly, he died a few years ago.'

'Oh. I'm terribly sorry.'

'I mourned him deeply.' He gazed into her eyes. 'I would like to show you Sittapore. My city.'

28

'Oh,' she said faintly. 'You have a city?'

'Well, of course,' he said lightly, as though it were the most ordinary thing in the world.

'I should love to see it,' she said.

'Then you shall.'

The music stopped.

'Your Highness.' Mountstuart Elphinstone bent over them. 'You'll forgive me, I know. But there is someone I am most anxious for you to meet.'

The Prince sighed. 'Duty calls. But I shall claim you for the next dance. May I?'

'Oh, I . . . you already have,' Laura stammered breathlessly.

'Well,' Marjorie said. 'What on earth are we to do?'

It was two in the morning, and they had just got home after the most exciting night of Laura's life. Everyone at the reception had been anxious to speak with her, when she hadn't been dancing with the Rajah, who had hovered about her most gratifyingly all evening.

As they said good night, he had told her he would take her riding this morning, early, before church. He had *told* her, not asked her! And she had dumbly nodded.

'At least we can be sure he's not after Laura because of anything Harrison may have left us.' Papa yawned as he spoke; he had had a great deal to drink.

'Because he wears a few jewels?' Marjorie snorted.

'Because I had a word with Elphinstone's secretary. Sitraj is one of the richest men in India, if not in the world. He has his own emerald mine.'

'But he is after our Laura,' Marjorie said. 'A Hindu! He probably has a dozen wives already. And as for what they practise!!'

'Really, my dear, you are being improper,' Carmichael protested.

'What *do* they practice?' Laura asked.

'Nothing *you* should know about, miss,' her father said. 'Off you go to bed.'

Laura obeyed, although she knew she would not sleep. Of course she knew that the Hindus were a race apart. Not only

29

were they of a different colour and a different religion, but they dressed differently, and they did things differently. Everyday things. Therefore . . . other things as well.

The trouble was, she didn't even know how Christian Englishmen and women did it; Mama had never been very forthcoming on the subject. It was as if, having conceived out of wedlock, she had resolutely turned her back on sexual matters. Certainly she had never conceived again.

But when she thought of Mr Bartlett . . . he had done nothing she would not have expected an Englishman to do. And everything he had done, she had wanted. But she could not imagine Rajah Sitraj being so hesitant and apologetic, or wanting so little! The thought of him lying on the sand beside her made her feel quite giddy.

And he was coming to take her for a ride tomorrow. No, today. Of course, Mama would have to come too. But even so . . .

When she awoke the sun was streaming through her window. It was past eight o'clock. Mr Bartlett would have been waiting for two hours.

Poor Mr Bartlett!

Bombay 15 June 1825

I am the most damned and despairing fellow on earth! I will never look at another woman if I live to be a hundred.

Miss Laura Dean is, I believe, no better than she should be. Indeed, that is what is said of her.

The wretched girl actually lay in my arms, while I behaved most correctly. She then made an assignation, when all things would have been possible. I had already proposed marriage, and had every intention of conducting our courtship in an honourable fashion.

So I attended this tryst, and she did not. Instead, I received a note to say that she overslept. A thousand apologies, etc, etc. Why, being a fool, I might have accepted this excuse, had I not already learned of her caprice of the previous night, when she spent almost the entire evening in the arms of a Prince of Scindhia – waltzing! I had always supposed that dreadful dance to be indecent; now I am certain of it.

The Prince of Scindhia is a Hindu! Bombay is set by the ears. One night's tête-à-tête would have caused gossip. But in the past week the Prince has squired the young lady every-where, taking her hither and yon in his phaeton, smiling at her every word. I have seen them.

I need hardly say that the fellow is disgustingly rich, and can be observed at a distance because of the sun reflecting from his jewels.

Opinion is considerably divided in the Presidency. On the one hand there are those who feel Elphinstone should put a stop to it, as the sight of a young English lady being monopolised by a dark-skinned gentleman, however wealthy, is bad for morale, and for our relations with our Indian subjects. On the other, there are those who feel that Miss Dean deserves whatever is coming to her; there are veiled allusions to disgusting Hindu practices!

She seems oblivious of it all, and merely smiles and looks contented, like a beautiful cat who has come across an unsuspected saucer of milk.

In despair, I have taken to the bottle and worse, and in a fit of drunkenness I sought the company of my dusky charmer.

This was quite an experience, although not one I would recommend to any but the most agile.

David Evans and I sallied forth; Evans apparently knew just where to go. In a dank and dark establishment we were treated to an exhibition of dancing which was obscene, but interestingly stimulating.

The girls are called nautch dancers, the word nautch being a corruption of the Hindu word nach, or dance. But of course they are much more than mere professional dancers. They wear nothing except gold bangles, and their bodies are coated in coconut oil. Thus unadorned they perform the most sensuous movements, revealing all, and from time to time they invite the caresses of the spectators. It is very difficult to resist this sort of thing, even when sober. And we were far from sober.

The dancing completed, the customers are invited to take their pick and retire to the private rooms with the wench of their choice. I was given first choice, and did very well. I will not shock the reader with the details, but I emerged with a monumental headache, a lighter wallet, an even lighter feeling in my loins, and a memory I shall carry to my dying day. I feel utterly miserable as I imagine Miss Dean subjecting herself to such obscenities to please her Hindu lover. Surely her natural delicacy would forbid it!

Amazingly, I continue in good health.

I am now actively training Rufus to bite all Hindus, with the exception of Ramjohn. This point of view is generally applauded by my brother officers.

There is not a great deal more to report. The Thug attacks continue on Company land, but not so close to Bombay as the murder of poor Harrison Dean. We send out column after column, but they always return empty-handed. The unfortunate fact is that the local people are either terrified of these bandits or in league with them, and all a Thug has to do is discard his weapons and his strangling noose and sit down among his dark-skinned compatriots, and he is indistinguishable from any law-abiding worthy, if such there be.

To defeat them we will have to adopt far more stringent methods than are at present employed. This is not apparently to the taste of our Governor, but the rumour is that Elphinstone is to retire, to be replaced by a soldier rather than an administrator, something which will be greatly appreciated by the military here.

2

The Rani

'Thank you again for a lovely drive, Highness,' Laura said, as
the phaeton drew up before the bungalow. To either side,
curtains rustled as the ladies of Bombay surreptitiously
inspected the pair, but Laura no longer cared about that.

'Thank you, again, for accompanying me,' Sitraj said.

'Will you take a cup of tea?'

'That will be very nice.'

This was a formality they went through at the end of every
drive. At first she had been reluctant to invite so grand a person
as the Rajah into so humble a home, but he had been as natural
there as in one of his own palaces. She admired that in him
greatly.

But today, as one of the Rajah's attendants came to help her
down – Sitraj drove himself, but four of his people always
followed on horseback at a respectful distance – he rested his
hand on her arm.

'Before we go in, there is something I must say to you.'

She turned, immediately breathless.

'I am returning to Sittapore next week,' he said. 'Duty calls.'

'Oh,' she said.

Of course she had known this moment had to come, but had
refused to think about it. For a week she had been the most
important woman in Bombay. Now she must return to being
the most unimportant . . . and the most disliked as well, she
supposed. However much the other white women might
criticise her, there was no doubt that they were all jealous of
her. As for the men . . . even Guy Bartlett turned away from
her when there was a risk of a meeting. She had sent him a note
of the most abject apology – something she had made him
promise never to do – and it had made no difference. He had

34

apparently joined the majority in condemning her relationship with the Rajah.

On the other hand, even if he had accepted her apology, would she not still have wished to have had this magical, unforgettable week?

Marriage, after all, was no longer a practical possibility, for soon enough the truth about her father's inheritance, or lack of it, would be known.

'I shall be sorry to see you go,' she said.

He still held her arm. 'You said once that you would like to see Sittapore.'

'Oh, I would!'

'Then, if I asked you to come with me, next week, would you say yes?'

Now she was utterly breathless. Go to Sittapore, with the Rajah? But as what?

He could read her expression. 'You would come as my wife, of course.'

His wife! The wife of a rajah. She would be a rani. But . . . he was a Hindu, and therefore probably already had several wives. And then as a Hindu, he would wish to . . . she had no idea. He had always been the perfect gentleman with her, had never touched more than her hand, nor had she had the courage to flirt with him as she had done with poor Guy Bartlett. But every Englishwoman in Bombay whispered about Indian lovemaking, how unnatural it was. As if they knew anything about it!

'That prospect does not please you?' Sitraj enquired softly.

'Oh, it . . . it . . . it pleases me very much, Highness. But . . .'

'I know. There are difficulties. But difficulties are there to be overcome. Let us begin at the beginning. Have I your permission to speak with your father?'

'Oh . . . yes. Yes, of course,' she stammered.

'Mr Carmichael Dean is here to see you, Your Excellency,' the Governor's secretary said.

'Dean! Yes. I supposed he would come to me, soon enough. Very well, Rodgers, show him in.'

Mountstuart Elphinstone leaned back in his chair, arranging his features into a suitably severe expression. The

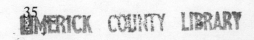

Governor was an easy-going man, who believed in getting on with everyone, but this was too much. He could not believe that Sitraj, who was a very good sort of fellow, would ever commit the slightest impropriety, but he could well believe that a silly girl like Laura Dean might suppose he had. It was all Dean's fault for allowing his daughter to see so much of the Rajah in the first place. If he was now seeking redress for some imagined insult from one of the Company's most loyal supporters, he had another think coming.

'Mr Carmichael Dean,' Rodgers announced.

Carmichael came into the Governor's office, slightly over-awed. He had never been in here before.

'Well, Dean.' Elphinstone did not get up. 'Take a seat.'

'Thank you, Your Excellency.' Dean sat down.

'Now tell me what your problem is.'

'Well, Sir . . .' Dean swallowed. 'It's this rajah fellow, Sitraj.'

'Ah. You have a complaint to make about His Highness?'

'Complaint, Your Excellency, well . . .' Dean took a long breath. 'He wants to marry my daughter. Asked to see me, proper as you please.'

'Good God!'

The Governor dined with Sitraj every evening, as the Rajah was a guest at Government House, and while he was aware that the young devil had been vastly taken with Miss Dean at the ball and had been seeing a great deal of her ever since, it had never occurred to the Governor that he would go so far.

'Quite,' Dean agreed.

Marriage, between the Rajah of Sittapore and a white girl? Whatever would the Directors say?

Oh the other hand, the boy's infatuation might well be entirely to the Company's advantage.

But to have chosen Laura Dean . . .

'Does the Rajah know who you are?' he asked. 'I mean – forgive me, my dear Sir – does he know you are a . . . well . . . a writer?'

'Oh, yes. He has been to my house several times. Of course he knows about Harrison's death, but I don't suppose anything I might have inherited would make much difference to him.'

'Even supposing you had inherited anything,' Elphinstone remarked drily.

Dean flushed.

'I'm afraid I do require to be kept informed of everything that happens in my Presidency,' Elphinstone pointed out. 'However, I entirely agree that even if your brother had left you his every penny it would not interest the Rajah. I assume he has not raised the matter of a dowry?'

'Well, no. In fact, he suggested that there might be a lot coming the other way, if you follow me.'

Then he was absolutely serious, Elphinstone thought. With the carelessness of omnipotent power and inexhaustible wealth, he had seen something he wanted, and was determined to buy it. Well, then, serve the young rascal right. He should at least enjoy himself.

'Oh, I do, Dean. I do. Let me get this absolutely straight. The Rajah, in full knowledge that you are nothing more than a clerk, and that you have not got two pennies to rub together, and that your daughter has been brought up in these penurious circumstances, has never known any other life, and has no dowry, has asked for her hand in marriage?'

Dean gulped. 'If you choose to put it that way, Your Excellency, yes.'

'And has even suggested that he might pay you for the privilege. How much?'

'Well, he asked if twenty-five thousand pounds would be sufficient.'

'Twenty-five . . . So what exactly did you wish to see me about, Dean?'

'Well, Your Excellency, my daughter is an English lady, and this fellow is . . .'

'A rajah, which is all that truly matters, surely. As well as being, of course, a very wealthy man.'

'But we know nothing about him,' Dean objected.

'Well . . .' Elphinstone enjoyed the opportunity to pontificate. 'You will no doubt know that the Scindhia family are basically Marathas. The Marathas gained their independence from the Mughal Emperors about a hundred years ago, and for most of that hundred years were a formidable military power.

However, in the course of time they split up into several principalities, of which that held by the Scindhia family, and known as Scindhia, remained the most recalcitrant. Why, thirty years ago, this boy's grandfather, Mahadaji Scindhia, took possession of Delhi and set the then Emperor up as his puppet. He had a large army, trained and commanded by French mercenaries. We had to put out a considerable effort to defeat him. But it was done, by the Duke of Wellington and General Lake, and the Scindhia territory was split up into smallish jaghirs, each given to one of the princes of the house, on condition they became clients of the Company. Sitraj happens to be one of these princes. Sittapore was actually given to his father, but he died very soon afterwards. There was some suspicion of foul play, I believe, something to do with a jealous brother. In any event, Sitraj sorted the situation out, and although very young, only eighteen when he succeeded, has proved a most successful ruler and, I may say, a very good client of the Company. His jaghir, centred around the city of Sittapore, is not very large, but very rich in produce as well as precious stones.'

Carmichael was showing signs of impatience; he knew as much about Indian politics as the Governor.

'What I meant was, Your Excellency, I know nothing about his . . . personal habits. He is a Hindu . . . well!'

'Ah. Yes. I take your point. Hm.' Elphinstone allowed himself to imagine the luscious Laura in the arms of a Hindu lover. 'Well . . . all marriages are to a certain extent a business of give and take, Dean.'

'Your Excellency, are you seriously suggesting I agree to this proposal?'

'Well . . .' Elphinstone scratched his ear. 'As I have mentioned, it is my business to know what goes on in this Presidency. You left England because of an undischarged debt, Dean. What was the amount?'

'Two thousand pounds,' Carmichael muttered.

'Eighteen years ago. With interest at say, two per cent, that is probably close to three thousand by now. But three thousand taken away from twenty-five leaves a very tidy sum. How old are you?'

'Forty-eight.'

'Well, you see, in a few more years you will have to retire. What then? You could not afford to remain here. But if you return to England without the wherewithal to pay the debt you will go straight into gaol, no doubt for the rest of your life.'

Carmichael gulped. He knew the awful situation only too well.

'Whereas twenty-two thousand, invested in Consols, could bring you in a modestly comfortable income for the rest of your life. Besides, if you put your situation honestly to the Prince, he might increase his offer.'

'But Laura . . . it seems so much like selling her.'

'My dear fellow, when is marriage not a case of making the best bargain possible? If your daughter has allowed herself to be squired by the Rajah for the past week, she cannot actually be repelled by him.'

'Well . . . she isn't. She seems quite taken with him.'

'Look here, Dean, why do you not put the matter to your daughter? I know it is not usual, but this is an unusual situation.'

'What will people say. . . ?'

'It will not matter what people say, Dean. You and your wife, if you so choose, will be on your way home to England, and your daughter will be the wealthiest woman in India.'

'But what about suttee?'

'We have outlawed suttee.'

'On Company land. But Sittapore is not Company land.'

'I happen to know that Rajah Sitraj has also outlawed suttee in his jaghir. However, I am sure if you mention your misgivings to him, he will agree to insert a clause in the marriage contract to the effect that your daughter will not be subject to any Hindu laws, religious or otherwise. Come to think of it, that might be a very good idea.'

'Suppose this fellow has other wives?'

'The Rajah will, I am sure, be reasonable,' Elphinstone said.

'Your father is a very protective man,' Sitraj said. He was sitting beside Laura on the verandah of the Dean bungalow.

They were quite alone, yet not alone. Mama was hovering

39

just inside the door, Papa as well, no doubt. The Prince's servants waited at the gate by his phaeton. And every surrounding bungalow was in darkness, suggesting that their owners were out, but in reality, as Laura well knew, to enable the windows overlooking the Dean household to be manned in force.

But at least they could not be overheard, as long as they kept their voices down.

'I am his only child,' she said, hardly aware of what she was saying. She felt rushed off her feet, as if it were all a dream. Papa had needed several stiff drinks after the Prince had spoken with him yesterday. Sitraj had then departed, saying he would return for an answer this evening; he had almost made it sound like an ultimatum. Papa had then gone rushing off to see the Governor this morning, had this evening received the Prince again in private . . . and then she had been invited to sit on the verandah, in the dark, and converse with him.

'Here is what I have agreed with him,' Sitraj said. 'I had no idea that he was in straitened circumstances. So I have agreed to make him a settlement of forty thousand pounds, which should enable him to liquidate his debts and live the life of a country gentleman in England.'

'Oh, Highness,' she gasped.

'I have also agreed that you will be my principal wife. I do have others, as well as concubines. Well, it is the custom amongst my people. But you will be Rani of Sittapore.'

'Rani of Sittapore,' she whispered. It sounded incredibly romantic.

'I have also agreed that we shall be married in a Christian church, here in Bombay. The Hindu ceremony can take place when we return to Sittapore. But the Christian ceremony will make us man and wife. This ceremony will take place the day after tomorrow.'

'The day after . . . that's not possible.'

'Everything is possible, my dear Laura, when one wills it. But it will not be possible unless you accept my proposal. Your father has left the final decision to you.'

'Oh!' But was she going to refuse? She had already virtually accepted, perhaps feeling almost certain that Papa would reject the idea out of hand. But he had not. And now . . . Did she love him? She had no idea. He was an attractive man, and the idea of marriage to him had seemed infinitely preferable to remaining poverty-stricken Laura Dean, or even if she were to be honest, the equally poverty-stricken if respectable Mrs Guy Bartlett. Sitraj would sweep her away from all that. She would be Rani of Sittapore!

But would she be marrying simply for money and position? Surely not. Sitraj was a man she could very well come to love, given time. And he would never hurt her.

'So?' he asked.

'I would very much like to be your wife, Highness,' she said.

'In that case, you will now call me Sitraj in private, Highness only in public.'

'Oh. Yes.'

'I have a present for you.' He felt in one of the pockets on his tunic, and held out an emerald. She gasped, for it was as big as her thumbnail and winked at her even in the gloom, catching the stray ray of light from the window. 'I will have it made into a ring for you when we reach Sittapore,' he said. 'But I wish you to have the stone, now.'

He placed it in her hand.

'And now,' he said, 'before we go in to your parents, I believe there is an English formality.'

She turned her face up for his kiss. It was a mere brushing of the lips, but as he kissed her, the tips of his fingers drifted forward and stroked, with the lightness of a feather, across the bodice of her gown. She had to repress a start, for the shock ran right through her. Before she could catch her breath, he was standing, and holding out his hand for her.

He had taken possession.

For forty-eight hours, life in the Dean household was chaotic beyond belief. Every seamstress in Bombay moved into the house, seduced by the Rajah's fortune. Marjorie Dean, who had appeared to be in a state of shock over the preceding two days, came to with a start when she discovered that her daughter's wedding dress was to be an emerald green sari.

'I'll have no such thing,' she declared. 'Laura is pure. She will wear white.'

'But white is the colour of mourning, memsahib,' explained the head seamstress. 'No bride can be married in mourning.'

Laura opted for the green. She was leaving European custom behind.

Marjorie subsided again. But on the morning of the wedding she summoned Laura for a little chat.

'We have never spoken of marriage,' she remarked.

'No,' Laura agreed.

'It is, I suppose, a very proper business, ordained by God. And you will be married in a Christian church, which is something to be thankful for. Afterwards . . . Oh, Laura!' She burst into tears.

Laura held her close. 'I shall be well cared for, Mama. Sitraj is a gentleman.'

'Laura, whatever he demands of you, whatever he inflicts upon you, remember always that you are a Christian lady.'

Carmichael was in a far better humour. The tailors had been busy about him as well, and he was resplendent in a new suit of best grey broadcloth. He had bought himself a watch and chain, and a gold-headed cane, and was very much the gentleman of means. He had already sent in his resignation to the Company.

This was something else that had upset Marjorie. 'You cannot mean to sail away and leave Laura all alone,' she complained.

'She will not be alone,' Carmichael pointed out. 'She will be with her husband. In Sittapore. That is more than a hundred miles from Bombay.'

'England is ten thousand,' Marjorie moaned. But she was again reassured by Laura, who was very happy at the thought of her parents departing. Much as she loved them, she knew they could only ever be an embarrassment to the Rajah, and to herself as Rani. Rani of Sittapore! How she loved the sound of that.

The church was crowded because, overnight, Sitraj had had sufficient invitations handwritten to be sent to every member of the Bombay community who was anyone at all, and there were very few who did not attend, even at such short notice.

42

The streets were crowded as well, as news got around that the Rajah of Sittapore was marrying an Englishwoman, and as Laura and Carmichael were driven to the church in their hired coach there were cheers and shouts.

Governor Elphinstone had turned out the military to keep order. No doubt Guy Bartlett was amongst them, but Laura did not see him. She did not wish to. He remained a stain on her conscience, partly because of any hurt she might have caused him, but more importantly because the future Rani of Sittapore had lain in his arms. Thank God her commonsense had saved her from making an irretrievable error.

The aide-de-camp, Colonel Mujhabi, acted as best man, obviously in a state of total confusion as to what was going on. Sitraj himself had to be led through the service by the bishop, but he responded well, smiling at Laura as he did so. And again his kiss was the gentlest touch imaginable. Yet she could see his desire for her in his eyes. She wondered what he could see in hers?

Elphinstone had decided that, as even with the Deans' sudden enormous wealth their bungalow remained quite unsuitable, and as Sitraj was in any event his guest, the reception would be held at Government House, and thence the Rajah of Sittapore and his wife drove in an open carriage, shaded from the afternoon sun by huge umbrellas, through cheering crowds. Every woman in Bombay who had ever sniffed and turned her head away as Laura Dean had passed by, every man who had ever ogled her, now had to curtsey to or kiss the hand of the Rani of Sittapore. She felt a glow of triumph.

Suddenly she found herself gazing at Guy Bartlett.

He had clearly been on duty, and was just about the last of the guests to come in. Now he bowed over her hand. 'My congratulations, Your Highness,' he said. 'May I wish you great joy . . . and prosperity.'

Laura caught the deliberate hesitation. No doubt he assumed she had married for money. No doubt a great many people assumed that.

She looked him in the eye. 'Why, thank you, Mr Bartlett. May I in turn wish you all the good fortune in the world.'

43

He then shook hands with the Rajah, but Sitraj had heard the exchange. 'A friend of yours?' he asked softly.

Laura knew it would never do to lie to her husband. No doubt he was kept well informed of Bombay gossip, and she could not tell to how many of his fellow officers Guy had spoken of his proposal.

'Mr Bartlett asked me to marry him, only a few days before you did.'

'You did not tell me of this.'

'Because I refused him.'

'Ah.' He smiled. 'I am glad this took place before I asked you, Laura. Shall we join our guests?'

There was champagne to be drunk, sweetmeats to be eaten, and speeches to be listened to. These went on until it was quite dark, at which time Marjorie, who was having the time of her life as the mother of a rani, found herself next to Laura.

'It has all been so rushed,' she whispered, 'I have not even found out where you will spend the night, but I am sure you should withdraw to put on some decent clothing.' Although the seamstresses had assured Marjorie and Laura that the sari was the most modest garment imaginable, Marjorie still felt it to be rather improper.

'I will have to speak with His Highness,' Laura said.

Sitraj had, as usual, been keeping his eye on her even as they mingled with the guests, and immediately he saw her looking for him, disengaged himself from his conversation and came towards her.

'My mother feels it is time I withdrew,' she said.

'I think that is an excellent idea. We will both do so.'

'Ah . . . in all the excitement we quite forgot to establish where we will be spending the night.'

'Why, on the road. I am leaving just as soon as you are ready, which you seem to be.'

'But . . . do I not have to change?'

'That will not be necessary, my dear Laura. Come, let us find His Excellency and thank him for this splendid party.'

People quickly became aware that the Rajah and Rani were preparing to leave, but they were confused by the odd manner in which it was happening. So was Elphinstone. But he shook Sitraj's hand for the tenth time, and kissed Laura for the third.

'Safe journey,' he said. 'Oh, safe journey.'

Marjorie was scandalised. 'Going off, just like that!'

Carmichael was very drunk. 'There's a whole lot of elephants at the door,' he announced. 'Ten of 'em.'

The guests ran outside to see. Laura and Sitraj went out among them. There indeed were ten elephants, draped with flowers and fine stuffs, surrounded by attendants, each with a richly dressed mahout, standing patiently in the flickering light of the flaming torches.

'You have ridden in a howdah before?' Sitraj inquired.

'Only once.'

'Kara will carry us all the way back to Sittapore,' Sitraj said. 'It will not take longer than a fortnight.'

A fortnight? On the back of an elephant? And when would they consummate the marriage? Perhaps he did not wish to until he was in his own house. Laura thought that might be rather a good idea; it would give them time to get to know each other.

There was a hum of excitement as the ladder was brought. Sitraj's men waited to assist Laura if she needed them. She looked for Mama and Papa, gave them each a kiss, and waved to all the guests. She caught sight of Guy Bartlett at the back of the throng. She climbed up, to find at the top less a howdah than a small room, with an ornate curved roof, and containing a divan. She sat down with a gasp, and a moment later Sitraj appeared, also waving to the crowd.

'My clothes!' she said, in sudden alarm.

'Everything has been taken care of,' he assured her. He sat down beside her, spoke to the mahout in Hindustani, and the elephant began to move. 'I think we should wave,' he told Laura.

She sat up, and waved at the people below, indistinguishable in the darkness.

'You will think me very remiss,' she said. 'But I know very little Hindustani.'

'Then you will learn,' he told her. 'There are a great many things you will have to learn.'

'I know,' she said. 'I do want to, really.'

'Then you shall. I think we have amused them long enough.' The elephant was at the end of Government House drive. The howdah was equipped with curtains, and these Sitraj now drew, completely isolating them from the outside world.

There was a small jewel-encrusted lantern hanging from the roof of the howdah, to give them light.

Sitraj smiled at her. 'Would you like something more to drink, or eat? There is a hamper there, with champagne, and food.'

'I think I have had enough,' she said.

'Good. I also have had enough.' He put his arm round her shoulders and brought her against him, kissing her mouth. She surrendered utterly, and felt his touch on her breast again. She made no protest as he unfastened the tunic and put his hand inside, warm and gentle, finding its way through the folds of her sari and the blouse beneath to cup the flesh and play with the nipple. She had dreamed of having this happen to her for so long; she had almost wanted Guy Bartlett to be more forceful that day on the beach, and again thanked her lucky stars that he had not been.

The fingers left her breast and slid down her ribs and stomach. Sitraj seemed to know a great deal about saris; the various folds just fell apart as he touched them, while all the while he was possessing her lips. Then she realised the hand was between her legs . . .

'Oh!' she gasped, jerking her head back.

'Enjoy it, my Laura,' he said. 'Enjoy it.'

She found herself panting; the sensation was irresistible.

'Is the movement of the elephant disturbing you?' he asked.

'No,' she said. 'No, it is lulling.'

'Good,' he said. 'Disrobe. Everything.'

She looked up at the light.

'No, no,' he said. 'I wish to look at you.'

He began to help her, taking off her tunic before unravelling the rest of the sari. She became filled with a tremendous tension, but it was the most delicious tension she had ever known.

'It is like unwrapping a parcel,' he smiled at her, as she sprawled naked on the divan. 'A very beautiful parcel.'

'Now your hair,' he commanded.

For this special occasion Mama had put the golden curls up in a vast chignon. Laura reached up and released the pins, and the hair tumbled around her shoulders.

'I am told there are many women in England with hair like yours,' he said. 'But none so beautiful in other ways, I am sure. Or why would any Englishman ever leave his country?'

She licked her lips, watching him, unable to guess what might be going to happen next.

To her consternation, he began to undress himself. She had supposed it would all happen in the dark, at least the first time.

Sitraj revealed a fine physique, well muscled and obviously very fit. But it was his lower half to which her gaze was irresistibly drawn. She had no brothers and though the Indian boys in Bombay were inclined to go about naked, it was the done thing always to avert one's eyes. In any event, on no boy had she ever seen anything so huge and demanding – would Mr Bartlett ever have looked like this?

Sitraj smiled at her. 'You must not be afraid of him. He will become your friend, in some ways your mentor, but at the same time your servant. He will bring you much happiness, and if you learn to make him happy in turn, he will never wish to seek another mistress. Now take him in your hand.'

Instinctively Laura half pushed herself away from him across the divan.

Sitraj lay on his elbow beside her, revealing not a trace of disappointment or impatience. 'You are still afraid,' he said. 'Your mother has been neglectful. Hindu girls are taught about such things from a very early age. But then, they are married at a far earlier age than the English. Do you know what they will say in Sittapore? That I have married an old maid.' He smiled and took her hand. 'But I have married a treasure. Come to me.'

Laura took a deep breath, and moved back towards him. He held her face and kissed her mouth, and at the same time pulled her against him. She could feel him against her thigh. Oh, my God, she thought, I am going to scream!

'In English,' he said, 'your words are harsh, unpleasant, distasteful. Penis, and vagina. Yours is a barbarous language.

47

But then, I often think your attitude to sexual matters is the same. It is a mixture of fear and lust and prurience. This is not so in India. A man should lust after a woman, certainly, but he must not take her unless he is sure that she in turn lusts after him. Oh, yes, my Laura, it is very possible for a woman to lust after a man. In fact, I sometimes think that women do more lusting than men. Now come. In my language, he is called a lingam. Say it.'

Laura opened her mouth and then closed it again.

'Say it,' he insisted gently.

'Lingam,' she whispered.

'And he wishes to embed himself in your yoni. Say it.'

'Yoni.' Her voice was stronger.

'Now hold him.'

She obeyed, tentatively, feeling the flesh swelling beneath her fingers.

'Now,' he said. 'I am going to play with your yoni, to make you ready for me. Do not be afraid. Lie back and enjoy what I am doing to you. It will be the most beautiful sensation you have ever known, if you surrender to it. Then I will hurt you. I must. Has your mother told you of this, at least?'

Laura nodded uncertainly. According to Mama it hurt every time; Mama had never spoken of any pleasure. As for beauty . . . but she still held him.

'I will hurt you as little as possible,' Sitraj promised. 'And after the first couple of times, there will be no pain at all. Only pleasure. A great deal of pleasure. Will you believe me?'

'I will believe you,' she whispered.

Laura awoke with a start. Never had she slept so deeply. As she had told Sitraj, the movement of the elephant was like a ship in a gentle sea, rocking her to and fro.

Never had she felt so languorously content, so aware of herself. Every inch of her body, from her toes to her hair, had been caressed at some stage during the night. Most of it had been kissed as well.

He had entered her three times. The first time they had lain facing each other, and he had taken her leg across his thighs; the second time she had been on her knees, and the third time

48

they had again both been lying down, but she had had her back pressed against him. That way he had been able to hold her breasts as he had surged into her.

There had been very little pain. Now she was only deliciously sore.

Could Mr Barlett have been as gentle, and yet as magnificent? But why did she keep thinking about Mr Bartlett? The sooner he was entirely forgotten the better.

The elephant had stopped. That was what had awakened her. She could smell spiced food being prepared. She was very hungry.

But where was Sitraj? The divan was empty but for herself. Laura sat up in alarm, and found herself looking at an Indian woman, quite old, dark and wrinkled, but smiling.

Hastily she reached for the covers. But there were no covers.

'His Highness is bathing,' the woman said in broken English. 'He awaits you.'

Laura looked around her, abandoning any attempt to cover herself. 'My clothes?'

'They are used clothes, Highness. You will wear new clothes, after your bath. This is what you must wear to the bath.'

She held up a dhoti.

'Just that?' Laura was aghast. 'I could not possibly.'

The woman smiled. 'His Highness understands your modesty. You will wear this blouse as well.'

It was of the thinnest cotton, and would conceal nothing. But it was better than nothing at all.

'Let me see to your hair,' the woman said. She knelt on the divan, behind Laura, and began plaiting the thick golden tresses, quickly and expertly.

Laura had not had her hair plaited since she was twelve years old.

'What is your name?' she asked.

'Miljah, Highness.'

'And you're a member of the Rajah's household?'

'I am his slave, Highness. I am your slave, now.'

'Oh.' There were no slaves in Bombay. It was forbidden by law.

'Tomorrow I will wash your hair,' Miljah said. 'But today it is still clean and sweet-smelling. It is your hair that first attracted His Highness. He has told me this. He said your hair had the quality of finespun gold. It is wealth I must possess, Miljah, he told me.'

'And now he does,' Laura said happily, as the plaits were gathered and secured on top of her head.

Climbing down from the howdah was an ordeal, because Laura knew she was as exposed as if she were naked, and while the men and women of the Prince's entourage pretended not to look, she was sure they did.

She had to wait for Miljah to follow her, and she gazed around, at the people, the encampment, and the jungle which surrounded them.

She had never been deep in the jungle before.

They were undoubtedly following a fairly well-worn trail, yet to either side the great trees clustered, rising out of the matted undergrowth, reaching for the sky and the sun. As it was quite early in the morning, the sun was not yet to be seen.

Miljah led the way along a narrow path towards the river, where Sitraj was already in the water, swimming lazily to and fro.

'It is quite cool,' he told her.

Laura allowed Miljah to undress her, and stood on the bank, feeling almost as foolishly anxious as she had the night before, and only just repressing a scream as she saw a man in the trees, hardly twenty feet to her right.

'He is guarding us against crocodiles,' Sitraj explained. 'He will never look at us.'

'Crocodiles?' Laura gasped, peering at the dark water.

'There are none in this stretch of the river,' Sitraj assured her, and held up his arms.

She slid down the bank and found herself being towed into the centre of the stream.

His hands slid over her shoulders and he turned her on her back and cupped her breasts, her head resting on his shoulders.

50

'Now my hair is wet,' she said happily. 'After all Miljah's work.'

'It will dry.'

Sitraj took Laura into his arms and kissed her.

'Put your legs round me,' he said.

Everything that had gone before was as nothing to this. Surely no woman could ever have been so abandoned – no English woman, anyway.

She felt him enter her. She wanted to scream, but it would have been a scream of sheer pleasure. She had never known, never dreamed, of such sexual freedom.

'I love you,' Laura told him, as he helped her up the bank.

'As I love you,' he replied, and kissed her.

Once Laura had been dried and dressed in a brand new sari – she discovered that Sitraj had had several made for her, and that her European clothes had simply been abandoned – they breakfasted with the rest of the party. Sitraj was on delightfully informal terms with his people, who treated him with the greatest respect, but were clearly his friends.

Then they climbed back on to the elephant for a long, delightful day's ramble. Several times Sitraj drew the curtains and made love to her.

'Surely everyone will know what we are doing?' she asked in some embarrassment.

'Of course. Is that something to be ashamed of?'

The thought of Mama and Papa, or herself and Mr Bartlett for that matter, announcing to the world that they were making love, was impossible to envisage.

Oh, damn Mr Bartlett, she thought.

That night, instead of continuing on their way, they camped in an elaborate tent. Its goatskin walls provided three rooms, an antechamber where their guards slept, a larger inner chamber in which they took their meals, and a yet larger chamber in which they slept. Carpets covered the ground, piled high with cushions.

'I will have to rock you to sleep tonight,' Sitraj said with a smile.

There was something utterly wanton about rolling naked on silken cushions with a man in her arms. She wondered how many women in Bombay had ever known such sensations as she was experiencing, or ever would.

'Do you not fear Thugs?' she asked lazily, in between coupling.

'Thugs? Ah. I was told of your unfortunate uncle. It was very unwise of him to take a rich caravan on a long journey, without proper protection.'

'He did so because Thuggism was unknown in southern India, until last April.'

'Thugs are bandits. And bandits are everywhere,' Sitraj said seriously. 'If they are now spreading into southern India, then your Company will have a serious problem on its hands. The only answer is strength, and protection.' He smiled, and kissed her. 'We are well protected, my dear Laura.'

The journey was a delight, as was Sitraj's company. They passed by villages whose inhabitants came out to cheer the Rajah, where they bought provisions, but deliberately avoided larger towns. This was because Sitraj did not wish to have to take part in any elaborate ceremonial greeting. There was certainly no danger involved, as more than half the territory between Bombay and Sittapore was under Company control, while the Company boundary abutted that of Scindhia, and even though the old principality had been divided up, it was entirely ruled by Sitraj's various cousins and uncles.

They neither saw, nor heard of, any Thugs.

Once across the border, indeed, Sitraj's precautions notwithstanding, their journey became a kind of triumphal march, with people turning out to line their route and clap and cheer. Now it was necessary to keep the curtains open all the time so that Sitraj and Laura could smile and wave at the crowds.

'I feel like a queen,' Laura confessed.

'You *are* a queen,' Sitraj reminded her.

The realisation made Laura think about the future.

'Tell me about Sittapore,' she begged. 'My duties.'

Sitraj smiled at her.

52

'You will be seeing Sittapore in two days. That will be better than attempting to tell you of it. As for your duties, they will be the same as that of any wife: to love me and bear me strong children.'

She could think of nothing she would rather do.

As Sitraj had promised, they entered the jaghir, or principality, of Sittapore two days later. Messengers had been sent ahead, and at the border they were greeted by a regiment of cavalry, four hundred strong, resplendent in yellow tunics and dark blue breeches, with dark blue turbans, and armed with lances as well as swords.

'Your household troops,' Sitraj told her.

They certainly made a splendid display, and looked even better when Sitraj, having donned a similar uniform, left the elephant to mount a waiting horse and ride at their head, as apparently he would do all the way into the city.

But he came to her that night.

Now they were travelling through undulating hill country, each rise being followed by a sudden delightful and fertile valley. Every hamlet was decorated with multi-coloured flags and cheering people. The next day, as the caravan topped a last range of low hills, the white walls of Sittapore rose out of a valley. The land here was several hundred feet above sea-level, with mountain ranges to either side rising higher yet. The hillsides were covered in wheat, and the whole jaghir gave an impression of peace and prosperity.

Now, as they approached the walled city, invisible until one was within a few miles of it, hundreds of people emerged; young girls in pink saris strewed flowers before Laura's elephant; young men blew bugles and clashed cymbals. Laura at first was afraid Kara might take fright, but Miljah who rode with her, assured her that he was used to this kind of noise.

Today, Miljah produced from her clothes chest the most exquisite sari Laura had ever seen. It was deep green silk, trimmed with crimson, and looked wonderful against her fair skin. The crowds cheered loudly when they saw her.

Laura had to keep smiling at them and waving, but she was

desperately anxious to see her new home. Although situated in a valley surrounded by the hills, Sittapore was itself built on a small hill rising from the valley floor; a river flowed round the base of the hill. On top of this mound rose the white walls of the city, and within most of the houses were white. Kara made his way across the stream, by means of a ford, where more crowds of people were waiting to greet their new rani, and up a sloping road to the main gateway. This was quite medieval; in addition to castellated walls it contained a portcullis. Both the walls and the houses beyond were a mass of multi-coloured flags.

'We'll never fit under that,' Laura gasped; the jagged teeth seemed to be hardly higher than Kara's head.

'No, indeed, Highness,' Miljah agreed. 'This is where we get down.'

Kara had already been brought to a stop, his trunk almost touching the wall. Laura climbed down and found herself next to Sitraj.

'Are you ready to take possession of your kingdom?' he asked, smiling.

'Oh, yes,' she smiled back.

She was not the least nervous now. For the past two hours she had been cheered and made to feel like the queen she was. Laura Dean, the despised clerk's daughter, with no dowry and precious little fortune, seemed to be someone else, in another world.

Sitraj did not offer her his arm, but he walked at her side as they ascended the last few paces to the gateway itself. Here a small detachment of foot soldiers, wearing the Sittapore colours, presented arms. Beyond, the narrow street, thronged with people, continued to climb. For a moment Laura thought they might be mobbed, but although her new subjects pressed very close, and held out their hands to her, they were not the least aggressive. Their presence, however, added to the heat of the sun, which was intense, and she was assailed by such an overwhelming accumulation of odours, coconut oil, garlic, turmeric, coriander, that she felt almost faint. Sitraj immediately realised her difficulty, and now he did take her arm to assist her up the steep slope.

Fortunately after another fifty yards the road evened out, and almost immediately debouched into a large square.

Laura caught her breath. The glittering white palace was low, only two storeys high, but enormous and in every way magnificent. It was approached by a broad flight of stairs, which led into a huge hall. From its crenellated walls, on which the heads of the guards could be seen, multi-coloured flags waved in the wind.

Laura could hardly wait to get up to that blessed shade, but first of all there was a guard-of-honour to be inspected. There were some two hundred men on parade, standing rigidly to attention, their sergeants armed with halberds, looking every bit as smart and military as any unit in the Company army. Sitraj led her along the ranks, but although, having watched inspections in Bombay, she felt that she should stop and speak to some of the men, she felt too faint and hot to do so; she only just managed to keep smiling until at last she was escorted up the stairs and into the cool of the house.

Laura looked around her at the magnificent carved figures on the walls, the elephants and tigers, the gods and human beings, and men and women, naked and indulging in every form of erotic pleasure. How very different from English Bombay!

There were several men waiting to greet her.

'My cousin, Prince Batraj,' Sitraj said.

Throughout Laura's journey, indeed from the moment Sitraj had come into her life, she had been surrounded with nothing but smiling faces eager to please. Batraj's face was certainly smiling, and it was a handsome face, perhaps even more handsome than Sitraj's, with a strong jaw and big hooked nose, but his eyes were like pools of the deepest black night, and she had the strangest feeling that he was looking into her mind, and not liking what he saw.

Her feeling of faintness returned, as the Prince bowed to her.

'Greetings, Your Highness,' he said. 'I have always considered my cousin a fortunate man. Now I know he is the most fortunate man in the world.'

'I . . . thank you,' she managed.

Sitraj, who had not appeared to notice anything strange in

55

his cousin's greeting to his wife, now introduced her to his Prime Minister, Prithviraj Dal, an elderly man with twinkling eyes and a charming manner, whom she liked immediately, and several other members of his government, whose names she hardly caught.

'Now come,' Sitraj said.

Laura wished only to sit down and rest. She would also have liked to eat something, for breakfast seemed a very long time ago. But she was Rani of Sittapore now, and so she followed her husband down some steps into a magnificent garden. The centrepiece was a fountain, in which the water spouted from the mouth of a large stone tiger, head reared back and paw upraised to strike. In the shallow pool swam many-coloured goldfish.

Surrounding the fountain there was a gravel walk, and flowerbeds surrounded by colonnaded and roofed walkways, open to the breeze. Everywhere the friezes were exquisitely carved in the erotically lifelike Hindu style.

Here there was an army of bowing servants, each of whom Sitraj paused to greet, thus forcing Laura to do likewise. But at last they were past the servants, and being shown through double doors at the far end of the garden, into another high-ceilinged reception chamber.

'I would have you meet my mother,' Sitraj said. 'The Dowager Rani Bilkis.'

Laura was taken entirely aback; Sitraj had told her his father was dead, but he had not mentioned his mother at all; therefore she had assumed that the old queen was also dead. The idea that he should have decided to marry without first presenting his bride to his mother, or even informing her of the event until after it had been consummated, she found astonishing. The Dowager Rani was surprisingly tall, somewhat heavy but by no means fat; she wore the white sari of widowhood.

Her face was also heavy-featured; in fact she bore a startling resemblance to Prince Batraj who, of course, would be her nephew, Laura realised. She wondered what thoughts this old lady must have at seeing this new and strange daughter-in-law so unexpectedly foisted upon her. And what her reaction would be when she heard the terms of the marriage contract.

56

But Bilkis was smiling, extending her arms.

'Welcome to Sittapore, my daughter,' she said in English almost as good as her son's. 'Welcome.'

Laura was embraced, and felt a gush of warm happiness sweeping through her entire body.

'These are your sisters,' Bilkis said, turning to indicate the three young women standing behind her.

Laura gulped; these must be Sitraj's wives.

Vaguely she heard their names: Bibi, Chandra and Indra. They were obviously older than she, but seemed perfectly pleased to see her, and welcome her into their house.

'And these are your children.'

Three little boys and a little girl were led out. Sitraj must have given them some kind of a signal, because they broke away from their mothers and ran forward to throw themselves into his arms.

'This is your new mother,' Sitraj explained, as he set them on the floor again. They solemnly bowed. 'You will have to learn their names at your leisure,' he said. 'But now, I can tell, you are both tired and hungry.'

'I had not realised,' she said weakly, thinking less of the exhaustion than of the enormous family she had suddenly accumulated.

'You will soon become used to it. Mother, shall we eat?'

After the meal, Laura was escorted to her apartment, a place of open balustrades and cool breezes at the back of the palace, on the upper storey and looking down on yet another interior garden so that she could be overlooked by no-one.

Sitraj took her into the bedchamber, and showed her the huge, cushion-strewn divan. Miljah was already there, setting everything to rights, but she hurried off when her master and mistress arrived.

Sitraj sat beside Laura on the divan, and held her hands. 'Are you pleased?'

'I am delighted. But, Sitraj, your other wives ... how long have you been married to them?'

'The first, ten years, the second eight years, and the third, six years.'

Laura swallowed. 'Then they are all much older than I.'

'Not so much. In India we get married much younger than in Europe. Bibi, my first wife, is only twenty-two.'

Laura was aghast. 'You mean she came to you when she was twelve?'

'She was nubile,' Sitraj pointed out. 'The others were no older. Indra is the same age as you are now.'

'But . . . you said I would take precedence.'

'So you will.'

'I cannot possibly take precedence over Bibi, if she is twenty-two and has been your wife for ten years.'

'Laura,' Sitraj said quietly. 'It is I who decides the order of precedence of my wives, no-one else. I promised your parents that you would be my principal wife. My mother will understand this. And, lest you be in any doubt, the son you will bear me will be the next Rajah. This I will announce to my people tomorrow.'

'Oh, Sitraj,' she said. 'Will I bear you a son?'

He smiled at her. 'Of course. No matter how often we have to try.'

'Oh, Sitraj,' she said. 'I am so very happy.'

Bombay, Christmas Eve, 1825

It seems that the Burma campaign has now come to a successful conclusion.

I should explain that two years ago a Burmese army, led by one Maha Bandula, a general of great repute, invaded India on two fronts. Naturally we declared war. I deeply regret that I was not here when it began, for I would certainly have volunteered.

It was not an easy business. It took several months to organise a chastising expeditionary force under Sir Archibald Campbell. But this was eventually done, and in May of last year Rangoon was seized.

Those rascally fellows, however, refused to submit, and our lads were stuck in that dismal town in the monsoon, ravaged by fever and dysentery, literally dropping like flies. Naturally the savages pressed their advantage, Bandula shrieking victory the while.

Reinforcements, including a rocket battery, were got up to the city by way of the river, and these soon dispersed the natives. Thank God for the Navy, I say. Thus in February of this year, when I first arrived here, Sir Archibald was enabled to resume his advance, again supported by our gallant tars. In a battle at a place called Danubyu, in April, Bandula was killed. One would have supposed that the Burmese would then have cried: enough.

Not a bit of it. When Sir Archibald went into monsoon quarters around the city of Prome the natives, now commanded by one Maha Menyo, promptly commenced further hostilities. Despite the rain, Sir Archibald lashed out, and our latest report is that he has gained a complete victory, and that

59

the Burmese are prepared to sue for peace and make lavish concessions.

Serve the rascals right. I wish I had been there.

Life in Bombay has this year been unusually dull, since the exciting affairs of the spring. I have suffered my first monsoon, and an unpleasant business it is. The rain is not continuous, but when it falls it is so heavy that it gets in everywhere. I have discovered that the roof of my bungalow leaks like a sieve, and it is small comfort to know that the roof of every other bungalow is in a similar condition. The roads are quagmires, and it is impossible to attend parade without being coated in mud from the knees down.

Naturally there have been any number of sick, and even a suicide reported. I can well believe it.

Rufus has now improved his biting of Hindus to five a week. I am hoping to improve on this further still, as he is not yet fully grown. I am not of course entirely popular with the tradespeople but that is their lookout, say I.

I am toying with the idea of getting him a mate. But she will have to match him for size. Then I can begin breeding my own Bartlett hounds. They may yet bring me fame and fortune.

I should record that for all my determination never again to become involved with the opposite sex I have agreed to make an assignation for this evening's ball. I could hardly avoid doing so. The young lady's name is Prudence Partridge, and she is the Colonel's daughter. Having virtually been commanded to dance attendance on the young lady, I shall do my best. As a matter of fact, she is attractive in a dark, intense sort of way. I understand she is sixteen.

The news from Sittapore is that the Rani is, as the poets put it, great with child, or as we should say with more delicacy, in an interesting condition.

'Oh God! Tomorrow, in the hottest weather any of us has yet experienced, we shall have to struggle through mountains of turkey and plum pudding, and play childish games in the mess. What torment! I would give anything for a good English snow fall, the nip of an English frost. How I loathe this place. Can hell itself be any hotter? And above all, I hate the sly Hindu!

3
The Tragedy

'Are you pleased?' Laura asked.

Sitraj kissed her on the forehead. 'I am delighted. He is a splendid child. Was it very painful for you?'

'No, no,' she said. 'Your mother was magnificent. So were the girls. They gave me something to chew, and I never felt a thing. Indeed, I had very happy dreams.'

'It is called bhang,' he told her, 'and is made from the hemp plant. It is not a good thing to become addicted to it.'

'I can understand that. One would never wish to do anything else, but dream. Oh, Sitraj! I am so very happy.'

'Which is what I wish you to be,' he said, and kissed her again. 'I only want you to be able to return to my bed at the very earliest possible moment.'

'It will not be long,' she promised him. 'I feel better than at any time in my life. What will you call him?'

'What would you like to call him?'

'Oh!' She had not considered that the choice might be left to her.

'Would you like to call him after your father?'

'Carmichael?' She smiled. 'How can we have a rajah called Carmichael? It would make people laugh.'

'I suppose it would,' he agreed.

'Let us call him after your father.'

'Sivitraj? Are you sure?'

'Sivitraj,' Laura said carefully. 'Yes. I am sure.'

He kissed her a third time. 'It will please my mother.'

The choice of name also pleased the people of Sittapore. There were bonfires and firework displays to celebrate the naming of the future rajah.

Prince Batraj made the little Prince a present of a bag of emeralds.

Laura was becoming used to being surrounded by such wealth. The jaghir of Sittapore might earn its sustenance by its abundant wheatfields and its numerous flocks of sheep and goats, but the wealth of the reigning family came from the emerald mine just outside the city. Here the precious stones were hewn from the living rock before being handed to lapidarists for cutting. And the mine belonged to Sitraj and his cousin.

To Sitraj and his family, however, money was of not the slightest importance. It was there, because it had always been there. Even their final defeat by the British, within living memory, had been a military humiliation, not a financial one: the Company had been only too eager to maintain the various princes of Scindhia in power as long as they kept the peace within their domains, and allowed the Company to trade.

Laura had never known such financial recklessness. She had but to admire something and it was hers, express the faintest wish that something might be changed, and it was done immediately.

What was most disturbing was the amazing gap between the ruling Scindhia family, and the rest of the populace. The majority lived, so far as Laura could make out, in desperate poverty, yet total happiness, not the least concerned that their ruler might squander what was to them a lifetime's income, on a present for his wife.

She reflected that the same difference in living standards no doubt obtained in England. From all accounts the extravagance of King George IV, compared with the living standards of the poorest of his people, was such that incipient revolution was bubbling all the time beneath the surface. That at least could not be said of Scindhia.

Yet, for all her happiness in Sitraj's arms, she continued to feel a stranger, bewildered. There was such a vast number of things she had to learn about her new home, and her new people.

It had begun with her Indian wedding, surrounded by flaming

torches and flagrant erotica, openly spoken prayers for her fecundity and that she should please her husband.

The people of Sittapore, like their ruling house, were Hindus. Their religion was based firstly on the Rigveda and secondly on the Upanishads. The beliefs expressed in the Rigveda at least were far more ancient than those of the Christian Bible, and equally revered by their adherents.

But, as with Christianity, these beliefs were a strange mixture of philosophical and ethical concepts and ideals, and odd superstitions.

Sitraj and his family were kshattriyas; that is, they believed themselves to be the second highest form of human life, beneath only the Brahmins, who were the only people on earth entitled to offer prayers and sacrifices to the universal Supreme God, Brahman.

A very simple mythology accounted for this. The Brahmins claimed to have been the people who had conquered India from the north, beyond the mountains. They had defeated the dark-skinned aboriginal inhabitants and driven them to the south or made them slaves, and slaves they had remained, the panchamas or outcastes.

The caste system itself had developed slowly. According to legend, when the Brahmins had conquered India it had been a golden age. All Brahmins had been noble and brave and acceptable to the gods; all panchamas had been obedient and servile. As time went by, however, some of the Brahmins had abandoned the perpetual quest for righteousness, and thus lost their place in the ruling elite. They became the kshattriyas, or professional soldiers.

These were still happy times when the Brahmins and kshattriyas ruled a prosperous and orderly world. Then came a further decline, with men seeking to make money rather than their peace with god. These men, who sank lower than the kshattriyas, were the vaishyas, or merchants. In this age men first began to know unhappiness – apart from the panchamas, who of course, had never known happiness.

Alas, man had to decline yet one more stage, into misery because of sloth and veniality. Those who had so sunk became the shudras, or cultivators. This was the stage in which the world was at present, the Brahmins said.

The caste system, Laura supposed, was not in itself very different to the class system in England, except for its rigidity. In England, a young kshattriya named Arthur Wellesley could rise virtually to the top of the Brahmin caste as the Duke of Wellington, or a Norfolk farmer and shudra, Tom Coke, could reach the very top of the tree of wealth and acceptance in the highest circles. This was not possible in India. A man remained within the caste to which he was born for his entire life, nor would he marry beneath him – although he could take a concubine from any caste – and if a woman did so, she took her husband's caste and descended the social scale.

Laura decided that, being a non-Hindu, she was regarded as being outside the caste system. Papa, after all, had been no more than a vaishya.

Escape from the caste system could only be achieved through death and re-incarnation, until the state of moksha, when all earthly ambitions and lusts and fears were forgotten, was reached. Reaching such a blissful state was however no easy task. One was reborn according to one's behaviour in one's previous life. Thus one might begin as a snake and become a Brahmin, but even that did not guarantee moksha. For if the Brahmin's life was not virtuous, he would be reborn further down the scale, and might even become a snake again.

It was the same with the gods. The Hindu gods were everywhere, carved or painted, throughout the palace and, as Laura had noted on her first day, more often than not engaged in very human activities.

Brahman himself, the Creator, was seen as a trinity, but the other partners were very different from Jesus Christ and the Holy Spirit. Second of the gods was Vishnu, the preserver, the protector of the world. Like all the gods he was many-sided, and could manifest himself in any one of several avatars or incarnations, the most famous being Rama, the hero of the Ramayana, and Krishna, the divine cowherd.

The third member of the trinity, and the most disturbing, was Shiva. Shiva was both destroyer and restorer, a supreme ascetic and yet the epitome of sensuality.

64

Apart from the strangeness of the religion, and the economic inequalities, Laura found life in Sittapore a continuous delight.

Her every day could very well have been spent doing absolutely nothing, for there was no task for which she was responsible. But she had a naturally vigorous mind and nature, and gossiping with Sitraj's other wives did not satisfy her. The wives were charm itself, and revealed not the slightest hint of jealousy at her sudden elevation above them; they seemed as delighted with the baby Prince and future Rajah as she was herself. But their conversation was simply banal.

Laura preferred the company of her mother-in-law. Bilkis would tell her about the great days of the Marathas, about how the legendary Sivaji had more than a hundred years before resisted even the mighty Aurangzeb, the Mughal Emperor who had referred to himself simply as The Great Mughal, until he had at last been forced to surrender. Siraji had been taken to Agra, the Mughal capital, officially as a guest, but in reality as a prisoner. Realising this, he had feigned illness, and as a supposedly dying man had distributed alms to the Hindus in the city, as he was required to do. These alms had consisted of huge baskets of fruit, which had first to be carried in to Sivaji for his blessing.

One day the baskets had been carried in and out as usual, and the Mughal guards had not realised that one had contained, beneath the fruit, Sivaji, and the other his son Simbaji who had been sharing his captivity. Thus they had escaped, to resume their war of independence.

Bilkis clapped her hands with joy every time she told this tale.

The Mughals never succeeded in bringing Sivaji's successors to submission, and when Sivaji's line had grown feeble, the chief ministers, or peshwas, had taken over, founding their own dynasty on the lines of the old Japanese shogunates.

But in time even the peshwas had grown feeble, and had been defeated in war by the British and French East India Companies. Then the Maratha empire had split apart, and the largest part had been that ruled by the House of Scindhia, and known simply as Scindhia. Bilkis's eyes would gleam when she spoke of the power of her ancestors, and of the French mercenaries they had employed to maintain their independence, famous soldiers such as Benoit de Boigne and Perron, of whom even Laura had heard.

Laura took to exploring the city of Sittapore, accompanied always by Miljah and by several guards bearing parasols to keep the sun from her head and face. The people seemed amazed to see her in their midst, but were clearly delighted. She visited them in their homes and, as her Hindustani daily improved, spoke with them and their children.

'Is it not possible to have a school here?' she asked Sitraj.

'A school?' He frowned. 'What for?'

'Well . . . to teach the children.'

'Teach them what?'

'How to read and write, and count. How to better themselves.'

'A man learns what is necessary from his mother and father,' Sitraj pointed out. 'You would not expect the child of a shudra to be taught to read and write any more than you would expect our son to be taught how to milk a cow or plough a field. Wholesale education means anarchy.' He smiled at her. 'As so often happens in Europe.'

Laura didn't know if he was right or not, but she loved him too much to dispute the matter.

There were no English books in Sittapore, and Laura had brought only her Bible with her, so she settled down to learn Sanskrit, so that she would at least be able to read the old religious books. Sitraj was delighted, and gave her an edition of the Hindu love manual, the Kama Sutra, as well as its Persian equivalent, The Perfumed Garden. She had never read anything like these, had in fact no idea that books like that had ever been written in any language.

But consternation and embarrassment were soon replaced by interest and amusement, especially when she and Sitraj would read them in bed together and then try one of the different love positions.

66

'You are a delight,' he would tell her. 'I sometimes cannot believe that I was fortunate enough to meet you.'

'I suppose you have tried all these positions with Bibi and Chandra and Indra.'

'Yes, I have.' He smiled. 'But none was so delightful as you.'

'Why?'

'Because none has golden hair, and a white body, and such shy eagerness.'

He reached for her again.

But although the nights spent with Sitraj were marvellous, Laura found that even with her studies, the days still dragged. Her 'sisters' did nothing but drink tea and tell each other interminable stories, most of them obscene and accompanied by gales of laughter, and wait for the summons to their master's bed.

They would not even play any games which required thought, finding them far too enervating. They preferred to lounge on their divans while their hair was brushed and combed and plaited by their maids, or to splash about naked in the bathing pool, chasing each other through the water with a good deal of erotic horseplay. Laura was alarmed by this at first, but soon found herself joining in the fun – it all helped to prepare them for Sitraj's bed.

Above all, they were totally uninterested in the running of their little country, and never paid the slightest attention to any problems Sitraj might be having. If Sitraj had a fault it was his arch-conservatism; and he was quite put out when he found Laura discussing modernising the sewage system with Prithviraj Dal.

He was quite happy, however, to show Laura the emerald mine, and watch her gasp at the enormous wealth that lay in the hillside close by the town. Her engagement present had already been made up into a ring, and he also made her a present of a matching emerald necklace. Wearing the two she supposed she was carrying several thousand pounds about with her, and in addition he loaded her with gold bangles for her ankles and arms. He even asked if she would like to have her nose pierced for a ring, but this she declined. He did not argue about it.

Sitraj played polo at least once a week, and Laura invariably went to watch, even if the game terrified her.

She had seen it played in Bombay, as the young sahibs had quickly picked it up from the Indians, but never had she seen such reckless speed combined with superb timing as on the field below Sittapore. Usually the teams, composed of army officers, were captained respectively by Sitraj and Batraj, when the Prince was in residence. Laura would sit with her hands to her throat as her husband hurled himself around the field on his pony. Many were the tumbles, but Sitraj always landed on his feet, laughing as he remounted.

When she asked him if there were ever any serious injuries, or even deaths on the polo field, he laughed. 'Of course. But a game without risk is not worth playing.'

As she became more at home, and grew to feel that she was being accepted by the people of Sittapore, the only blight on Laura's total happiness was her cousin-in-law Batraj.

Batraj was the only man, apart from servants, who actually lived in the palace – although his apartments were far from hers – and whom, therefore, she saw with any regularity, apart from her husband. But where the servants all bowed as she approached and tried to be as self-effacing as possible, Batraj was more than likely to stop and engage her in conversation.

He was never other than totally polite, and he was always interesting, and yet she felt ill at ease with him. She was certain he desired her as much as Sitraj, and then asked herself what was so unusual about that. Every man in Bombay had desired her. What made the knowledge different in Sittapore was the constant presence of erotic statues in every niche and corner. She found it difficult to carry on a normal, polite conversation with Batraj when both he and she were looking at an erected male penis, not six feet away. Also there could be no doubt that he had also read both the Kama Sutra and The Perfumed Garden!

He travelled a great deal, but where he went, or what he actually did, remained a mystery: Sitraj said no more than, 'he is my ambassador.' But when Batraj came back his eyes almost seemed to be mocking her, and he looked at her more boldly than ever.

So she would remind herself that although he was a prince, she was Rani of Sittapore. She was beyond his reach.

She did once ask Sitraj about his father's death, but he would not go into details.

'My father died very suddenly,' he said. 'It must have been a heart attack.'

'I heard there was a rumour of poison.'

'There are always rumours of poison when someone dies suddenly,' he pointed out.

'Your father and his brother-in-law had quarrelled, had they not?'

'They had a difference of opinion,' Sitraj said carefully. 'Over our relationship with the Company. My father stood for closer ties, my uncle did not. But my father was Rajah, and it was his decision which mattered.'

'Do you and Batraj differ in your policy towards the Company?'

'Batraj is his father's son, as I am mine.' Sitraj smiled. 'But in this case also, I am Rajah.'

Laura had expected to be pregnant again soon after she returned to Sitraj's bed, but this did not happen. When she became concerned about it, he merely smiled as usual, and said, 'Perhaps we need a change of air. Would you like to visit Bombay?'

'Oh, could we?' she squealed in delight.

He laughed at her enthusiasm. 'Why not? We will go as soon as the monsoon is over.'

They made the journey south in November, and Laura wondered if they might possibly stay over Christmas.

She had been a little put out when Sitraj had decided against taking little Sivitraj. The baby was now eight months old, and Laura had never been separated from him.

'The journey is an arduous one,' Sitraj pointed out.

69

'Certainly for a baby. And he is my heir. He will remain with his grandmother. She will take good care of him.'

Laura knew he was right. It was a wrench which soon dissipated, however, in the excitement of returning to her home town in all her glory as Rani of Sittapore.

Her parents had by now long left, and according to their letters were moving in the best society in England. Mountstuart Elphinstone was still there, however, and after the elephants and outriders had paraded through the streets of the city in front of gaping crowds, he welcomed them to Government House, where they would be staying: how proud Mama and Papa would be, Laura thought. But Elphinstone himself was leaving the following year.

'Well, I've been in India thirty years,' he pointed out.

'You must have many memories,' Laura ventured.

'Oh, indeed, Your Highness. I was with Wellesley at Aswari, and then there was that business with the Peshwa ten years ago . . . oh, indeed. I shall be sorry to go, in some ways. But there are other places to see, Greece, Italy . . . and of course, dear old England.'

'I have never set foot in England,' Laura said thoughtfully, wondering if she ever would. Perhaps Sitraj could be persuaded . . . How marvellous to arrive in England as Rani of Sittapore! Perhaps she might even be presented to the King!

'Who is to be your successor, Sir?' Sitraj asked, more practical.

'Ah . . . Sir John Malcolm,' Elphinstone said, a trifle diffidently.

Sitraj raised his eyebrows, and Laura could understand his surprise. Sir John Malcolm was a very well-known figure in India. It was related that when, as a young boy, he had been taken before the Directors of the East India Company by his recently-bankrupt father in an endeavour to find him a place, and had been condescendingly asked by one of the great men, 'Well, little fellow, what would you do if you came face to face with Haidar Ali?' (for the great Rajah of Mysore was causing the Company all manner of trouble), Malcolm had replied without hesitation and in his strong Scottish accent, 'Cut off his heid!'

Throughout his career he had fought brilliantly whenever given the opportunity, had tumbled in and out of debt with great regularity, acted as British Ambassador to Persia, and applied for government posts, invariably without success until now.

It was also remembered that he had been a fair man, more so than some of his contemporaries. When Sir Arthur Wellesley, as the Duke of Wellington then was, had projected the destruction of the castle of Gwalior after his victory at Aswari, Malcolm had protested that it was the family home of the Scindhia, and that to destroy it would be an act of brigandage. His stand had not endeared him to the future Commander-in-Chief of the British Army, but he had won his point.

Sitraj remembered this.

'I do not think we could ask for anyone better, after yourself, of course, Elphinstone.'

'Do you know, I agree with you. But we are also to have a new Governor-General next year. Amherst has resigned. As to who will replace him, I have no idea, although I have a notion John Malcolm will probably throw his hat into the ring.'

'Better and better,' Sitraj agreed.

It was a tremendous pleasure to descend on the bazaar, followed by a train of servants, Miljah always at her elbow, with someone to hold a parasol over her, and others to carry the baskets which she filled with whatever caught her fancy.

The native stallholders remembered her, and welcomed her as one of them, while the English people she met were forced to bow to her or salute her. She felt it was the greatest triumph of her life.

It was an equal pleasure to sit in the Governor's box and watch Sitraj playing polo with the British Army, outriding them all and outplaying them as well with the ferocity and accuracy of his shooting.

Polo matches are leisurely affairs for the spectators, and she had ample time to look over the stand and the crowds, the English ladies all beautifully dressed, their husbands explaining the finer points of the game even if they themselves were indifferent horsemen, the Indian spectators a kaleidoscope of soft colours as they swayed with excitement.

71

Then she saw Guy Bartlett, seated below her in the stand. Beside him was a small dark girl, somewhat plain, Laura thought, but with abundant hair and a good figure.

She also observed that he now wore the insignia of a full lieutenant.

'Who is that lady with Lieutenant Bartlett, Your Excellency?' she asked Elphinstone.

'Ah, that would be Miss Partridge. Daughter of the Colonel of the Regiment, you know. Young Bartlett and Prudence are seen quite a lot together, have been for some time.'

Laura remembered Prudence Partridge, all teeth and puppy fat. She seemed to have changed.

'Don't know if anything will come of it,' Elphinstone observed. 'Bartlett hasn't two brass farthings to rub together, save for his pay. But then, neither does Partridge,' he added sadly.

Laura spent most of the rest of the game watching the couple in front of her. They seemed very friendly, often bringing their heads close together as they discussed the game, although as she remembered Guy Bartlett was most definitely an infantry officer; the last time she had seen him he had sat his horse on parade with a good deal of discomfort.

She asked without thinking, 'Will Lieutenant Bartlett be coming to the ball?'

'Why, do you know, I hadn't thought of it,' Elphinstone said. 'But of course he should. The Partridges will be coming. I'll certainly have Rodgers send Bartlett an invitation.'

The ball was a much grander occasion than the one in 1825. Laura was the guest of honour, and stood in line after Elphinstone and Sitraj to receive the guests.

How splendid it was to hear the Governor say, 'And may I present to you, Your Highness. . . .'

Guy Bartlett arrived early.

'Why, Lieutenant Bartlett,' she said. 'How well you look.'

'As do you, Your Highness,' he said. 'You look perfectly splendid.'

'Why, thank you, Mr Bartlett. Tell me, how is your dog? What was his name? Rufus.'

'Rufus is a father, Your Highness.'

She raised her eyebrows.

'Yes,' Guy went on, 'I purchased him a wife. It is the thing to do. With dogs, I mean.'

She glanced at him. How insufferably rude!

'May I hope for the privilege of a dance during the evening, Your Highness?'

'Why, Mr Bartlett,' she said coldly. 'You may hope for anything.'

Of course, he knew she would dance with him. The filling of her card had been left to the Rajah's aide-de-camp, Colonel Mujhabi, of which Guy would have been well aware, thus his early appearance. The colonel was under the strictest instructions to allow no guest more than one dance, reserving two for the Governor and four for the Rajah. Guy was certainly early enough to write down his name for one of the remaining dances. Well, she thought, she would dance with the wretch, and squash him like a fly.

She found herself face to face with the Partridges.

'Your Highness.' Florence Partridge curtsied. 'May I say how beautiful you look tonight?'

'You're so kind,' Laura said sweetly.

Partridge muttered something as he kissed her hand.

Prudence came next.

'Your Highness,' she mumbled, giving a somewhat uncertain curtsey. Laura had to grasp her hand to stop her from falling over.

'You should practise, Prudence dear,' she said, with her most charming smile. 'Mr Bartlett is already here, by the way.'

Prudence flushed crimson, and hurried off.

The night turned into a long succession of men, smiling nervously, sweating profusely, treading on her toes – few of them were familiar with the waltz. To dance from time to time with Sitraj, and Elphinstone, who also waltzed well, was an enormous relief. Between dances she was invariably escorted to sit with one of the elderly matrons. This was quite enjoyable, because they were all women who would not so much have

73

noticed her in the street two years before, but for that very reason conversation was limited.

'Every man in the room wished to dance with you, Highness,' Colonel Mujhabi laughed. 'I am afraid the majority have been disappointed.'

She smiled at him, and saw Guy Bartlett approaching. It was nearly midnight; he had clearly only just been in time to write his name in her card for all his early arrival.

During the first part of the evening he had danced almost exclusively with Prudence, Laura had observed. They had moved well together, and their conversation had been quite animated.

He led her on to the floor and bowed.

'I apologise for being so tardy, Your Highness. There were two vacancies before this one on your card, but I thought a waltz would be preferable to a gavotte or a polka. We have never danced before, have we.'

'How thoughtful you are, Mr Bartlett,' she said, as his hand settled on her waist, and he swept her into the rhythm of the music.

'Do you know, you are the most beautiful woman I have ever seen,' he said in a low voice.

'Mr Bartlett!'

Let him not think he could charm her so easily.

'I am sorry, Your Highness. It just slipped out.'

Perhaps he had been drinking; his face was certainly flushed.

'I once told you never to apologise,' she said, and realised that also had just slipped out.

'What a great many memories we share,' he said.

'Do you suppose Miss Partridge would approve of your flirting like this?' she asked coolly. 'I know I do not.'

The music stopped, and they stood, still gazing at each other.

'I could never flirt with you, Laura,' he said.

Hastily she stepped away from him.

'Thank you for the dance, Mr Bartlett.'

'Would you like to see Rufus again?'

'Rufus?'

74

'My dog. You asked after him. Would you, Laura?'

People were starting to leave the floor, and he was still holding her hand. Gently she disengaged it.

'I still take him for a walk on the beach whenever I am able,' he said. 'I shall do that tomorrow. At midday.'

'If I walk on the beach, Mr Bartlett,' she said, 'be sure I shall not be alone.'

'Please be there,' he whispered, and escorted her back to her chair.

'That was a splendid party, Your Excellency,' Laura said at breakfast. 'Do you know, I have no idea what time we got to bed.'

'About four, I think,' Elphinstone said.

'Good heavens. And what have you got planned for us today?'

'Well today, I'm afraid, I must attend church parade.'

'Oh!' Laura turned to Sitraj. 'Do you think I could possibly go to church, Your Highness? It has been so long.'

'Of course,' Sitraj said. 'You do not mind if I do not?'

'Oh, no,' she said.

'Colonel Mujhabi will accompany you.'

'That will be very nice,' she said.

She rode with the Governor in his trap, sat beside him in his pew, and enjoyed the stares and whispers. The bishop, although clearly taken aback at seeing a sari in his church, spoke with her afterwards while Elphinstone waited patiently.

'One would really like to see the Indian rulers allow more missionaries into their dominions,' he said. 'But now, with a Christian Queen of Sittapore, may we hope for a great advance?'

'It is certainly possible,' Laura said, trying to imagine what Bilkis would make of a Christian missionary, or what the missionary would make of the joyously erotic statues, or the nautch dancers who often entertained the royal family in the evenings, quite naked save for their jewellery.

Guy Bartlett had not been at church. And it was now nearly noon.

75

'I wonder,' she said to the Governor, 'if I might go for a walk on the beach before returning home? I feel in great need of some fresh air. All that champagne last night.'

'And the late hours,' he agreed. 'I think that is an excellent idea, Your Highness. Would you mind if I did not accompany you? I'm afraid even on Sundays I have some work to do.'

'Of course I shall not be offended. Colonel Mujhabi will escort me.'

Elphinstone's horse had been brought along by one of his servants, and now he mounted and rode off, while Laura got into the trap, Mujhabi obediently trotting at her side.

'What part of the beach, Highness?' asked the driver.

'Just go straight across the island,' Laura told him.

She smiled graciously at the various ladies they passed as they drove past the houses and down the track through the trees. Now Mujhabi had to fall behind the trap, as there was insufficient room for him beside her.

'Stop here,' she told the driver, as the trap reached the grass before the beach, and she looked out at the Arabian Sea.

Mujhabi immediately dismounted to assist her down. 'You should have a parasol, Your Highness.'

'I will carry it myself, Colonel,' Laura told him. 'It is the custom among Englishwomen. You remain here.'

She was sure the Colonel could have no idea that the coming meeting was not entirely an accident. She wondered whether Guy Bartlett might at the last moment get cold feet and abandon the project.

She strolled down the sand to the water's edge, gazing at the shimmering surface. She had never stood like this, utterly exposed to the sun and the wind, in a sari before. The parasol protected her head, but the thin silk fluttered against her skin in the cool breeze. It was a curiously exciting sensation.

She heard barking, and turned, her heart pounding. Rufus she recognised immediately, though he had grown considerably since she last saw him.

Mujhabi gave a shout of alarm and ran from the trees, his tulwar drawn. At the sight of him, the dog stopped and growled, teeth bared.

'Go back, Colonel, go back!' Laura shouted.

'But, Your Highness, the animal will savage you.'

'No, he will not,' Laura assured him, walking back up the beach. 'Come along, Rufus!' She gave a little whistle. 'Come along!'

Rufus cocked his ears and turned back towards her. Out of the corner of her eye she could see Guy just emerging round the little headland of trees; he had the sense to stop and wait for a moment before coming on.

'You go back to the trap, Colonel,' Laura reassured him, as Rufus lay down with his paws in the air. 'You see, he will not harm me!'

Mujhabi did as she requested, clearly amazed at the influence she had over the huge beast.

Laura stooped down to stroke and tickle Rufus, and listened to boots crunching on the sand. She raised her head. 'I think Rufus remembers me.'

'That fellow . . .'

'You did not expect me to come alone, did you, Mr Bartlett?' She stood up.

'I hardly expected to see you at all,' he confessed.

'I wished to see my old friend again,' she told him, patting Rufus's head.

'When do you go back to Sittapore?'

'Not until after Christmas, I think.'

'Laura, are you happy?'

'Are you not happy, Mr Bartlett?'

'I am the most miserable fellow on earth.'

'What, with Miss Partridge so obviously in love with you?'

'That is part of my misery. I do not love her. I love you, Laura. I loved you from the moment I saw you. Did you really marry that Indian fellow just for money?'

'You are being insulting, sir.'

'Then you did!'

'I married my husband because I fell in love with him, Mr Bartlett. I am still in love with him. If I had suspected you were going to carry on in this ridiculous fashion, I would certainly not have come. Now I must bid you good day.'

She turned away from him, and he caught her arm.

'Be careful what you do,' she said in a low voice. 'Colonel Mujhabi is most certainly watching.'

'I love you, Laura. I shall always love you.'

The words she had come to Bombay to hear.

'That is very sweet of you, Mr Bartlett. I shall always treasure those sentiments. But I am married to another. I do not think we should, or shall, meet again.' She held out her hand. 'Marry your Prudence, Mr Bartlett, and be happy.'

'Mujhabi has told me of your adventure on the beach,' Sitraj said that night. 'Attacked by a savage dog, which you quieted with a word.'

She smiled. 'I'm no magician, my love. I knew that dog two years ago. He belongs to Mr Barlett.'

'Ah! Was Bartlett the man you spoke with on the beach?'

'Yes. He was exercising his dog, and as usual he got somewhat out of control. Fortunately, as I have said, Rufus remembered me.'

'Mujhabi was quite upset,' he remarked. 'What did you and Bartlett have to say to one another? He did not, I hope, presume in any way, in view of your earlier relationship?'

'By no means. He apologised for his dog, and I congratulated him on his engagement.'

'His engagement?'

'To Miss Partridge, the Colonel's daughter. Did you not know of it?'

'No,' Sitraj said. 'I'm afraid I do not pay much attention to Bombay gossip.'

Was that a rebuke?

She lay on his chest. 'Sitraj, when can we go home?'

'I thought you wished to stay until Christmas.'

'Well, I do not think I do, any more. I would rather be in Sittapore for Christmas with Sivitraj.'

He smiled as he kissed her. 'But what about all your shopping?'

'I have done everything I came to Bombay to do,' she assured him.

'Well then, I have promised to play polo next Saturday

afternoon, for the Governor's Team against the Army. We shall leave the next day.'

'One week,' she said. 'That will be ideal.'

She did not leave Government House again all week, not wishing to risk encountering Guy. Instead, she buried herself in the library, starved as she was for English books in Sittapore.

Elphinstone was delighted. He was a great connoisseur of books, and the tragedy of his adventurous life had happened during 'that little trouble with the Peshwa' ten years before, when the residency at Poona had been sacked by the Marathas and his carefully-collected library destroyed. But he had set to work to replace the lost volumes, and although that had proved impossible, he had none the less re-created a very fine library.

Laura came across several of the novels of Miss Jane Austen, and these she thoroughly enjoyed. She thought she would start building up an English library of her own in Sittapore, ordering the books through the Company.

When she broached the idea to Sitraj, he was pleased.

'It is certainly my intention to have you teach Sivitraj English, and to understand the ways of the world beyond our narrow boundaries,' he told her. 'That is the way to continuing prosperity.'

She made a list of books she would like and gave it to the Governor. She included not only the novels of Jane Austen, of Richardson, Smollett and Defoe, but also translations of the classic Greek histories of Herodotus and Thucydides and Xenophon. The Governor was delighted and promised to give the list to the factor and have the books sent out at the earliest opportunity.

Then it was simply a matter of getting back to Sittapore as soon as possible. She made Miljah pack on Saturday morning, so that she would have nothing to do that night but enjoy herself, and that afternoon she rode with the Governor to the polo ground. Sitraj had gone on earlier for his usual pre-match practice.

The scene was as crowded and colourful as ever, and Sitraj was soon in the thick of the action, the ferocious sweep of his mallet sending the ball racing towards his team's goal.

Laura spotted Guy in the crowd, with Prudence at his side. They seemed as intimate as the first time she had seen them. But he loves me, she thought triumphantly.

She was recalled to the game by a surge of excitement from the crowd, raised her head to see Sitraj and one of the Army officers both racing for the ball, which had flown loose. So concentrated were they both that neither noticed the other until they were within a few feet of the other, then both attempted to swerve.

It was too late, and the horses careered into each other. The shock of the impact could be heard all over the ground, even above the hubbub. Horses and riders went down, Sitraj being hurled from his saddle for a considerable distance.

Laura found herself on her feet, both hands clasped to her throat.

Elphinstone was also on his feet, but there was nothing he could do. Already stretcher bearers were hurrying forward, as it was obvious to everyone that both men were badly hurt.

For several moments there was total silence round the enclosure, then a babble of excited sound filled the air.

'I had better go down,' Elphinstone said, and made for the gangway.

Laura hardly heard him. She remained staring down at the knot of men and horses, for both sides had of course ceased playing and were gathered round the casualties. She watched the stretchers being lifted, and suddenly came to life, hurrying behind the Governor.

Several people spoke to her, but she did not hear them as she stumbled down the steps and into the paddock, arriving at the same time as the stretchers. The bearers stopped when they saw her, and she gasped in horror. Elphinstone had been walking beside the stretcher, his face contorted with misery. Now he looked up, and then came forward to stand next to her, and put his arm round her shoulders.

'My dear,' he said. 'My dear, dear girl. I am so terribly sorry.'

No one had thought to cover Sitraj's face. Laura gazed at the stiff features, distorted with the effort of avoiding the collision.

'His neck was broken,' Elphinstone explained. 'I'm afraid he must have died instantly.'

Bombay, 17 December 1827

I am the most caddish of men, for I am feeling the utmost exhilaration and satisfaction at what is, I truly own, a most dreadful tragedy.

Yesterday on the polo field Rajah Sitraj of Sittapore was in collision with Major Levenson of the Dragoons, and broke his neck. Levenson got off with a broken collarbone.

Accidents are not uncommon, as one might expect, but fatalities are not frequent. The death of the rajah has set the entire Presidency by the ears.

And this Sitraj is the scoundrel who two years ago carried off Laura Dean from under my very nose!

I then swore never to have anything further to do with women, and if for this past year I have been dancing attendance on Prudence Partridge, this is because it has been expected of me by my colonel. Certainly I had given no thought to marriage; I am in no position to, in any event.

Thus I was mightily bedevilled to see Miss Dean return to Bombay some three weeks ago. I once described her as beautiful; now I am at a loss for words. She returned not merely enhanced by motherhood and maturity, but as Rani of Sittapore. That is virtually the same thing as queen, even if the kingdom in question is somewhat small. But here in India even small kingdoms are likely to be as large as England!

I wished to stay away. I wished to avoid her. I wished to hate her. But I could not. And when I actually held the gorgeous creature once again in my arms, I am afraid I surrendered, horse, foot and guns. Before I knew where I was, I was attempting to seduce another man's wife.

81

Actually, adultery is a pastime which occupies a good deal of time here in Bombay. It has been said that it is the commonest form of activity in the Presidency, far more indulged in than connubial relations. However, I had always hoped to be above such indecent goings-on. Yet here I was . . .

The Rani refused my importunities, very properly. But the way she did it, and the fact that she agreed to an assignation with me on the beach the following day, led me to suppose that her refusal was one of those entirely feminine manoeuvres, perhaps dictated by caution, but certainly designed to encourage a man to persevere. The assignation, I am bound to say, was equally unproductive, but I still had hopes. I had not yet formed my next strategy when yesterday's accident occurred.

The Rani is now closeted in Government House and is not receiving visitors, even those who would offer their condolences. I adore the woman! I believe she is susceptible to me. And she is now a widow. But at the same time she is a queen, and mother of a king. Yet she is also plain Laura Dean. My God, the temptation!

But into what sort of fire would I be jumping? Would she abandon her throne to be the wife of a humble lieutenant? Or would I have to leave the army and become some kind of king consort, or at least regent for her baby son? How imagination runs riot! I had never sought to rise so high.

Now, to confound the entire matter, I have learned by discreet inquiries that the Rani plans to leave Bombay tomorrow morning to return to Sittapore, as it is there that the Rajah must be buried. In Sittapore too is her son. But where does this leave me? I cannot possibly renew my courtship at this moment without proving myself an unfeeling cad. Neither can I desert my commission and go rushing off to this jaghir unless invited to do so by the Rani.

I have thus decided to pursue a policy of masterly inactivity, as recommended by all the best generals, for a while. This will allow the Rani to complete her mourning and consider her future, at which time I hope to obtain leave and travel up to Sittapore, and with good fortune bring her to a sensible decision.

82

As for poor Prudence – well, I feel very badly about it, but who would walk beneath the cold light of the moon when he could bask in the rays of the sun?

Rufus has just bitten his hundred and twenty-fifth Hindu.

4

The Widow

'Are you certain this is the best course?' Elphinstone asked.

He sat beside Laura in the drawing room at Government House her hands held in his.

'It is the only course,' Laura said. 'The Rajah must be taken back to his city, and I must accompany him. My son is there, and my family. Sitraj's family is mine, now.'

'Yes. Well . . . I hope they prove so. Now, I know this is a most indelicate subject, but in this heat . . .'

'Is there no way he can be preserved?'

'By embalming, of course. But I doubt we have anyone here in Bombay capable of doing that in a satisfactory manner. What I have done, if you will forgive me, is have the body placed in a cask of alcohol. This will preserve it, I believe, at least long enough for you to get it home.' He gave an encouraging smile. 'It is how they sent Lord Nelson home from Trafalgar.'

'Oh. Yes. I am very grateful, Your Excellency. Now, I must go and see that everything is ready.'

Elphinstone stood up with her. 'Have you thought of the future?'

'No. I cannot until I have spoken with the Dowager-Rani and Prince Batraj. Little Sivitraj is not yet a year old. I have no desire to rule Sittapore – I wouldn't have any idea how to go about it – but I cannot leave my son, at least until he is old enough to look after himself.'

'Oh, quite so, quite so,' Elphinstone agreed. 'You will always remember that you have friends here in Bombay. I shall not be here, unfortunately, but I am sure Malcolm will be happy to give you any assistance you require, the moment he arrives. You could even have a home here, if you wished to remain in India. I mean, after you have sorted things out in Sittapore.

84

Now, if you ever need support in that direction, you have but to send to us here, and assistance will be on its way immediately. I give you my word on that.'

'I will remember, Your Excellency. And I would like to thank you so very deeply for all that you have done, both for Sitraj and for myself.'

She kissed him on the cheek, and he watched her leave the room. Such a beautiful woman, he thought, and so self-possessed; she had hardly shed a tear, yet he had no doubt, on the evidence of his own eyes, that she had dearly loved her Indian rajah. To think that this regal, commanding woman used to be poor little Laura Dean. The Governor sighed. The problems she faced were immense. But she seemed to have the confidence to deal with them. And at least she was English. There was no risk of her being caught up in the dreadful consequences of being a Hindu widow; Sitraj had both guaranteed this in his marriage contract and abolished it in his kingdom.

But he thought, just in case any hotheads in Sittapore might wish to cause trouble, he would send someone with her, to remind them all of the Company's presence and power. And he knew the very fellow.

Laura sat on the bed as Miljah placed the last few items in her box.

She had the curious sensation of being outside herself, looking in.

She could hardly remember what it was like to be the poor, penniless Laura Dean of only two years ago. She could not imagine not being Rani of Sittapore. But then, she could not imagine Sitraj dead either. If she had shown no overwhelming grief as yet, that was because she had been in a kind of trance ever since she had seen him fall, and known instinctively that he had been killed.

It was a trance from which she was only just awakening; she could feel the tears lurking behind her eyes, waiting to be released. Perhaps, when she got home . . . But what would she find in that splendid, erotic palace, without him at her side?

Yet her son was there, and her son was now Rajah. If she had accumulated anything of real value during her two years as Sitraj's wife, it had been a sense of responsibility, as well as a love, for Sittapore and its people. She could pay Sitraj's memory no greater honour than to make sure that their happiness continued.

Would she be allowed to? Obviously there was a chance Batraj would claim the throne. But he had no right to it, as there was a living rajah. She would have to be very firm, and very strong . . . and remind him of the power of the Company, far more powerful than any force he could raise, and pledged to her support.

Then what of Bilkis? Bilkis was Batraj's aunt, but she was little Sivitraj's grandmother. Surely she would support the rightful claim of her grandson. Besides, Bilkis, Laura was certain, knew that Batraj was unsuitable to be the ruler.

Suppose he made advances to her? Laura wondered. He probably would, out of lust for her as much as lust for power. Well, she would have no trouble in dealing with that!

'It is ready, Highness. Will you change now?'

Miljah had laid out a white sari for her.

'I did not know I possessed such a thing,' Laura said, as she allowed herself to be undressed.

'It was the first made for you, Highness. Every wife must possess a white sari.'

'I suppose she must,' Laura said absently.

'Highness, you are going back to Sittapore?'

'Of course.'

'Highness . . . it would be better for you to remain here.'

Laura frowned at her. 'Remain here? My son is in Sittapore. And besides, do you not suppose I wish to see my husband buried?'

'He will not be buried, Highness. He will be burned. This is the Hindu custom.'

Laura shuddered, but she knew that to be true.

'I must be there,' she insisted.

Miljah said nothing more, and finished dressing her mistress.

'Me, sir?' Guy could hardly believe his ears, as he stood to attention before both the Governor and Colonel Partridge. 'You wish me to accompany the Rani back to Sittapore?'

'I think that would be best. You are a friend of the Rani's, are you not?'

'Well, sir . . . I suppose you could say that.' He could feel the heat in his cheeks, and cursed it.

'That's what I thought. You will take an escort with you. Not your entire company. . . .' The Governor glanced at the Colonel.

'I should think ten men and a sergeant, Your Excellency.'

'Yes. That should be sufficient. There must be no suggestion that we are in any way attempting to overawe the people of Sittapore, or to influence their decisions or customs in any way. Your official purpose will be to represent the Company at the Rajah's funeral. The situation is a very delicate one, Lieutenant Bartlett, and must be handled with the utmost care. As I have said, we must not in any circumstances offend the people of Sittapore, but we have a responsibility to the Rani, as she is one of our own. Do you understand what I am speaking about?'

'Yes, sir! The infant Prince. You wish to be sure there is no trouble to stop him becoming Rajah.'

'That certainly,' Elphinstone agreed. 'However, we are more concerned with the safety of the Rani. She is now the widow of a Hindu, and more over, of a Hindu rajah.'

Guy frowned at him. 'You mean . . . suttee? My God! I beg your pardon, sir. But I was under the impression that it had been abolished, by Company order.'

'It has been abolished, Lieutenant, in all territories directly controlled by the Company. And we have made our disapproval of so horrible a practice clear to all our client princes. Sitraj understood this well enough, and I happen to know that he has forbidden it in his jaghir. He also guaranteed in the marriage contract that the Rani should never suffer such a fate. But Sitraj is now dead, and I do not propose to take any risks with the Rani. I wish this understood.'

'Yes, sir. How long am I to remain in Sittapore, sir?'

'Until you are satisfied that the government is in the right hands, and that the Rani can be safely left.'

'Yes, sir!' Guy said, growing more enthusiastic with every moment. He wondered what Laura was going to say when she discovered who was to command her escort.

'I wish you a safe journey, my dear, and after . . . great success in your endeavours.'

'Thank you, Your Excellency. I shall always treasure the memory of your friendship.' Laura went outside, and surveyed her caravan. The elephants had all been draped in white, and the escort wore white armbands, while the servants were also dressed in white.

Sitraj's coffin was in a howdah on the first elephant; he would lead them back to Sittapore.

Then Laura saw the ten red-coated Indian soldiers and their sergeant, standing to attention in a guard of honour. And none other than Guy Bartlett in command!

'Your escort,' Elphinstone explained.

'My escort? But I do not need an escort. I have my own soldiers.'

'The Company wishes to be represented at the funeral of the Rajah,' Elphinstone said deviously. 'I would come myself did I not have pressing responsibilities here.'

Laura glared at him, knowing that he was lying. 'And Lieutenant Bartlett!'

'Is he not a friend of yours?'

'Well . . . yes.'

Elphinstone frowned. 'He has not been improper, I hope, Your Highness?'

'Good heavens, no, Your Excellency.' She could not possibly get poor Mr Bartlett into trouble when she had accepted his advances in the first place. 'It is just that I am sure he cannot welcome the idea of marching all the way to Sittapore.'

'As you see, his men are provided with mules, so they will be able to keep up with you. And Mr Bartlett is a soldier, Your Highness. He goes where he is sent.'

Laura gave up. In fact, the thought of having a Company officer at her elbow when she faced Batraj was reassuring.

She gave him a cold smile as she went down the steps. 'Good

afternoon, Mr Bartlett. I gather you are to accompany me home.'

'It is my pleasure, Your Highness.'

'I'm sure it is,' she agreed, and mounted into her howdah.

Colonel Mujhabi was in command of the caravan, but he took his orders from Laura, and every day they kept going until it was dark before camping.

Much as Laura wished to push on, however, it was impossible to reach Sittapore in under nine days, and so they were still on the road, although within a march of the Sittapore border, on 25 December.

Laura had no real desire to celebrate Christmas, and she doubted that any of her Indian entourage would even know what it was, but she felt it would be churlish of her to leave Mr Bartlett all alone on such a day, so she invited him to dine with her.

She half expected him to decline, but at the appointed hour he arrived, looking very smart in his uniform.

'Merry Christmas,' she said, as he kissed her hand.

He sat in the other camp chair. 'Is it, for you, Highness?'

'No. But I suppose life must go on.'

Food was served, and with it cane rum, well watered.

'How long do you anticipate staying in Sittapore?' she asked.

'As long as is necessary.'

She frowned at him. 'Necessary for what?'

'My instructions are to make sure there are no hitches in the succession of your son.'

'Elphinstone sent you to do that?'

'Yes. Do you resent that?'

'Oh, good heavens, no. I am rather grateful for it. But . . . I should hate to have any trouble.'

'I have not come to cause trouble, Laura, only to prevent it.'

'With ten men.' She smiled at his earnest confidence.

'My ten men represent the power of the Company. Your people will understand that.'

'I'm sure.' She was eating little, but she took another glass of rum.

'Laura . . . I know I should not speak of this, at such a time. But have you given any thought to your future?'

She turned her head to look at him. 'My future is to be my son's mother until he is old enough to rule.'

'I understand that. But will it not be a lonely existence?'

She gazed at him for some seconds. She had not known him to be so thoughtfully serious before. 'I think that is to be my karma.'

'I should hate to think that,' he said.

'I think perhaps we should speak of this at a later date,' she said.

'Tell Colonel Mujhabi that I wish a messenger to be sent ahead to inform the Dowager-Rani of the death of the Rajah,' Laura instructed Miljah next morning.

The slave looked doubtful; she had in fact worn a very long face ever since leaving Bombay.

'Do you think this is wise, Highness?'

'The Rajah's mother must be informed, Miljah. And I should hate to be the one who has to break the news. Better that she be prepared.'

'Yes, Highness,' Miljah said reluctantly.

The messenger had obviously done his job thoroughly. The border guards wore white armbands, and there was no celebratory firing of muskets on this occasion, while as they approached Sittapore, they could hear nothing but the clashing of cymbals and the mournful blowing of bugles.

White flags flew from the palace.

When Sitraj's coffin was carried up the sloping street beneath the gateway the crowds moaned and wept, women screamed and rolled themselves in the dust.

Laura walked immediately behind the coffin, Mujhabi at her elbow. Then came a solitary drummer, beating a slow cadence. Guy and his Company soldiers followed, then the Sittapore soldiers and the servants.

People stared at Laura as if she were a stranger; there was no greeting. But she hardly noticed the hostility. Twelve men carried Sitraj's coffin, but Laura saw that they were exhausted when they finally lifted it up the steps on to the palace verandah, where Bilkis and Sitraj's three other wives were waiting, as well as his children. Sivitraj was in the arms of his nurse.

Prithviraj Dal was there too, and other members of the government.

Laura bowed before her mother-in-law. 'My husband, your son, the Rajah, broke his neck falling from his horse,' she said simply.

'You have brought great misfortune upon Sittapore,' Bilkis said.

Laura's head jerked, but she knew she had to expect this for a while. It would be self-defeating to take offence.

'The greatest misfortune is mine,' she said quietly. She looked for Batraj, but he was not there. That at least was a relief.

She turned away from Bilkis, and went to Sivitraj. The baby gurgled happily to see his mother, and she kissed him. And then remembered Guy.

'This is Lieutenant Bartlett of the Honourable East India Company,' she explained to Bilkis. 'He has come to represent the Company at my husband's funeral.'

Bilkis's gaze remained cold. 'It will be tomorrow,' she said.

Laura turned to Prithviraj Dal instead. 'Lieutenant Bartlett and his men need quartering, Excellency.'

Prithviraj Dal bowed, his hands together in front of his face.

Laura looked at Guy. 'His Excellency will attend to you. Perhaps you would join me at supper.'

Guy saluted. 'It will be my pleasure, Your Highness.'

Laura took Sivitraj from the nurse and went into her apartment.

She kissed the child and hugged him, sat with him on the divan she had shared with Sitraj. As she had anticipated, the tears now came very fast, and the little boy stared at her in distress.

'It's all right, sweetheart,' she promised him, rocking back and forth with him in her arms. 'Everything is going to be all right.'

The door opened and Bilkis came in. Her mother-in-law had never entered here before. Now she did so without knocking. But Laura still refused to take offence.

91

'Why did you come back?' Bilkis asked boldly.

'Should I not come back, with my husband's body? This is my son.'

'You should not have come back,' Bilkis said. 'And with Company soldiers!'

'They are a mark of respect!' Laura cried. 'Why are you behaving so cruelly to me? Do you think I killed your son? I loved him. You know how he played polo. He was too reckless!' She began to sob.

Bilkis gazed at her, her face expressionless.

Laura laid Sivitraj down and dried her eyes. 'Where is Prince Batraj?'

'He is away. I have sent people to find him.'

'Thank you. There is much to be done.'

'You should not have come back,' Bilkis said again. 'It will cause much trouble.' She left the room.

Obviously Bilkis was not going to help, Laura realised, at least in her present mood. She was more than ever grateful for the presence of Guy and his small band of men; indeed, for the first time she wished Elphinstone had sent more. But if there was some attempt to replace Sivitraj as Rajah, could she not count on Colonel Mujhabi and his men?

In any event, if that were going to happen, would it not have happened whether she had returned or not?

She sent for Miljah, had a bath, and got rid of most of the tear stains by liberal applications of kohl, the heavy dark eye make-up used by the Indian women; against her pale complexion and yellow hair it made her eyes appear huge and luminous.

When she was dressed in all her splendour, wearing her gold bangles and her emerald necklace as well as her ring, she sent for the Colonel, receiving him in her private sitting room.

Sivitraj was in his high chair beside her.

'I sent for you to tell you how grateful I am for your assistance, Colonel,' Laura said.

The Colonel bowed, clearly somewhat embarrassed.

'And to introduce you to the new Rajah of Sittapore.'

The Colonel bowed to the little boy.

'There will be difficult times ahead, Colonel,' Laura said. 'But I have no doubt that with the aid of loyal friends like yourself and the army, and with the wholehearted support of the Company, we shall surmount this tragedy.'

Mujhabi bowed. Laura wished he would say something, but she could not command him to do so.

'Thank you, Colonel,' she said.

Mujhabi bowed.

Laura then sent for Prithviraj Dal. She felt it was vitally important to establish that she was in control in Sittapore, acting both for her dead husband, and for her son.

Prithviraj Dal was even more embarrassed than Colonel Mujhabi, at being summoned into the Dowager Rani's apartments, and when Laura gestured him to a seat he perched uneasily.

'In the absence of Prince Batraj,' Laura told him, trying to sweeten the pill as much as possible, 'whom I am prepared to delegate as my son's representative on the Council, I intend to take that position myself. In this regard, as you know, I am presently insufficiently informed about current matters here in Sittapore. I would therefore like you to have your secretary prepare a résumé of the current financial position, and of any other matters to which my late husband would normally have attended on his return from Bombay.'

Prithviraj Dal bowed, his hands together in front of his face.

'I would like that information to be delivered to me tomorrow afternoon, and I wish a full Council summoned to meet the morning after.'

Prithviraj bowed.

Laura wanted to get up and shake him. But she kept her composure. 'I know it will be unusual to have a woman at your council,' she said, 'but I must act for my son. Sittapore must be governed, and I intend to do it until my son is of an age to assume the responsibilities of his position. I may say that this is the wish of the Company as well. Please tell me that you understand and agree.'

'Tomorrow afternoon,' Prithviraj Dal muttered, bowed again, and left.

*

Laura entertained Guy to supper that evening, although with sufficient servants present to make sure there was not the slightest risk of impropriety.

'Are you satisfied with your quarters?' she asked.

'Mine are very comfortable. I'm a little far away from my men, but I suppose that is inevitable. But this . . .' he looked around. 'This is quite palatial.'

'It is a palace,' she reminded him.

'These statues . . .' he stammered.

'Yes. They would shock in an English drawing room. But they represent the gods. Hindu gods are refreshingly earthy beings.'

'I can see that. Laura . . .'

'It would be better to call me Your Highness, Mr Bartlett. Some of these servants have a word or two of English, and I would not like them to suppose that we were more than acquaintances.'

'Of course.' He added, 'It struck me your welcome was not entirely . . . well . . . a welcome. Did you know there is quite a large crowd gathered outside the palace?'

'I did hear a noise. I have not gone to look at them. They are very emotional people, and their Rajah is dead. I will see them tomorrow, at the funeral.'

'They were shouting and chanting,' Guy said. 'I'm afraid I could make little of it, but it had to do with the Rajah, certainly. And the Rani.'

'I'm sure.'

'You're not concerned? What about this fellow Batraj?'

'He is not here, thank God. Things will have quietened down by the time he returns.'

'Hm,' Guy remarked. 'You don't suppose I should send back to Bombay for some more men?'

'If you think you should,' she said carelessly. She did not wish him to know she was herself a little frightened. And besides, what happened next would have to be decided long before a messenger could bring any adequate force from Bombay.

'Well, that mob out there . . .'

'They are mourning their ruler, Mr Bartlett. It is an act of respect. If you are worried about me, please do not be. These people love me. I have always been their friend.'

Guy could see no point in arguing further. But when he left the palace at midnight, the crowd was still there, and it seemed to him that it was definitely hostile.

His room was in the officer's quarters of the Sittapore army. He found Ramjohn waiting there for him.

'It is very worrying, Guy sahib,' Ramjohn said. 'Do you know what those people are chanting?'

'Tell me.'

'They are chanting: destruction to the white witch who has caused the death of our rajah.'

'Are you sure?'

'Yes, sahib. It is not good.'

'Hm. Mobs do chant silly things . . .' he came to a decision. 'Do you think you could leave the city secretly, Ramjohn?'

Ramjohn grinned. 'I can do this, sahib.'

'Then I wish you to leave, now. I will give you a message for the Governor in Bombay. I wish you to return there as quickly as possible, and deliver this message. Can you do this?'

'I should take a horse, sahib.'

'Take mine. Will you get out of the gate with a horse?'

Ramjohn grinned again. 'Oh, yes, sahib. I came in with the Rajah's servants. None of the guards noticed me. I will do it.'

'Good fellow. Ramjohn . . . this is a most urgent matter.'

'I will do it, sahib.'

Laura was awakened by Miljah just after dawn.

'It is time, Highness,' the slave said.

She looked, as she had for the past week, unutterably doleful.

'What time is the cremation?' Laura asked.

'In the fourth hour, Highness.'

Miljah fussed about her, bathing her and dressing her in her white sari. To Laura's surprise, the maid had also laid out all her jewellery.

'You must wear your very best,' Miljah said.

95

Laura supposed she was right. If ever she needed to look like a queen it had to be now.

'Are there still many people outside the palace?' she asked.

'There are many people everywhere, Highness. This is a sad occasion.'

'Yes,' Laura said.

She wished it were done. But it was an ordeal which had to be undergone.

To her surprise, once she was fully dressed and bejewelled, Miljah opened the door, and Bibi, Chandra and Indra filed in, also dressed in their best and accompanied by their children. Each bowed low before Laura, and Bibi took her hands and kissed them; all the women were obviously in deep distress, and Laura's heart went out to them.

Baby Sivitraj was also dressed in his finest clothes. Laura took him from his nurse and herself carried him to the front of the palace, but before she got there, she had to pause and greet each of her personal servants, who were lined up in a row, and who seemed more distressed than anyone. Bilkis waited on the porch, together with Prithviraj Dal and the government ministers. Colonel Mujhabi was there looking very solemn, supported by some hundred of his men, as well as Guy, equally solemn, with his escort.

Sitraj's body lay on a large bier of flowers, some six feet wide and ten feet long. The alcohol had worked very well, and he was dressed in his finest robes, his hands pressed together on his chest as if in prayer.

Bilkis nodded to the soldiers. She had entirely taken over the proceedings. Well, Laura thought, she was welcome to it.

A dozen soldiers picked up the bier and carried it down the steps, into the midst of the huge silent crowd gathered there.

'You will follow,' Bilkis said.

Still carrying Sivitraj, Laura went down the steps and into the people. Last night they had been chanting and shouting, today they were silent. One or two even smiled at her, and called out to Sivitraj. That was reassuring.

She did not look back, but knew there was a long procession of wives and notables behind her. Although it was only a

96

quarter to ten, the morning was very hot. Laura began to sweat and shiver, and wondered how long the ceremony would take.

The bier was carried to the banks of the Sittapore River, where a huge pyre had been constructed, consisting of dried wood to make sure it burned well, and green leaves to ensure a huge column of smoke which would be seen for miles around. Waiting beside the pyre were four men with torches already alight.

Here too there was a large crowd, now swelled by those who had followed the bier down the hill.

The bier was carried up specially prepared steps, and laid on top of the pyre. Laura stood among the other members of the royal family, while the priests droned interminable prayers, and the morning grew ever hotter. But at last it was done, and Laura turned to Bilkis. Presumably the old woman intended to give the signal.

'Are you ready?' Bilkis asked.

'Yes,' Laura said.

'Give the Rajah to his nurse,' Bilkis said.

Laura obeyed, wondering what other ceremony remained.

'You are being very brave, my child. I forgive you for the misfortune you have brought upon us. Here.' Bilkis held out her hand and offered to Laura what looked like a small nut.

'It is bhang,' Bilkis said. 'Chew it, and you will feel less pain. Inhale the smoke as quickly as you can, and it will be done.'

Laura had no idea what her mother-in-law was talking about.

'It is time for you to join your husband,' Bilkis said.

Laura froze in horror.

'No,' she said.

'You must,' Bilkis said, still in a low voice. 'Do not make a spectacle of yourself.'

'Suttee has been abolished in Sittapore,' Laura said, trying to speak evenly to prevent panic from clawing at her. 'And it was written into my marriage contract that I was not subject to your laws.'

Bilkis regarded her with patient pity. 'Foolish woman. My son was an apostate, who would sacrifice all to pander to the friendship of the Company. But he is dead. And those of us

97

who remain will have no dealings with the invaders. Now you will mount the pyre with dignity. Or must you be bound in place and die in humiliation?'

Laura swung round. 'Guy!' she screamed. 'Guy! Help me!'

'She has lost her senses,' Bilkis snapped. 'Take her.'

Laura was surrounded by men led by Colonel Mujhabi.

'Colonel,' she gasped. 'You are my friend. Colonel . . .'

'It is the law, Highness,' the Colonel said regretfully.

Men seized her arms, her thighs, her ankles, and she was lifted from the ground. She tried to fight them, but there were too many of them.

'Guy!' she screamed again. '*Guy!*'

The men half carried and half dragged her up the ladder to the top of the pyre; her legs and arms and body were bumped and bruised on the steps as she attempted to fight them, and her sari became disarranged. Other men brought ropes and she knew she could fight no more. She was laid beside her husband, her wrists and ankles tied together so that she could not move, a rope passed round her body and secured to a strut of the bier to keep her from rolling.

She could just see Sitraj beside her, his features now slightly puffy from the heat.

She gasped and panted, and screamed again. Bibi and Chandra and Indra had climbed the steps to file past her. Then Bibi stooped, and kissed her forehead.

Even through her terror Laura realised that had she not returned, Bibi, as the next senior wife, would have been lying here in her place.

'Help me,' she begged. 'Somebody . . . help me!' she wept in desperation.

Bilkis stood above her. 'With good fortune, you will be together in the next life, my daughter,' she said, and went down the steps.

Laura smelt smoke, and heard the crackle of flame. She screamed again, though she knew nobody could hear her.

At Laura's first shout, Guy instantly understood what was happening. 'Follow me,' he shouted to his men and pushed his way forward. But the Company escort had gradually been shunted to the rear during the procession down the hill, and he had not wished to give offence – as instructed by the Governor – and had thus allowed it to happen.

He had never supposed it could come to this.

Now he found himself surrounded by Hindus, who pressed so close it was impossible even to draw his sword, unless he intended to kill someone.

'We cannot do it, sahib,' shouted the havildar. 'Let us get back.'

Guy hesitated. It was his first independent command, his first face-to-face confrontation with the reality of India. But Laura was in danger. Even had he not been in love with her, her safety was his reason for being here.

'Go back,' a Hindu growled, pushing his face close. 'Go back, or you will all be killed.'

'Damn you!' Guy snapped.

Then there was a tremendous drumming of hooves, an explosion of firearms, and a chorus of shrieks and yells. The entire crowd began to fall back, running this way and that, and the small band of red-coats was carried with it, trying desperately to avoid being trampled.

Guy struck two men with his fist, and at last got his sword free, but by then it was too late. The funeral pyre, from which plumes of smoke were already rising was surrounded by horsemen, scattering the women and servants who stood there. One of the horsemen snatched the baby Rajah from the arms of his nurse. Another climbed the ladder on to the pyre, and with two strokes of his knife cut Laura free. Then he threw her over his shoulder, her golden hair uncoiling and drooping down his back.

The man faced the crowd and waved his tulwar, uttered a great shout of defiance, and leapt on to his waiting horse and galloped away, followed by his men, one of whom held Sivitraj in his arms.

Behind them the smoke billowed, and the body of Sitraj began to burn.

Guy sheathed his sword and pushed forward. The women

were still picking themselves up, aghast at what had taken place, while the flames roared above their heads.

He found the Dowager-Rani. 'Do you know what has happened?'

'That was my nephew, Batraj. He has defiled his cousin's funeral, and proved himself an enemy of his people.' Each word dripped from her lips like vitriol.

'Batraj? Why should he have done this?'

'He covets the Rani,' Bilkis said. 'And the throne. Now he has the little Rajah. But to desecrate the suttee for desire of a woman . . . that will not be forgiven.'

Covets the Rani, Guy thought. My God! To think of Laura in the hands of that scoundrel . . .

'Where will he take the Rani?'

'Into the hill country.' She gestured to the north.

'I will follow.'

'You?' Bilkis's lips curled in contempt. 'Batraj will take your manhood with his own hands.'

'I will follow,' Guy said. 'And you, Highness, look to yourself. There is a column of Company troops marching upon Sittapore at this moment.' It was necessary to exaggerate: he could only hope Ramjohn was on his way.

'My people will fight them,' Bilkis said.

'You had better hope they have more sense. Havildar, have the mules saddled and prepare to move out.'

Laura was for some minutes too dazed to understand what was happening. She had inhaled a lungful of smoke deliberately, to send her senses reeling, so that she would die before the flames got to her. Then she had found herself, it seemed, flying through the air. And now she was galloping away from Sittapore, held in the arms of . . . Batraj?

He grinned at her. He had taken her from his shoulder and carried her in the crook of his arm; she realised he must be tremendously strong. 'You are safe now,' he told her.

She gasped, and tried to think.

'I do not think they will even follow,' Batraj said. 'In any event, they will not catch us.'

100

'But . . . why?' Her brain was reeling. Surely with her out of the way Sittapore was his.

'Are you not grateful to me?'

'Yes. But . . .' she was feeling more and more uncomfortable, held as she was tightly against him by his left arm, her thighs and legs bumping against the horse. 'Can I not sit properly?'

'Of course.' He reined in, and swung her round so that she was sitting on the saddle in front of him. It was only marginally less uncomfortable.

She looked over his shoulder at his men. There were at least a hundred of them, armed to the teeth; none of them had she ever seen before. But one of them carried Sivitraj. The little boy was too excited at this sudden adventure to be afraid.

'Sivitraj!' she said.

'He is safe. He is our Rajah, is he not?'

'I do not understand,' she said.

'You will understand,' he said. 'When it is time.'

They rode for three hours, then Batraj called a halt. By now they were in the hills to the north of the city.

They stopped by a stream. It was all done with military precision. Sentries climbed to the higher ground, the horses were hobbled, a fire lit, and within five minutes a delicious spicy smell filled the air. Flat loaves of unleavened bread were put to roast on stones by the fire.

Sivitraj was brought to her and one of the horsemen brought her a bowl of mare's milk, known as kumiss for him.

'It will make him sick,' she protested.

'He will get used to it.' Batraj had brought her a bowl of water, and sat down beside her.

'What do you want?' she asked, half-fearfully.

Batraj grinned. 'Are you not glad to be alive and free, and to have your son in your arms?'

'Of course I am. I am most deeply grateful to you. But I do not understand why you have done it. Surely . . .' she bit her lip.

'Surely with you dead, I would have been in a position to dominate Sittapore? You do not know my aunt. It is that little boy she will wish to see on the throne. She is a great believer in legitimacy, and she hated my father. She hates me. With you dead, she would have declared herself regent. And I . . . I would have been nothing.'

Laura had been trying to get Sivitraj to drink some of the milk, not very successfully; the baby kept blowing bubbles. At least he was not apparently hungry. Now she hugged him closer. 'Then you mean to harm my son?'

'I hope that will not be necessary.'

She felt her stomach muscles begin to tighten. She had not, after all, been rescued.

'You would disrupt the entire jaghir, to obtain me?' she asked in a low voice.

'Are you not worth it?'

She said nothing, and only held the baby tighter.

'I could of course take you by force,' Batraj pointed out. 'There are men enough who would willingly hold you down. But I would rather have a partnership. You are Dowager-Rani of Sittapore. No matter that those fools, inspired by my aunt, I may say, sought to burn you on my cousin's pyre. All India knows that Satraj had outlawed suttee. They will accept the fact of your rescue, and honour me for it.'

'Then could you not just have ridden in there with your men, and put a stop to it?' she asked.

'One hundred against an incited mob of several thousand? Even with the aid of your gallant platoon of Company redcoats?' He grinned. 'Had I received sufficient warning of what was happening, I might have attempted such a coup d'etat. But I only heard of Sitraj's death two days ago, and I had no time to prepare more than this. In any event, this is better. We will remain in the hills until the furore has died down. Meanwhile my agents will be sniffing out people in Sittapore who are sympathetic to me, suborning them in my favour. When the time is right, we will return, clandestinely, enter the city by night, seize the palace and the person of my aunt, and proclaim the new Rajah.'

'With you as regent?'

Batraj grinned. 'No, no. It must all be very proper. Or the

102

Company may be angry and send an army. You will be regent, Highness. I shall merely be your husband.'

She gasped at his effrontery. But for the time being it was necessary to stay calm, in order to stay alive. 'But my son *will* be Rajah?' she asked insistently.

'That is entirely up to you, Highness. Or may I call you Laura?'

She inhaled, slowly. She said nothing, in order to give herself time.

'I will be good to you,' he said. 'This I swear. I have wanted you from the moment I saw you. I have worshipped you. My lingam calls upon me to possess your yoni every time I see you.'

Once again she was left breathless at his crudeness.

'And I have risked a great deal for you,' he went on. 'I have saved your life. By all the laws of history you belong to me. I will have you, Laura. But if you will have me equally, are there any heights we may not climb together?'

'You must give me time to consider your proposal,' she said. 'I will give you my answer after we have returned to Sittapore.'

'You will give me your answer now, this minute, Laura.' He smiled. 'And then you may consider my proposal, until we have reached our destination.'

Laura fought to keep herself from exploding in outrage and anger, and despair. She was absolutely helpless. He would have her but it might still be possible that he would have her only on her terms. She had never been afraid to look facts in the face before. The only thing she must not become now, was afraid.

'If I surrender to you,' she said. 'Will my son be Rajah?'

'He shall.'

'Do you swear to this, by the wrath of Shiva and Vishnu?'

'I swear it.'

Laura drew a long breath. 'Then I accept.'

'You are a sensible woman.' He stood up. 'The Rani is mine,' he shouted.

His men cheered, and Laura felt her cheeks scorching with embarrassment.

'Now let us make haste,' Batraj said.

*

103

They finished their meal, mounted, and rode again. Laura was given a horse of her own, and rode next to the man carrying Sivitraj. She would have liked to be able to hold the boy herself, but was simply not a good enough horsewoman; there was no side-saddle, and this was the first time she had ever ridden astride.

She felt a jumbled mixture of emotions. She had just consented to go to Batraj's bed! All for the sake of her little baby son, who kept smiling at her.

She had turned her back forever on her own people. Her business was survival, for herself and for Sivitraj, until they regained Sittapore, and she could make contact with Bombay.

Remember, Elphinstone had told her, that we are your friends, always. Call on us when you need us. She would do that. And then Batraj might proclaim to the world that she was his wife; *she* would tell the world differently!

Survival. She almost looked forward to the challenge.

They rode all afternoon, and by the time Batraj called a halt Laura was exhausted. She feared that he would now seek to possess her, but he did not; a tent was erected for her and she was allowed to sleep with Sivitraj in her arms.

Perhaps he was not going to be so difficult after all.

Next morning they resumed their journey, climbing high into the hills, a place of sudden defiles and precipices; Laura was in mortal fear for Sivitraj, but Batraj's horses were as sure-footed as goats.

'This is my land,' he told her. 'All the rest is but an empty show.'

He laughed and joked with his people, and with her, all the time; he was enjoying his triumph.

In the middle of the afternoon they suddenly came upon a village. About a hundred people, men, women, and children, with their dogs, all crowded forward to greet the Prince.

The houses themselves were poor, as in most Indian hill villages, but there was a flock of goats, and a bubbling stream, and a communal fire blazing in the centre.

'I am afraid life in the hill country is primitive,' Batraj said as he lifted her down. 'But it is a good life.'

104

'Are we still in Sittapore?' she asked.

'Certainly. But we are close to the borders of the next jaghir. Up here we are safe. Only a madman would seek to find us in these mountains, which we know so much better than anyone else.' He took her hand. 'Now come.'

She looked down at herself, all dusty and dirty. She had been hoping for a further respite. 'Can I not bathe first?'

He grinned. 'I wish you the way you are, smelling of sweat rather than perfume. I am not like my cousin.'

Laura swallowed. But she had agreed, and she was still in his power. 'Where?'

He pointed to the largest hut. 'That is my house. Our house.'

'What of the Rajah?'

'He will be cared for by the women.' Batraj turned to them. 'I give you – your Rajah!' He held Sivitraj high, and the baby crowed happily. Batraj handed the boy to a waiting woman. 'And now I take possession of the Dowager-Rani, in the name of the great goddess.'

The men and women shouted their approbation.

'Is it necessary to humiliate me?' Laura hissed.

'Should a man and a woman be ashamed of coupling?' Batraj inquired. 'Come.'

Laura followed him to the hut, hesitated at the doorway. It was dark in there, and smelt unwholesome.

'Come!' His voice echoed out of the gloom.

Laura hesitated still. She had no real idea what was going to happen to her. Sitraj had been so gentle; there was nothing gentle about Batraj.

She looked back at the men and women gathered behind her. They were all watching her. She was in the midst of a den of wolves; if anything were to happen to Batraj she would be at their mercy.

'Come!' Batraj said again, more peremptorily.

Laura went into the hut.

The light was poor, but after a few seconds Laura found she could see, and hugged herself in dismay, for Batraj had already stripped, and was more than ready for her. Never had she seen anything so huge and menacing.

105

'He is impatient,' Batraj grinned. 'Let me look upon you.'

Laura knelt, and took off her sari. Batraj had already spread blankets on the ground. When she would have sat down, he stopped her.

'Stay like that,' he commanded, and knelt against her. She shuddered as he began to explore her, not brutally – indeed his hands were surprisingly gentle – but with slow and complete thoroughness, almost as if he were a blind child discovering a new toy with his fingers.

'I have watched you, and dreamed of you, and desired you, for two years,' he said. 'These breasts, they are divine. These buttocks, they are perfection. This hair . . . can there be an equal of it in the world?'

The terrifying thing was that he was beginning to excite her in turn, where she wanted only to hate him, reject him, suffer him in pain and anger.

'I could play with you all day,' he said. 'But my lingam grows impatient. Why, he has been impatient for two years. And now your yoni is impatient too. Come to me.'

He sat down with his legs folded, and drew her forward on to his lap. Her knees were parted, and he made her sit on him. She felt him enter her, deeper than she had ever been entered before.

'Scream,' he commanded her. 'Scream your ecstasy.'

Laura screamed.

When he let her go, she collapsed in a heap. She was afraid to think. Sitraj had never made her feel so much, had never made herself so aware of herself as a woman. Nor could she imagine Guy Bartlett even approaching such sexual splendour.

Was this then the man she was destined to love? She could not believe it, did not wish to believe it.

But supposing they *did* manage to regain Sittapore, and place Sivitraj on the throne, with Batraj and herself as joint regents . . . heady thoughts filled her mind. Lascivious thoughts too, of endless hours with Batraj.

His hand stroked her shoulder, and she turned her head. He could not possibly be ready again so soon.

'You are everything I hoped for,' he told her. His hand

slipped up her shoulder to her neck, and caressed her throat. 'And to think that my first desire, when Sitraj brought you home, was to wrap my rumal around this neck, and tighten it slowly, and watch your eyes start from your head and your tongue loll out as you died.'

Laura rolled on her back, lazily.

'Did you hate me that much? For marrying your cousin? Or because I was a Christian?'

'I did not hate you at all, Laura,' Batraj said. 'I merely thought what a magnificent offering you would make to Kali, my goddess. A far more splendid offering than your aged uncle.'

Sittapore, 8 January 1828

I feel myself to be a failure, a mass of uncertainties, the most miserable fellow in the universe. Yet, I am at the same time excited beyond measure. For I am about to go to war, and on behalf of the most beautiful woman in the world.

Oh, cruel fate! I had believed that my every dream had come true. I was chosen to represent the Company at the funeral of the Rajah of Sittapore. There was of course more to this than met the eye; the Governor wished to have a representative to keep an eye on the situation, and ensure that the infant Rajah was duly proclaimed the rightful king.

For this purpose he chose me! I was the happiest man in the world.

Elphinstone could as well have sent an ass. Well, he did send an ass.

Laura was not very pleased to see me. I suspect she was afraid of compromising herself before her servants. But I was content. And the night before Christmas Eve, she entertained me to supper, tête-à-tête apart from a few dozen servants.

What is more, she did so again when we arrived in this place Sittapore, where she seems to have lived in splendour which quite puts the Brighton Pavilion to shame.

Contemplating her beauty, I was quite bewitched. I was already aware that her return had not been as satisfactory as she might have hoped. Her relatives are a grim-faced lot, her people even more so. She claims they love her, but I saw no evidence of it.

I now know that, no matter how hard she protested, I should have seized her there and then and carried her out of the city, while sending post-haste for reinforcements. I did send for reinforcements, but foolishly left her in the grandeur of her palace, and apparently in power.

Disaster befell the next day, the day of Sitraj's funeral. There is a dreadful custom amongst the Hindus, called suttee, which requires that a man's widow be burned upon his funeral pyre. Burned alive! My readers will ask why Miss Dean, or her parents, did not take this into consideration before her marriage. The answer is that they did, and a solemn marriage contract was drawn up specifically excluding Miss Dean from any Hindu religious obligations.

But the man who signed the contract was dead! This was a sad oversight on our part. The result was that Miss Dean was seized, most shamefully manhandled, and tied beside her husband's rotting corpse to be consumed by the flames.

And what was I doing the while? Endeavouring to reach her, of course. The situation was desperate, flames and smoke already rising from the pyre, when we were surprised by a cavalry charge, and in the twinkling of an eye Laura and her baby son had been removed, and carried away to the hills.

But she had not been rescued, merely kidnapped, by a dastardly scoundrel named Batraj, a cousin of the dead Rajah and from all accounts a lecherous lout.

Worse, the older Dowager-Rani, a hard-faced hag named Bilkis, tells me that this Batraj is actually a Thug. The Bilkis woman preferred not to go into details about it, but says she has her suspicions, even that Batraj may have been responsible for the murder of Harrison Dean, and for other incidents over the past two years.

And Laura is in his power! For all I know, she may already be lying dead, a knotted cord around her throat. Certain it is that she is his plaything. The gossip in the Presidency leads me to believe that Hindu methods of coupling are indecent and unChristian.

When I think of Laura being subjected to such horrors my blood boils. The only saving grace is that presumably she suffered as much at the hands of her husband, and seems to have survived.

Naturally I wished to go after them at once. I was dissuaded

109

from this course by both the dreadful Bilkis female, and my own havildar. Of course they had commonsense on their side; how could ten foot soldiers mounted on mules hope to catch a hundred horsemen? And suppose we did catch them: what could ten do against a hundred, every man armed to the teeth and a professional assassin?

I thus submitted. But I cannot feel I acted the hero in any way.

However, at last I am to be given an opportunity to redeem myself. Yesterday, after a forced march, Colonel Partridge arrived with the regiment, mounted on mules and looking very fierce. Having reported the situation to him, I then sought permission to seek out this Batraj fellow with a sufficient force to deal with him, and at the same time rescue the Dowager-Rani and the young Rajah. The Colonel demurred at first. I'm afraid he regards Laura with some disapproval, and holds the opinion that as she has undoubtedly already been forced by Batraj, she is hardly worth rescuing.

However, I pressed the point that Batraj is the leader of a Thug gang, and a most wanted man. I also reminded him, respectfully, that his orders from Governor Elphinstone were not only to restore law and order in Sittapore but also to make sure that the rightful ruler is established on the throne, and that this can only be done by capturing Batraj.

The Colonel is now in a state of some perplexity, following a conversation with the hag Bilkis, as to what Batraj's future intentions might be. My own desire was to place the wretched woman under arrest, as she has freely admitted that it was her decision to burn Laura beside her son. This she claims is Hindu law, and she despises her son for having agreed to change it.

Colonel Partridge will not arrest her; he feels she is the only person capable of governing Sittapore at the moment. Possibly he is right. But there are deeper reasons, I have no doubt. The Colonel is an unromantic fellow, and cannot conceive that anyone would overturn an important religious ceremony merely for the sake of a woman. Bilkis agrees with him in this, and is certain that Batraj means to return to Sittapore and set himself on the throne at the appropriate time, using the little

110

Rajah to accomplish this. Obviously the best and quickest way to deal with this is to lay hands on the fellow.

Thus tomorrow I set forth at the head of a full company of the regiment, eighty strong. Jefferson will accompany me. We shall be mounted on mules, and will have natives to guide us into the hill country, where everyone is certain Batraj is to be found.

It is assumed that eighty Bombay rifles will be more than a match for a hundred Thugs, and I personally have no doubt of it.

However, our Colonel, devious fellow, is also laying a trap, which is known only to the officers of the regiment. As I leave with my men, the Colonel will leave with the remainder of our force, ostensibly to return to Bombay. Thus Sittapore will be left defended only by its own army, a totally ineffectual body of some seven hundred men.

The Colonel entirely agrees with Bilkis that it is Batraj's intention to return at the earliest possible moment and attempt to usurp the throne. Colonel Partridge reckons that the rascal will evade a battle with my column, for no sensible Hindu would wish to fight disciplined troops led by white officers. Having been informed that the rest of our people have left Sittapore and that it is therefore at his mercy, Batraj will undoubtedly make straight for the city. But the regiment will, in fact, be only two marches away, in a secluded valley known to the Colonel from a previous campaign. He will have scouts out, and the moment Batraj has placed himself in a vulnerable position he will be attacked and destroyed.

I hope that the Colonel is wrong, and that the Thug will attempt to do battle with my troops.

So I am off to my first campaign, as commander-in-chief, no less!

And I shall rescue the fair Laura, like the very best of knights errant!

Then I shall marry her, no matter what her fate meanwhile – on this I am utterly determined – and we shall live happily ever!

5

The Thug

Laura rolled away from Batraj as violently as she could, and rose to her knees against the far wall of the hut.

Batraj smiled at her. 'A man should have no secrets from his wife.'

'You? You killed my uncle?'

'With my own hands.'

She gasped, unable to believe her ears. And she had just submitted to him, been satisfied by him ... desperately she fought to keep her emotions under control. 'But why?' She managed to speak normally. 'Why did you have to kill an innocent old man? And all his people? To sacrifice to your filthy black goddess?'

Batraj's eyes narrowed. 'You will speak of the great Kali with respect,' he said. 'Or I will thrash you to within an inch of your life. Yes, I offered him and his people as a sacrifice. But there was more to it than that. Sooner or later the Company will have to take action against my Thugs. They will send a punitive column to seek us out. To find me they will have to enter territory which is not their own. If, by the time they act, I am Regent of Sittapore, they will have to mount an invasion. My relatives and neighbours will hardly be able to allow that to happen. That will cause war, and war is what I seek.'

Laura was shaking her head in disbelief. 'War? You wish to go to war with the Company?'

'How else can they be driven from India? Our people are weak. Once we Marathas were great warriors. We were feared the length and breadth of the land. Now, because the Company managed to defeat us a generation ago, people like Sitraj and his father wish to live in peace with them. That was not the behaviour of our ancestors, of the great Sivaji. He

112

fought until he died. My father was determined to fight like Sivaji, but Rajah Sivitraj the First would have none of it. So my father poisoned him. He had planned to take power, but his own sister turned against him. Bilkis led the people in demanding vengeance for their dead rajah, and my father was forced to flee. I was but a boy then, but I fled with him, and shared his exile. Thus I worshipped at the shrine of Kali, and was inducted into the ranks of her followers, and I took the sacred oath.' His eyes gleamed, the veins stood out on his forehead, and his voice was strident. Then it quietened. 'Now I am a man, I must redeem that oath. I must take up the fight. I must force my people to war, as I must make the Rajputs join with us, to drive the British into the sea where they belong. This will happen.'

'If you fight the British, they will kill you and all your people,' Laura said, as reasonably as she could. She sensed that inside this unusual man there were two personalities fighting for control. One was undoubtedly that of the Thug, fired with a desire to avenge his father and carry on his father's work, but the other was a sensitive man with a sense of honour.

Batraj grinned. 'We are many. They are few. Even with their so-called sepoy soldiers they are few. They cannot kill us all. But we can kill them. Now come back to me. I am ready for you again.'

'No,' Laura said. 'Never. I could not. You are a murderer, a betrayer of your people.'

'Do not anger me, Laura. My anger is a terrible thing.'

'If you attempt to touch me I will fight you.'

He grinned. 'You, fight me?' He reached for her. She struck at him, but he was closer than she had thought, and her swinging hand with curved nails slashed into his cheek and sent him reeling backwards, blood pouring down his face.

His eyes narrowed. She knew that she had just committed suicide, or worse.

It was worse.

He pulled on his breeches and went outside. She heard him calling his men, and braced herself for the coming ordeal.

She looked to see if there might be some way out of the back of the hut, but there was none. The opening darkened as two

113

men entered, grinning at her. She remembered Sivitraj. She was still helpless. There was nothing she could do, save submit.

The men pulled her outside. The sun immediately scorched her naked body. She was dragged through the village, surrounded by people who stared at her, to where Batraj was waiting by the stream. She could not believe he would so expose her, but he too was smiling as he continued to wipe the blood trickling down his face.

'It is good that my men should look upon you,' he said, 'and see how beautiful you are. And also that they know you are my slave. Even the beautiful Englishwoman, the beautiful Rani, is the slave of Batraj. It is good for them to know this.'

Laura felt as if her entire body was a blush of shame as the men looked at her, appraising her, grinning and chattering amongst themselves. The men kept jerking on her arms, so that her body jerked as well; her gold bangles jangled against each other, and her emerald necklace swayed from breast to breast. To her horror the woman holding Sivitraj held the baby boy up to see his mother, but Sivitraj did not understand, and merely laughed.

Batraj stood beside her, and spoke to his men. While he did so, he fondled her breasts, drove his fingers into her hair and pulled her head backwards so that her mouth opened and she gasped with pain.

'I am telling my people that when we have driven the British out of Bombay we shall have all of their women, and that there are many like you in Bombay.'

'There are none like me in Bombay,' she spat at him, still refusing to give in now she saw that Sivitraj was not apparently in any immediate danger.

'We shall see.' He touched the scratch on his cheek. 'Now you must be punished. My people must see you punished.'

He took the necklace from round her neck, but did not touch her ring. He gave more orders, and the two men holding her arms forced her to her knees. Other men came to seize her legs and drag them away from her backwards, so that she found herself lying on the hot ground, on her stomach, trying desperately to keep her face from the earth, while her hair

114

clouded around her, the men pressing on her wrists and ankles to keep her still.

Batraj stood above her. 'You will receive twelve strokes of the cane,' he told her.

Her head jerked. 'No!' she shouted. 'You cannot.'

No Indian would dare whip a white woman. And as for whipping a rani . . .

'Twelve strokes,' he said.

'You . . .' the pain was like a knife across her buttocks, and her words became a scream.

Before she could draw her breath the cane slashed into her again, and again. She found it impossible to breathe properly; her face was ground into the dirt, and the pain was paralysing. The ground beneath her was wet with sweat and blood, and as blow after blow thudded into her, she collapsed.

When the flogging ceased, she did not realise it for several seconds. Her entire body was a mass of agony, and she only slowly understood that the men holding her wrists and ankles had released her. But she did not wish to move. To move would bring a renewal of the pain.

Then she heard Sivitraj wailing, and her head rose instinctively.

'You have caused His Highness to cry,' Batraj said severely. 'Get up and comfort him.'

Laura couldn't move.

'Get up,' Batraj said, 'or would you like to be caned some more?'

Laura slowly pushed herself to her knees. Tears were streaming down her face, and her body was coated with dust. She found she was shaking so that she could hardly stand. The pain was severe, but it was the pain in her mind which was the harder to bear.

She did not look at the men and women standing silently about her as she went towards the baby boy.

'It's all right, my darling,' she said, trying to keep her voice steady. 'Mama and Uncle Batraj were just playing a game.'

She could not take him because she was so dirty, so she stretched out a hand and stroked his head. He stopped crying.

'The mother's touch,' Batraj commented. 'Now wash yourself clean. There is the water.'

Laura hesitated. She wanted to defy him, but she was too exhausted, and in too much pain, to offer the least resistance.

She slid down the bank into the stream and her bottom touched the earth. She gave a little whimper of pain and threw herself forward into the water. It was surprisingly cool, and relieved her tortured flesh. She did duck her head, to rinse her hair again and again. The water also was deeper than she had imagined, and she had a tremendous urge to stay beneath the surface and take great breaths, and drown.

But she could not, because of Sivitraj.

She washed the dust from beneath her bangles, and from under the emerald on her finger. She was the wealthiest woman she had ever known, and she was a slave.

'That is enough.' Batraj called from the bank. 'You are clean. Come out now.'

Laura climbed up the bank.

'Go into the house,' he commanded.

It was as much as she could do to walk back through the village in the hot sun, her wet hair plastered to her neck and shoulders, and hold her head high. She came at last to the cool darkness and the blessed privacy. But immediately the doorway was darkened. He was following her.

'Now come to me,' he said.

She turned. 'I am in pain.'

'That will be interesting, will it not?'

One day, she thought, when Sivitraj is safe, I will drive a dagger into your heart.

Scouts sent out by Batraj brought news that there was no sign of any pursuit.

Batraj grinned. 'They are a spineless people, as is your Lieutenant Bartlett. But it is too soon to return. I must let my agents work on the minds of those who would oppose me. Yet I must occupy my men, or they will wish to share you, my sweetest Laura. There is an English mission at Slopan. We will pay it a visit.'

'No,' she begged. 'For God's sake, are you not satisfied?'

'Kali is never satisfied,' he told her, and made her come to him.

This was the most terrifying part of her ordeal. She hated him and everything about him. She could never forget her humiliation before his men, or the pain he had caused her. Yet he could arouse her, and leave her gasping in loathsome ecstasy.

But to be forced to take part in one of their terrible raids, with murder at the end of it, was more dreadful still.

'Batraj,' she said. 'No more raids, I beg of you. Please, spare the mission, and . . .' she drew a long breath. 'I will never oppose you again.'

He grinned. 'But you will never oppose me again anyway, Laura. I must occupy my men, and offer a sacrifice to Kali, that she may bless our return to Sittapore with success. And you will come with us.'

She was forced to leave Sivitraj in the care of the Thugs' women and ride with her husband to Slopan.

Slopan was situated some hundred miles south of Sittapore, and was just within Company territory. The Thugs approached it from the north, after a surprisingly rapid march of three days, and made camp in the hills above the village.

'We will attack at dawn,' Batraj said. 'And wipe it from the face of the earth. You will wait until our victory is complete, then you will come to me, there.'

'Me? For God's sake, Batraj . . .' she protested.

'Some people will get away. That is inevitable. They will flee to the nearest Company station and report what has happened. They will also report that riding with the Thugs was the white Dowager-Rani of Sittapore. Oh, this will distract the Company.' He grinned at her. 'Do not forget your son waits for us in our village.'

Laura felt almost physically sick. She had not slept, had even toyed with the idea of attempting to sneak away during the night and warn the village of the catastrophe which was hanging over it. But, as always, she was prevented by the impossibility of abandoning Sivitraj.

Now her reins were attached to those of her guard, a large man named Bedi, to prevent her from even considering escape. They rode at the rear of the company.

In the darkness of the pre-dawn they filed their way down the hillside. Batraj had reconnoitred the area thoroughly, and knew the way. When they were within half a mile of the village, he divided his force, and fifty men rode off to the south-west.

A dog barked, and was silent. Nearer at hand, some goats bleated. The animals could tell there was danger, but the humans slept soundly, secure in the protection of the Company.

Laura shivered. It was in fact quite chilly, but it was the thought of what was going to happen which made her cold.

Bedi smiled at her. 'You will soon be warm, Highness. Very warm. His Highness will burn the houses when we have finished with the people.'

Laura shuddered.

Batraj had a European watch, a present from his cousin. This he consulted from time to time as he waited for his men to get into position.

In the village a cock crowed, and the dog barked again.

Batraj put away his watch and drew his tulwar. With an immense rasp of steel his men did likewise. The darkness was beginning to turn to grey.

Batraj raised his sword and pointed it, and the Thugs galloped forward. Batraj shouted, 'Kali!' and his men responded.

The village came to life. People ran out of their houses, saw the horsemen thundering down upon them, and ran away.

But from the far side of the village came another roar, and the second wave charged.

Bedi kept a tight hold on Laura's rein, as both horses became restless.

They waited for half an hour, while the screams and yells and shrieks of the villagers rose into the steadily lightening sky. But eventually the noise began to die down; even the dogs ceased to bark.

'It is time,' Bedi said, and led Laura down the slope.

A family lay in a cluster outside the first house they came to, father, mother, two sons and a daughter, all cut down by the Thugs. Men were still looting the house, laughing as they rifled the family's pathetic belongings.

Every few yards, Laura saw another family, ruthlessly slaughtered. Everywhere the Thugs were looting and shouting at each other in triumphant glee.

In the centre of the village there was a cleared space, with a church, and the missionary's house beside it. This was of course the prize, and the hubbub from within was tremendous. Gathered in the square were some twenty captives, and these, Laura saw with a lurching heart, included several white people. As she drew closer, her horror grew: she had met some of them in Bombay several years before, when they had first arrived from England, full of enthusiasm for their self-appointed duty of converting the Hindus. Now they were being forced to kneel in the dirt in their nightclothes.

And they, as they raised their heads, knew her too.

'It has been a triumph,' Batraj shouted. 'A triumph!' He took Laura's rein from Bedi, and himself guided her to the huddled group. 'You know them?'

'Yes,' she said. 'Please . . .'

'They will please Kali. There is but one thing wrong. Our attack was so successful that no-one has escaped. We must leave evidence that you have been here.'

'Yes,' she gasped. 'Yes. Let the white people go. They have seen me.'

Batraj grinned. 'Oh no, they will die. But we shall leave evidence that they have seen you. Make them pray to Kali,' he told his men. 'Not the little boy. Keep him for Kali herself.'

Laura turned her face away and wept, as one by one the prisoners were garotted with the dreadful knotted silk. Only those captured women who were attractive were spared, for the pleasures of the camp. The factor and his wife and daughter were kept until last.

The little boy watched in bewilderment; he was too young to understand what was happening.

'Can you permit this, Your Highness?' the husband shouted to Laura. 'For God' sake, madam . . .'

The silk was placed round his throat.

119

His daughter was killed next, her childish wailing cut to a sinister silence.

His wife seemed to be in a trance, overwhelmed by the catastrophe which had suddenly overtaken her. Perhaps she did not even know she was dying, Laura thought, as the woman was strangled.

'Give me your emerald,' Batraj said.

She closed her hand around it. Apart from Sivitraj, it was the only tangible reminder she had of her happiness with Sitraj.

He pointed to the ring. 'The emerald,' he said again.

He reached up, forced her hand open, and took the ring from her finger. 'You have worn this in Bombay,' he said. 'Everyone will remember the Rani of Sittapore's emerald.' He stooped, opened the dead woman's hand, and placed the stone in it, then closed the hand around it. Then he grinned. 'They will think you strangled her with your own hand, while she fought you.'

'Are you human?' Laura spat at him.

'It is the will of Kali,' he told her.

Torches were applied to the houses and the factory, once everything of value had been removed, and the Thugs rode back to the hills with huge clouds of smoke billowing behind them.

The little boy was carried across the saddle of one of the Thugs, but to Laura's relief there was no attempt to ill-treat him.

When they regained the hill village Laura was amazed to discover a large number of people waiting for them, several hundred men and quite a few women.

'My people have been at work,' Batraj said. 'These have left Sittapore to be with me.'

Laura saw with consternation that quite a few of the men wore the yellow jackets and blue breeches of the Sittapore army.

She was allowed to dismount, and immediately went in search of her son, and found him in the arms of Miljah.

'Miljah!' she cried, and hugged both the slave and the boy together, to Miljah's embarrassment. 'What are you doing here?'

120

'Are you not my mistress?' Miljah asked.

'But . . . what is happening in Sittapore?'

'Sittapore is an unhappy place, mistress. Brother is divided against brother over Prince Batraj's actions.'

Batraj had known this would happen.

'But who rules?'

'I do not think anyone rules at this moment, mistress. There is much confusion.'

'And Lieutenant Bartlett and his people?'

'There was much confusion there too, mistress. First it was said he would leave in pursuit, then he did not. Then a Company regiment came, but after spending a day in the city, they went away again.'

Laura sighed. Even Guy had abandoned her.

'Oh, Miljah,' she said. 'I am so happy to have you with me. I am in such trouble.'

'We are all in much trouble,' Miljah said, refraining from pointing out she had virtually prophesied disaster were Laura to return to Sittapore.

'But you will stay with me,' Laura begged.

'I am your servant, mistress,' Miljah said simply. 'I was given to you by Rajah Sitraj. It is my fate to share yours.'

Laura wept.

That night there was a great celebration, and the captured girls were parcelled out amongst the men. The women already in the camp, almost certainly gained in the same fashion, seemed quite resigned to sharing their favours. Perhaps they were glad of it, Laura thought; she would cheerfully have shared Batraj with any other woman.

But she knew something horribly sinister was about to happen, and sat with screaming nerves while the celebrations continued.

She observed several of the new arrivals spending some time talking with Batraj. He listened impassively to what they had to say, and then nodded and dismissed them. Then he sat by himself for a while, thinking, before getting up and calling a halt to the proceedings.

'It is time,' he said, 'for my wife to join us. Hitherto she has

121

done no more than witness our achievements. Now she will become an initiate into the cult of Kali.'

Laura gulped, and swallowed. She felt sick.

A statue of the goddess herself was brought from one of the houses. It was even more hideous than the one in the palace at Sittapore.

The statue was placed upon the ground, and the entire camp knelt before it to pray. Laura did not understand what they were saying, but she thought it best to kneel with them, Sivitraj in her arms. The little captive boy was close beside her. He had been fed and, to her disgust, given bhang to chew, and he clearly did not have any idea where he was.

Batraj stood in front of the statue, his arms folded. 'Bring the sacrifice,' he commanded.

Laura immediately threw her arm round the boy. But she could not protect him and he was torn from her grasp and dragged forward. He seemed to think the whole thing was a game.

'Now bring forward the initiate,' Batraj commanded.

Miljah held out her arms for Sivitraj. Laura hesitated, but she knew she could not resist them. She gave the woman the little boy, and stood up; two men waited to take her arms. Apparently this was part of the ceremony, whether she was willing to go or not.

They marched her forward until she stood in front of Batraj, then they took the sari from her head and shoulders, and also removed her blouse, so that she was naked from the waist up. She shivered in the cool breeze coming down from the hills, but she no longer felt ashamed to be exposed to them; they knew all of her secrets now.

Batraj drew the knife from his waistband, and held it out. 'Take this,' he said. 'And come to Kali.'

Laura, scarcely believing what was expected of her, took the knife. Then she saw the little boy being presented to her.

'Cut his throat, Highness,' said the man beside her. 'And bathe in his blood.'

Laura's head jerked. 'No,' she said.

'It is the will of Kali,' Batraj told her.

122

'No!' Laura shouted. 'No! Kill me. Kill my son. I will not commit murder for you!'

Batraj glared at her, but realised that he had perhaps pushed her too far. He snatched the knife away from her, and cut the boy's throat himself. Laura wanted to faint, but was held upright as blood was smeared on her face and shoulders, her breasts and stomach. Then she was violently sick, but the ceremony continued for some time, with prayers and incantations. Even then she was not allowed to wash the blood away, but had to sleep in it, and accept Batraj in it too.

It was next morning before she was permitted to go to the stream, and wash the blood away, while Miljah waited with her sari.

'Now you are one of us,' Batraj told her.

'I will never be one of you,' she replied, dressing herself.

'I think you will. Come with me.'

He led her to her horse. They mounted and rode away from the village, following the course of the valley and the stream until they were out of sight of the other people. She supposed he wanted to rape her again, in some private place, but instead he walked his horse out of the valley, and followed a maze of trails between the hills which he obviously knew well.

They must have ridden for two hours, and she was becoming exhausted – she had had very little sleep over the past few days – when at last he held up his hand and dismounted.

Laura slipped from the saddle. They were in a narrow defile, quite high up between two hills. Leading his horse by the bridle, Batraj went forward, until the path ended abruptly, the hillside falling away beneath them.

Laura saw a wide valley which stretched for several miles to the next range of hills. Marching across this valley was a column of red-coated men, mounted on mules, with two officers on horses, while behind them a standard bearer proudly carried the Union Jack.

Laura caught her breath, and Batraj smiled. 'It seems that your friend Lieutenant Bartlett sent for reinforcements. My agents have told me that the entire regiment arrived in Sittapore but nine days after you had left. They must have

123

marched very quickly. However, as you say in English, they found that the birds were flown, and they can hardly have been welcomed by Bilkis. Indeed my agents tell me that there were some words between my aunt and the English colonel. The result was that the British evacuated the city and returned whence they came. Save for this one column, which has been sent to find you, and presumably me. We have been watching it since it left the city. See if you recognise the commanding officer.'

He reached into his saddlebag and produced a telescope, which he gave to her.

Laura levelled the telescope, and caught her breath.

'The ubiquitous Mr Bartlett,' Batraj commented. 'I suppose he feels guilty for being unable to prevent me carrying you off.'

Laura lowered the glass. 'What are you going to do?'

'Eighty men? We shall kill them all. Kali will be pleased.'

Part Two

THE FUGITIVE

In Camp, 10 January 1828.

By this time tomorrow I shall have won my spurs and my lady! I write this today, because by the same token I may also be dead. I will send my journal back to Sittapore by my faithful Ramjohn, who will deliver my despatches to the Colonel, and I pray that it will find its way back to England, as a record of my adventures. If I am dead, I shall not mind it being read, though I would not wish dearest Mama to be distressed, nor my brother Dick, the Reverend Richard Bartlett; though I have always chaffed him about his extreme Godliness, I hold him very dear. If you read this, Dick, pray for your foolish brother, and tell Mama and Papa that I was thinking of them with gratitude and affection.

We have marched long and well for the past two days, following a trail which my guides have found remarkably easy to read; Batraj has not made the slightest attempt to hide his tracks. Now my guides tell me that they are positive he is concealed somewhere in the hill country immediately ahead of us. I have thus pitched camp here on the plain, to rest my men and prepare my dispositions. My first battle, and I am in command!

There is at present no sign of the scoundrel, nor of his brigands. Presumably, he feels there will be no pursuit and is in a state of complete confidence. We shall soon disabuse him of that!

We start our manoeuvres at dawn!

I would not have my reader suppose that I am afraid; I am a soldier, and I joined the Company army in the full knowledge that it might be my allotted fate to stop a bullet or a sword thrust, although to be sure by far the greater number of our fellows die of fever or alcohol.

If I am to die, what shall I leave behind me? Very little I fear. Evans will, I hope and trust, keep and nurture the dogs; they are a happy little family. Prudence may shed a tear or two. Dick, if you read this, remember only that I will have died as an Englishman should. If my body is recovered and has not been looted, I leave you my sword and Company badges, as well as that magnificent pair of pistols you gave me, which are with me now. These warlike appurtenances may look unseemly in your vicarage, but you can keep them in the attic, for who knows, you may have a son who may wish to emulate his uncle and be a soldier.

To you also I leave my chess set and board, and my books.

But suppose I conquer, and triumph without a scratch? Why should I not? What then?

I will be honest and admit my purpose is less to bring this dangerous bandit to justice than to rescue, or if need be, avenge Laura Dean. She may be dead. In which case I shall take the greatest pleasure in hanging this Batraj by the neck until he is also dead.

But if she is alive, what sort of a woman shall I find? If she has survived she will have been most shamefully mistreated. Can I therefore hope to make a wife of her? I believe I can. I have no doubt that such a step will be criticised by my fellow officers, and even more by their detestable wives. But I also know that no matter that she has been the plaything of a Thug, I love her, and will always do so.

6

The Bargain

Laura watched as the little company came to a halt, and began to pitch their tents. She could almost hear the shouts of command as the men scurried to and fro.

Batraj grinned. 'They think they are on a parade ground. Do you know what my men will do to them tomorrow? I will make your Mr Bartlett eat his own genitals before I put the noose around his neck.'

Laura attempted to take refuge in defiance.

'You will not find a company of soldiers as easy to kill as you did defenceless villagers,' she told him. 'Those are disciplined men.'

'I am sure they are,' Batraj agreed. 'On a parade ground. Or even on that plain where they are now situated. But we are not going to fight them where they can form ranks and fire by volleys. Their guides are in my employ. They will lead them into these hills. The place where we will destroy the redcoats is already chosen, and my men are already occupying it.'

He seemed to have thought of everything.

'They will send others,' Laura said. 'Many, many more. The whole regiment will come to avenge its dead.'

'That is what I am hoping will happen, certainly. Then the entire country will come to war.'

Laura knew that familiar trapped feeling.

'No,' she said. 'Please . . .'

Batraj raised his eyebrows. 'Are they that important to you? And Bartlett? Why did he really accompany you back to Sittapore?'

'To act as the Company's representative. But . . . we did know each other, before I married Sitraj.'

'Did my cousin know of this . . . connection?'

'Of course.'

'But not that you were an adulterous woman.'

'I am not an adulteress,' she snapped. 'We were friends, nothing more. But I would not like to see him killed. Please, Batraj, if you value me in the least . . .'

'I value you greatly, my dear Laura. Especially now that you have become a worshipper of Kali. But we must kill them. Especially Lieutenant Bartlett. I am going to castrate him personally. I have conceived a great dislike for him.'

Laura fell to her knees. 'I am begging you.'

Batraj grinned. 'You do so delightfully. Now let us be returning to camp.'

She caught his hand. She had only one last card to play. 'Batraj . . . you know that you have forced me in everything.'

'It has been my pleasure.'

'But then you know that I hate you for it, that I will resist you the moment I have the opportunity. That I will bring you down if I have the chance.'

He studied her. 'I believe you may try.'

'And do you not suppose I will one day succeed? You dream of returning to Sittapore as regent. When you get there, do you suppose you can keep me a prisoner for the rest of my life?'

His eyes narrowed. 'Are you attempting to threaten me? You? When the British find your emerald at Slopan, you will be damned as a criminal.'

'By some people, not by all. The evidence will be circumstantial. Batraj, would you not prefer to have me standing loyally at your side, throughout the rest of your life?'

He was frowning now. 'You offered me this, before Slopan. But you have nothing to offer me that I cannot take, have not already taken.'

'Do you suppose so? I would declare my love for you to all the world, bring Sivitraj up to honour and respect you, and obey you in all things.'

'Even when, as Regent, I lead my people to war against the British?'

'If that is what you are determined to do.'

'You would do that?'

'If you spare the lives of those men.'

130

Why had she not thought to make such an offer earlier, and save the village? Because Guy Barlett's life had not been at stake then?

But what an offer. It condemned her to a lifetime of misery, and indeed treason, for the sake of a man she really hardly knew.

But a man who had declared his love for her!

'You would do these things?' Batraj asked. 'How can I know you will do them?'

'I will swear, any oath you wish. I will swear it upon the Christian Bible. I will swear it upon my son's life.'

Batraj stroked his chin. 'You will swear to be my wife in all things, to grant me anything I wish of you or your body and take pleasure in it?'

Laura's nostrils flared as she breathed. 'I will swear.'

'And you will not try to escape me, at any time?'

'Never.'

He turned away from her to look back down at the little encampment.

'I need those muskets and powder and balls,' he said, half to himself. 'I must have them.'

'Then take them prisoner. But let them go again.'

'Do you think they will surrender to me?'

'Yes. If you have them surrounded. I will make them surrender.'

Batraj considered some more. What she was offering was a greater asset than the mere murder of a hundred men, especially if he could obtain their weapons into the bargain. And it need not interfere with his original plans. With the regiment having evacuated Sittapore, there was nothing to prevent him occupying the city. And that would certainly be considered an act of war.

'Then swear,' he said.

The Company soldiers began to file through the pass. Poor Guy Bartlett had very little idea of the dangers of campaigning in India Laura thought. He had thrown out an advance guard of six men, some quarter of a mile in front of the main body, but they were absolutely useless; none of Batraj's Thugs intended

131

to show themselves until signalled by their leader, and the six men could be allowed to pass through and rounded up afterwards.

The others rode in a column of twos. Not one man had a weapon in his hand; the muskets were carried in holsters behind the saddles. They might even be unloaded.

'They are fools,' Batraj said contemptuously.

Laura had to agree with him. Batraj had two hundred men on the hillside below them, hidden in the long grass and behind the boulders. Another two hundred waited on the hillside opposite. And she knew two hundred and fifty were waiting down the slopes, mounted, to block the rear of the defile, while a further two hundred were gathered ahead, to block the exit. Few of the men were armed with anything better than spears and swords, but their superiority in numbers was overwhelming. As Batraj had said, given the opportunity to form square and fire by volleys to resist an open attack, the Sepoys might be capable of withstanding odds of even ten to one. But they were not going to be given that opportunity. It was the most perfect trap any general could lay.

The column came on. Batraj handed her the telescope, and she found Guy's face. He was chatting with his fellow officer. Both men were watching the slopes to either side, but they could see nothing.

Batraj waited, as did his men, with immense patience; when the entire Company force was within the defile, save for the advance guard which had emerged from the northern end, he pointed his musket into the air and fired.

The sound of the explosion reverberated through the hills, and caused confusion among the Sepoys, with the mules braying and bucking, some of the Sepoys promptly sliding off with cries of alarm, Guy drawing his sword and looking up at the hillside, perplexed. Clearly he could not comprehend the meaning of the single shot.

Batraj was calmly reloading his weapon, with great care. He knew his orders would be obeyed.

The other officer was pointing, and Guy was staring ahead of him now, at the two hundred horsemen who had suddenly appeared, out of musket shot, but blocking any further progress. Behind them there were some scattered shots as the advance guard was overrun.

Guy gave an order, and the bugler riding at his shoulder blew a call which Laura, having lived all her life before her marriage close to the Bombay barracks, recognised as a retreat. But it was too late. The rear of the defile was also now blocked.

The Sepoys were setting up a tremendous hubbub of alarm, but Guy rode amongst them shouting orders, and trying to restore discipline: he was certainly no coward. Under his leadership the men all dismounted, as did he; the mules were brought into a group, and his force formed into two lines, one facing front and the other back, with the mules between. Obviously he expected to have to receive a simultaneous charge from each end of the defile.

Having taken their position, the Company soldiers waited, muskets at the ready, bayonets fixed. But the horsemen waited as well. The valley was suddenly silent, save for the still agitated shuffling and braying of the mules.

The sun rose higher and began to play upon the scene, and the red tunics began to darken with sweat.

Laura glanced at Batraj, and he grinned. 'Let them sweat,' he said. 'That is as much fear as heat. They know they are dead men.'

He waited for another hour. Using the telescope Laura could see the Sepoys beginning to whisper to each other. They wanted their officers to get them out of this mess. Guy was standing between the two ranks, with his companion and the company sergeant major, obviously trying to decide what to do. But there was nothing they could do. Infantry could hardly charge cavalry at odds of one to four.

Batraj fired his musket a second time. Instantly every man on the two hillsides stood up and uttered a mighty shout, before falling back to the ground. The echoing noise was tremendous, and the quick movement obviously convinced the Sepoys that there were several thousand men in the hills around them. Several threw down their muskets, and one or two even pulled off their red jackets; they had to be caned into resuming their places by their sergeants. Several others fired their pieces, at nothing that they could see.

Laura felt truly sorry for Guy, so inexperienced, and faced with such a foe.

'Now you may go and talk to them,' Batraj said. 'Remember, if you betray me, they all die, and your friend Bartlett will do so very slowly . . . beside you.'

'I have given you my word,' Laura said, with as much dignity as she could muster.

She stood up. She was wearing her green sari, and Batraj had also made her put on all of her remaining jewellery. Now the faint breeze ruffled her garments and her hair, for she had left it loose, so that even at a distance they would know who she was.

She felt curiously exposed as she made her way slowly down the hill: it needed only one man to lose his head, from either side, and she would be dead. As she passed, Batraj's men grinned at her from behind their boulders and clumps of grass.

'My God!' she heard Guy say as she approached. 'It's Laura. The Rani. Hold your fire!' he shouted.

Guy stepped out from the ranks of his men. His sword was still drawn, and he carried a pistol in his left hand; another was thrust through his belt, and he looked very determined, but completely bewildered.

His aide, whom she now recognised as Second-Lieutenant Jefferson, appeared equally bewildered.

'Laura?' Guy asked. 'My dear girl, are you all right?'

'I am as you see me,' Laura told him.

'But . . .' he looked past her at the apparently empty hills. 'These men . . . was their purpose simply to return you to us?'

Laura sighed. 'No, Guy. I have come to tell you to surrender.'

'Surrender?' He frowned.

'You are surrounded by more than a thousand men, well armed, well disciplined, and utterly determined. You have no hope of fighting your way out.'

'Then we must die,' Guy declared. 'The Company army does not surrender.'

'For God's sake listen to me,' she said. 'Do you want to die?'

'I have my duty to perform,' he said stiffly.

'What duty? Why did you come here? To rescue me and the

134

Rajah? You cannot do it, Guy. It is impossible. The Rajah is beyond your reach, and so am I. I belong to Batraj now. I can never belong to another.'

'It makes no difference. I have come for you, and I have found you. And I will take you back to your own people.'

Laura wanted to burst into tears. It only made her the more determined to save his life.

She took a long breath, knowing that Batraj was watching through his telescope.

'Guy, I do not wish to be rescued. I have told you, I am now married to Batraj. I am his wife in all things. I will not return to Bombay. I will not return to Sittapore, save as his wife. Please try to understand that.'

He stared at her.

'She has become deranged,' Jefferson said. 'Mistreatment and too much sun. Or they have given her bhang.'

'I am not deranged in the slightest,' Laura said evenly. 'I am trying to save your foolish lives. Batraj wants your weapons. Lay them down and go back to Bombay, and I will guarantee your safety. You can do nothing here, save die.'

Guy still seemed speechless.

'Well,' Jefferson said. 'If what you say is true, we can at least place you under arrest, Your Highness.' He spoke her title with great sarcasm, and stepped forward to grip her arm. 'We'll see what this husband of yours makes of that.'

'I would advise you to let me go, sir,' Laura said. 'If you attempt to harm me, all of you will die, now. He is watching us.'

Jefferson hesitated, glancing at Guy.

'Oh, let her go,' Guy muttered. 'Is it true, what you have said?'

'Yes. Yes, it is.' She was holding her breath.

'Then be damned to you,' he spat. 'Go back to your murdering Hindu lover. Crawl on your hands and knees to him. I despise you.'

Laura flushed, but Jefferson's fingers fell away.

'And you will surrender?' she asked.

'No, we will not surrender,' Guy snapped. 'We did not come simply to rescue you, Your Highness. We came to arrest Prince

135

Batraj, for Thuggee and murder.' He paused. 'Did you know your "husband" is a Thug?'

'Yes,' Laura said calmly. 'I too am a follower of Kali.'

'My God!'

'That is surely grounds for arrest,' Jefferson protested.

'Simply belonging to a religion is not a crime,' Guy said. 'But I am not returning to Bombay without Prince Batraj manacled and under guard. You tell him that, Miss Dean.'

'Do you think he is going to come down and hand himself over?' She was in despair.

'Now we know where he is, we shall come and take him,' Guy said.

'My God, my God! Please listen to me.'

Guy took out his watch.

'If you truly wish to return to his side, Highness, you have my permission to do so. I will give you five minutes. At the end of that time, I will lead my men up the hill to his position, and place him under arrest. I will, of course, instruct my men not to harm you, but I cannot guarantee your safety. Good day to you, madam.'

She stared at him for several seconds, unwilling to believe her ears.

'You now have only four minutes, madam,' he said.

Laura turned and ran up the hill, tripping and stumbling, losing her breath, gasping. Still Batraj's people grinned at her; they had no idea what was going on, but were content to wait on their leader's orders.

Batraj came down a few yards to greet her.

'He has surrendered?'

'He won't!' She was sobbing. 'He seems to have gone mad. When he heard I was your wife he lost all reason.' She collapsed in an exhausted heap at his feet. 'Now he says he is coming up the hill to place you under arrest. In about one minute.'

Batraj smiled.

Slowly Laura regained her breath, and rose to her knees to look back down the hill. Guy was marshalling his men into three ranks, facing the hillside on which he now knew Batraj

136

was to be found, and completely ignoring the watching horsemen; he was clearly determined to stake everything on laying hands on the Thugs' leader. Well, she supposed, if he was determined to fight, that was indeed his only chance.

But it was no chance at all. The Sepoys were clearly unhappy at being commanded to commit virtual suicide, and were looking up at the hill, muttering amongst themselves. Batraj, who equally was not a coward, left Laura's side and went down among his men, telling them what to do.

Guy drew his sword and gave the command to fire. The Sepoys obeyed, blasting the lower slopes with their volley. One or two of the bullets struck home; Laura heard men cry out and watched one of the Thugs tumble to the ground, a sprawl of disordered cloth. Then, without waiting to reload, Guy led his men forward, trusting to cold steel in the very best British tradition.

Jefferson and the sergeant-major were at his shoulder, but the rest were less enthusiastic. The charge was over before it could even begin. As Guy scrambled up the lower slopes he was set upon by four Thugs, who wrestled him to the ground. Jefferson and the sergeant major were not so fortunate; both were shot at point-blank range by two Thugs rising out of the grass. The disappearance of their officers proved too much for the Sepoys, who gave a collective shriek of despair, threw down their weapons and attempted to run away, straight into the mounted Thugs, who were now cantering forward, swinging their swords and lances.

There were a few seconds of frenetic activity, swirling dust, screams of pain and shouts for mercy, then the massacre was completed.

Laura felt as if turned to stone; she was certain that if she attempted to move she would faint clean away. She watched Guy being pulled to his feet; his shako had fallen off and he appeared to be only half conscious. He was dragged down the hillside and thrown across a horse. Thugs were gathering up the discarded muskets, stripping the dead Sepoys of their cartridge belts. Laura moaned as she watched the breeches being torn from Jefferson and the sergeant major, their genitals sliced away and tossed into the air. The same

137

mutilation was performed on the Sepoys, and from the screams, not all of them were dead.

Batraj grinned at her. 'Was that not well done? It was a great victory.'

Laura slowly got herself under control. 'What are you going to do to Mr Bartlett?'

'Why, nothing, my dear Laura. I gave express orders that he was not to be harmed more than necessary. Was that not our bargain? I have kept my part, now you must keep yours.' He held out his hand to her. 'For the rest of your life.'

They went down the hill, into the stench of death and the groans of the dying. Guy was starting to come round, blinking and shaking his head.

'You should have taken the Rani's advice,' Batraj told him. 'Did you suppose an old friend would lie to you? You *are* old friends, are you not? I am told you once proposed marriage to my wife? Let us look upon what you have to offer. Strip him,' he told his men.

'No,' Laura said. 'Please.'

Batraj grinned. 'Have you no wish to look upon a man you nearly married?'

'Our bargain . . .'

'Was that he should not be harmed, and that he should be released. I will keep my bargain. Strip him.'

The Thugs laughed as they ripped away Guy's clothing, pushing him to the ground to pull off his boots. When he was naked they dragged him back to his feet and held him before Batraj and Laura.

'Look at him, Laura,' Batraj commanded.

Even half conscious, Guy was panting with anger and humiliation, but then, so was Laura.

'You may touch him, if you wish,' Batraj invited.

'No,' Laura said. 'Please, Batraj.'

Batraj laughed. 'Put him on a mule, and bring him to our people,' he commanded.

The Thug encampment was *en fête*. The men danced and drank as the victory was celebrated. But Kali had to be thanked as well. Two of the Sepoys had been captured alive; they were now forced to kneel before the statue of the dread goddess to have their throats cut. Then their blood was scattered across the revellers. Laura, sitting beside Batraj, had the horrible liquid smeared on her face. Some was even smeared over Guy, who made no move to resist, but sat silently staring in front of him, clutching the rags of his uniform about him, refusing all food and drink. He was utterly crushed.

Batraj was at his jovial best, laughing and talking, shouting to his people. He forced Laura to take off her sari and dine in only a dhoti, and from time to time he fondled her breasts to leave Guy in no doubt that she was his woman. But not even this could arouse any response in him.

It was one of the most terrible evenings of Laura's life, and it ended as always, in Batraj's arms.

'Today we begin our march on Sittapore,' Batraj told Guy, the next morning.

The lieutenant had spent the night bound hand and foot, and had clearly not slept; the young girls in the camp had been encouraged to torment him as much as they chose. A stubble of beard clung to his chin, and his eyes were bloodshot while his body was coated in dirt and sweat and blood. And Laura could do nothing for him.

His feet were released and he was mounted on a horse, his hands tied to the reins, which were in turn secured by a long rope to the reins of Bedi's horse.

He had watched the preparations with deadened eyes, which had not shown life even when Laura and the other women had bathed in the stream. But now for the first time he reacted. 'You mean to assault Sittapore?' he asked.

'If that is necessary. But I anticipate that the gate will probably be opened to me, when I return in such triumph.' Batraj pointed to the Union Jack which one of his men was carrying. 'Besides, my agents have been busy amongst the people, and I do not think they will resist me. You will be pleased to know that once I have installed my cousin as Rajah, with myself as Regent, I will permit you to return to Bombay with news of your mishap.'

'Why?' Guy asked. 'Why did you not simply murder me as you did my men?'

'Because my wife asked for your life. Should a man not grant his wife what she asks from time to time?'

Guy looked at Laura, and then away again. She could only keep her face impassive.

The Thugs moved down from the hills. As every man was mounted they made good time, and had covered half the distance to Sittapore by nightfall.

Laura was relieved to observe that Guy seemed to have recovered some of his spirits. He actually ate and drank, then submitted to being tied up without demur. How she wanted to tell him the truth of her situation, that she wanted him to escape and ride for the regiment, and bring an end to Batraj's murderous career, even if it meant her own death.

But always her thoughts came back to the little baby Rajah being carried by Miljah, to the rear of the army. His very presence left her helpless.

By the following afternoon they were within striking distance of the city, and Batraj rode forward with his scouts to see the situation for himself. He took both Laura and Guy with him. They dismounted as they approached the top of the northern hill to look down on the valley; those farmers they had encountered had been taken prisoner until after the assault had been completed.

The city looked as peaceful as ever, basking in the rays of the setting sun. The flags were still white, and through Batraj's telescope they could make out the remains of Sitraj's funeral pyre. Laura could not subdue a shudder as she looked at it.

Batraj inspected the defences very carefully, but there seemed to be no more men on the walls than usual.

'Where do you suppose your regiment is now, Lieutenant Bartlett?' he asked.

'Probably back in Bombay,' Guy replied carelessly.

'Hm.' He swung his telescope over the hills, and Laura heard Guy catch his breath. Her own heart began to pound, as she remembered that Guy's spirits had only lifted when he had

140

heard that Sittapore was to be attacked. Yet the hills appeared empty.

Then there was a flash of light to the east, followed instantly by others, a whole succession of flashes, red in the sun's rays.

Batraj saw them as well. 'There are armed men up there,' he snapped. 'Vijay Dal, take a hundred men and find out what they are about.'

The Thug second-in-command nodded, and rode off, followed by his troop.

Batraj turned to Guy. 'You knew of this?'

'I did not,' Guy replied. 'They must be your cousin's people.'

'Perhaps you are right. Vijay Dal will find out. We will camp tonight. The assault will be at dawn.'

Laura was sure there was something going on of which she had no inkling. When Vijay Dal returned his news was disappointing to her, if reassuring to Batraj.

'There were some horsemen, Highness,' he said. 'But they rode off at great speed when they saw us approaching.'

'How many?'

'Not more than six, Highness. I sent some of my people in pursuit.'

'Were they Hindus, or Christians?'

'Oh, they were Hindus, Highness.'

'Mujhabi is less of a fool than I thought,' Batraj commented. 'He will have circled behind the city to gain it. Still, it will make no difference. They must know we are here. We will attack at dawn.'

Again Laura hardly slept, because Batraj would have it so. He was at once excited and apprehensive, and wanted her again and again. By dawn she was exhausted.

At first light they struck camp; the men armed themselves, and mounted. As before, Laura was left in the care of Bedi, on the hilltop. Guy was left bound to his horse, guarded by two Thugs.

Batraj made a leisurely approach to the city, his thousand men spread out behind him; he knew he was expected, so he was putting on the most confident display he could. Early as it

141

was, he was quickly seen by the sentries on the walls, and Laura could hear the bugle calls summoning the garrison to arms.

Batraj had left her his telescope. She watched the walls fill with the familiar yellow and blue uniforms. But there were not enough of them. Everything would depend on the attitude of the people, and of this Batraj seemed very confident.

Guy was breathing heavily, and darting quick glances at his Thug guards.

Oh, my God, she thought, he means to make a break for it. That would give Batraj a perfect excuse for killing him.

She didn't know what to do. Bedi and the other two were totally absorbed in watching the approaching battle. Laura bit her lip and looked back down at the valley. Batraj had halted his army out of musket shot of the walls, and an emissary was sent forward. Through her glass she could make out Bilkis on the walls above the gate, together with Colonel Mujhabi. Laura could not tell what was being said, but Bilkis was certainly not making any submissive gestures, and finally the envoy turned and rode back to Batraj.

Suddenly, Guy made his move. He kicked his horse violently, so that it charged forward causing Bedi's horse to rear and snort. Guy swung his manacled hands, and managed to hit Bedi hard enough to tumble the big man from his saddle. Guy then seized both reins and broke into a gallop.

'Laura!' he shouted. 'Follow me!'

How she wished she could. Instead, she calmed her startled horse and forced it to stand still. In any event, Guy was surely committing suicide, for the other two Thugs promptly gave chase, waving their tulwars.

Below them, the Thug army was just beginning to move forward, its banners – including the captured Union Jack – streaming, its cymbals clashing. But suddenly there came a flurry of bugle calls from the hills to the east. Batraj raised his arm to call a halt, and a line of redcoated Sepoys emerged above the wheat stalks, followed by another and then another, the early sunlight flashing from their swords and bayonets. At the same time, there came the explosions of cannon, and roundshot went bounding into the little valley.

The effect was instantaneous. The two men who had been

chasing Guy immediately turned and rode back, and Guy plunged onwards into the safety of his comrades.

Batraj was waving his sword and summoning his men to retreat; he knew he was no match for an entire Company regiment, supported by artillery. He had been caught in a trap every bit as devastating as that he had sprung on Guy. The roundshot was already tearing through the ranks of his terrified people, and they were scattering in every direction, while the Sepoys, led by Company officers, advanced with measured tread to the beat of their drums.

The gates of the city opened, and Colonel Mujhabi brought his cavalry squadrons down the slope to join in the overthrow of the Thugs.

Laura caught her breath; she had never seen a battle before. But this was not a battle; it was a rout. The Thugs were already fleeing, some up the hill, others to the western end of the valley. Batraj's army was no more.

Bedi seized Laura's bridle. He knew nothing of her promise to Batraj, and wished to make sure she did not try to follow Guy to safety. She made no effort to resist him. She could only wait, and see what happened to Batraj himself.

Batraj had managed to rally a few of his people, led by Vijay Dal, and they were galloping up the hill as fast as their blown horses could manage. Batraj's face was twisted with rage and frustration.

'Where is the English officer?' he shouted.

'He has escaped, Highness,' Bedi said.

Batraj turned his anger on Laura. 'Your doing? By the great Lord Krishna . . .'

'The Rani had nothing to do with it, Highness,' Bedi said. 'It was my fault.'

'Fool!' Batraj struck him across the face with his whip. 'And you have lost your horse? Mount behind the Rani! Haste now! Haste!'

The Company soldiers were still advancing steadily, but now they had little to do; the last of the Thugs had fallen or fled. Colonel Mujhabi's cavalry held the field, waiting for the advancing troops. They were making no effort to pursue their enemies; too many of them were their own kinsmen.

'You have lost the day, Prince Batraj,' Laura said. 'Why do you not end this senseless dream, and surrender?'

'And be hanged?' he sneered. 'Yes, I have lost the day. But I have not yet lost my head. I will yet drive those redcoated devils into the sea. To the camp.'

And they rode away from the city.

Bombay, 28 January 1828

This has been a terrible time for me; I have contemplated suicide.

Never can a man have been so grateful for the loyalty of his friends. I lost the battle, and not my life. I know now that I sadly mismanaged the whole affair and totally underestimated the scoundrel Batraj. Thus I was forced to watch my command cut to pieces. I was the only survivor.

They stripped me naked as the day I was born, and paraded me before their womenfolk, who were encouraged to do their worst. But no knives were drawn. Perhaps it would have been better had they been.

The true cause of my shame and misery is also the reason for my survival: the intervention of Laura Dean.

I loved her. In my nightmare midnight hours I love her still. And she is the most black-hearted harlot who ever drew breath. Yes, I say such harsh things of the woman who saved my life!

Yet against that isolated act of charity must be set the murder of my men, my own humiliation, and the fact that she is now an acknowledged Thug, who virtually drinks blood, who flaunts herself before her people and rides to battle like a Valkyrie. It was she who summoned me to surrender, and she who presided over the ghastly celebration of my defeat.

I have looked upon her naked body, smeared with blood. I have looked, and desired and wanted to strangle her at the same time.

But worse yet was the news that greeted me on my return here. A village on Company territory was recently attacked by

145

these Thugs, and every living creature within it massacred save those carried off for sport. That it was Batraj who perpetrated this foul deed is undoubted, and that Laura rode at his side there too is equally certain; one of her rings, an emerald the size of a quail's egg, which everyone in Bombay has seen and admired, was found amidst the carnage!

At least she and her frightful paramour have been checked in their career of horror. They took their army straight into the jaws of the trap we had laid for them, and were soundly beaten. My poor fellows have been avenged.

But Batraj and Laura escaped back into the hills, and although an immediate pursuit was this time launched, they have vanished. I suspect Colonel Partridge was not sorry to see them go. Batraj's force has been entirely dispersed and thus he is without power, and the Colonel was somewhat reluctant at having to place Laura, an Englishwoman, upon the scaffold.

At the commencement of the fight I managed to make my escape. I even called upon Laura to follow me. What a fool I was! But at that time I did not know of the massacre at Slopan, although I doubt she would have come anyway, so besotted is she with this Hindu lover of hers.

Naked as I was, I rode into our ranks. This caused some ribaldry but also, oddly, a great deal of admiration. Colonel Partridge steadfastly refuses to blame me for the loss of my command, and instead praises my courage in surviving; apparently he had anticipated the loss of at least a company upon the campaign. Thus I am returned to Bombay something of a hero.

Of course word of what happened got about fairly rapidly, and the ladies are looking at me strangely, whether out of respect or curiosity I am reluctant to guess.

Following my return, I sank into the depths of despair, at Laura's hideous perfidy, at my failure as a soldier, and at my own stupidity. But most of all because I still love her. I am the most cursed of men.

Now I must pick up the pieces of my life and resume my career.

Today I was invited to tea by the Partridges, and placed next to Prudence, who gazed into my eyes with the utmost devotion. In

146

Bombay Laura is regarded as a murderous wanton, and Prudence clearly feels that I rescued myself from a fate worse than death. I suppose I will marry the girl. If nothing else, it will clearly advance my career.

Our new governor, Sir John Malcolm, is expected daily. He is by all accounts a fire-eating Scot, who will settle once and for all with these Thugs, I have no doubt. I intend to volunteer for every possible mission. I have a great deal to learn about soldiering in India, and I intend to do so, to wipe out the memory of my disgrace, and carry the war to the enemy.

Was there not a Greek philosopher who, having fallen into the gutter, reflected that the only course left to him was to rise?

7

The Mountains

The remnants of Batraj's army straggled back into the camp.

'We have lost a battle,' Batraj declared. 'We have not lost faith in ourselves.'

His men looked doubtful; they had certainly lost faith in him, as he could tell.

'For the time being we will split up,' he told them. 'Scatter and make your own ways. When the time comes, I will summon you again to my standard. Then I will command a great army, and victory will lie at our feet.'

'Where will you go, Highness?' asked Vijay.

'I will seek my own salvation. You will accompany me, Vijay, with my wife, the nurse, the Rajah, and five men. Pick them yourself, and tell them to choose their women; they can bring one each.'

'Batraj,' Laura said. 'You have lost. You will never become Rajah of Sittapore, or even regent. Can you not at least let the boy go back to his people?'

'The boy is my passport to power,' he told her. 'We made a bargain, you and I. Keep your part of it, or I will cut his heart out, and send him back without it.'

Batraj was in mortal fear of being captured, so he and his small group rode out within the hour, leaving the rest of the Thugs to make their own escapes.

'There is no doubt that the Company will turn my own family against me,' Batraj said. 'And the spineless cowards will obey. We must find someone who will fight for us. And I know the very person. The Begum Sombre. We will ride for Agra.'

Laura had of course heard of the Begum Sombre. Her origins

148

were obscure. Some said she had been a Persian slave who had been bought by a French soldier of fortune during the wars of the previous century. This man, Renaud, was of such viciousness that he had been given the soubriquet Sombre, but he had had the talent to carve out a jaghir for himself south of Delhi, including the fabled city of Agra, once capital of the Mughal Empire. When Renaud had died, his wife, now calling herself the Begum Sombre, had seized power, and kept it with the aid of a series of military commanders, all of whom had apparently been her lovers.

The tales about her were endless: she had blown her enemies from the mouths of her cannon; she had once buried two slave girls alive and sat on their grave smoking her hookah; she had been bound naked to a cannon by her rebellious soldiers, and yet survived to resume her reign. In her time, she had been the most beautiful woman in India, and she accepted no man as her master.

It took several days to reach Agra. They travelled in the hills, avoiding the valleys and the villages except for buying food, or stealing it when possible. Batraj's energy was, as ever, unquenchable, and after the first day, he was even good-humoured again.

'You had never thought to see so much of India, Laura,' he smiled. 'Is it not a fabulous country? But you have seen nothing as yet.'

Laura had to agree that it was a fabulous country, even if only because of its size. The way Company officials, including her own father, had spoken of Company conquests, had rather encouraged her to think that Delhi and Agra might be a couple of marches from Bombay or Calcutta.

Now she looked at range after range of hills; at valley after valley under wheat; at herds of cattle grazing contentedly, and flocks of sheep waiting to be slaughtered.

'This place is called Malwa,' Batraj told her. 'It is the most fertile part of Hindustan.'

Now that he judged himself to be well ahead of any possible pursuit, he actually seemed to be enjoying himself.

As the march continued, Laura's saris began to disintegrate.

149

At the same time her complexion began to redden and peel, and her hair lay undressed in a tangled golden mess on her shoulders and down her back. Her feet blistered and then hardened again, for before long she was as barefoot as Miljah, and as dusty; she was determined to preserve one garment for when they reached Agra, and took to wearing simply a dhoti, like Milkah and the other women. Her breasts and shoulders were exposed to the sun and started to burn, but this seemed unimportant.

But her collapse as Rani seemed to make no difference to Batraj's desire for her.

'What will we do when I become pregnant?' she asked.

'Continue as before. Indian women do not stop their labours because they are pregnant.'

'I am not an Indian,' she shouted.

He laughed. 'I am making you into one, my dear Laura.'

Then she hated him.

The eight women in the little party – for in addition to the men, Vijay had brought his favourite, Nanja – shared the cooking, and in true Indian fashion, waited on their men. Laura did her share, for gone were the heady days when she had been reared as queen. She found she enjoyed the work. She had helped her mother with the cooking in Bombay as a girl, and could make as good a curry as any Indian; she liked the companionship of the other women too.

Yet often enough she lay awake in the small hours, and nearly wept with despair as she wondered what was going to become of her and little Sivitraj. Batraj might have the most exotic dreams, but she knew none of them would ever come true: the Company was simply too strong for him.

Even so she contemplated the rest of her life with horror. She had committed herself entirely to a bloodthirsty murderer. That he could also be a charming and irresistible lover only increased her self-loathing. She was not quite twenty-one years old, and she was doomed to spend the rest of her days at this man's side. Only in the prospect of Sivitraj growing to manhood and rescuing her or avenging her could she find a spark of hope for the future – and that future was a very long way away.

*

'There!' Batraj pointed to a brilliant light in the distance.

'Is it a fire?'

He grinned. 'It is the morning sun reflecting from the walls of the Taj Mahal.'

As they descended into the valley of the Jumna they approached first the abandoned city of Fatehpour Sikri, which Akbar had built for his favourite wife, the Rajput Princess Jodha Bai. The spectacular buildings and magnificent palaces were mostly deserted, for Akbar had turned his back on the city forever when his queen had died.

Then they came to the Taj Mahal, and Laura gazed in wonder at the marvellous tomb, erected nearly two hundred years before by the Mughal Emperor Shah Jahan for *his* favourite wife, Mumtaz Mahal, the Light of the Palace. The tomb itself, an immense dome with four high, exquisitely tall minarets, one at each corner, and the formal gardens, was an architectural wonder. It was the opalescent and many-faceted marble that caught and reflected the sun's rays.

They stopped by a stream to bathe and dress themselves properly. Laura put on her white sari and her jewellery, and Batraj his yellow and blue uniform as an officer in the Sittapore army. Laura could do nothing about her ruined complexion, so she kept a fold of the sari across her face as they rode towards the city.

The armed guards bowed when told that the Rajah of Sittapore and his mother wished an audience with the Begum Sombre, even if they looked somewhat surprised that so illustrious a personage should arrive with so small an entourage.

They were admitted within the walls, and Laura found herself in a teeming, bustling community which quite reduced Bombay to the status of a village. Here, too, there were architectural gems to be admired, in particular the red sandstone Lal Qila which occupied the centre of the city. Inside this palace there was a splendid mosque of white marble which, Batraj told Laura, had been erected by Akbar himself; the Emperor's tomb was not far distant, outside the city.

They were admitted into an inner courtyard, where a

151

chamberlain received them. Here was far greater splendour than Laura had known at Sittapore, although there was also some evidence of decay. It was almost uncanny to think that the legendary Mumtaz Mahal, or her even more famous aunt Nur Jahan, might have stood in this very spot, or that Akbar the Great might have strode by on his way to war.

She shivered. What sort of reception would they receive from the equally legendary Begum Sombre?

The chamberlain beckoned, and Laura went forward. Vijay and the remainder of the party waited in the courtyard, but Batraj accompanied Laura, and they were followed by Miljah, who carried the little Rajah.

They were escorted through richly decorated marble halls, past armed guards who stood to attention, and thence into a reception chamber which was the biggest Laura had ever seen.

The room was filled with richly dressed men and women, but devoid of furniture save for a single highbacked chair in the centre, and in this chair sat the Begum Sombre.

The Begum, Laura calculated from what Batraj had told her, must be not less than seventy-five years old. She saw a tiny figure, glad in a cloth-of-gold sari, her fingers covered in huge ruby rings. Her complexion was pale. As Laura approached, she saw that the signs of age were very evident; blue veins stood out on the Begum's hands, and wrinkles fled away from her eyes and mouth, and marked her neck. Yet she realised that she was still looking at a remarkably beautiful woman. The small features remained exquisitely fashioned, the green eyes continued to sparkle, the teeth were white and even.

'The Rani of Sittapore,' she said, in accented but good English. 'I had heard that Rajah Sivitraj had taken a very beautiful woman to wife. Come closer, child.'

Laura went right up to the chair, and the two woman gazed at each other.

'Will you not show me your face?' the Begum asked.

Laura hesitated, then let the fold of silk drop.

'You have been over-exposed to the sun,' the Begum agreed. 'But true beauty can never be destroyed. I was exposed to the sun once, for three days, bound to the burning barrel of a cannon . . .' just for a moment her face hardened and became

152

almost frightening, as she remembered the outrage. Then she smiled. 'But the men who did that to me are all dead. And I am alive. And still beautiful. Your complexion will recover, child, as did mine. And now I am told your husband is dead. Can this be true?'

'A fall at polo, Highness,' Laura told her.

'Polo,' the Begum said contemptuously. 'It is the curse of India. But . . . your husband was a Hindu?'

She was clearly puzzled.

'Indeed, Highness,' Batraj said, coming forward as well. 'And the Dowager Rani was placed upon his pyre. But I rescued her.'

The Begum turned her gaze on him for a moment, and appeared to like what she saw.

'Why did you do that?' she asked.

'Could so much beauty be allowed to perish, Highness?'

'So now you are fugitives,' the Begum said. 'Outcasts who have violated the law of their people.'

The Begum, of course, was a Muslim, if she was anything.

'We sought to regain control of the city, Highness,' Laura told her. 'But were defeated by Company soldiers. Prince Batraj is a worshipper of Kali.'

Batraj gave her an angry glance.

'It is the truth,' she said, suddenly feeling that this strangely beautiful old woman might after all help her.

The Begum looked from one to the other. Then she said, 'You have travelled far, and fast. You are weary, and you, my child, have suffered. Let my women attend to you.'

'The Rajah . . .'

'He may accompany his mother,' the Begum said.

Batraj looked as if he would have protested, but then changed his mind.

Laura could hardly believe her ears, as she and Miljah and Sivitraj were escorted through a delightful enclosed garden, and into what appeared to be a bedroom, full of divans and soft cushions. The Begum's women divested her of her clothes, with much chatter in Urdu, a language she did not understand, although she gathered that they were exclaiming over her beauty and her height, and her sun-burned complexion.

A huge tin tub of lukewarm water was brought in, and Laura was bathed, the girls gently washing her with sweet smelling soaps. It felt very good to be so treated after so long. She closed her eyes and enjoyed the soft fingers, the perfumes, the caress of the water.

Laura was dried, then made to lie on a divan where she was massaged with oil of roses. The girls worked in relays, two or three at a time; all had discarded their clothes and were kneeling beside her or astride her as they rubbed the oil into her shoulders and breasts, her thighs and legs and feet. The massage was as sensuous as it was soothing, and Laura felt herself drifting into the most relaxed state she had known since making love with Sitraj. Meanwhile Miljah was bathing little Sivitraj, who splashed and crowed and chattered happily to the women, without anyone understanding what he was saying.

Food was brought, perfectly prepared and delicious, but no wine so Laura supposed the Begum might after all be a devout Muslim.

She knew she should be worrying about what Batraj was up to, and making her own plans, but she felt so delightfully drowsy, truly aware for the first time of how exhausted she was, that all she wanted to do was lie down and close her eyes.

'I feel that we have stumbled upon some kind of a paradise, Miljah,' she said.

'Let us hope it stays this way, Highness,' Miljah said, as pessimistically as ever. No doubt she too had heard the stories of the Begum's cruelty. But so far, no-one could have been kinder.

After the meal, a divan was prepared for her, and the girls indicated that she should indeed lie down. She nestled amidst the cushions and called for Sivitraj to be given to her. He was as sleepy as she, and within seconds they were both dead to the world.

When Laura awoke with a start, Sivitraj was no longer there. It was clearly evening, as lamps were glowing in the room. And she was alone . . . save for the Begum Sombre.

Laura sat up, reaching for the cushions, embarrassed by her nakedness.

154

'Where is my son?' she asked, surges of alarm hammering at her brain.

'With his nurse,' the Begum told her. 'You have slept soundly. You needed that sleep.' She stretched out her hand and stroked golden hair from Laura's brow. 'Such marvellous hair. But then, you are such a beautiful woman.'

Her hand slipped to Laura's shoulder. Laura couldn't make up her mind whether to resist her or not; she was terribly aware of being entirely in this woman's power.

'Such breasts,' the Begum said, and stroked them. 'You must make Batraj very happy.'

Laura licked her lips. After all she had been through during the past month, she could not feel that to be seduced by the Begum Sombre would be the least unpleasant. She was more concerned with what advantage she might be able to gain.

'He is my captor,' she said.

'He says you are his wife.'

'Because he has declared it to be so, Highness.'

'My name is Aljai,' she said. 'I would have you call me Aljai.'

'Aljai,' Laura said, her heart beginning to pound.

'Tell me the truth, of you and Batraj,' Aljai invited, her hands sliding over Laura's body.

It was difficult to concentrate, but Laura told her everything. The Begum was not a woman from whom one could hide very much.

'You would like me to help you,' the Begum said, and stood up.

Laura fell back on the cushions. 'If you would return me and my son to Sittapore . . .'

The Begum removed her sari; for all her age and her experiences, she had the figure of a young girl. 'You would be arrested by the British,' she said. 'Are you not also a devotee of Kali?'

'Batraj forced me,' Laura said. 'Please believe me.'

Aljai stretched out on the divan beside her. 'I have been blessed in my life,' she said. 'So many beautiful people . . . George Thomas . . . my Frenchmen . . . and Richard Bryant . . . do you know of them?'

'I have heard their names . . .'

155

'And now you, the most beautiful of them all, come to visit me in my old age. Am I not blessed?'

Laura smiled. 'It is I who am blessed, Aljai. Will you help me?'

Aljai smiled. 'We will talk about it. Later.'

After Aljai had left, the girls came in to perfume Laura and dress her for the evening. They brought a beautiful new white sari, but no sandals, and she gathered she was to go barefoot, like the Begum. They spent half an hour dressing her hair, first of all combing and brushing it, and then twining it into a thick golden plait, almost as if she had been a girl again.

Her knees felt weak as she was escorted out into the garden, where Aljai sat on one divan and Batraj on another. What would Batraj say if he knew that his wife had been seduced by another woman and had enjoyed it?

'Come and sit beside me,' the Begum said. 'You look truly splendid tonight. But then, you are beautiful, Laura. Do you not agree, Prince Batraj?'

'With all my heart,' Batraj said.

Laura said nothing. I have escaped your clutches, she thought, without your even being aware of it. No matter what I have had to do, I have escaped you.

She sat beside the Begum and Aljai squeezed her hand. 'I have some entertainment for you.'

She clapped her hands, and a sitar player entered the garden followed by several nautch dancers, naked save for gold bangles at wrist and ankle.

'Do you like to watch them dance?' Aljai inquired, softly.

Laura looked at the girls with entirely new eyes.

Afterwards they ate, while Aljai talked about the great days of the past, about her love-hate relationship with the huge Irish adventurer George Thomas who had gone into battle wearing chain mail and wielding a gigantic two-handed sword, and about her true love, the Englishman Richard Bryant.

'Like you,' she said, 'he came to me a fugitive from the Company, and stayed to command my troops.' Her liquid eyes played over Batraj. 'There are no men like him any more.'

Batraj merely smiled.

156

After the meal, Laura was returned to her bedchamber. She understood that she was a prisoner, that perhaps the Begum had not yet made up her mind what to do with her or Batraj. But after that afternoon she did not doubt that she was going to succeed. She thought, I'm no better than a courtesan, willing to do anything to return my son to his inheritance. And she laughed.

She felt almost noble, and at the same time excited. Surely Aljai would wish to come to her again this night?

But to her disappointment, Aljai did not come.

She was awakened by Miljah, bringing Sivitraj to her for his morning cuddle.

'When will we leave this place, Highness?' Miljah asked.

'When the Begum permits us to do so.' Laura told her. 'Do you not like it here?'

'It is evil,' Miljah said.

'I am beginning to think all of India is evil,' Laura said. But I am part of it now, she thought. I have been swallowed into its erotic embrace.

She was bathed and dressed and fed. Suddenly then the girls squealed in excitement. 'The Prince comes!'

Laura stood up, Sivitraj in her arms. Batraj smiled at her. 'We are to leave here today.'

'Leave? For where?'

He gave a little shrug. 'We will go to Afghanistan. I know the Amir, Dost Mohammed. He will give us shelter while I prepare my plans. He hates the British.'

'I will stay here,' Laura declared. 'With the Rajah.'

Batraj did not get angry. 'Do not be foolish, Laura. You are my wife. Besides, there is our bargain. Where I go, you go. You will enjoy Afghanistan.'

'I will stay here,' Laura repeated. 'The Begum wishes me to stay.'

'Perhaps you should ask her,' Batraj suggested.

What could have happened? Was Batraj simply attempting to assert himself? Laura refused to despair.

'I will do that,' she said. 'Do not try to stop me.'

Batraj stepped aside, and held the door open for her.

Laura glared at him and went out into the garden. No-one was there, but the door on the right was open, and she went towards it. A horrifying wail of agony came from within. She hesitated, and another heart-rending scream tore the morning apart.

Maids hurried forward to stop her.

'I wish to see the Begum,' she demanded.

Another scream, which subsided into a kind of whimpering agony. Laura pushed the girls aside and entered a large hall.

'Laura, my child.' Aljai emerged from an adjacent room, serene in red silk. 'You have come to say goodbye.'

'What is happening?' Laura demanded.

'Oh, I am punishing one of my women. Come and see.'

Aljai took Laura's hand and led her through the inner doorway. On the floor inside was the naked body of a young girl, held there by several others, writhing and moaning in agony. Beside the victim there was a bowl of . . . Laura stared at it in horror. Red pepper!

The girl's nipples and breasts seemed swollen to twice their normal size.

'You will destroy her!' she gasped.

'Not there, if I wished to destroy her I would put the pepper between her legs,' Aljai said contemptuously. 'Oh, yes, then they die.' She sighed. 'But that is frowned upon nowadays.'

'What has she done?'

'Done? Why, nothing. It amuses me to remind these bitches that I still have teeth. Now, let us bid each other farewell.'

Laura felt as if she were choking. 'I thought you would help me,' she muttered.

'Believe me, my child, I have considered the matter carefully. I would like very much to keep you here. You are a delight, and would bring me much happiness. But I cannot antagonise the Company. They are strong, and I . . . in my old age I am weak.'

'But they are my people!' Laura cried, desperately.

'You are a criminal to them,' Aljai said. 'Prince Batraj has told me of this. If they knew I was giving you shelter here they would send to arrest you, and perhaps me as well. I have no soldiers now with which to fight them. I wish only to live in peace.'

158

'Batraj is a liar!' Laura shouted.

'Will you deny that you have worshipped at the shrine of Kali?'

'I was forced to it.' Laura protested. 'I have told you this.'

'It is the deed that matters,' Aljai pointed out. 'You and Prince Batraj, and your son, are expelled from my jaghir. On pain of death should you be found within my boundaries at this time tomorrow. Now go.'

'Your Highness, Aljai, I beg of you. After what we have . . .' she bit her lip. After what I allowed to happen, she thought . . . to be thrown out, like a prostitute!

'There will be others, if you wish it,' Aljai said. 'Now go.'

She left the room. Laura made to follow her, still hoping to persuade her, but was prevented by the women.

'You must leave this place, Highness,' one of them whispered. 'Do not anger the Begum, I beg of you, or it will be very hard for you. And it will be very hard for us.'

As if to underline the warning, the girl inside screamed as Aljai applied more pepper to her tortured flesh.

Laura's shoulders drooped as she was escorted through the door. Never had she felt so humiliated. To have allowed herself to be seduced by that horrid old woman . . . and to be cast aside at the end of it . . .

'I should have you whipped,' Batraj said as they rode out of the city. 'Do you consider you were keeping our bargain to tell the Begum that we are Thugs, and wanted by the British?'

'I told her nothing but the truth,' she said. 'Our bargain did not say that I must lie for you.' She drew a long breath. She had at least a spark of revenge to throw at him. 'Shall I tell you that the Begum came to my bed yesterday afternoon, and used me carnally?'

She waited for an explosive reaction of disgust, of revulsion, or of anger, but he was not in the least put out. 'But last night she summoned *me* to her bed, Laura. She is omnivorous.' He gave a shout of laughter. 'I wonder which of us she enjoyed the more.'

After Agra, Laura realised she was beaten. Even after Sitraj's death, even after her bargain with Batraj, she had yet dreamed of somehow escaping the consequences of her madness. As they rode north, she understood that she was Batraj's woman, and must remain so for the rest of her life.

Batraj did not beat her. Instead he humiliated her by making her show him everything that Aljai had done to her, which was far worse. He seemed delighted by the incident, which left Laura feeling even more devastated yet, in a strange way more relaxed than she had been since Sitraj's death. As she could no longer resist the world, she might as well allow herself to sink into its embrace, abandon herself entirely to the senses, which seemed to be all that was required of her.

She had felt it somehow shameful to think of Guy Bartlett before. That night when Batraj mounted her, she closed her eyes and remembered every detail of Guy's naked body.

After what had happened at Agra, however amused he had been by it, Batraj decided it would be dangerous to allow Laura to work her charms on any other potentate, especially the Mughal Emperor in Delhi. That august personage might have sunk a long way from the fame and splendour of Aurangzeb, his dominions no more than a few square miles around the city, and his survival entirely dependant upon the pension paid him by the Company, there was a British Resident in the city, and a regiment of Sepoys camped outside it. Batraj was sure that news of the fight outside Sittapore would not yet have reached this far north, but he would not risk Laura being able to talk to any of her compatriots.

Thus from Agra he turned north-west, away from Company-controlled territory, and into Rajputana. Here the British had no direct influence, although the Rajput princes were well aware of the looming power to their south and east.

Batraj now travelled as an Afghan merchant on his way home. He was still well provided with funds and found little difficulty in obtaining food and shelter. The Indian women made up a dye, and Laura's magnificent hair was dyed black, and her white flesh darkened to a sallow brown. Nothing could be done about her blue eyes, of course, but it was certainly an adequate disguise from a distance.

160

'And there are Pathan women with blue eyes,' Batraj told her. 'I have seen them.'

He had apparently taken refuge in the north following his father's death and his first failed attempt at a coup, and had only returned to Sittapore when Sitraj had extended the hand of welcome.

How foolishly generous had her first husband been, Laura thought.

January and February were two of the best months in the Deccan. Although the nights were cold on the high plateau after leaving the valley of the Jumna, once the little party descended into the huge plain watered by the Indus, the weather was again very pleasant.

Although Batraj was apparently known in several towns, he gave the impression that he was merely travelling, as usual, on a mission for his cousin: the news of the death of the Rajah of Sittapore had not yet reached the north. Even the Rajputs, however, had heard that Sitraj had married a golden-haired Englishwoman, but no one was allowed to get close enough to Laura even to suspect that she was not what she seemed, a Hindu concubine.

But for her circumstances and her fears for the future, Laura knew she would have found the journey fascinating.

It was not that her immediate circumstances were particularly unpleasant or uncomfortable; she found the continuous travelling exhausting. Batraj was still ahead of the news from Sittapore, and intended to remain that way. But he was good humoured and tolerant, and they invariably found a place in one of the caravanserais which lay close to every large town. These caravanserais were huge walled hotels, in which any traveller was welcome to stay free of charge for three days: this was to encourage tradesmen to visit the area. They were extremely comfortable, with apartments for families and a large area for animals. They were also extremely noisy when there were several caravans all in residence at the same time.

As they left Sargodha, however, and began the ascent towards the Hindu Kush, it became apparent that it was still winter in the mountains which were their destination. Now the

161

wind came whistling down from the north, it was bitingly cold, and they huddled beneath blankets even as they rode.

There was no snow on the ground as yet, and they reached Peshawar safely enough. Peshawar lay in a vast depression in the hills, although still a considerable height above sea-level, and was surrounded by mountains, forbiddingly snow-covered, which reach up to the sky.

'How far is Kabul?' she asked Batraj.

'From here, not far at all. But it is in the mountains,' he told her.

They remained several days in Peshawar, because Batraj was waiting to join a caravan bound for Kabul and then the trade routes of Central Asia.

'One needs strength in the mountains,' he said. 'The people are very bad.'

Strange words for a Thug, she thought.

But she understood what he meant as they traversed the Khyber pass. It was now paralysingly cold, but worse than the weather were the men who sometimes came close to look at them and, when they stopped for the night, to trade. They were all armed with ancient muskets and long knives and swords and spears.

'They will cut a man's throat as soon as shake his hand,' Batraj told her. 'And to those that fall into their hands after a battle their women are absolute devils.'

Laura was glad he had waited after all; the caravan numbered several hundred souls, and was obviously too strong to attack.

The next day, although it was almost April, they experienced their first snowstorm. Laura rode with Sivitraj in her arms all the time; she was afraid the little boy, so unused to this climate, might catch his death of cold.

But they all remained very healthy, and after only a week of really hard travelling, they topped yet another line of hills and looked down on Kabul.

Bombay, 16 September, 1830

Yesterday afternoon, Prudence and I returned from our honeymoon in Madras.

The wedding, as weddings go, was a quiet affair. There was some criticism of Colonel Partridge, my father-in-law, for throwing his only child to a junior officer with no fortune and little prospects. The fact is that he wished Prudence, who is now twenty-one and has even less prospects than I, to be a wife, and I was her first choice.

In the circumstances, therefore, it was deemed proper to have a very quiet wedding.

Thus I find myself a very married man. I use the word 'very' advisedly. Prudence is a dear sweet girl, but with set ideas on when and how and even where certain events should take place.

It is not that our marriage has not been consummated. Far from it; it has been consummated time and again, with total acceptance upon the part of my dear wife. However . . . damn it, if a man cannot confide in his own journal . . . The fact of the matter is that Prudence understands that our marriage has been consecrated by God, and that it is her duty to submit parts of her body to my male lust in the hopes that she will one day – soon she prays – perform her female function and become pregnant. In this regard she recognises that such part of her body as lies between her navel and her knees, in front, must be exposed for this purpose, and is prepared to raise her nightgown for the required few minutes, while herself assuming the position of a corpse. She raises no objection when I seek to touch her breasts so long as I do not linger. However,

163

she steadfastly refuses to bare them, and there is all the difference in the world between naked flesh and that same flesh covered with cloth. And my seeking, during our initial moments of passion, to possess those far larger and more gracious curves at the rear, earned me a buffet which made my head spin.

When I think of my dusky charmer, who would present her plump little cheeks for my adulation, confident that I should seek to prosper by that route and no other . . . my imagination cannot envision Prudence's reaction should I ever seek to roll her on her face. My head would be spinning for a month.

But there it is. Half a loaf is better than no bread at all, and if I am required, as the Colonel's son-in-law, to appear the most happily married man in Bombay, no doubt I shall be, in the course of time.

Actually, I doubt it. Prudence unfortunately does not like dogs. Being a dear sweet girl who understands men's weaknesses, she has not gone so far as to command me to get rid of my little family, but she has instituted certain rules. Rufus, Regina and the puppy are forbidden the house and must sleep in a kennel in the yard, where they howl most dolefully as they recall the happy nights they spent snuggled in my warm bed. Indeed, sometimes I feel it was warmer then than now.

Yet, all is not darkness and gloom. I have, as the Colonel's son-in-law, *some* prospects looming on the horizon. Smythe has been invalided home, so there is a captaincy vacant in the regiment. Partridge has hinted that it may well be mine, so I live in hopes.

Politically, it is quiet here. With the disappearance of Batraj, Thuggish activity has quite died down. What has happened to that scoundrel is anyone's guess. We did receive a report that he sought asylum in the jaghir of a woman known as the Begum Sombre, a lady who has a reputation for every vice known under the sun, and some which are best only practised in darkness. However, it appears that she turned him out for fear of vengeance.

John Company is a terrible adversary!

Thus the scoundrel has disappeared, and with him, needless to say, the perfidious Laura. No doubt they have both long since been murdered by bandits. A fitting end for a Thug. But Laura . . . I have to confess that I still dream of her, and dream too of holding her in my arms.

But she is only a dream.

There is one political matter which holds out some promise of a break in the monotony. It seems that there has been a revolution in Afghanistan. This mountainous country, situated far beyond our dominions, is as old as the hills in which it resides, and has gone under a variety of names, of which Bactria, Gandara, Transoxiana, Tukharistan, Ghazni, and now Afghanistan are but a few. In its olden days it even received the phalanxes of Alexander the Great, who founded a host of cities, named, as was his wont, after himself. These names have largely been corrupted, but I understand that his is still a revered name in those parts.

More recently the country has acted as a pathway for men like Tamerlane and Babur the Mughal. No-one who has anything to do with India can forget that it was through those mountain passes of Afghanistan that Timur descended upon northern India and sacked Delhi in 1398, or that Babur followed the same route in 1526 and Nadir Shah less than a century ago. Since then the power has lain south of the Hindu Kush rather than north of it. But times change, and in recent years it has always been of interest to John Company to know just what is going on in that remote land. This is one area in which the Rajputs of Rajasthan and even the Sikhs in Kashmir make common ground with us: they mortally fear the forces that lie beyond the mountain. Now this force is again a most powerful one: Russia.

Thus it has behoved the Company to make sure that in Kabul there is a ruler who will keep his mountain passes closed. Heaven knows we have no desire to go north. All we want is for him to make sure no Cossack army comes south. To this end, in 1809 we reached an agreement with the then Amir, Shah Shuja, that as long as he resisted any encroachment upon his territory, we would come to his aid with all possible despatch were he assaulted by the Tsar.

Alas, we were not dealing with Europeans. The palace politics of Asiatic kingdoms almost defy description. Shah

Shuja only obtained the throne of Afghanistan by rebelling against and deposing his brother Mahmud, who had in fact deposed his elder brother, the rightful amir Zaman Shah. Mahmud had the foresight to blind his poor brother, and thus put him permanently out of the question. Shuja omitted to take this desperate step, with the result that only a year after we had signed our treaty, Mahmud led a counter-revolution and regained his throne. Shuja escaped and made his way into our territory, where he has remained ever since, importuning our governors-general to reinstate him, as he claims we are bound to do.

However, our treaty with him called for us to defend him against foreign encroachment, not an internal revolt, and especially one where he was in the wrong. On the other hand, Mahmud naturally turned his back on any agreements made by Shuja. Fortunately, he was able to set up quite a strong kingdom, with the support of a soldier and leader named Fath Ali Khan, whom he appointed vizier, or prime minister, and who appeared hostile to both Russia and Britain.

Then Fath Ali Khan and his master fell out, Mahmud was again put to flight, and the Khan became amir. Still there was little cause for alarm here in India, save amongst the adherents of the unhappy Shuja.

However, in 1826 Fath Ali Khan died, and was succeeded by his brother Dost Mohammed. This was considered of no great importance to the company, but now, word is being received that Dost Mohammed is entertaining Russian ministers and officers at his court in Kabul.

For the time being, we are simply going to make representations, and wait to see what the outcome of these will be.

One thing is certain, if an expedition should be determined upon, even if it means a lengthy separation from my dear wife, I intend to volunteer.

8

The Conquest

The walled city of Kabul lay in a valley between the Asmai and Sherdawaza mountain ranges, but even the valley was nearly six thousand feet above sea level.

Laura knew that Kabul was one of the oldest cities in the world, having been in existence for more than three thousand years, its importance lying in its position, dominating the best trade route from Central Asia to India.

Here she found herself in an even more bewildering world than Agra; though the city was not as large, it seemed to be more crowded, and most people spoke a variety of Persian, which she could not understand.

Batraj was taken immediately before Dost Mohammed, and he made Laura and Sivitraj accompany him. Laura found herself in a splendid and clearly very old palace, but the court was truly barbaric; she was surrounded by Pathan and Afghan chieftains, with tulwars thrust through their sashes, and pistols and daggers, while their faces were covered in bristling beards and moustaches.

No women were present, and she realised that she was now in a totally Muslim country. For that reason she was wrapped up in a bourka which concealed her entirely, leaving her only a little woven grille to see through.

Batraj now revealed yet another facet of his remarkable personality by speaking fluent Persian, as he explained his situation to Dost Mohammed. The Afghan ruler had a strong, evil face, in which nose and bearded chin and eyes were all prominent. When he looked at Laura she could not repress a shudder.

'His Highness would look more closely upon you, and the boy,' Batraj said, and beckoned her forward.

She clutched Sivitraj to her breast as she advanced.

Dost Mohammed stared at her for several seconds, before smiling and speaking.

Whatever he said pleased Batraj, who also smiled as he replied. Then Dost Mohammed got up. For a moment Laura thought he was going to touch her, and her knees shook. But instead he tickled the baby Rajah and made Sivitraj laugh.

Then they were dismissed, and escorted to apartments in the palace. Laura continued to be impressed by the evidence of ancient wealth and power, the carved and inlaid wood, the domed ceilings, the soft rich carpets on the floors.

'We will have a home of our own as soon as one can be arranged,' Batraj told her. 'The Amir is pleased to welcome us here. He regards the Company as his greatest enemy. Are you not pleased?'

'I am pleased to be finished with travelling for a while,' Laura said, and set Sivitraj on the floor.

'So am I,' Batraj said, and took her hand to lead her into their bedchamber. 'Do you realise that you and I have never slept in true comfort before?'

The room was certainly comfortable, and beautifully appointed. The divan was even bigger than the one she had shared with Sitraj, strewn with rugs and cushions, and the doors at the back gave access to a delightful garden with the invariable bathing pool.

'I had never imagined such luxury could exist in such an inhospitable place,' Laura observed.

'Kabul is one of the centres of the world. This palace once belonged to Babur, indeed he is buried in the city. There is much evidence of past greatness in Central Asia. It is the part of the world from whence all greatness stems,' Batraj said reverently. 'From here I too will seek greatness. Now come . . .' he unwound her sari. 'Lie with me in our new home, and know happiness.'

He was irresistible, even had she possessed the strength or the means to resist him. Two months later she realised she was pregnant.

Laura was horrified.

Batraj was delighted. 'Now you are truly my wife,' he said. 'You will give me a strong son.'

'I cannot bear your child,' she cried.

'You mean you do not wish to. You most certainly can. You above all women are made for child-bearing.'

'Let me lose it, Batraj,' she begged.

'You will bear the child,' he told her. 'And love him as much as you do Sivitraj.'

She had felt a prisoner ever since arriving in Kabul. Because Muslim women were naturally prisoners in a European sense, Afghan society was complex in that a good proportion of the population was not Muslim, and those women went about freely and unveiled, but only among the lower orders. Certainly a dowager rani was expected to live a very discreet life.

For the first two months she had been slowly, by means of continuous bathing and washing, getting rid of the dye; Batraj was anxious to have her pale skin and yellow hair back in his embrace. Apparently he had told Dost Mohammed of her beauty, and however sinful it might be for a true believer to look upon another man's wife, Dost Mohammed wished to do so, and Batraj wished to humour his host in everything. Thus he would not permit her to leave their apartment until her colour had been fully restored, and this tedious operation had only just been completed when she discovered her condition. Now she went into a far more complete purdah than before, with only Miljah, Vijay's woman Nanja, and Sivitraj for company.

When she was nearly restored to her proper complexion she was escorted down secret corridors and shown into Dost Mohammed's harem, where she was introduced to the Amir's wives, concubines and children. There were a great number of these, and they were all very interested in Laura's golden hair, which was so strange to them, but as Laura had as yet picked up only a word or two of Persian she could take little part in their excited chatter. The whole atmosphere of the harem made her feel uneasy, as most of the women clearly had close relationships with each other, while the eunuchs moved about them with obvious intimacy.

169

Although Batraj spent as much time with her as ever, from the day Miljah confirmed her condition he never attempted to touch her. In one way this was a blessed relief, but it still confused her.

'What will he do?' she asked the slave. She could not imagine Batraj existing without a woman.

'The Amir has given him two concubines,' Miljah said.

Laura could not decide whether to be pleased or anxious. One half of her, which still clung to her English ideals, hoped that his new women would please him so much that he never came back to her; but the other was almost jealous – she did not know if *she* could now live without a man.

It was a great relief to Laura when, as promised, the exiled Rajah of Sittapore was given a home of his own.

This was a small palace not far from the Amir's, situated next to the Bala Hissar or central square of the city. Hardly more than a large house, it was very comfortable, enclosing a centre courtyard with a pool and a fountain. There was a retinue of servants. It was during the move that Laura first met Batraj's concubines, and was disgusted to discover that they were hardly more than fourteen or fifteen. They giggled all the time, especially when they looked at the Dowagar Rani.

As Laura was now several months pregnant and looking, she felt, at her worst, she burst into tears once she gained the privacy of her apartments.

'Why do you not whip them?' Nanja asked.

'What?'

Nanja, although she had elected to follow her husband into the ranks of the Thugs, was the daughter of one of Sittapore's wealthiest citizens. Dark-skinned, voluptuous and boldly handsome, she had rigid concepts of power and responsibility, certainly within the home. 'You are the Dowager Rani, and Prince Batraj's wife, Highness,' she said. 'You have absolute power within his household. If the girls offend you, whip them.'

Laura had never considered her status before. While she had been Rani of Sittapore, she had never in any way considered herself superior to Sitraj's other wives. And since his death, she had thought of herself only as Batraj's slave.

Now she realised that what Nanja had said was indeed true. Batraj had introduced her to Dost Mohammed and to all Kabul as his wife. In a Muslim community he must obey Muslim laws, and that made her absolute mistress of his household, no matter how many other wives he might take. His rights over her consisted of the privilege of taking her to bed, which he could not presently do; of beating her himself, which again was not at the moment possible, as he dearly wanted her child; of killing her if he found her guilty of adultery; or of divorcing her if he grew weary of her.

But was not to be divorced by Batraj something to be dreamed of? On the other hand how could she survive in this wild land, save as Batraj's wife? The possibility of being claimed by one of those ferocious mountain chieftains, or even by Dost Mohammed, was too terrible to contemplate.

Laura decided against whipping the two girls. The idea was attractive, both in itself and as a release for her tensions and frustrations, but to give way to such a desire would be to lower herself one more rung of the ladder into becoming entirely Indian. She knew that her only hope of eventual salvation was to preserve as much of her English upbringing, the mores and morals of her childhood, as possible.

So she put up with the giggles and the snide remarks behind her back.

But, pregnant as she was, she insisted on taking over the running of the household. Vijay, who had naturally stepped into the position of Batraj's chamberlain, was astounded and concerned. He complained to Batraj, but Batraj was amused and, Laura soon realised, pleased that she was at last taking her proper place instead of waiting to be driven or dragged.

Thereafter she and Vijay became good friends, as they discussed the various renovations which the house needed. It had belonged to one of the followers of the rightful Amir, Shah Shuja, who had fled with his master, and thus it had remained empty for some years. Laura became entirely involved in her new life, and from time to time had to stop and remind herself that she had no right to be happy.

Yet happiness was difficult to resist. Sivitraj was growing up

171

into a delightful little companion, and Batraj was invariably in a good humour. Early in 1829 Laura gave birth to a daughter. She gazed at Batraj with anxious eyes as he held the babe and peered into its face. He had been so determined she would give him a son that she feared an outburst of anger.

But he merely remarked, 'She has your blue eyes. She will be a beautiful woman. What will you name her?'

'I, name her?' Laura asked.

'I will name our son,' Batraj told her. 'You may name the girl.'

She wished the girl to be as English as possible. She named her Mary.

With the birth of Mary, life in Kabul assumed a contented pattern. Laura fed the baby for three months, as she had Sivitraj, then Miljah found her a wet nurse, because Batraj wanted her back in his bed. His passion for her was all the victory she required over his concubines, who were banished to their harem while he rediscovered the delights of his beautiful Englishwoman.

He still, more than anything, wanted a son. But although Laura twice became pregnant during the following two years, she miscarried both times, and it seemed clear that he was going to be disappointed. Nevertheless, that did not lessen his ardour for her.

Laura's thoughts often drifted back to her life in Bombay, and to her parents in England, who no doubt joined the rest of the world in condemning her as a debauched murderess. Since it now appeared that Kabul was going to be her home at least until Sivitraj was grown up, she worked hard at learning Persian until she was fluent. She ran her household with the closest attention to detail, and accompanied Vijay to the market, suitably veiled, to oversee the weekly shopping.

She made a friend of Nanja, and the two women often gossiped and reminisced about the past while their four children played at their feet. They also indulged in excursions together, exploring the magnificent mausoleum of Babur the Mughal, and sometimes picnicking with their children in the hills surrounding the city.

Why, Laura thought, I am living a civilised existence. Even had she lived in England, she could still have found herself bound to a man she hated and feared, without even the promise of ecstasy every time she was summoned to Batraj's bed.

Gradually Laura noticed certain changes in Kabul, white faces and European clothes began to appear. From the cut of their uniforms and their round fur hats, she understood the newcomers to be Russian. As she never left her house except heavily veiled she did not suppose they ever knew her to be European herself, although they were not above glancing at the statuesque woman walking the streets with her attendants behind her, and undoubtedly she was pointed out to them as the Dowager Rani of Sittapore.

Then, in the summer of 1832, as she left the market, she noticed several men, who were unmistakeably British, issuing from the Amir's Palace and appearing somewhat hot and bothered.

Laura hastily returned home, where she awaited Batraj with some anxiety.

'There are Company officials here,' she said as he entered her bedchamber.

'They have been here for some days now,' he said.

'And you did not tell me?'

'I did not consider it any concern of yours.'

'Not my concern? Have they not tracked us down, to demand our return to Bombay?'

Batraj smiled. 'We are not *that* important to the Company, my sweet. No, no, these people are here in an endeavour to dissuade the Amir from becoming too friendly with Russia. He will ignore their representations, of course. Now does not that conjure up a promising spectacle? Britain and Russia locked in combat over Afghanistan?'

'My God!' Laura gasped. 'You can hope for something like that?'

'It is out of such conflicts that a man like myself might pluck a kingdom,' Batraj said seriously. 'Unfortunately the Company will never send an army this far north; it would mean opposing the Sikhs, at the least, if not the Rajputs as well. However . . .'

he sat beside her. 'Your first fear is a very true one. The Company people did not come to Kabul looking for us, but now there are here they will most certainly learn of our presence. And who knows what Dost Mohammed may do. He is the most treacherous of men. If he granted us asylum, it is because it suited him to do so. If he felt he could buy off the Company . . .' he sighed. 'He wishes to entertain you.'

'What?' Laura cried.

'He has coveted you from the moment he set eyes upon you, especially when I told him of your true beauty, which he then could not see. But he looked upon you, from a hidden position, when you were in his harem, and coveted you even more.'

'I am a married woman,' Laura said, trying to keep from screaming. 'Is not adultery the most heinous of all crimes to the Muslim?'

'It is a serious crime, to be sure,' Batraj agreed. 'But Dost Mohammed is not a serious Muslim. He is an Afghan robber chieftain who happens to have made himself Amir, and has found it convenient to join his people in paying lip service to the Koran.'

'Batraj!' Laura seized his hands. 'You cannot be serious.'

Batraj sighed again. 'Do you think I wish you to do this? I have resisted his importunities for two years, by claiming you have been pregnant. Alas, you are not pregnant now, and the Englishmen are here. And the Amir repeated his invitation to you to attend a banquet at the palace only yesterday. I told him I would have to investigate your condition, but now, we must accept.'

'Batraj . . .'

'He does not wish you to be veiled. As he points out, you are an infidel, and infidels do not wear the veil.'

'Are you coming to the banquet?'

'Of course. But I may leave early.'

'Abandoning me there? Batraj, you cannot do this to me. You are asking me to prostitute myself!'

'Listen to me, Laura. In the eyes of the Company you are a Thug and a murderess. If they manage to take you back to Bombay they will hang you by the neck until you are dead. In public. Do you wish that to happen?'

174

Laura found she was clasping her throat.

'I do not wish to give you to Dost Mohammed,' Batraj went on. 'I know him for what he is. But for the present time he is our only hope of survival. As for your moral scruples, you did not hesitate to prostitute yourself to the Begum Sombre when you thought she might help you escape me.'

Laura bit her lip. She had no defence.

Batraj smiled at her, and stroked her hand. 'You must forget that you were once the daughter of a clerk. You are now a great lady, and great ladies play for high stakes with every weapon that God has given them. He has given you a very powerful weapon, Laura. You must use it.'

Nanja and Miljah both assisted Laura to dress. She wore a white sari, to remind everyone that she was a widow, and her emerald necklace and all her gold bangles. Her nails were hennaed and her eyes outlined with kohl. Her complexion had quite recovered from its ordeal during the flight from Sittapore.

Her hair was brushed and combed and then dressed in the typical Indian chignon. As she inspected herself in the brass mirrors, she felt more of a sacrificial victim than she had when she was laid on the funeral pyre beside Sitraj.

Laura and Batraj walked to the palace, attended by their servants. Over her sari she was dressed as a Muslim woman, and she kept her veil in place as they were ushered into the reception chamber, her back as straight as ever.

She was astounded to realise that she was not, after all, the only woman present; there were two others, wearing European evening dresses and revealing a good deal of decolletage. They turned out to be the wives of the Russian diplomats who had recently taken up permanent residence in Kabul.

They and their husbands gazed in amazement at the Dowager Rani as, on Batraj's muttered instructions, Laura unveiled herself to bow before the Amir.

She was duly introduced to the Russians; the men kissed her hand, and the woman actually curtsied – she was, after all, a queen. Then she was presented to the English party.

She had been terrified it would include someone she knew,

175

but all the faces were strange to her. Their leader was surprisingly young, only a few years older than herself, short and plump and with a good-humoured face. He bent over her hand, his lips just brushing her flesh. 'Alexander Burnes, at your service, your Highness,' he said with a delightful Scottish burr. 'Dare I say how much I have looked forward to this meeting?'

His aides, who were mostly older, were not quite so pleasant. Definitely, they knew all about her.

Laura was seated on Dost Mohammed's right, with Burnes on her right. The meal was served at a single long table set against one end of the room, so she was effectively separated from Batraj, who was some distance away, between the two Russians. She could see that he was uneasy about her closeness to the company envoy, but there was nothing he could do about it.

Dost Mohammed was kindness itself, and himself filled her wine glass, proving even more that he was a man first and a Muslim second.

'You are the most beautiful woman who has ever adorned this palace, Highness,' he remarked.

'I find that impossible to believe, Your Excellency,' she protested, surprised that she could speak at all, so dry was her throat. She drank some of the wine, the first she had tasted in some time, and found it astonishingly good.

She turned to Burnes.

'Does Bombay still prosper?' she inquired, in English.

'It grows every day,' the Scot said.

'I should love to see it again,' she ventured.

'And I wish you could,' he agreed.

She turned her head to gaze directly at him.

He smiled, a trifle sadly. 'But it would be difficult. Your name is still much discussed, and . . . there remains an unserved warrant for your arrest on a charge of murder.'

'Of which I am entirely innocent.'

He sighed. 'It is the proving of it, Your Highness, the proving of it . . . But is Kabul not now your home?'

'My . . . husband finds the climate congenial,' she replied.

'I am sure he does. There are many people in Bombay who

176

would like *him* to revisit them. And no doubt in Sittapore, as well.'

'Perhaps one of these days we shall gratify their wish,' Laura said. 'When my son is old enough to take his rightful place as Rajah.'

'Ah. Your son is with you, here in Kabul?'

'Should a son not be with his mother, sir? Will you tell me who is currently acting as regent in Sittapore?'

'Why, the Dowager Rani Bilkis. For her grandson, the Rajah Partaj.'

Bibi's son, Laura thought.

'Prince Partaj is an usurper, sir. Whatever crimes I may be accused of, my son is innocent, and he is the rightful heir.'

'Then the sooner you bring him back the better, I would say,' Burnes remarked.

'Would you assist me to regain my son's inheritance?' she asked boldly.

'Why, Highness, it would be a great honour. But . . . I cannot guarantee success, and the risk would be enormous.'

'If something is worth having, is it not worth risking all for?' Laura enquired, with her most dazzling smile. She felt a great glow of warmth. Had she found a friend?

'Of what do you speak with that man?' Dost Mohammed inquired.

'Of my son's jaghir, Your Excellency,' Laura replied.

'It is sad, to lose one's inheritance,' Dost Mohammed said, enigmatically.

During dinner sitars played in the background, but as it came to an end, the music increased in volume and the nautch dancers came in. Clearly the Russian women had never before been subjected to such a display of unbridled sexuality, and they hid their embarrassment behind their fans. Laura watched the girls, but her thoughts were on other things; the sympathetic conversation with Burnes was full of promise for the future, but the immediate problem was Dost Mohammed. She had finished her third glass of wine and would have drunk more had she been given it, but when she raised the glass again to her lips she found it had been filled with water.

Dost Mohammed smiled at her. 'I was concerned lest you become too sleepy to enjoy the evening, Highness,' he said. Laura felt like putting out her tongue at him.

The girls having completed their dance, the guests rose. Laura realised she was absolutely sober. And now people were starting to leave. Laura discovered that Batraj had already gone. The Company contingent followed him, bowing over her head as before.

'It has been a great pleasure, Highness,' Burnes said. 'I hope we shall meet again. And if I can ever be of any assistance to you, be sure of my support.'

She wondered if the cheery little Scotsman understood that she had been abandoned for the night by her husband?

The Russian ladies certainly did so, and cast glances from her to Dost Mohammed, who stood close by, smiling his evil smile.

At last the hall was empty, save for the servants who waited to clear away when the Amir had left.

'I am glad you have remained behind, Highness,' Dost Mohammed remarked. 'I have long wished for an opportunity to hold a private conversation with you.' He walked to the rear of the room, where a majordomo held the door open for him. 'Come, let us seek some fresh air.'

Laura forced her legs to move, to go forward. You are a great lady, Batraj had told her, and must act the part. She went through the doorway, and was escorted along various corridors into the heart of the labyrinthine palace. Soon they encountered eunuchs, and she knew they were near the harem, but instead of entering there Dost Mohammed took her through another set of doors and into yet another reception chamber. Inner arches gave on to one of the secluded gardens so beloved of Muslim architects, with the inevitable pool and fountain, the whole lit by flaming torches to give a very dramatic effect.

'Sit with me.' Dost Mohammed threw himself on to one of the several divans, and Laura understood she was to do the same. As she sat down, eunuchs appeared with trays of iced sherbet.

'They cool the blood,' Dost Mohammed told her. 'But

178

nothing will cool my blood tonight. Nor yours, I hope, Highness.'

Laura ate her water ice as the eunuchs bowed and withdrew, closing the doors behind them. She attempted to decide how to handle the approaching ordeal. She could just close her eyes and let it happen. But that would hardly please the Amir, which was what she was here to do. Or she could pretend to enjoy it.

She felt his hand on her shoulder, sliding down her arm, and then up again, beneath the folds of her sari.

'Tell me of yourself,' Dost Mohammed said.

Laura swallowed her water ice, and obeyed. Perhaps if she could keep him listening to her, he would fall asleep. So she began with her childhood, and told him of Bombay and how she lived before Sitraj came into her life. But as she spoke, his hands wandered over her, gradually removing the sari and then unfastening the blouse beneath. His touch was gentle enough, but the very thought of him, of what she was being made to do, made her unable to suppress a shudder.

'You fear me,' Dost Mohammed said.

'I fear the crime you commit, my lord,' she said.

'Adultery is only a crime when committed by Muslim with Muslim,' he pointed out. 'I have established this point with the mufti. You are an infidel, so there can be no crime, especially as your infidel husband is agreeable to what we do.' He had uncovered her breasts, and now stroked them very knowledgeably, so that she felt her nipples hardening. 'And your body accepts me,' he went on, pleased at her reaction. 'Therefore your mind must, as well. Do you suppose I would ever harm such a magnificent creature as you?' Gently he pulled her back so that she lay on the divan; the half emptied sherbet glass fell from her fingers and shattered on the marble floor, but he was not distracted. 'Your countrymen, now, they seek to harm you. They asked me why I do not send you back to Bombay. I asked them, what will you do with her there? And they said . . .' he smiled, his teeth white in the black of his beard, 'oh, we shall undoubtedly hang her for murder.'

Laura could not believe Burnes had said that. But the others . . . oh, she could believe it of them.

'I am innocent,' she said. 'I was forced to become a Thug by my husband.'

'I believe you,' Dost Mohammed said. Suddenly Laura realised that she was almost completely naked. Now he rose to his knees the better to look at her. She wanted to draw up her own knees, but made herself lie still. The sooner it was done, the better.

'Such hair,' the Amir said. 'My women do not have such hair.' He touched it, and she shivered again.

'If you do not accept me,' he said, 'then I may hurt you. I should not like to do that.'

'I will accept you,' Laura said.

'Then disrobe for me.'

There was not much left to do. Laura stood up and let the disordered sari settle about her ankles, stepped out of it and then out of her undergarments, kicked off her sandals.

Dost Mohammed gazed at her. 'Truly are you a gift from Allah,' he said. 'Now, undress me.'

Laura gasped. She was apparently going to be spared nothing. Tentatively she removed his belt and unfastened his tunic. Then she took off his shoes, returned to his tunic, removed it, and lifted the silk shirt beneath. He had a splendid torso, broad and deep and covered in a mat of thick black hair.

He lay down, and waited for her to remove his breeches. She drew a long breath, and did so, and the oddly-shaped drawers he wore beneath. His size made even Batraj seem like a boy, and here too there were masses of hair.

'You see how anxious he is to receive you,' Dost Mohammed said. 'But I would have him entertained. Dance for me.'

Laura stared at him in consternation. 'But there is no music.'

'That is unimportant. I wish to see you move, as a woman. Dance for me.'

Laura pushed herself off the divan and made herself move as she had seen the nautch girls do.

'Loose your hair,' he commanded.

As she danced, she put up her hands and released the pins holding her hair, which promptly tumbled over her shoulders.

'Magnificent,' he said. 'Magnificent.' He watched her body begin to gleam with sweat. 'Now come to me,' he said.

She went to his arms. 'Will you send me back to Bombay, Your Excellency?' she asked.

He laughed, and kissed her before arranging her to his satisfaction. 'As I have said, that would be a waste.'

It was difficult not to feel an afterglow of contentment as she lay in his arms, even if she was determined not to, to hate everything that had happened to her. The Amir was clearly at least as big a monster as Batraj, but he was an equally formidable lover. Perhaps, she thought, I was born to be a courtesan amongst bandits and robber chieftains.

'Do not the British wish my husband returned to them as well?' she asked.

'Indeed they do. I think they want Batraj more than you.'

Laura sat up to look down at him. 'Will you surrender him?'

Dost Mohammed smiled. 'After he has sent you to my bed? That would be an act of treachery, would it not? In any event, why should I humour the John Company? They are my enemies, and Batraj may well be useful to me in the future. Do not fear for your husband, my dear.'

And Laura was pulled back into his arms.

She supposed she had now plumbed the very depths of degradation, for Dost Mohammed sent for her at least once a month thereafter. What his own wives and concubines thought of it, she dared not suppose.

Batraj pretended to be outraged, but she soon realised that he was secretly pleased to be sharing his 'wife' with the Amir; it made them something closer than brothers-in-law.

Dost Mohammed lavished presents upon her, mostly of jewellery, and Batraj felt he had to match his rival, although his store of money and emeralds was by now rather low. She was also established as one of the great aghas of Kabul, entirely abandoning the veil, and in good weather she walked abroad, accompanied by Nanja and Vijay, and by Miljah and her children, with complete freedom, her head held high and her back as straight as it had ever been, while proud chieftains

181

bowed to her and stepped out of her path. Again this was approved by her lovers, who wanted the whole world to see the beauty which submitted to them.

Dost Mohammed, indeed, was utterly blatant in his adoration. He introduced her to his sons, grave young men who clearly disapproved of her. Laura began to wonder if Batraj was as safe in Kabul as he supposed, not from the Company but from his host.

The thought of being forever incarcerated in the Amir's harem kept her awake at night.

To Laura's surprise, she was even invited to tea by the Russian ladies, who could converse with her in very limited Persian. They were of course consumed with curiosity, both as to her past, of which they had heard the wildest rumours, and her present, which clearly at once scandalised and titillated them. Laura saw no reason to be the least reticent with them, as they knew her position in Kabul society, and indeed, rather enjoyed the temptation to shock them. So she confessed freely that she was a high priestess of the goddess Kali, and left them aghast . . . and eager to ask her again.

Thus life settled in to a very regular pattern. The winters in Afghanistan were very cold, and for several months all intercourse with the outside world was ended. Then it was a time for staying at home curled up in front of a roaring fire, teaching the children English and about England. But in the summer, it seemed all of Central Asia came to Kabul. Caravans came from China in the East, and from the Ottoman Empire in the west, and the Afghan capital became a huge continuous market, in which the most exotic goods, from silk and perfumes to girls and boys, could be bought at will. Laura indulged herself to the utmost. As Miljah was growing infirm, she actually purchased a Chinese girl named Wu Li, principally as a nursemaid for Sivitraj and Mary, but also as a personal maid for herself. Wu Li, who was fourteen, was pretty and energetic as well as intelligent, and tremendously anxious to please; she rapidly learned a smattering of both English and Persian. Laura grew very fond of her.

In 1836, Sivitraj was ten years old, and already nearly as tall

182

as his father had been, thanks to Laura's own height. Mary was seven. Laura herself was twenty-nine and, she felt, in her very prime. It was a shame that her beauty had to be wasted upon robber chieftains, yet it nonetheless continued to ensure her domination of Afghan society.

She supposed she would end her days in Kabul. Batraj seemed to have entirely given up his dreams of leading a holy war against the British, or even of regaining Sittapore; he had taken a command in the Afghan army, and was content to be one of the Amir's tuman-bashis, or divisional commanders. Sittapore itself seemed like another world. Laura felt that Sivitraj's birthright was forever lost, but then she reflected that he was probably happier in Kabul, where he had made many friends and where he was not forced to undertake any responsibilities. Only the knowledge that in a few years Batraj would wish him to become a soldier bothered her, but now Afghanistan was at war with no one.

However, in 1836 Dost Mohammed's kingdom was invaded by the Persians.

The Russians, who had become fed-up with Dost Mohammed playing them off against the British, wished to bring matters to a head without actually becoming involved militarily.

When the news of the Persian invasion of the western borders, several hundred miles from Kabul, was received, there was great excitement and some hysteria. Returning from the market one day, Laura and her servants watched in horror as some Persians were chased into an alley by the mob; the men were castrated and the women raped before having their throats cut.

They hurried home, and encountered Batraj, wearing his uniform and preparing to leave. 'The army is marching for Herat,' he announced grandly.

In fact, the Afghan army was incredibly slow to mobilise, as men had to be summoned from their mountain villages and armed and equipped. A Company army could have taken over the entire country before the army finally marched out, almost a year after the first act of war. Fortunately, the Persian advance was even slower, and finally ground to a halt before the city of Herat, some four hundred miles due west of Kabul.

The Persian offensive began in November 1837, and the Afghan army did not attempt to mount a relief until the following spring. The situation was saved by a British officer, Captain Eldred Potter of the Company's Army, who made his way to Herat in disguise, offered his services to the Afghan commander, and so organised the defences that a huge Persian assault was repulsed. The Persians then settled down to a regular siege, while both besiegers and besieged were cut off from the outside world by heavy snow. When the Afghan army finally approached in the summer, the two forces skirmished for weeks without ever actually coming to grips in a major battle, and then, in September 1838, the Persian king Mohammed Shah called the whole thing off and took his army home.

As wars went, Laura thought this one could be considered a complete fiasco, but it was to have momentous consequences for them all. Throughout the two years of hostilities, the Russian embassy remained in Kabul, officially condemning the Persian action. This hypocrisy was accepted by Dost Mohammed, who wished to continue his policy of matching British and Russian interests against each other for his own profit. But as the Russian armies conquered the Syr-Darya valley and thus brought their empire to the very borders of Persia and Afghanistan, the Governor-General, Lord Auckland, determined to act. To the consternation of Dost Mohammed, Auckland concluded a treaty with Ranjit Singh of the Sikhs, and announced his intention of restoring Shah Shuja to the Afghan throne.

Kandahar, 30 April 1839

Yesterday we occupied this city, one of those founded by Alexander the Great so many centuries ago (Kandahar is apparently a corruption of Alexander). I have been mentioned in despatches, both for efficiency in scouting for the advance guard and for my behaviour in combat. I must confess that this is most gratifying, as it is the first concrete evidence of any approval from the powers-that-be of military ability on my part.

I can scarcely claim to have fought a battle, as the enemy simply melted away in front of us, yet it is impossible not to feel a sense of exhilaration at this first triumph. Undoubtedly there will be battles enough ahead, before we march into Kabul. The thought makes my blood tingle.

The first we knew of it was when Sir John Keane arrived, and told us, 'We are going to Kabul,' and mobilisation began.

Ever since Burnes returned from his embassy in Kabul seven years ago, to tell the world that he had sat next to the Dowager Rani of Sittapore at a banquet in Dost Mohammed's palace, I have found it difficult to prevent myself thinking of that far off place.

Laura was alive and living in splendour! She was still married to her Hindu husband, of course. Had she then risen forever beyond my reach, or sunk forever beneath my grasp? It was difficult to decide which. I only knew that she was there, and would haunt me forever.

But that was seven years ago. Does she still live and prosper? Is she still as beautiful as ever? It is now eleven years since I have laid eyes on her, or she on me.

And what will be her fate when we enter Kabul? There is no Statute of Limitations for murder . . .

Naturally I volunteered. There was some suggestion that married officers might be omitted from such an arduous campaign, but – I may as well admit it – my marriage has not been blessed. I have no children; my dog is dead, and my wife wishes only to leave India and follow her parents to England. When I explain to her that this is impossible, as we shall have nothing to live on, she merely becomes angry or tearful, according to her mood at the time.

I wonder I do not let her go by herself, to do the best she can. Pride, I suppose. And perhaps a sense of duty, that as I allowed myself to accumulate this burden I must shoulder it to the bitter end.

When I told my wife that I was accompanying my regiment to war, she stared at me as if I were mad, and in fact said she thought I was, on several occasions. I suspect she hopes I shall not return, leaving her free to follow her own inclinations. Whereas, to escape Prudence on a regular campaign has always been my dream.

Lord Auckland's decision to replace Shah Shuja upon the Afghan throne has not been received with universal acclaim amongst the pundits. It seems that Bentinck, one of Auckland's predecessors here, has called the project an act of incredible folly, and it is rumoured that even the Great Duke, when he heard of it, spoke of it as being certain to engage the Company in endless war. However, our master has been urged on by the gallant McNaghton, who has lived most of his life in India and has made a lifelong study of the people and their leaders, and is acknowledged as the greatest expert on local affairs in the sub-continent. He has expressed repeatedly the opinion that most Indians, and particularly the mountain men, are like children, who need only to be shown the stick to retreat into a corner.

On the evidence of what we have seen so far, McNaghton is correct, and such gentlemen as Bentinck and Wellington are out of touch with the realities of India, or the power of John Company.

This is not to say that our opponents are not a mob of vicious and beastly murderers. On our march through the mountains one of our patrols was ambushed and taken prisoner. We found them the next morning, staked out on the hillside, stripped naked, and with their privates cut away, as well as their eyelids, ears, noses and tongues, and with their eyes gouged out. Our guides tell us that this horrible deed was undoubtedly perpetrated by the Pathan women!

But such terrors merely harden our hearts for the triumph that lies ahead, when we shall exact a full and just retribution.

We muster twenty-one thousand men. The Bengal Division, commanded by Sir Willoughby Cotton, has for this great adventure been united with the Bombay Division led by Keane, who is in overall command. Only a small proportion of these are British, of course, but the Sepoys make a brave show and, stiffened as they are by our own good lads, seem to be more than a match for the Afghans. It is our intention to be in Kabul well before the onset of next winter for, as we have recently found, winters in these mountains can be severe.

When I mentioned twenty-one thousand men, I am of course referring to the fighting elements of the Bombay army. For the rest, we muster very nearly a hundred thousand all told. With us march Shah Shuja's army, a band of desperadoes who remind me of the Iron Duke's remark during the Penisular War that some of his new recruits from England frightened him far more than they were likely to frighten any enemy. Whether we actually need quite so many people is open to question. I know of an officer in the Lancers who is travelling with a retinue of forty servants. My own establishment, consisting of the faithful Ramjohn and five others, is far more modest.

However, the army needs to be supplied every inch of the way. We have a large baggage train, containing everything that an army might need, from bullets to boots, from whisky to water, from grain to girls; this means we have to employ a huge retinue of civilians; thus the baggage train has to be made even larger, to feed them, and so on in a horrifying geometric progression.

Ranjit Singh, the wily old Sikh leader, although declaring himself to be our ally against Dost Mohammed, has refused us permission to march through his territories. Thus we have had to come up through Baluchistan, or Sind as it is sometimes called, a vast area of desert, *and* where there is no food or fodder to be had; we are accompanied by thirty thousand camels.

The Baluchis, I may say in passing, are a sullen and mutinous lot who pay lip service to the Company and no doubt mutter rebellion behind our backs.

From Baluchistan we used the Bolan Pass to enter these forbidding mountains and come to this place.

The next thing is the coronation of Shah Shuja, which will take place within the next fortnight, following which we will march upon Kabul.

My one disappointment is that my brave Rufus is not with me. How he would have loved the opportunity to snap at some Afghans' heels. But no doubt he is looking down from his dog-heaven and urging me onwards: he was fond of Laura, and would eat from her hand.

Who can tell what I will find at my journey's end, triumph or tragedy?

9
The Reunion

'They are marching on Ghazni,' Batraj told Laura. 'We will meet them there, and destroy them. You would do well to remain indoors until my return.'

He kissed her farewell, and left to join the army. It was the second time in three years that the Afghan soldiers had marched off to war.

Laura watched from the upstairs windows of her house; remembering the fate of those hapless Persians three years ago, she had no intention of venturing out, even if she found it difficult to believe that anyone in Kabul would wish, or dare, to harm her.

She was more uncertain of her own emotions. After more than eleven years' total separation from her own people, of any contact with them save for that one meeting with Alexander Burnes, they were seeking her out. More than twenty thousand of them, Batraj had said.

Perhaps they were not actually seeking *her*, but they would know she was there. And now she was identified not only with Batraj but with Dost Mohammed, the man they were intending to overthrow.

She wished the British would go away again. But she knew that would only happen if the Company army were to be defeated, for if it were to be defeated in these mountains, so far from its base in Bombay, it would be annihilated. She could not bring herself to wish for that.

So what could she truly wish for? Only that there might be a negotiated peace before Kabul was actually occupied. But that would necessarily entail Dost Mohammed's abdication, and what would then become of her?

*

It was a matter of waiting, as spring turned into summer. News came back from the Afghan encampment outside the historic city of Ghazni, where Dost Mohammed was preparing to halt and defeat the invaders. The Company army was slowly making its way over the mountains, but no one could say when the battle would be fought.

July came, and Kabul baked in the inevitable summer heat. The fact that the country was at war seemed to make little difference to the traders, and the usual number of caravans made their way south from Balkh to keep the city busy.

By now Laura had got over her fear of being attacked as an Englishwoman, and had resumed a normal life. Both Batraj and Dost Mohammed were at Ghazni, and thus her time was entirely her own.

Yet she too waited for news, until she was distracted: upon unexpectedly entering Sivitraj's apartment one afternoon she found him and Wu Li naked on the divan.

They both sat up in surprise, while Laura stared at them, no less dismayed. Of course Sivitraj was now thirteen, and she could tell at a glance that he was entirely mature, but the idea of him being old enough for this had not crossed her mind.

Wu Li realised that she, as the older of the two and as the slave, would have to be the one to suffer. Without a word she left the divan and knelt at her mistress's feet, her back arched to receive the whipping she anticipated.

'It was my wish,' Sivitraj said.

'Is this the first occasion?' Laura demanded.

Sivitraj hesitated. 'No, Mother.'

'I see. Can you give me one reason why I should not flog you both?'

Another brief hesitation. 'No, Mother.'

Wu Li trembled.

But Laura's anger was already fading. Of course the boy had to have a woman, and her own slave was the obvious answer. It gave her a hold over him with which to combat Batraj, who would undoubtedly wish to provide a woman of his own for his stepson.

'Stand up, girl,' she told Wu Li.

190

Wu Li scrambled to her feet, still trembling.

Laura looked her up and down. Although of very slight build, she was a decidedly attractive young woman.

'Make my son happy,' Laura told her, and left the room.

News from the front arrived on 23 July, in the form of a tavachi, or aide-de-camp of the Amir, who rode a failing horse into the city, and told in the market place of the terrible disaster which had overtaken the army.

Apparently the Company troops had attacked, and swept all before them. The tavachi's voice trembled as he spoke of the terrible bayonets, advancing in line and destroying every man that attempted to stand up to them.

'Where is the Amir?' he was asked.

'Fled,' he told them. 'Dost Mohammed is a fugitive.'

Laura and Nanja had joined the throng to listen, and Laura could hardly believe her ears. She managed to get close to the tavachi. 'What news of Prince Batraj?' she asked.

'The Prince fell in battle, Highness.'

Laura stared at him. 'He is dead?'

'I saw him fall from his horse, Highness. I believe he is dead, but I did not see him die.'

'And my husband, Captain Vijay Dal?' Nanja asked.

'I do not know. He was with the Prince.'

Laura hurried back to her house, Nanja at her heels.

'Our husbands are either dead or prisoners. What will you do?' asked the Indian woman, who was now her closest friend.

Laura tried to think. Batraj is dead, she thought. Batraj is dead! My eleven years of imprisonment are finished. Batraj is dead.

'Will you flee this place?' Nanja asked.

Flee? Into the mountains, to become again the plaything of a robber chieftain?

'We shall wait here, for the British to come,' Laura said.

Nanja looked doubtful. 'Will they not hang you?'

'I do not believe so. My son is the rightful ruler of Sittapore, and I am the rightful Regent. I will swear that you and I were forced to become Thugs. It will be their duty to take Sivitraj and ourselves back to Sittapore, and instal him as ruler.'

191

Nanja continued to look doubtful, but she had nothing better to offer.

A fortnight after the defeat outside Ghazni the people of Kabul heard the screech of the fifes and the thunder of the drums, as the British came sweeping down from the mountains.

It was some considerable time since Kabul had fallen to an invader, and no-one knew quite what to do. The garrison had originally been determined to defend the city, but the news that Dost Mohammed had himself fled into the mountains had had its effect, and the men had melted away. At the sound of the fifes and drums their officers followed them.

August was normally a very busy month in the Bala Hissar, the great marketplace, but the traders too had taken their leave; they had no desire to be caught in the crossfire. Now Kabul was a city of old men, young boys and frightened women, waiting to feel how heavy might be the hand of the conqueror.

Most windows were boarded up. Laura had seen to this immediately, while there had been some risk of resistance, but she and the children, Miljah, Wu Li and Nanja went up on to the flat roof to watch the British arrive.

A regiment of horse came first, proud turbanned fellows with long lances, a glitter of blue and gold, led by British officers. They looked to left and right as they walked their horses through the empty streets, aware that they were being watched, ready to respond to the first shot.

Behind them came a infantry British regiment, with red jackets and white trousers, knapsacks on their backs secured by white crossbelts; squares of white cloth hung down from their shakoes to protect their necks from the sun. They marched with muskets at the slope, their bayonets fixed, a glittering column of steel; these were the weapons which had driven the Afghans from the field in panic.

Behind the first foot soldiers came a great number of generals and dignitaries. Some wore uniform, their breasts adorned with medals and stars; others were in civilian clothes but none the less arrogant for that; and quite a few were in Afghan dress. Among them rode Shah Shuja. It was now some thirty years since he had been expelled from Kabul, and Laura saw an old and stout gentleman, very richly dressed to be sure, but also obviously terrified. In that moment she realised the expedition was going to be a failure.

But also in that moment she recognised one of the two Englishmen riding close behind the new Amir. It was Alexander Burnes.

Laura could not believe her good fortune. She wanted to rush out and call out to him, there and then. But commonsense told her to wait until the parade was over. He was her friend, and he had promised her his assistance; another hour or two would not hurt her.

The rest of the army followed the dignitaries. Several regiments of Sepoys, with their British officers, then the artillery, then another regiment of lancers, and a horde of Afghan irregulars, the followers of Shah Shuja. Lastly came a huge wagon train which stretched out of sight, attended by a moving nation of men and women, goats and chickens, children and dogs. After the officers had passed by, Laura left the roof.

She had to prepare herself.

Laura dressed with great care, in a white sari. She discarded her gold bangles, but wore her emerald necklace, as well as an emerald bracelet given her by Dost Mohammed.

'Will the soldiers not rob you?' Miljah inquired.

'They will not dare,' Laura said, as confidently as she could.

The Bala Hissar, or market place, had become a vast military camp. Bugle calls punctuated the afternoon, orders were barked, horsemen galloped to and fro raising yet more dust.

As it became apparent that the city was not to be given over to the sack, doors opened and people, especially children, ventured out on to the street to peer at the soldiers.

Laura wrapped herself in a haik and wore a veil, so that only her eyes showed as she left her house accompanied by Nanja and Miljah, similarly attired. Thirteen-year-old Prince Sivitraj accompanied them, his finest clothing concealed beneath a rough robe.

The generals and dignitaries had of course taken possession of the palace, and there were armed guards, English soldiers, on the gates. There was also a large crowd of petitioners, seeking an audience with the conquering general, mostly men of the merchant class, for all the Afghan nobility had fled with Dost Mohammed, fearing the vengeance of Shah Shuja. There was no order; people jostled and fought to speak with the Afghan dragoman who stood with the Captain of the guard. Most were told to stand back and wait until the general or the envoys or the new Amir had the time to see them.

Laura pushed and shoved her way through the throng until she reached the front. The soldiers frowned as they realised that here was someone rather different from the rest.

'I wish to speak with Mr Burnes,' Laura said in English.

Heads turned within the gates, and the Captain came closer. 'Who are you?' he demanded, also in English.

'I am the Dowager Rani of Sittapore,' Laura told him. 'With me is my son, the Rajah of Sittapore.'

The officer looked her up and down, and Laura took the veil from her head, just enough to reveal the golden hair beneath.

'By God!' the Englishman commented. 'Miss Laura Dean!'

'The Dowager Rani of Sittapore,' Laura corrected him.

'Open the gate and allow this woman to enter.'

'And my people,' Laura said.

The captain hesitated, then nodded.

The gate was opened just enough for Laura and Sivitraj to squeeze through, followed by Nanja and Miljah. The crowd set up a great babble and pressed forward, but the gates were forced shut again.

'You'll take command here, sergeant, until I return,' the Captain said. 'Allow no-one else in. Please come with me, Highness.'

Laura followed him into the palace and up the wide front stairs.

Several red-coated officers stopped to stare, but she ignored them as she was ushered into a great reception room filled with more officers, Afghan and British. She was led through double doors at the end into a smaller chamber, where desks had hastily been placed to accommodate the military secretaries. A short, red-faced man, whose scarlet tunic was a mass of gold braid and military orders, looked up angrily as they entered.

'What's this?' he demanded. 'I gave orders that no-one was to be admitted at this time.'

'With respect, sir,' the Captain said. 'This is the Dowager Rani of Sittapore.'

Laura took the veil entirely from her head, and looked the officer straight in the eye.

The General's reaction was the same as his subordinate's. 'Good God!' he commented. '*You*, madam, have come to *us*?'

'Are you in command here?' Laura demanded, certain that she would only triumph by being as arrogant as he.

'I am in military command. Sir John Keane, at your service. No, that is incorrect. I am *not* at your service, madam.'

'My son and I have been held prisoner in Kabul for eleven years, sir,' Laura told him. 'Now I seek a restoration of Prince Sivitraj's rights, and mine.' Sivitraj had moved forward, urged by Miljah, to stand beside his mother, and he also took off his cloak to reveal himself to the General.

'Rights,' Keane muttered, looking from one to the other. 'This is a civil matter,' he decided with some relief. 'You had best see Sir William. See to it, Carpenter.'

'Yes, sir. If you'll come this way, madam . . .' Captain Carpenter ushered Laura and Sivitraj to the door, followed as always by Miljah and Nanja. Laura realised that she was being passed on like an unclaimed parcel, but she could do nothing about it. Maybe it truly was a civil matter.

She was shown into another reception room, where there were more desks and secretaries, and more streams of orders being dictated. But these men were all civilians. Dominating them was an Englishman, standing in the centre of the room, who glared at the intruders even more formidably than Keane had done.

'My apologies for this interruption, Sir William,' Carpenter said. 'But General Keane is of the opinion that you would wish to interview this lady.'

The man had ridden behind Shah Shuja on his entry into the city Laura remembered. He was tall and clean-shaven, but with an unutterably supercilious expression on his face. 'You must be Laura Dean,' he remarked.

'I am the Dowager Rani of Sittapore,' Laura told him. 'And this is my son, the Rajah of Sittapore.'

The room fell silent as men raised their heads to look at her.

Sir William gave a slight bow. 'Sir William McNaghton, Her Majesty's Commissioner for Afghanistan,' he said. 'What is it you wish of me, madam?'

'Why, sir, as I have just been released from eleven years' captivity, I now seek to be returned to Sittapore with my son, that he may take his rightful place upon his throne. The gentleman with whom I wish to speak is Mr Burnes.'

McNaghton stared at her for some seconds. Then he said, 'I think you must mean Sir Alexander Burnes. You had best come in here, madam.' He nodded, and a secretary opened an inner door.

Laura stepped through. Sivitraj made to follow her, but was checked by McNaghton.

'We wish to speak with your mother alone, Sir,' he said, and followed Laura into the inner room, closing the door behind him.

Laura opened her mouth to protest, and then thought better of it. She was prepared to use every weapon at her disposal to gain her end, and it was probably better that Sivitraj not be present. At another makeshift desk, covered in papers, Alexander Burnes sat. Laura was intensely relieved to observe that he seemed to have changed not a whit in the seven years since they had last met, being as stout as she remembered, and possessed of a face which was clearly still used to smiling. There was no-one else present.

'You will never credit whom we have here, Burnes,' McNaghton said.

Burnes stood up. 'The Dowager Rani!'

'The very same. Demanding restitution to her jaghir, for herself and her son, no less.'

There was only one chair in the room. Burnes brought this round in front of his desk, then held Laura's hands and kissed them. 'Do be seated, Your Highness.'

'You seem surprised to see me, sir,' she remarked as she sat down.

'We expected that you would have fled Kabul,' Burnes said. 'With your . . . ah . . . husband.'

'My husband, Prince Batraj, was killed in the battle outside Ghazni,' Laura told them. 'As for fleeing with him, I have been his prisoner ever since he abducted me from Sittapore in January 1828, as I once explained to you.'

'You mean you were his accomplice in crime,' McNaghton corrected.

'I was abducted, sir, together with my son.'

'Do you deny being a devotee of the Goddess Kali?'

'I was forced to it, sir.'

'As no doubt you were forced to commit murder at Slopan.'

'I did not commit murder at Slopan, sir.' Laura spoke quietly, determined to lose neither her composure nor her temper. 'I was forced to witness what happened there, and afterwards my ring was left to establish my presence. This was part of my husband's plan to bind me to him.'

'And you have remained bound ever since,' McNaghton said contemptuously.

'That is correct,' Laura said.

'Do you really expect us to believe that?'

'It is the truth.'

'The truth can only be decided by a court of law, madam.'

'I am the Dowager Rani of Sittapore,' Laura declared. 'I am not subject to Company law or English law.'

'You think so, madam? Well, let me tell you . . .'

Burnes, who had been listening in silence, cleared his throat, and McNaghton glared at him.

'I think it would be best to keep our tempers,' Burnes said quietly. He addressed Laura. 'The situation is a difficult one for us all, Highness. Let me put it to you very plainly. You were, as you say, Dowager Rani of Sittapore. But you forfeited that status by your marriage to Prince Batraj . . .' he held up his hand as Laura would have spoken, '. . . even though you were forced into that alliance. As for your not being subject to Company or English law, you happen at this moment to be in

Afghanistan, and Afghanistan is now under British military rule.'

Laura gazed at him in consternation, feeling a slow tightening of her stomach muscles.

'Additionally, your husband is a proscribed robber and murderer, both in Sittapore and in all territories governed by the Company, and you are regarded as his accomplice. Now, it may well be that you are telling the absolute truth, and that you were forced to participate in everything of which you are accused. These are matters, as my colleague has said, which can only be finally resolved by a court of law. But you should consider that, lacking any witnesses in your favour, you may find the verdict of the court against you.'

Laura sat very straight. 'Am I under arrest? You once promised me your assistance, Sir Alexander.'

Burnes glanced at McNaghton, and then looked at her again. 'I am endeavouring to fulfill that promise, Highness. To arrest, and then try, an Englishwoman on a charge of Thuggee would be very distasteful, and would do little credit to our affairs here in India. Especially if things went badly for you. I am sure you will understand that.'

'What are you trying to tell me?' Laura demanded.

'That it will be in your best interests simply to continue to play the role which fate has given you, and in which . . .' he allowed his gaze to wander up and down her sari, noting the richness of the material, her jewellery and her obvious health, '. . . you would appear to have prospered. As your present husband is dead, I would recommend that you return to your house, and live there as a Hindu widow should, attending to your personal matters and your children. For our part, Sir William and I will forget that this interview ever took place.'

Laura stared at him, unable to believe her ears. 'You are condemning me to spend the rest of my life in Kabul?'

'It is your home, is it not?' McNaghton asked.

'But what of my son? He is Rajah of Sittapore!'

'Sittapore already has a rajah, Highness,' Burnes said. 'Rajah Partaj has now been on the throne for eleven years, and is accepted by his people and by the Company as the rightful ruler. The return of your son would only lead to discord and

198

perhaps civil war, especially were he to be accompanied by yourself. In that case, the Company would have to take steps to correct the situation. I would therefore most strongly advise you to make no attempt to regain your son's inheritance.'

Laura stood up. 'I had never thought to hear such words spoken to me by my own countrymen.'

'You have just claimed no longer to be English,' McNaghton reminded her. 'So we are hardly to be considered your countrymen.'

Laura glared at him, then marched to the door and opened it. She seized her son's hand, and led him to the outer room, where Miljah and Nanja were still waiting.

'We shall go home,' she told them, and went towards the outer porch and the stairs.

At the top, she saw an officer coming up: Guy Bartlett.

They stared at each other, and Laura realised that in her angry haste to be away from the British envoys she had forgotten to replace her veil.

Guy was equally taken aback, but before he could say anything she had swept past him and down the stairs, pulling her veil over her head.

She almost ran home, dismissed her servants and her son, retired to her bedchamber, and threw herself on the divan to burst into tears. That she might be so utterly rejected – and by Burnes of all people – had simply not occurred to her. She was innocent of anything more than a desire to preserve her son, but she was condemned to a life of . . . she had no idea, sat up and looked around her in the wildest dismay.

Was this house, then, to be her prison? Batraj had left her a considerable amount of money, and she had her jewels. Presumably she could live here, if she practised a careful economy until Sivitraj was grown up and able to support her.

But she had only ever brought him up to be Rajah of Sittapore. His stepfather might have had dreams of making him into a soldier, but his stepfather was dead.

And how was the boy to be told that his dreams of inheriting his kingdom were now also dead?

How she hated the Company, and everything to do with it!

They should have been defeated, and massacred in the mountains.

And now, to top it all, Guy was here. She had last seen him bound naked to the back of a horse. But he had lived and prospered, as she could tell by looking at him. He had clearly shed much of the callow youthfulness she remembered.

She knew he was going to come to see her. But whether to receive him or not when he did so, she had not yet made up her mind.

The servants were all very curious to know what had passed between their mistress and the English envoys, but Laura did not immediately tell them. She wanted her own emotions to settle down first. When Nanja came to her to say that there was an English officer at the door, the woman obviously supposed the visit was a continuation of their morning confrontation at the palace.

By then Laura had washed her face and changed her clothing; she was wearing the pale green that suited her best.

Why *had* he come? He could have nothing but hatred for her in his heart after she had apparently been a party to the destruction of his company.

And if he were to learn what she had done since . . .

Yet she could not send him away. Just to see him again would bring a touch of sanity into her tortured life.

'I will receive the officer, Nanja,' she said. 'Please show him in.'

Nanja hesitated, obviously considering that it would be more appropriate for her mistress to receive the Englishman in the main part of the house rather than in her private apartment, but she bowed and left. Five minutes later Guy was ushered in.

'Highness!'

'Major Bartlett. Thank you, Nanja.'

Nanja again hesitated, then left the room and closed the door behind her.

'It is good of you to call,' Laura said.

'I . . .' Guy swallowed. 'I heard that Prince Batraj was killed in battle.'

'Yes,' Laura said.

200

He seemed at a loss for words, so she gestured to the other divan. 'Will you not sit down?'

'Ah . . . thank you.' He seated himself, somewhat awkwardly with his sword.

'You may remove your sword,' Laura suggested. 'There is no danger here.'

'Ah . . . thank you.' He stood up again, unbuckled his sword belt, and laid it beside his shako on the divan, then sat down again.

There was a knock on the door, and Nanja entered, carrying a tray of iced sherbet, which she placed on one of the low tables, bowed, and left, casting a hard look at her mistress as she did so.

'I am afraid, as we are in a Muslim country, there is no alcohol to be had,' Laura explained.

'May I ask what your intentions are now, in all the circumstances?' Guy ventured. 'Will you be returning to Sittapore? Or Bombay?'

'Neither. I shall be remaining here.'

He raised his eyebrows.

'I have been informed that if I return to either Bombay or Sittapore I will be put on trial for my life,' Laura told him.

'Well, I suppose that would be inevitable,' he said. 'I would offer testimony on your behalf.'

'You? What would you say?'

'That you tried to save the lives of my people by getting them to surrender. You did try to do that, didn't you?'

'Yes,' Laura said. 'Why did you not accept my advice?'

'Do you suppose Batraj would have kept his word?'

'Yes,' Laura said. 'He would have kept his word.'

'How can you be sure?'

Had he forgotten what she had told him, so long ago? Or had he disbelieved it? She had not chosen to use her pact with Batraj as a lever with McNaghton; she had felt sure it would not have influenced that unpleasant gentleman at all. But why should she keep any secrets from Guy, now? 'We had made a bargain, the lives of you and your men for . . . my faithful allegiance.'

'My God,' Guy muttered. 'Then it was true.'

201

'Do you not believe me?'

He swallowed. 'Oh, I believe you. I wanted to, then. I did. But when I learned of the massacre at Slopan . . .'

'I was forced to watch that. I did not take part in it.'

'Laura, have you told McNaghton all this?'

'I have declared my innocence to him. I have not told him of my arrangement with Batraj. I do not think it would serve any purpose. Your Mr McNaghton has conceived a powerful dislike for me. Had it not been for Mr Burnes I suspect I would have been hanged by now. But even Mr Burnes did not give me the support I had expected.'

'He is constrained by Company policy, but he is a good man at heart. But do you mean that since that day, you have followed Batraj . . .'

'Because I had sworn to do so, if you lived.'

Guy crossed the room to sit beside her on the divan. 'Then I owe you my life.'

'At that time . . .' she bit her lip.

'At that time, I loved you,' he said.

'At that time, I loved you.'

'I love you still. Seeing you . . . Laura . . . Batraj is dead.'

'Yes.'

Their faces were very close together. What am I doing? she asked herself. What am I permitting? We may have loved each other once, but this man and I are as far removed from each other now as it is possible to be.

'I love you still,' he said again, and took her into his arms.

To her surprise, but also her relief, the hesitancy and shyness had gone with his youth. Now it was on her side.

She did not know what he wanted, how easily he would be shocked. Batraj and Dost Mohammed had both wanted to be imprisoned in her hands as part of their loveplay, but she had no idea if Englishmen indulged in such things. As he opened her sari to hold her breasts she remained very still, trembling, but when he lowered his head to kiss her nipples, she could not prevent stroking the front of his breeches.

His head came up.

'I am a wanton,' she said. 'I have been taught to be so.'

202

'Then be so, I beg of you. I have dreamed of you for so long.'
He stood away from her, to strip, and she also undressed, while
her hair came away from its chignon and shrouded her
shoulders.

When he came to her, she held him, as he kissed her mouth,
and sent his own hands roaming over her.

Then he possessed her, and gasped with sheer ecstasy.

'Oh, Laura,' he said. 'Laura, Laura, Laura. How I have
dreamed of you, all the time certain we would never meet
again.'

She lay on her back and gazed at the ceiling. She had noticed
the ring on his left hand. 'Does your wife know of me?'

He raised himself on his elbow. 'My marriage is a sham. It
has always been a sham.'

Laura smiled. 'Is that not the protestation of every man bent
on seduction?'

'In my case, it is true.'

'I do not doubt you, Guy. What of your children?'

'We have none. I do not even have my dogs any more. Laura,
my dearest, dearest Laura, will you come back to Bombay with
me? I will obtain a divorce from Prudence, and marry you.'

'Dear Guy, I have told you that I cannot return to Bombay,
or anywhere controlled by the Company.'

'That is absolute nonsense. When I tell them the truth of the
matter . . . have I your permission to speak of the pact you
made with Batraj?'

'Certainly.' Her heart began to pound. Could it be possible?

'Then you may leave your case in my hands. Will you marry
me, Laura?'

She hesitated. If she were permitted to return to the south,
would it not be her duty to attempt to re-instate Sivitraj? It
would clearly have to be done through diplomatic rather than
military channels, and her own position might be the stronger
for being the wife of a Company officer.

Mrs Guy Bartlett, she thought. Fourteen years before she
had been about to assume that name, and had allowed herself
to be led astray by wealth and position. Well, she had surely
suffered for it. Now it was time to return to the fold, and
perhaps be happy.

'Yes,' she said. 'I will marry you, Guy.'

He stayed to dinner, met all of the family, and then stayed the night. Nanja, having surreptitiously opened the door earlier in the evening, had seen them wrestling together on the bed and gone away again.

They loved again and again, all through the night. By the end of it their intimacy had become sufficient for her to guide him in the ways she had become used to, and which she most enjoyed, and he sighed his ecstasy as her back nestled against him, and he was able to use his hands as well as his manhood at the same time.

When Guy left at dawn, he promised to return that evening, with the lifting of her proscription an accomplished fact.

But when he returned he was at once furious and despondent.

'They would not listen,' Laura said, as soon as she saw his face. Her happiness which she had always known to be a delusion, drained away.

'They would not listen,' he confirmed. 'Never have I met two such hidebound fools. To them there are only two sides to a coin: it is simply a choice between placing you on trial, which they feel will be bad for British India, or forgetting you exist.'

'And they have opted for the latter course, and feel that they are doing me a great favour,' Laura pointed out. 'There is no point in being angry.' She smiled, sadly. 'We had one night of dreams.'

'Do you think I am going to be put off by those idiots?' he demanded. 'I intend to write to the Governor of Bombay, the Governor-General, and the directors in London if I have to.'

'I cannot ask you to undertake so much on my behalf, Guy. You will do your career little good.'

'Damn my career. It is you I am concerned with. Oh, Laura, my Laura . . .'

In his arms she could forget the impossibility of her situation. But she knew her dream had been even more of an impossibility. Kabul had become her home, and was to remain her home; that was clear.

*

Over the next few months, the Afghan capital began to resemble any other British-controlled city in India. For a while it was necessary to continue campaigning against the Afghans and their Amir, but then Dost Mohammed was captured and sent into exile in India.

As soon as it was considered that all possibility of resistance was at an end, the Company forces moved out of the Bala Hissar and into cantonments outside the city where, as the British inevitably did, they settled down to making themselves comfortable. A race course was laid out, and a cricket pitch. Card parties and polo matches were held, and by the following spring nearly all the married officers had brought their wives up to join them in what appeared destined to be a lengthy occupation. The Company apparently intended to maintain a military presence in Kabul until Shah Shuja's rule was firmly established and, although Sir John Keane and the main part of the army departed as soon as the passes were open, Sir Willoughby Cotton was left in command with a brigade of nearly five thousand men under Brigadier General Sir Robert Sale, including the British Regiment, a force regarded as amply sufficient to keep the country in subjection.

With the arrival of the women, parasols and poke bonnets, hooped skirts and swinging reticules appeared in the market places and on the streets of the city, while the Afghans stared in wonder.

Prudence Bartlett did not make the journey north. Undoubtedly news of her husband's carrying on with the notorious Dowager Rani of Sittapore had percolated back to Bombay; it was certainly widespread gossip in Kabul.

'Are you sure you know what you are about?' Laura would ask Guy. She would not dream of refusing to receive him, but with every visit she was certain he was damning himself more and more in the eyes of his fellow officers and his superiors.

'If I am to divorce her, I must give her the necessary ammunition,' he said. 'Will you be ashamed to be named as co-respondent?'

'I shall be proud,' she told him. If it ever happens, she reminded herself, refusing to believe in it. Her fears were well-founded. In July 1840, just under a year since the

Company army had marched into Kabul, Guy came to her house looking more distressed than she had ever seen him.

'I have been ordered back to Bombay,' he said. 'My petition has been refused, and I am considered an embarrassment to everyone by remaining here.' He raised his head. 'I shall resign, of course.'

'You will do no such thing,' Laura told him.

'But, my dearest girl . . .'

She held his hands. 'Guy, we have been given twelve glorious months together, far longer than I, at least, deserve. But your career is the army. What, would you become an Afghan chieftain? That is a savage and uncertain game, which invariably ends in death. Guy . . . go back to your own people, and prosper.'

'You have had enough of me,' he said bitterly.

'If you believe that, then have we truly wasted our time together.'

'Oh, Laura, Laura!' He swept her into his arms. 'What will become of you?'

'I will remain here, until opinion in Bombay changes. Then you will send for me, and I will come to you.'

'Yes,' he said fiercely. 'Yes. It will change. I will make it change.'

'And I will be content to wait for that,' she said.

'But Laura . . . to leave you now . . .'

'Not now,' she reminded him. 'Tomorrow.'

The next day Laura stayed in bed and wept her heart out. She had been so close to happiness, but all the while, in reality it had been as far away as ever. She could hardly restrain herself from running after Guy, and shouting, 'Yes, resign, and live here with me. Become a renegade, like me, and let us seek what happiness we can, for as long as we can.'

But she knew that that would take away every standard by which he had always lived, leave him less than half a man. It would be a crime. She had been criminal enough, in allowing him to love her at all, to put his career in jeopardy. Now he must be forgotten.

And she must weep.

Oddly, with Guy's departure, Laura found herself, if not accepted, certainly taken up by British society. She knew perfectly well that this was mainly a result of curiosity on account of her notoriety. 'My dear, you'll never guess with whom I took tea yesterday? The Dowager Rani of Sittapore, Laura Dean that was. My dear, she is a Thug, who smears blood on her naked body and strangles people with a knotted noose.'

The first invitation actually came from Florentia Sale, the wife of the Brigadier, a gracious lady who was at great pains to defer to Laura's rank.

'You do take tea, Highness?' she inquired, having blinked at her guest's sari-clad figure before politeness restored her self-control.

'Thank you,' Laura said.

Servants scurried to and fro, and Lady Sale settled herself. 'Kabul is such a delightful place,' she ventured.

'In the summer,' Laura agreed. 'It is very bleak in the winter.'

'So I have been told,' Lady Sale agreed. 'Well, we shall just have to make the best of it. As you have done, Highness.'

With Lady Sale was her daughter Barbara, a young woman not yet twenty, Laura estimated. Then other guests arrived, obviously deliberately late, having been informed of the identity of the guest of honour. Laura smiled and talked with them all, about clothes and food and servants, and thus told them nothing of what they truly wanted to hear. But she duly invited them back, and most of them came, to gape at the luxury of Laura's house, the evidence of wealth.

Even Florentia Sale was somewhat taken aback, having clearly expected evidence of Thuggism to be visible on every hand. 'It must have taken you considerable time to adjust to the Indian way of life, Highness,' she remarked.

'Why, yes, Lady Sale' Laura said. 'I have been adjusting, as you put it, for fifteen years.'

She longed for a letter from Guy, but there was none before the first snows fell and word arrived in Kabul that the roads were blocked. No doubt, she thought, he has realised his folly now that he can no longer come to my bed, and is anxious to forget me.

But she slept badly that night, and awoke with a start of mingled horror and ecstasy to find a man standing by her bed. It was Batraj.

Laura sat up, staring at him in consternation.

He wore ragged clothes and had not bathed for some time. But he looked as fit and strong as she had ever known him. 'I was told you were dead,' she whispered.

'No doubt.' He began to take off his clothes, throwing them on the floor. 'I was carved by a bayonet. Look.' He stood close to her, and she saw a hideous scar curving round the side of his body. 'I should have died, but Vijay Dal saved me, put me on his own horse and, although wounded himself, carried me to safety.'

'Vijay is alive?' How happy that news would make Nanja.

'He died of his wounds. I did not die of mine. But regaining my health has been a tedious business.'

'Batraj . . . the Company will hang you.'

'Only if they know I am here.' He knelt on the bed, drove his fingers into her hair to raise her head so that she winced with pain. 'Will you tell them?'

'No,' she panted. 'No, I will not. But they will find out.'

'Not until I am ready for them to do so.' He threw her down and lay on her, moving his body on hers. 'Laura, my Laura. How have I missed you. I feared you would have made your peace with the Company, and been lost to me.'

'The Company wants no peace with any associate of yours,' she gasped.

'Then you did try.' He knelt astride her. 'Now tell me of this Major Bartlett who has shared your bed.'

Laura tried to move, but his knees and his weight kept her pinned to the bed.

'Tell me,' he said.

'I thought you dead,' she said.

'And considered it your right to indulge yourself with an old lover. I should whip you for not mourning me.'

'Mourn you?' she asked. 'Why did you come back? Do you think I will come with you into the mountains?'

He grinned. 'No, no, my Laura. You may remain here. I have come back on a mission for Prince Akbar.'

Laura frowned at him; Akbar was Dost Mohammed's eldest son. 'What mission?'

'To alert our people, here in Kabul, that the time is nearly ripe. Oh, the British may suppose that they have set this Shuja on our throne, but they know nothing. Shuja is hated throughout the land. When the time is right, we shall rise up and deal with him, and all of his supporters. Including the British.' His teeth gleamed at her. 'It will be war! War such as I have always dreamed of. And you will be at my side, my Laura.'

Bombay, 12 August 1840

I have been forced to abandon Laura! I hope and pray this may be only temporary. But even a temporary separation after the joys we shared last winter is a harrowing experience.

In the New Year, I was filled with the happiness of fulfilment. Oh, any man who has lived and not held Laura Dean naked in his arms has never lived at all!

As it happens, many have known that sublime happiness. But they are all dead. I am alive.

I cannot pretend our liaison has made me immensely popular with my compatriots, but that means nothing to me. Nor have my constant letters insisting upon her innocence and demanding her forgiveness by the Company, her acquittal of all charges – of which she is *entirely* innocent – made me very popular with my superiors. But that means nothing either.

And now this peremptory recall to duty.

I was tempted to remain in the softness of Laura's arms. But Laura would not permit me to take so desperate a step, and on reflection I must admit that she was right. She has no more desire to end her days in Kabul than have I, and her only hope of escaping that foul place is for me to arrange for a pardon for her, and a triumphal return to Bombay.

This I certainly intend to do. If I fail, well, at least I know where she is, and that she is waiting for me.

In Afghanistan, it all seems very settled. We gave them a good drubbing outside Ghazni, and of course several of their leaders were killed. The rest seem anxious to make peace, and a good number of the hill chieftains have entirely submitted to Company rule. Just to make sure of their loyalty, we are paying them each a kind of retainer as Company servants, so long as they keep the peace in their villages.

Best of all, of course, Dost Mohammed is in our hands. He simply presented himself for surrender, being tired of the whole business. Naturally Shah Shuja wanted his head, his eyes, or some other even more important portion of his anatomy, to make sure he could not change his mind at some future date, but John Company does not deal in such barbarities, and the ex-amir has been sent down into India and perpetual imprisonment. It is a pity that his equally rascally son Akbar remains at large, but we are assured that his credit with the Afghans is now very low, and the chances of his mounting a counter-offensive slight indeed.

Naturally there are born pessimists like old General Nott, whom we left in command of the garrison at Kandahar, who writes in all directions imploring for vast reinforcements to be sent. Otherwise, he says, not a man of us will ever see Bombay again. This is clearly an absurd point of view. We simply have not got the men to spare; it would be a waste of time and money; in any case, these people are thoroughly cowed. As McNaghton says, they are like a bunch of unruly but essentially timid schoolboys; send one to stand in a corner and the rest fall immediately to heel.

There is even talk of reducing the garrison next year. Afghanistan seems certain to become yet another province of the Company, and we shall all thumb our noses at the Russians.

Meanwhile, here I am back in Bombay, after a journey through the worst of the monsoon. I arrived dripping wet and in rags. Not for the first time I find myself the cynosure of all eyes, but although my military reputation has never been higher, thanks to Keane's despatches, the glances I receive are now entirely disapproving.

The most disapproving glances of all emanated from my dear wife. Yesterday she took ship for England to rejoin her parents, having moved out of my bed the moment I moved into it. Divorce proceedings have already been instituted. I shall have to fabricate some evidence of my own wrongdoings. Well, this is as it should be, and as I desire it. To many it will appear that my life is irretrievably ruined, but I know better. I love, and am loved. No man in that happy position, providing only that the object of his adoration is worthy of it, can ever be less than enormously wealthy.

I seem to be becoming a philosopher in my old age!

Ramjohn is out looking for a new dog. Thus I shall have company, and my dreams, and much to look forward to.

10

The Massacre

Batraj's return left Laura in a state of terror, partly that his presence would be discovered and the whole family arrested, and partly because of his threats against the occupying forces. During his stay she never left the house, and had to decline several invitations to take tea.

But his departure left her in a greater quandary than ever. To betray him was to risk her death and that of Sivitraj, but how could she allow him to plot unhindered against her own people, even if they had rejected her? She could not help but realise that the only way she would ever be rehabilitated as an Englishwoman was to prove her loyalty.

She was handicapped by knowing nothing of what Batraj had in mind; she could not even understand what he *could* do, with the British so firmly in control of the situation. She did raise the matter in a tentative fashion with Lady Sale, whom she regarded the most intelligent and perceptive of the memsahibs, not mentioning Batraj by name and still pretending to be a widow, but allowing herself to wonder aloud if the Afghan chieftains were as cowed as the British commanders thought them.

'Oh, they are absolutely reconciled to their defeat,' Florentia told her. 'They have discovered that Sir William McNaghton is no man to cross. But of course, my dear, you know that.'

Laura felt she could do nothing more for the time being, and had to assume that both the envoys and the military were in as full control of the situation as they assumed, and that Batraj's survival was a personal misfortune with which she would have to cope. In any event, soon after Batraj's reappearance winter set in, the passes both north and south became blocked, and Kabul was totally isolated from the outside world.

The English community, few of whom had any experience of weather of this sort, began to turn in on itself. Laura found herself, with her knowledge of Afghanistan winters, in much demand at the supper parties which replaced the race meetings and polo matches. Her beauty and sophistication, as well as her reputation and the hideous crimes which were attributed to her, made her very much a celebrity, and she supposed she must have reached the pinnacle of success when she was actually invited to dine at Sir William McNaghton's house.

Sir William was courtesy itself, but when soon afterward she wrote to him asking if her position could not be reviewed and her return to Bombay considered, she received only a note from his secretary to the effect that thanks to the efforts of Major Bartlett the whole business had been taken out of His Excellency's hands, and he could no longer offer an opinion on the matter.

Laura all but despaired.

In the new year Batraj re-appeared, and with him came a dark-visaged and heavily bearded man: Akbar Khan.

'By Allah, you have grown in beauty, Highness,' Akbar said. 'Do you not remember me?'

Laura swallowed.

'It is a privilege to have you in my house,' she lied. 'But I fear for your safety, and that of my husband.'

Akbar took her hand and led her to a divan. 'Who will betray us? You, Highness?'

He made her sit beside him.

'You know better than that,' she told him.

'My father has spoken to me of you,' Akbar said. 'He said that to mount you is like taking a step towards paradise.'

Laura gasped and looked at Batraj, who was smiling.

'I will leave you,' he said. 'The Amir has matters to discuss.'

'Do you mean to prostitute me to the whole Afghan nation?' she asked in English.

Batraj continued to smile. 'All of those who are of use to me, certainly, my dear Laura. You are living gold. And remember that if you betray me, I will cut off your nose, and the boy's.'

'What does she say?' Akbar inquired.

'That she is unable to believe her good fortune, my lord amir.'

He closed the door behind him.

Akbar smiled at Laura. 'We will make much good fortune together, Highness, as you did with my father.'

Laura could think of only one last defence. 'I fear, my lord, that for a son to couple with his father's mistress may be against the ruling of the Koran.'

'What care I for the Koran?' Akbar asked, as he slipped the sari from her shoulders.

Batraj and Akbar stayed three days, leaving the house by its side entrance, wrapped up in the meanest of goatskin coats, to mingle with the common people, and tramping through the snow to the Bala Hissar where they met with their spies and agents.

Once again Laura was in a quandary, even more so than usual. For three days she had virtually been shared between the two men, had almost feared they would assault her together, but this at the least was not acceptable under Muslim law. Remarkably, Akbar was a man of considerable refinement beneath his rough exterior, far more so than his father or Batraj. He never treated Laura with anything less than extreme courtesy, was gentle in his love-making and often witty and sophisticated in his conversation.

Yet of his hatred of the British there could be no doubt. Akbar was no mere bandit. He was the son and heir of a long line of mountain chieftains, and regarded Afghanistan as his by right of conquest. His father had lost the kingdom to the British, and he had every intention of getting it back, and of settling with Shah Shuja as well. All of this he told Laura, without imparting any plan he might have to achieve it. Once again she felt obliged to drop hints to McNaghton and Burnes and Sale and his wife, only to be met by polite smiles at her naivety, especially when she suggested that far from being in hiding in the mountains Dost Mohammed's son might actually be close at hand. What they might have said were they to discover that she had actually entertained the prospective Amir in her bed did not bear consideration.

215

During the winter she had become friendly with one of the army surgeons, Dr John Bryden. Bryden was no mere time-server, but was deeply interested in both tropical medicine and in the effects of frostbite. As Laura, during her long stay in Kabul, had gained considerable knowledge of both, he frequently sought to pick her brains. This was gratifying, and she even suggested she actually view the stricken men, but this the doctor would not permit.

'Hospitals are no places for ladies, Highness,' he told her.

That seemed ridiculous, after her experiences. 'I am sure you are the only English person in Kabul who actually so considers me,' she pointed out.

He smiled. 'Then the rest of us are singularly unobservant.'

After that their friendship grew, and when she had failed to make any impression upon the command, she ventured to mention the matter to him. He listened to what she had to say, stroking his chin. When she was finished, he remarked, 'You speak almost as if you knew something was going to happen, Highness.'

'I speak only from my knowledge of the Afghans, doctor,' she insisted.

But he was too intelligent to treat her simply as a silly woman, and he knew her too well.

But for the time being she was forced into inactivity, while as the snows melted and the sun shone, the British settled down to a great deal of sporting activity of their own, watched with wonder by the natives.

The big event of the summer was to be the marriage, in August, of the Sales' daughter to Lieutenant Sturt of the Engineers. Also, the Company had now been occupying Afghanistan for nearly two years, and it was felt that it was time to rotate the troops. Thus it was announced that Sale's Brigade would be replaced by that commanded by Brigadier Shelton. To reassure everyone it was pointed out in the Gazette that the composition of the new Brigade would be the same, one all-British regiment, the 44th, and four Sepoy battalions. At the same time, Sir Willoughby Cotton was being returned to duty in the south. In addition, McNaghton himself had been promoted to the governorship of Bombay, and would be

216

leaving with Sale's Brigade when it marched out. It was thus essential to hold the wedding before the departure of the parents of the bride; Lieutenant Sturt was not one of those being relieved.

All of this was thoroughly disagreeable news to Laura. Not only was Florentia the nearest thing she had to a friend amongst her own people, except perhaps for Bryden, but with McNaghton in command in Bombay she had no idea how she or Guy were ever going to achieve anything. She was further depressed by the arrival of the first of Guy's letters since the winter; he was obviously at a low mental ebb, relieved only by having found himself another dog, which he had called Rufus the Second, and which he claimed was even larger and fiercer than Rufus the First.

How she wished she could be with him, enjoying such simple pleasures as walking the dogs on the beach.

But just as she was feeling her very worst, while attending race meetings and tea parties and even the Sale wedding with a bright smile and glittering in jewels, she heard that Cotton's replacement as military commander in Afghanistan was to be Major-General William Elphinstone, who had been in command in the south.

This was the best news Laura had heard for a very long time, for the new commander was a distant cousin of Mountstuart Elphinstone, who had been such a good friend to her during her marriage to Sitraj. He was also, Lady Sale told her, a most distinguished soldier, who had so covered himself with glory at Waterloo that he been made a Commander of the Bath, a Knight of the Order of William of Holland, and also of St Anne of Russia. Since then he had served mainly in England, until being sent out to Bombay as military commander of the Benares division of the company army in 1839, from whence he had been appointed to succeed Cotton.

All of these moves took time, and the year was well advanced before Elphinstone actually reached Kabul, escorted by Shelton's Brigade. As usual, all the city turned out to see the ceremonial entrance of the Company army. This was a far grander display than the last time, for of course Sale's Brigade had not yet left, and was also on parade, while the regimental band vied with each other in playing military marches.

Laura joined the crowds with Sivitraj, who was now fifteen and very anxious to join an army. For all her careful education of him, Laura could not be entirely certain which army he had in mind, for while he clearly admired the brilliant uniforms of the British, he also undoubtedly found his stepfather's dreams fascinating.

At the moment, however, she was far more concerned with the arriving troops and their commanders, and felt an icy hand clutch her heart.

The procession was led by a squadron of cavalry. The band followed, and then General Elphinstone rode alone. He hardly presented a dominating figure, for he slouched in his saddle as if he found riding an intolerable burden, and gazed straight ahead of him, eyes half-closed against the fierce sun.

Behind him, Brigadier Shelton also rode alone, and suggested an entirely different personality. His head was high, his eyes darting from left to right, as if warning the onlookers that a soldier had come amongst them. This was reassuring, but studying his face as best she could – she no longer had Batraj's spyglass – Laura saw only a disturbing mixture of sullenness and arrogance. His right sleeve was pinned armless to his breast, for he had lost the limb during the Peninsular Campaign in Spain against the French more than thirty years before.

Even more disturbing was the demeanour of his troops, for if the Sepoys presented a reasonably military appearance, the English soldiers of the 44th marched in a most slovenly fashion, seeming to take little heed of their officers, and openly ogling the Afghan women and girls who lined their route.

Maybe, Laura told herself optimistically, they were simply exhausted at the end of a very long march.

The next day she presented herself at Elphinstone's headquarters.

She had written a note, in which she said, 'Your cousin did me the great honour of being my friend, and I hope and pray that friendship may be extended by Your Excellency.'

She was kept waiting for some time, and was then showed into an inner room, where to her distress she saw the general, in his dressing gown and with one foot on a chair, lacking a shoe but apparently with more than one stocking pulled over it. This was at eleven in the morning.

'You'll forgive me not rising, Highness,' Elphinstone said. 'I am afflicted with this damnable gout.'

Laura reckoned he was afflicted with more than that; his face was grey and his eyes dull.

'I am sure you will find the climate in Kabul most agreeable, sir,' she ventured.

'I doubt it, madam, I doubt it. I am too old for this posting. I told them so, but they would have it. Now, what can I do for you? You'll not be importuning me about returning to Bombay, eh? It won't do, madam. Think of the scandal. That damned fellow Bartlett is a scandal all by himself. Add you to him, and the place will never be the same again.'

Laura was speechless.

'I know you were a friend of my cousin Mounstuart. But he is a damned peculiar fellow. Damned peculiar. We come from different branches of the family. Now tell me, madam, what did you wish of me?'

'Why, nothing,' Laura said coldly. 'Save to inquire after your health. As that appears irremediable, I will wish you good day, sir.'

Laura was cast again into despair. Judging by what Elphinstone had said, Guy was unlikely to be able to achieve anything of value. Her only relief was that Batraj had not been in Kabul since the spring, but at the same time she could not tell what he was up to.

In September, when Sale's Brigade was about to begin its march back to India, without any warning the Ghilzai chieftains from the south of the country, who had been residing in Kabul for some weeks, left the capital. They had been there to argue about reductions in the monthly 'retainers' being paid by the Company to 'loyal' Afghans, and the official reaction was that they had left because McNaghton had

219

refused to reconsider his instructions, which had been to cut down on the costs of the occupation.

Whatever the truth of the matter, the Ghilzais fled to their tribesmen in the mountains above the Khyber Pass, and these promptly blocked the roads leading to Jellalabad, the fortress which covered the Pass and thus the shortest route to and from Peshawar and India.

Colonel Monteath was therefore despatched as an advance guard to open the passage, Sale's Brigade following behind; McNaghton decided to remain in Kabul until the road was open before travelling south. The women and children were also told to remain until the Ghilzais had been dealt with.

The Brigade marched out with as much ceremony as it had marched in two years earlier. Once they were gone, although it was now well into October, since there was as yet no snow the British community settled down to winding up the racing season and playing a few last cricket matches.

Returning home from one of these, Laura found Batraj waiting for her.

Her first reaction was relief that Akbar was not with him. Her second was alarm at his evident delight with the situation.

'The hour of deliverance is at hand, my dearest Laura,' he told her.

'You are mad,' she protested. 'The British are as strong as ever.'

'They are but a shell. Sale is gone. His people will never reach the border.'

Laura swallowed. 'Four thousand soldiers?'

'They will be overwhelmed, by our people. The Ghilzais have given the signal for a general rising of the Afghans. Akbar Khan himself is with them. As for this rabble, commanded by a sick man whose brain is addled, they will fall like plums shaken from a tree.' He hugged her. 'Consider their dispositions. They lodge themselves in cantonments outside the city. They are using their outlying forts as commissariat storehouses, with but an ordinary guard in each. Are these not the acts of fools or madmen, drunk with their own arrogance? And this Brigadier Shelton has his men yet a mile further off. He fears to involve

220

them in the life of the city because of their lack of discipline. These are the men who will hold Afghanistan?'

'The Company is planning to leave it to Shah Shuja to hold the city,' Laura said desperately. 'Have you seen the garrison encamped in the Bala Hissar?'

'They too are a rabble, and have already been suborned by our agents. I promise you, Laura, you are about to witness the greatest defeat ever suffered by British arms in India. Not one of them will escape. And you and I will be avenged for many an insult.' He held her in his arms. 'But more important, Dost Mohammed will then be restored, and Kabul will again be our city.'

Laura shuddered.

Batraj stayed for several days, before leaving the house secretly clad as an ordinary hillman. But Laura could no longer doubt that his plans, and those of Prince Akbar, were just about finalised.

Nor could she doubt that every member of his household was absolutely faithful to him. Even Miljah, though she hated the thought of Thuggism, hated the British more. As for Nanja, she could only regard them as the people who had killed her husband.

Laura could not even confide in Sivitraj, because she was unsure where his loyalties lay, while Wu Li, though quite uninterested in Afghan politics so long as she had two meals a day, was too scatterbrained to share secrets, and Mary was far too young.

So the burden was hers alone. After Batraj had left, assuring her that the next time he returned it would be for good, Laura virtually invited herself to tea at Florentia Sale's. To her disappointment, there were several other women there, happily discussing their arrangements for Christmas. Laura grimly sat them all out. After the last one left, Florentia began to show some signs of impatience that her friend was still there. 'I'm afraid I am rather tired,' she began.

'I must speak with you, in confidence, on a most urgent matter,' Laura said.

Florentia sat down. 'Well? I hope these are not more fears

about Afghan revolts. My dear Laura, it simply will not do. Sir William is well aware that you are producing these chimeras in an effort to be allowed to return to Bombay. He is not going to be taken in.'

Laura sat beside her. 'They are not chimeras, Florentia. You know that I am married to a Hindu and a Thug, Prince Batraj.'

Florentia frowned. 'I know that you are his widow.'

'I am his wife. Batraj is alive and well, and was in my house three days ago. He has been in Kabul several times. Last spring . . .' she gave an involuntary shudder, 'he was accompanied by Prince Akbar.'

Florentia's frown had deepened. 'Is this true? Why did you not report it at the time?' Then another thought crossed her mind. 'Did you know this when you were, ah . . . seeing Major Bartlett?'

'No, I didn't.'

Florentia looked sceptical, and most disapproving. While she was broad-minded enough to accept the idea of adultery on the part of a man with a widow, the idea that Laura had also been committing adultery was clearly unacceptable. 'But you decided not to report it at the time,' she said again.

'Do you have any idea what would have been done to me, and to my son, if I had betrayed my husband and the Prince?'

'But you are betraying them now.'

'I have no choice. Listen to me.' She held her friend's hands. 'This Ghilzai revolt has nothing to do with their being paid less money. It is all part of a plan. Your husband's brigade is going to be wiped out in the mountains.'

Florentia's entire body stiffened.

'Once that is done, there will be an Afghan uprising here in Kabul. It is all planned. They mean to massacre every man, woman and child who is attached to the British cause. And they will do it, Florentia. You do not know these people as I do.'

Florentia gazed at her. 'My husband . . . have you any proof of what you have just said?'

'No. But it is the truth.'

'You must come with me at once to Sir William. And General Elphinstone.'

'Do you suppose they will believe me?'

'They will have to,' Lady Sale declared. 'It is my husband's life we are speaking about.'

But Elphinstone and McNaghton were only interested in the fact that Batraj was still alive.

'And you have entertained that Thug and Akbar in your home, without reporting it to the proper authorities?' McNaghton demanded. 'Do you realise, madam, that not-withstanding any agreement we may have come to, I have every right to place you under arrest for harbouring wanted criminals?'

'Oh, stuff and nonsense,' Florentia Sale snapped. 'A woman can hardly be expected to turn in her own husband, however despicable he may be.'

'And the Dowager Rani would have been in considerable danger had she done so,' Burnes, who was fortunately also present, pointed out. 'It seems to me that we should address ourselves to the news she has now brought us despite her personal danger.'

'Oh, I agree this trouble with the Ghilzais is very provoking,' McNaghton said. 'It is delaying my departure for Bombay, and I am most anxious to get there. But your husband's brigade is the one that defeated the Afghans two years ago, Lady Sale. There can be no doubt that he will clear the passes, and before the snow sets in.' He glanced contemptuously at Laura. 'Wars are not won by either rumour or faint-heartedness.'

Elphinstone was slightly more forthcoming. But he was as usual only half-dressed and clearly in considerable discomfort. 'There have been reports of some severe fighting in the south,' he agreed. 'But as far as I know General Sale is overcoming all obstacles.'

With that Florentia and Laura had to be content.

'I can only hope and pray that you are wrong, Laura,' Florentia said. 'But I am nonetheless grateful for your loyalty. Be sure I shall remember it.'

That was a small crumb when Laura had no doubt they all faced catastrophe.

Three days later, on 2 November, Laura was awakened by a tremendous noise. Quickly dressing herself, she sent Nanja out to discover what was happening. Nanja returned within a few minutes. 'There is a great crowd around the Treasury House,' she said. 'And also the house of Sir Burnes. They are breaking down the gates.'

'My God!' Laura said. 'What are the soldiers doing?'

'The Sepoys in the house are shooting our people,' Nanja said angrily.

'They are protecting the envoy,' Laura snapped. 'What of Shah Shuja's men?'

'Oh, they are helping our people, Highness.'

Laura realised that the revolt had begun. She told Sivitraj and Mary to dress, all the while trying to arrive at a decision. Her safest course was to remain in her house, but that was safe only in the short term. Even if the Afghans would never attack the residence of Prince Batraj, as they surely knew he was still alive, if they conquered and the British were driven out of Afghanistan, she would be tied irrevocably to Batraj for the rest of her life. And if the rising was put down the fact that she had warned the occupying army would almost certainly become known, and she would not be able to remain in Kabul without having to face Batraj's vengeance.

Yet she hesitated for half an hour, a period punctuated by shots and screams, and shrieks of agony and vengeance. She ran on to the roof in time to see the naked body of the unfortunate envoy, whom she still regarded as one of her very few friends, being carried by on the points of several spears. He had been castrated and beheaded, and his blood dripped on to the cheering faces beneath him. Behind him were carried his brother and Lieutenant Broadfoot, similarly mutilated.

Laura gasped in horror. But at least such a tragedy would surely force even Elphinstone into action. She had warned them it was going to happen. She ran downstairs, and gathered up her children.

'Where are you going, Highness?' Nanja demanded.

'I am going to the British,' Laura told her. 'Will you come with me?'

'Never!' Nanja declared. 'You are betraying our master.'

'The decision is yours,' Laura told her. 'I am sorry for it. I had thought we were friends.'

'How can I be friends with a betrayer of our cause?' Nanja spat.

'I am sorry for that, too,' Laura said. 'But do not try to stop me. Miljah?'

'I will come with you, Highness,' Miljah said, as Laura had known she would.

The women put on their veils while Nanja gazed at them with smouldering eyes. Then they stole from the house, mingling with the crowds who were playing football with the heads of the three murdered men.

Holding Mary tightly against her and attempting not to look at the horror being perpetrated, with Sivitraj, Wu Li and Miljah close behind, Laura made her way through the crowds until she reached the commissariat fort in the suburbs of the city. Here she was admitted by the sentries and taken before their commander, Captain Mackenzie. The Captain had heard the tumult in the city but was unaware of the reason; there were tumults almost every day in Kabul. Now he listened with horror to what Laura had to tell him.

'My God!' he said. 'You were right all along, Highness.'

'You must evacuate this post and join the brigade,' she said.

'I cannot abandon the commissariat without orders,' he said. 'We will defend it.' He immediately gave orders to his Sepoys, who took up their positions, while a horseman was despatched to the cantonment to inform General Elphinstone of what was happening. The fort was a round building with thick stone walls, small windows which were nothing more than loopholes, a heavy wooden door, and a flat roof with crenellated upper walls; it was certainly easily defensible by a hundred determined men, so long as the garrison had ammunition and food and water, and the enemy had no heavy guns.

'You have my permission to leave, if you wish, Highness,' Mackenzie told Laura, 'but I am afraid I can spare no men to escort you.'

Laura hesitated. It was a long mile out to the cantonments.

'On the other hand, if you stay here,' Mackenzie told her, understanding her predicament, 'I have no doubt that the

225

brigade will come down, both to our rescue and to punish these rascals, the moment my messenger gets there.'

Laura decided that was the safest course. She had definitely burned her bridges now, and for her children as well. It was her only chance of getting out of Kabul, and free of Batraj. That it should have happened so unexpectedly filled her with a tremendous sense of exhilaration, which was tempered by fear and her horror at the dreadful death of poor Burnes.

Over the next half hour several other women with their children sought refuge in the little fort, and fairly close behind them came a huge crowd of Afghans, mainly men, although there were some women with them, brandishing their weapons.

'Hold your fire until they make a hostile move,' Mackenzie told his men. 'Ladies, kindly sit on the floor.'

They obeyed, huddled together, although Sivitraj was plainly disgusted at being included with them. The other refugees were mainly wives of merchants who were known to be friendly to the British. All of them knew Laura by sight, but none of them knew her socially, and they stared at her with wide eyes as she sat with them. Laura realised that for the first time in her life she was actually about to come under fire; she hugged Mary, and smiled at Sivitraj who glowered at her; his loyalties were too divided.

The attack began at midday. The Afghans surged forward, and were met by determined volleys from the company of Sepoys. Some of the attackers got right up to the barricaded door of the fort, but could not force an entry, while the men on the roof poured musket fire down on them. Women screamed, and smoke eddied about, making breathing difficult. Mackenzie was everywhere, sword in hand, and the Afghans at last retired, leaving several dead behind.

'Cease firing, reload,' Mackenzie snapped. 'Havildar, attend to the wounded. Every third man may withdraw for water. Ladies, is any of you hit?'

None was, and only half a dozen of the Sepoys were wounded.

'Surely this is our business?' Laura asked.

Mackenzie frowned. 'To tend the wounded? I have never heard of it.'

'You need all your people to defend the fort,' Laura insisted. 'Ladies, shall we not play our part?'

Thus encouraged, the other women came to her aid, even climbing the ladder to the roof to bind the wounds of the men up there; none of them was very seriously hurt, although there was a great deal of blood and insufficient dressings, so that soon enough the women were tearing lengths from their petticoats to make bandages.

Mackenzie watched in amazed admiration.

'Will they attack again, sir?' Mary asked him.

'Oh, they'll come again, my dear. But we'll hold them until the brigade arrives.'

In fact the Afghans did not immediately attack again, but settled down to shooting at anyone who moved inside the windows or on the roof. Mackenzie had with difficulty to restrain his men from replying, both because that involved showing themselves and to conserve their limited store of ammunition. Meanwhile they got hit anyway, as bullets came in through the windows and ricochetted to and fro. Laura was in mortal fear for her children, but they survived unharmed. Several of the women were struck, and had to be attended to, as well as an increasing number of Sepoys. The already-crowded floor became slippery with blood and encumbered with bodies.

Nevertheless, Laura resolutely prepared a meal for all the defenders, and insisted that they eat. Food was no problem in a commissariat store, but she was concerned at the shortage of water.

And still no help arrived, nor any sign of it.

'The General will be preparing his attack,' Mackenzie told his people.

It was certainly not a good idea to let anyone suppose help was not coming.

A second Afghan assault took place in the middle of the afternoon, when a determined attempt was made to break down the door, by piling brush against it and setting it on fire. Lacking sufficient water, there was nothing the garrison could do except endure the scorching heat and swirling smoke, shooting again and again into the mass of men outside.

Once more the Afghans were driven back by the intensity of the resistance, and as soon as the fire had burned itself out Mackenzie had his men pile bags of meal in the doorway to resist the next attack, but now the situation was desperate. Several of the Sepoys had been killed, a good half were wounded, the door was broken in, and even in the cool of November the bodies which had been lying outside the building for several hours began to stink.

'Either your messenger did not get through, Captain, or General Elphinstone has decided not to send his people to your aid,' Laura pointed out, putting the unthinkable into words. 'And there is only a single ration of water remaining.'

Mackenzie chewed his moustache in frustration. He was as aware as Laura that, given the General's reputation for indecision, the latter was the most likely.

'We'll have to fight our way out,' he decided. 'As soon as it is dark.'

'And the women?'

'They'll have to come, or stay and be massacred. What of yourself?'

'I will come with you, Captain. Have no fear of that.'

The preparations were made carefully and quietly, but at dusk there was another Afghan assault which had to be driven back, and another lot of wounds to be tended, so that it was not until midnight that all was ready for the break out.

'Please understand, ladies,' the Captain told them, 'that once we leave the building we cannot stop for any purpose whatsoever. You must keep up.'

Bayonets were fixed, and every musket loaded. The Sepoys formed a hollow square, with the women and children in the centre. When all was ready, Mackenzie lit the powder train to the stores they were being forced to leave behind, and gave the word; the advance guard pulled away the last of the sacks barricading the doorway, and the small body marched out.

The Afghans were taken entirely by surprise; indeed, most of the besiegers seemed to be asleep. Before they could gather their wits the Sepoys had charged through them, using their bayonets to clear the way. Then before the besiegers could rally, the abandoned fortress exploded, which further confounded them. By the time they had worked out exactly what had happened, the little detachment was hurrying towards the cantonments. But no effort was made to come out to the fugitives' rescue, and they had to withstand several assaults before they were safe beneath the fire of the guns.

The march took them about half an hour, and while the darkness certainly confused their attackers, many of whom were firing on each other, several more people were hit. They arrived with scarcely anyone unwounded, save for Sivitraj; Mary had a scratch and Laura found several bullets in her clothes; fortunately the Afghan powder was of very poor quality, and she suffered no more than bruises.

Everyone was exhausted but happy to have survived. Laura went straight away to see Elphinstone. She had never been so angry in her life.

She found McNaghton with him.

'Well, gentlemen?' she inquired.

'What is the meaning of this riot?' McNaghton demanded.

'Did you not get Captain Mackenzie's message?'

'We got a message, but we could scarcely credit it.'

'And you did nothing? While your colleague was being murdered. And several other good people besides?'

'By your friends,' McNaghton remarked.

'I warned you of the probability of this happening, Sir William,' she reminded him. 'Not once but several times.'

'What to do,' Elphinstone mumbled. 'What to do. You do not know our problems, Highness.'

'She may as well,' McNaghton snapped. 'Everyone else will know it by morning. We would have come to your aid, madam, but when General Shelton commanded his English regiment to march on the city the poltroons refused.'

'Oh, my God!' Laura said.

'Oh, they will defend us here,' McNaghton said. 'If only because they are also defending themselves. But offensive action is another matter. You had best take my advice, General, and send for Sale and his people. He cannot be that far away. Until he arrives, we will act only on the defensive.'

'Can you not see that is the one thing you must not do?' Laura cried. 'The Afghans are now convinced that they have won a great victory. Their morale will grow, and more people will join them, unless they are defeated now.'

'Hark at who is giving me military advice,' Elphinstone grumbled.

'We must wait for Sale,' McNaghton said. 'If the 44th will not fight, we have no other option. And now, madam, I am sure you are very tired . . .' he looked her up and down, taking in the torn and bloodstained sari. 'You are certainly in need of a change of clothing. And the General and I have a great deal to discuss. Good night to you.'

Laura took refuge with Florentia who, like everyone else, was awake. Her daughter Barbara was with her.

'I know, it is a terrible business,' Florentia agreed. 'And it is being hopelessly mismanaged. But as soon as Robert gets here the tables will be turned and we will settle it all. Poor Burnes. And poor Broadfoot. It really is a most sad affair. But at least you are safe, dear Laura, and your dear children.'

They were given a bath, and hot tea, and Laura exchanged her tattered sari for an English gown and underclothes, for she and Florentia were much the same size. It felt extremely odd to be so constrained after so many years of almost total freedom, but she also felt it marked her final break with the life she had been forced to live throughout those years. Dr Bryden came in to dress Mary's wound, which was very slight, and then Laura slept heavily, despite her discomfort and her fears for the future.

The complacency with which the British accepted the murder of Burnes and his colleagues astonished Laura; it was apparently held that men who accepted positions in 'heathen' countries must accept these risks as a matter of course.

Even more disturbing, however, was the utter chaos within the cantonments. Elphinstone was apparently unable to think of anything save defence, and he now called in his detachments from every one of the outlying forts, apparently oblivious of the fact that those forts not only contained most of his reserves of food and ammunition, but that they overlooked the British position which they had been intended to defend. As soon as the British marched out, the Afghans marched in.

Not all of the forts were evacuated without loss; from one of them came news that the British officers had been cut to pieces by their own Sepoys, who promptly joined the rebels. While this catastrophe was in progress, the entire brigade, more than four thousand men, watched. Although the 44th manned the walls of the cantonments, they steadfastly refused to attack the rebels, and as they would not, the Sepoys also refused to do battle. The idea of British troops behaving so badly, and not immediately being punished for it, was quite unacceptable, but there was no means of enforcing discipline save by using the Indian troops to overawe the white, and that was apparently not considered. When Laura thought of the way Mackenzie and his gallant company had first defended themselves and then marched right through the Afghan ranks, she wanted to weep. She seemed to have jumped from the frying pan into the fire, for she could have no doubt that Batraj had by now joined the Afghan forces, and the thought of falling into his hands after she had broken their pact and attempted to escape made her blood run cold.

In these circumstances she found her new position as resident heroine something of an embarrassment. Mackenzie told everyone how she had tended the wounded during the defence of the commissariat, and Florentia equally told everyone how she had given a positive warning of the coming insurrection, which had been ignored. Laura found that everyone wished to speak with her, save of course for Elphinstone and McNaghton.

With every day the insurrection grew in strength, and the defenders were driven from position to position until they held only the cantonments themselves. Meanwhile, from the city there came the most dreadful noises as Shah Shuja's officers were hacked to pieces, although the Shah himself was apparently being held captive, possibly with a view to future negotiations.

From Laura's point of view it was like re-living the attack on the commissariat force, save that there was now no possibility of any brigade coming to their rescue. A messenger got into the cantonment just before it was entirely surrounded to say that Brigadier General Sale was unable to return owing to his own losses and the numbers of men massed against him, and that he was fighting his way through to the fortress of Jellalabad, which he intended to hold until reinforcements came up from India. He could only hope and pray that the garrison of Kabul would do the same.

Laura was with Florentia when the news was received. Lady Sale squared her shoulders. 'If Robert says he cannot return, then it is clearly impossible,' she declared. 'As for holding Jellalabad, that is the obvious course; the Khyber Pass must be kept open for the relief column which is on its way.'

Her optimism was admirable, but bore no relation to reality that Laura could see. McNaghton had despatched riders to the south requesting assistance immediately after Burnes's murder, but there was absolutely no certainty that any of them had got through. Even if one had, she knew from experience how long it took not only to regain Bombay, but then to raise an army and march it north. They were talking in terms of at least a year, she estimated, and a year was a good deal too long. By the end of the first week in December the garrison was very short of food, although there remained ample water from the wells within the cantonment.

Refusing to be downhearted, the English ladies continued to prepare for Christmas, and Laura and Mary were required to join them in making paper chains and other decorations. Sivitraj watched the proceedings with brooding anger. Laura could not penetrate his reserve, and could not therefore be sure whether he was angry at the British inefficiency or at the Afghans' failure to attack; although they kept up a desultory fire in order to make the defenders' lives a misery, the besiegers made no effort to come to grips. They had no reason to; they knew the state of the British food supply.

Thus on 11 December McNaghton, realising that his people could hold out at best for another fortnight, sent out a white flag and called for a parley with the besieging chieftains, which was agreed. Almost the entire garrison lined the low walls surrounding the cantonments to watch as McNaghton, accompanied by his staff, descended the slight hill to where the Afghan chieftains waited. Laura strained her eyes, but the distance was too great to make out any faces, and there was no means of knowing if Batraj was there.

McNaghton returned in a good humour. 'Children,' he said contemptuously. 'I have always said they are children. They are willing to agree all of my terms. All they wish is for us to leave Kabul.'

'Will they send in food supplies?' Florentia inquired.

'Of course. But it will take time. You must understand that things are difficult for them, now that the snows have started.'

Indeed it was snowing, not heavily, but with a quiet persistence, and the hills were white.

'There is also the matter,' the Envoy told them, 'that the chieftains themselves have no power to agree to anything binding without the consent of Prince Akbar. He has been sent for, and will be here in a few days. It merely requires us to be patient. I know it will be said that we have suffered a defeat, and been forced to march away in shame. But we will do so with all the honours of war, and in the certainty that we have done our duty.'

Laura could only contrast this attitude with his arrogance of a few weeks before. But now he sent for her.

'It is time to consider your position, Your Highness,' he said. 'Amongst the chieftains with whom I spoke was your husband.' He held up his finger as she would have spoken. 'I understand that you warned us this would be the case, when it was too late for me to do anything about it. However, there it is. Prince Batraj, not unnaturally, is demanding the return of his wife and family.'

Laura clasped her throat. 'He will murder me.'

'I am aware of the difficulties of your position, madam, just as I am aware that these difficulties are largely self-inflicted. May I ask what you wish of us now?'

'I wish to accompany you when you leave Kabul,' Laura said.

'To Bombay and a trial?'

233

'Yes, if that is what it comes to. I have deserted my husband, and I have betrayed his plans to you. If I stay here, I will be murdered.'

'And if your surrender is made a part of any possible agreement with Akbar Khan?'

Laura inhaled, slowly and deeply. 'Then I must rely upon your honour as an English gentleman.'

'You, a self-confessed Thug, have the nerve to appeal to my honour as an English gentleman? Madam, you amaze me.' He waved his hand. 'Oh, do not remind me, you were forced to it. What do you suppose would be the reaction of the people for whom I am responsible, given the choice; your life or theirs? I shall do my best for you, madam, because, as you say, I am an English gentleman. But I do so with no great feelings of sympathy, or indeed, much hope of success. Good day to you.'

Laura was utterly crushed. She fled to Florentia's room and collapsed in tears in her arms.

'Wretched man,' Florentia remarked. 'Do not fear, my dear; Batraj will not get his hands on you again.'

But whenever McNaghton went down the hill to confer with the Afghans Laura was in tremendous fear. The worst of all was not knowing; he did not send for her again to tell her how things were going. She did, however, gather that everything was awaiting the arrival of Akbar Khan, but she could not see that improving her position: Akbar might well wish her for himself.

Meanwhile it snowed, and grew steadily colder. There was almost no fuel left inside the cantonments, and the defenders crowded against each other for warmth, Florentia, Barbara, Laura, Mary and Wu Li in a huddle, wearing every piece of clothing they could fit on. Lieutenant Sturt was a tower of strength, always cheerful and confident, and apparently oblivious of discomfort. Sivitraj brooded, and did not even seek Wu Li's company. And Miljah kept entirely to herself; she seemed already to have accepted death.

The cold was accentuated by their hunger, for the Afghans had not yet delivered any of the promised supplies, and they were down to quarter rations. They gazed down the hill at the lights and smoking chimneys of Kabul with hungry eyes, Laura remembering the huge warm fires her servants had built for her, and the succulent dishes they had cooked for her. But at last, three days before Christmas, there was a great clashing of cymbals and blowing of bugles, and a huge assembly of banners. Akbar Khan had arrived.

Next morning, 23 December, McNaghton and his staff rode down the hill as before to meet the Prince, and finalise the details of the British withdrawal.

There was a huge assembly of Afghan chieftains, and large numbers of their people as well. Again Laura could make out no faces, but she could tell where Akbar was from the banners which clustered behind him. McNaghton and his officers were swallowed up in the throng, and the watchers could only wait for them to re-emerge.

Instead, after quite a short period, there was a sudden upheaval of movement in the midst of the crowd, which spread rapidly in every direction, while the sound of a single pistol shot echoed up the hill.

'Oh, my God!' Laura muttered, and hugged Mary against her.

Beneath them the tumult spread, and now they caught a glimpse of one of the British officers, half naked, being thrown about like a sack of corn.

'For God's sake!' Florentia Sale shouted. 'Fire into them, General.'

'Fire on our own people?' Elphinstone demanded.

'Those men are being murdered. You cannot save their lives. You can only avenge them.'

Elphinstone pulled his moustache in uncertainty, but it was in any event too late. Laura watched the naked, mutilated bodies of the four men being hoisted on spears and carried triumphantly back towards the city.

However much she had quarrelled with McNaghton, and indeed loathed the man, she felt sick.

The garrison was numbed by the disaster. Elphinstone seemed

235

most numbed of all. 'What's to be done?' he muttered. 'What's to be done.'

'What is going to happen to us, Mother?' Mary asked, as they ate a very frugal luncheon.

'We are all going to be killed,' Sivitraj said savagely. 'Because these British do not know how to fight.'

'Whatever happens,' Laura told them, 'we must be prepared to die with honour.'

She wondered if the little girl had any idea what she was talking about.

To their surprise, that afternoon an Afghan came up the hill, under a white flag, and spoke with Elphinstone. It was the request of Akbar Khan that the British resume negotiations. The envoy explained that McNaghton had secretly been plotting with various chieftains to betray Akbar and reinstate British rule, and that when this treachery had become known, the Prince's loyal chieftains had fallen upon the British party and cut them to pieces before they could be restrained.

'It is a complete lie, of course,' said Major Pottinger, the senior remaining political officer.

'Nevertheless, to resume negotiations is our only hope of survival,' Elphinstone said.

Pottinger was left with no option. But he was generally felt to be a singularly brave man as he descended the hill on Christmas morning. All thought of celebration was forgotten as the spectators wondered if they would ever again see him alive.

He returned, unharmed, a few hours later.

'We are allowed to march out, with whatever we can carry,' he said bitterly.

'What of food?'

'There is none to spare. We must manage as best we can. We are also to take with us all the people of Kabul who supported Shah Shuja.'

'But you are talking of thousands!' Elphinstone protested.

'Quite.'

'That is impossible.'

'Those are Akbar's terms. Or we can sit here and starve.'

236

Elphinstone pulled his moustache. 'Can we reach Jellalabad, Major?'

'I believe some of us may do so,' Pottinger replied.

The news was received with mingled fear and hope. No-one could suppose the march to Jellalabad, through snow-covered mountain passes, would be anything less than terrible. But it held out a prospect for survival for some of them, as Pottinger had said.

Yet once again there were alarming delays. Several of the women were pregnant, and one unfortunate actually gave birth during the waiting period, while Akbar would not permit the defendents to leave until all those who had shown some loyalty to Shah Shuja had been accumulated. The Shah himself, however, was retained as a prisoner, and the British made no great effort to obtain his release to accompany them; Laura could not imagine what the poor old gentleman's feelings might be.

Thus the withdrawal did not begin until 6 January. During the intervening time the beseiged had to put up with the insolence of the Afghans who, now that there was actually a truce between the two sides, came right up to the cantonments to stare at them and make obscene remarks and threats. Laura was in a sweat of fear that Batraj would renew his demand for her return, or indeed appear before the walls to claim her, but he did not. She dared not speculate on his absence, but she could hardly wait to start moving.

The brigade now numbered some four thousand, five hundred armed men, of whom approximately seven hundred were British and the rest Sepoys. To this had to be added several thousand camp followers.

Brigadier Shelton and Elphinstone commanded the main body of troops, with whom were the women and children, the sick and wounded, and what baggage they had been able to accumulate, together with the food supply; as it was considered impossible for any of the white women to walk, they were either mounted on mules or carried in huge panniers suspended from camels, of which there were a good number. Laura and Mary shared a mule, riding astride, and Sivitraj, Wu Li and

237

Miljah walked beside them. Behind them and around them swarmed the immense horde of Afghan women and children, and quite a few men. These were in mortal fear of their lives, and with reason, for as the British marched out of the cantonments, the Afghans broke in. Heart-rending screams came from those who had not evacuated fast enough and were being murdered, while almost immediately the last of the British was in the open, firing began, replied to by the rearguard of fifty men.

'They mean to kill us all,' Barbara Sturt cried.

'We always knew it would come to this,' her mother said. 'Now we must just face it out.'

Laura could only hug Mary against her as the mule plodded on, listening to the terrifying noises from behind them. Soon the gunfire ceased, however; they never saw the rearguard again.

Now the Afghans surrounded the main body, hooting and jeering, and firing into the shapeless mass as the fancy took them, while occasionally they even rushed at stragglers and cut them to pieces. Laura could not believe that this was actually happening, that a British army was allowing itself to be systematically destroyed. Surely it would have been better to have stood their ground, and fought to the last man. When she thought of the way Guy had commanded his men to do or die against Batraj . . . but his men had abandoned him then, as these men had clearly abandoned all obedience to their officers. No orders were being given. If a soldier chose to fire back at their tormentors, that was entirely up to him. For the main part they merely plodded onwards, and the women and children followed them.

When darkness fell, the mass just stopped moving. Again there were no orders, and no attempt to make a defensive perimeter. Men and women fell where they stood. Laura and Mary, Barbara and Florentia, Wu Li and Miljah huddled together as the temperature plummeted below zero. They had only a few cups of cold soup to drink. Sturt joined them to make sure his wife was all right, but had to return to his batteries; already two guns had had to be spiked and abandoned as their mules had been shot.

All night the Afghans kept up their cacophony from every side, but even this was often drowned by the wails and shrieks of the camp followers, few of whom had any warm clothing or food.

When dawn came it was possible to see that they had moved no more than six miles from the cantonments. Now the very last of the discipline had broken down. Again no order was given, no bugle blown. The mass of people merely heaved itself to its feet and commenced moving, save for those who had died of exposure during the night, or who were incapable of going on; these shouted and screamed and begged for help, but there was none forthcoming.

Almost in a dream, Laura and Mary mounted their mule and resumed their march, following Barbara and Florentia. Laura had no feeling in her feet, and her cheeks were equally numbed. Her belly ached with hunger and every muscle protested at every movement. The alternative was to lie down and die.

It looked as though death might come more quickly than that. In the middle of the morning a large body of Afghan horse, who had been keeping pace with the refugees, suddenly charged into their midst, waving their tulwars and screaming. People scattered in every direction as blood flew. Some of the soldiers rallied sufficiently to open fire, but most just kept on marching, their brains numbed by the cold. Both Laura and Mary were thrown heavily as their mule went down, and Mary screamed as she struck the ground. Laura rose to her knees, the little girl clutched in her arms, and looked up to see a mounted warrior coming straight at her, his sword raised for the blow. She bowed her head, thinking what a waste of a life hers had been, when there was a shot. The Afghan gave a shriek and tumbled from his saddle to discolour the snow with his blood, and Laura raised her head again to see Sivitraj standing beside her, a smoking pistol in his hand.

'Oh, Sivitraj!' she wept, and hugged him against her.

*

239

The Afghans departed again, and the refugees tried to nerve themselves to continue. Mary was alternately screaming and whimpering, and it was obvious that she had severely hurt herself in her fall. Laura sent Sivitraj to find Dr Bryden, and he came as soon as he could, examined the child, and diagnosed a broken rib. He bound her up as best he could, but had no laudanum with which to dull the pain.

'I should recommend rest,' he said. 'But as that is impossible . . .'

'What is to become of us, John?' Laura asked.

'I am afraid we are doomed,' he said. 'I do not know whether Akbar is practising treachery, or whether his people are really unable to restrain these brigands, still . . .' he smiled at her, 'we must do the best we can. Nil desperandum.'

The mule had run off or been killed. Most of the ladies were now on foot, and struggled on until they arrived at the village of Boothak. Here there was a considerable force of hillmen and, to Laura's dismay, Akbar.

Akbar professed his concern at what had been happening, and again professed that he was unable fully to control the Gilzhai tribesmen. He offered personally to escort the refugees the rest of the way, but demanded hostages . . . in case the Company soldiers should attack him! Elphinstone was now totally incapacitated by a violent attack of gout, and what was left of the command devolved upon Pottinger, for Shelton merely rode at the head of his men in a brown study of depression.

Pottinger believed that his sole duty was to rescue as many of his people as possible, and felt forced to agree to the terms. Thus Captains Lawrence and Mackenzie were surrendered. The harassed political officer then was forced to beg for some food, for there was absolutely none left for either man or beast. Akbar assured him that supplies would be forthcoming, and with this the refugees were forced to settle down for another night of endless misery, as the temperature again fell and the snow with it.

By this time all attempts to find mounts for the white women had been abandoned, there were no mules or horses left, and they were struggling through the snow on foot like the Indians;

those who were unable to walk for a variety of reasons – one was nursing the baby born on the very day they had departed from Kabul – were again loaded into panniers on the sides of camels.

Florentia Sale had been shot through the arm during the day's skirmish, but bore her wound with her usual indomitable resolution, although even she burst into tears when Lieutenant Sturt's body was brought to her. Barbara fainted, but when she had recovered, the lieutenant was buried with full military honours in the freezing darkness.

Bryden was right, and we are all going to die, Laura thought, as she huddled between Mary and Sivitraj, Miljah and Wu Li, all shivering, their teeth chattering, their bellies rumbling with hunger. How I have fought and struggled and prostituted myself to keep these two children alive, and all for no purpose.

And dear Guy, writing his letters and seeking her rehabilitation, would not even know how she had died, because assuredly there were going to be no survivors from this catastrophe.

During the night the Afghan attacks continued, and several white women and children were carried off, screaming piteously. The Hindus were particular targets of the Muslim Afghans, and some of these unfortunates were found terribly mutilated, the women with their breasts, noses, and ears cut off, and their throats slit, while some of the children had been hacked in two at the waist.

In the morning, when they heaved themselves to their feet, Miljah did not move: she had frozen to death during the night.

There was no time even to bury her, for the mass which had once been an army was already on the move, and Laura dared not be left behind. She could only mutter a prayer to Vishnu; Miljah had been her most faithful friend.

The third day of the march was the worst, as they entered the Khoord-Kabul Pass, known even by the Afghans as the Jaws of Death. Here the hillmen could no longer come amongst them, but they kept up a steady fire from the heights to either side, and someone fell every few minutes.

Now entirely without food, forced to cram snow into their

241

mouths as a substitute for water, many of the refugees were on their hands and knees. All the artillery had been abandoned, save for a single gun, and the soldiers merely staggered forward, using their muskets as crutches. When they finally emerged from the Pass any resemblance to a military force was gone.

Now they again encountered Akbar and his men, again apologising for the attacks of the hillmen.

'It grieves me sorely to see such gallant ladies and their children exposed to such horrors,' Akbar said. 'If you will yield them to me, I will make myself personally responsible for their safety.'

Pottinger and Shelton looked at each other in some perplexity.

'That we could never do,' Shelton declared.

'I give you my sacred word, sworn on the Koran, that no harm shall befall any of your wives or children,' Akbar said.

Again the two officers exchanged glances. They knew that the army was doomed to almost certain destruction, and everyone with it, including their women. If there was the slightest chance that the Afghan leader could be trusted . . .

'Their husbands will never give them up,' Pottinger objected.

'Then let their husbands accompany them,' Akbar said jovially. 'Once I can protect them from these mountain men, they will be safe.'

For a last time Pottinger and Shelton looked at each other. Then Pottinger agreed. 'Be sure that if our women are massacred, Akbar Khan, or violated, the Company will never rest until you are destroyed.'

'I am a man of honour,' Akbar said. 'Have all your women brought to me. Including the wife of Prince Batraj, the Dowager Rani of Sittapore.'

Part Three

THE SWORD OF EMPIRE

Peshawar, 1 February, 1842

All British India is in a state of shocked misery.

An entire British army destroyed! Four thousand five hundred men, with but a single survivor, the gallant Bryden, who reached the fortress of Jellalabad alone, unarmed, beaten and bloody . . . but unbowed.

My own grief and loss are almost too overwhelming to bear. Laura is gone, this time, I fear, irretrievably.

I must strive to write coherently.

How did it happen? A multitude of mistakes, is the answer. And I will be the first to admit that I shared the over-confidence of last year. Then there was the appointment of Elphinstone, a decrepit desk general who happened once, many years ago, to cover himself with glory, and the replacement of Sale by Shelton.

But the true cause of the disaster, of course, was McNaghton. The assault on, and occupation of, Afghanistan was his idea in the first place. He it was who convinced Auckland of the practicability of the scheme, in the face of the most determined criticism from anyone who knows anything about India. Well, he has paid for his folly, for his belief that the Afghans were 'children', as he kept repeating, with his life. But what of all the other lives sacrificed to pander to his ambition and over-confidence?

I will be brief; the tale is too tragic for expansion. Suffice to say that despite all the warnings, some, according to Lady Sale, given by my own dear Laura, the occupying force persisted in its blind confidence while a storm brewed all around it, to erupt in the murder of Burnes at the beginning of November. There can be no doubt that prompt action on the part of the British

245

would then have nipped the revolt in the bud; Elphinstone disposed of more than four thousand men, and our reputation was still high.

But nothing was done! Elphinstone himself was incapable. He is now in the hands of the Afghans, but nothing can excuse his dreadful supinity, or the incompetence of those who appointed him. Well, then, what of Shelton, a brave and experienced officer, but a man of well-known sullen temperament, who was so at loggerheads with his own troops that they would not follow him. Ah, if only Sale, gallant fellow, had still been there! But he was fighting his way into Jellalabad, in a desperate attempt to keep open the passes into India, aware all the time that his wife and daughter were trapped in Kabul.

The only sensible thing anyone did was send for help. A messenger was despatched to old General Nott, holding Kandahar, but he too was beleaguered and could do nothing more than hold. But the message was also received in Delhi, and forwarded with the greatest despatch to Bombay and Calcutta, as the seriousness of the situation was immediately realised. By then it was understood that the British forces with their noncombatants were besieged in the cantonments outside Kabul, that Sale was similarly besieged in Jellalabad, and that an expedition at least as massive as that of 1839 was required to retrieve the situation.

Auckland, whatever his many shortcomings, is a man of decision, notwithstanding that he had been informed that he is to be relieved this year. He immediately mobilised every man who could be spared, called for volunteers in addition, and appointed, Sir George Pollock to march to the rescue. He could not have made a better choice. Sir George has campaigned in India virtually all his life, and is a man of unbounded energy and determination. Within a fortnight of his appointment he was on his way and, realising that to travel by way of Kandahar would take too long, negotiated with Ranjit Singh's successor to allow us to proceed directly through Sikh territory in order to take the Khyber Pass, the most direct route to Kabul. Fortunately the Sikhs had also been alarmed by reports coming out of Kabul, and were willing to agree to our request. Thus we are here in Peshawar, only two months after receiving the appeal for assistance, with less than two hundred miles to go. And yet I feel the dreadful certainty that we are too late.

I naturally volunteered my services, and however bad the odour I may be in with certain of my superiors, Sir George was happy to accept me, both because of my reputation as a fighting man, and because I know the country over which we will be campaigning. I conceived that I was setting out to rescue Laura!

It was only on our arrival in Peshawar yesterday, that we learned the awful truth of the situation.

Having done nothing to retrieve their position, or adequately to strengthen their defences, the garrison lingered, surrounded, until they ran out of food, and had to treat. It was then that McNaghton was murdered. And still the garrison saw no alternative but to treat, and accept the most humiliating terms from the Afghans, unaware that we were already on our way.

Thus, offered safe passage by the dastardly Akbar, they set off, men, women and children, horse and guns, through the Afghan winter. Can any one possibly imagine the conditions under which those poor people marched and died? For those not slaughtered by the Afghans soon perished of starvation and exposure.

At every halt, Akbar Khan and his generals appeared, apologised for their inability to control their hill people, promised food and protection and took hostages, thus robbing the expedition of all its commanders. And the murderous rascal then demanded that they hand over the women and children, for their protection! One can only imagine the feelings of our gallant Englishmen at that moment. But there was nothing for it.

Thus the remnant, struggling on through the snow and constant harassment, having lost all their guns and most of their ammunition, lacking their officers, died one by one. Only Bryden, alone, rode into Jellalabad!

There is one remarkable thing about this story, which would be unbelievable were it not attested by Lady Sale, wife of the gallant defender of Jellalabad. Her son-in-law was murdered

247

by the enemy and she is therefore not disposed to regard them as any better than they are. The women were not violated! In fact, they seem to have been treated with a good deal of kindness, clothed and fed and restored to health. All this is contained in a letter written by Lady Sale to her husband, and the mere fact that the captured women were allowed to write at all is a measure of their treatment, nor can we doubt for a moment that if Lady Sale had been forced to write lies she would have found some secret way to inform her husband of this.

For me, what the good Lady Sale had to say of Laura is the most important thing in her letter. It seems that my darling girl not only played the heroine by risking her life to warn the supine McNaghton of his danger, but she then helped to defend a beleaguered position against the enemy. She yet again proved her worth during the catastrophic march. Surely now the clearing of her name is certain.

But, alas, her ladyship can give no good news of Laura's safety at this moment. She knows that Batraj was amongst the Khan's generals, and that he sought the return of his wife and family. On the surrender of the women, Laura and her children were removed from the rest and have not been seen since, so there can be little doubt that she was indeed returned to her husband. Lady Sale fears for her life, as it was well known that my beloved had attempted to warn the British of their situation. But there is another thing, known only to me: she had agreed a pact with Batraj, many years before, that if he spared my life she would remain forever at his side. That pact she obviously broke when she sought to escape with the British.

My poor Laura! I am forced to envisage her with her throat cut, and no doubt her children in a similar state, after having suffered heavens knows what indignities. My blood boils, and then becomes ice-cold.

She will be avenged. They will all be avenged. We are here, and we are more than twenty thousand strong. We shall relieve Sale, who still holds Jellalabad, and then march on Kabul. We shall reclaim our women and any other of the hostages who may still be alive, and we shall wreak the most terrible vengeance upon Akbar and his cohorts. My only dream is that I shall at last discover Batraj at the end of my sword.

And perhaps I shall look upon dear Laura's grave.

11

The Avengers

The women and children were gradually gathered together. The beleaguered troops watched with sad and sullen eyes; whatever was going to happen to them, none of the soldiers had much hope of survival.

The husbands were outraged, and at first reluctant to abandon the main body. Shelton had to order them to do so. They left the British ranks and trudged or limped towards the waiting Afghans.

Dr Bryden had just redressed Lady Sale's arm for the last time, and Mary's rib as well. Now he saluted them. 'Courage, ladies,' he said. 'You will be avenged.'

Laura half carried Mary. She above all others had wanted to refuse to be surrendered, and had then realised she could not. Whatever fate awaited *her*, she could at least hope to save the lives of Sivitraj and his sister.

Sivitraj had to carry Wu Li. The Chinese girl lacked the stamina of the others, and was incapable of walking.

Akbar himself greeted them.

'May we inquire after the fate of our officers?' asked Lady Sale.

'They are well,' Akbar assured her. 'With the exception of poor General Elphinstone, who is very ill with dysentery. But my physicians are doing what they can for him.' He turned to Laura. 'Highness,' he said. 'I am so relieved to see you safe, and your children. Prince Batraj will be overjoyed.'

Laura could not prevent herself from looking around, but she could not see Batraj.

Akbar smiled. 'Your husband is wounded. He was hurt in an engagement with General Sale's army. Do not fear for him,

Highness. He will soon be well. But he is anxious to have you at his side.'

'My children and myself were surrendered as part of the agreement with General Shelton,' she said. 'Our safety was guaranteed by yourself, my lord.'

Akbar nodded. 'Your safety *is* guaranteed, Highness. But I did not undertake to keep all you ladies together. Nor can I keep a wife apart from her husband when he seeks her return.'

Laura drew a long breath. 'My lord, if I am returned to Prince Batraj, he will kill me, or at least torture me most savagely.'

'No, he will not,' Akbar said. 'I have told him that you must not be harmed, and that you are under my personal protection. I will give you a letter, under my seal, reminding him of this, and that I will have you examined by my women when I return to Kabul, to make sure that I am obeyed. Now go with my women, to be bathed and dressed, then an escort will take you to your husband; he is already on his way back to Kabul.'

'And my children?'

'Your daughter will accompany you. Your son has played the boy for too long. He will remain with me, as my tavachi, and learn to be a man.'

Laura opened her mouth to protest, then saw Sivitraj's eyes dancing. He might have killed an Afghan in defence of her, but at heart he was one of them.

She realised she could do no more. She turned to Lady Sale, who had overheard the conversation. Florentia clasped her hands.

'Courage, my dear girl. If the prince does not keep his word, then we will all die. We must put our trust in providence.'

'I will never see you again,' Laura said.

'Never is a very long time, my dear.' Florentia embraced her, holding her close for several moments. 'God keep you, dear Laura. Be sure that if I survive, I will tell the world of your heroism, and have every last stain removed from your character.'

She was weeping as Laura and Mary and Wu Li were led away.

*

After the horrors and the physical agony of the march, it was like entering another world for Laura to find herself inside a snug felt tent, with all the food she wished, and all the water she could drink. Mary's rib was re-bound, and soon the girl ceased shivering with cold and fear.

Laura was bathed by attendant women, who exclaimed over the swollen state of her feet, and tenderly washed them, and washed and brushed her hair, and then put her to bed on soft cushions.

How her heart went out to those unfortunates who were still struggling along the road to Jellalabad. She wondered if any of them would ever get there.

Next morning, when she was mounted with Mary and Wu Li beside her, well wrapped up in their haiks, she saw no sign of the other women. Laura could not repress a shudder as she thought that they might already have been murdered, or given to the Afghan soldiery. But she, above all others, had to have faith in Akbar's word.

The snow continued to come down as they made their way north, but not even the snow could hide the evidence of the massacre which had been perpetrated. Every minute, their horses seemed to stumble over a corpse. Because of the cold most of the dead might have been killed only an hour before, instead of several days, and the sight of them evoked terrible memories. Mary started to cry all over again.

Laura had some hope of discovering Miljah's body, and giving it a decent burial, but she could not find it, and her escort were unwilling to delay while she made a proper search.

They did not catch up with Batraj on the road; instead, three days later, they rode into Kabul.

The capital was still in a state of high excitement and triumphant exhilaration. Laura gazed in consternation at the mangled bodies of Burnes and McNaghton, still strung up in the Bala Hissar, while people continued to jeer and throw stones at them. The cantonments were just a blackened ruin. But the city itself was undamaged, and the escort were greeted with cheers as they rode through the crowds. The women were

252

too heavily veiled to be recognised, even Laura's hair being totally concealed.

The escort delivered Laura, Mary and Wu Li directly to the door of Prince Batraj's house. Outside, several armed men were lounging, who regarded Laura's tall figure with interest, but made no effort to prevent her going to the door, which was opened for her by Nanja.

They stared at each other, and Nanja's nostrils flared. 'You dare to return here?' she asked in a low voice.

'I understand my husband is wounded,' Laura said haughtily. 'Stand aside.'

Nanja hesitated, then obeyed, and Laura swept into the house. 'Show my daughter to her bedchamber,' she said. 'And put her to bed.'

Mary was drawn and pale after the exertions of the ride.

Nanja hesitated, them summoned some of the household maids to assist her.

'You go with her, Wu Li,' Laura said.

She went towards her own apartment. Her muscles were tense, but she was quite cool. Akbar's precious document was in her hand.

There was a man waiting outside her bedroom door.

'I have come to visit my husband,' Laura said, and he bowed and opened the door for her.

Laura looked at those so familiar surroundings, and at the divan on which Batraj lay. He was heavily bandaged; from his shoulder and across his chest, but apart from that he looked surprisingly well, although he had lost weight. Like Nanja, he stared at her for several seconds. Then he said, 'You have betrayed me, and your oath.'

'I feared for the lives of my friends,' she said. 'And indeed, for my own life. Your children were also in danger.'

'Danger,' he snarled. 'Could they have been in greater danger than upon that foolish march? You exposed them to that. Where are they now?'

'Your daughter is in her bedroom. She broke a rib in a fall, but she will recover. My son is now with Akbar, serving as an aide-de-camp. And any danger we were in was caused by the treachery of your people, who had promised us safe conduct.'

253

'Safe conduct,' he sneered. 'Your generals were fools. Do you suppose we ever intended anything but their destruction? But you, oh, you will suffer for your betrayal. I am going to take the skin from your back. Ramdas!' he bellowed.

The door opened and the guard came in.

'Fetch four men, and a cane,' Batraj told him.

Ramdas hurried off.

Laura refused to lose her self-possession. 'I think you had better read this,' she said.

She held out Akbar's letter, and he snatched it from her and glared at it.

'The Amir is a man of his word,' Laura reminded him. 'And thanks to your encouragement, he has a great weakness for me.' She could not resist that.

The men came in with the cane, Batraj glared at them in turn, while Laura stood absolutely still.

'Who returned from the Amir's camp with the Dowager Rani?' Batraj demanded.

'Your daughter, and the slave Wu Li, my lord.'

'Bring the slave to me.'

Wu Li was brought.

'You were with my wife when she was received by His Highness?'

Wu Li licked her lips, and glanced nervously at Laura. But Laura could give her no instructions, even with her eyes; she had no idea what information Batraj was trying to obtain. 'Yes, my lord.'

'Then tell me, where is His Highness now leading his men?'

'To the assault of Jellalabad, my lord.'

'Ha,' Batraj said. 'That will take not less than a week, and then it will be at least another week before he can return here.'

Laura caught her breath. 'Do you not suppose I will tell him, my lord?'

Batraj glowered at her. 'You will have to prove your words.' But he was hesitant. Much as he wanted to make her suffer for betraying him, he knew that if he did indeed have her thrashed insensible, there might still be marks in a fortnight's time. And he also knew that his survival depended on Akbar's favour.

Then he smiled, his lips drawing back from his teeth like

those of a wolf. 'We will learn from the Begum Sombre. Pepper,' he said. 'Bring pepper. The swelling will have gone down in a fortnight.'

Laura gasped, and turned for the door, even as she knew it was hopeless.

'Send for Nanja,' Batraj said. 'She will carry out the punishment. She will enjoy that. She will wish to hear her mistress scream.'

Laura screamed. The men held her on the floor while Nanja annointed her nipples with the red pepper. She writhed and tried to fight them, but they were too strong for her. Her wrists were tied behind her back so that she could not help herself in any way, and she was left there, still screaming and whimpering with pain, unable to keep still, rolling to and fro and rubbing herself on the carpet in an attempt to relieve the agony, while Batraj watched her and grinned, for forty-eight hours. Then he gave permission for her to be bathed and dressed.

Even then the swelling took two more days to go down, and every waking moment was agony, while her nights were a mass of hideous nightmares.

And even when the pain diminished, and finally faded altogether, her suffering was not yet ended, for then she was required to attend Batraj's bed, as he was all but fully recovered from his wound. When she was not in his company, she was in Nanja's. Her former friend was appointed her gaoler, and never let her out of her sight, except to go to her master.

Then news came, brought by Akbar's own troops, hurrying into Kabul through the snow, attempting to hide their discomfort beneath a show of bravado. The British were coming back! With four thousand five hundred men Elphinstone had hidden in his cantonments until forced out by lack of food. With considerably less than that number Sale, when Akbar had neared Jellalabad and set up a siege, had sallied out, charged the Afghan army at odds of several to one, and put them to flight. Admittedly he had been assisted by a severe earthquake which had terrified the besiegers, but it had

255

also destroyed most of the defence of Jellalabad. Sale knew that if he had treated for an evacuation, a massacre would undoubtedly have ensued.

Sale had lacked sufficient force to follow up his astonishing victory, and Akbar might have been able to rally his people and resume the siege, but then the news had come that a relieving Company army commanded by the famous Sir George Pollock was actually in Peshawar, and about to storm the Khyber Pass.

Thus the Afghans had come fleeing back to Kabul.

Akbar came to see Batraj almost the moment he entered the city, accompanied by Sivitraj.

'I see you are restored to health,' he remarked. 'About time. There is grave news. You told me that once we had driven the British out, that they would never come back. Well, we have not even succeeded in driving them out, and they are back. Pollock has twenty thousand men.'

'This time we will fight him and defeat him too,' Batraj said.

'Are you mad? He will destroy us.'

'What do you suppose he will do if you flee?'

'We will at least be alive.'

'I came to Afghanistan to fight the British,' Batraj said. 'Not to run away from them.'

Had there ever been a more contradictory character? Laura wondered. Confident, brave, generous in victory save where his fearful goddess summoned him to vengeance, learned, intelligent, a gentle and consummate lover . . . and a vicious monster when his passions were aroused.

Certainly he re-invigorated Akbar, and Sivitraj's eyes shone with hero-worship.

'I shall bring you back an English flag, Mother,' the Rajah said, as Laura held him close.

'Just bring me back yourself,' she told him.

'But you hope that *my* body will be left dead in the snow, I have no doubt,' Batraj commented.

'Should I not?' she demanded. She had not wasted her time in attempting to tell Prince Akbar how his orders had been ignored, but she knew there was no way she could be ill-treated

256

with both the Prince and her son in Kabul. 'As you have so shamefully misused me?'

'And did you not shamefully betray me?' he demanded. He held her against him, kissed her mouth. 'Why cannot you love me, as I love you, sweet Laura?'

'Because I hate you.'

He grinned at her. 'But I am your husband.'

And he rode off with the army.

Not for the first time in her life, Laura was reduced to waiting. It was tempting to suppose she might be able to escape from the city with Mary, and find her way into the British ranks. But she well knew that was impossible, even as the weather warmed and the snow melted. With the death of Miljah, her only friend in the house was Wu Li, and the Chinese girl was too terrified to be of any help, while Laura knew that for herself and Mary and the maid to be alone in the mountains and at the mercy of the tribesmen would be a fate even worse than waiting for Batraj's return.

Besides, there was always the hope that he would not return.

Sir George Pollock advanced slowly and carefully, but with unceasing determination. The Afghans attempted to hold the Khyber Pass, and were driven back. Jellalabad was relieved on 16 April and then, as the summer grew hotter, the British army moved closer and closer to the capital. The Afghans fought with desperate courage, but nothing could prevail against the superior discipline and firepower of the invaders. By the beginning of August Laura, standing on the roof of her house, could hear the distant rumble of the guns, and a few weeks later men began hurrying into the city, pausing only to gather their families and what belongings could be carried before then scurrying away to the north.

'They are devils,' they would say. 'Red-coated devils.' And they would speak in awe of the bayonets.

Could these possibly be the same men who had hooted and jeered at Elphinstone's command, and ridden amongst them with careless murder in their hearts? Certainly their utter dejection terrified the inhabitants, who began a general exodus.

At the end of the month Akbar himself returned to Kabul accompanied by Batraj and, to Laura's great relief, by Sivitraj. All were unharmed, but all were chastened by their successive defeats.

Unlike Akbar, however, Batraj was still full of fight.

'They will never take Kabul!' he declared. 'We will defend it to the last man.'

'You are dreaming,' Akbar told him. 'You are a dangerous man, Prince Batraj. You have led my people into disaster. You fled to Afghanistan to escape the hangman's noose. Then you saw your opportunity to draw us into your private war. Well, that is now finished. I have ordered my people to evacuate Kabul and withdraw to the hills. We will continue the fight from there.'

'I will not accompany you,' Batraj said.

'You will surrender to the British?' Akbar was amazed.

'I will never surrender to the British,' Batraj declared. 'But once you retreat to the hills, you are finished. They will not make the same mistake again. If you will not fight them before Kabul, I will go to someone who will.'

'Who will that be?' Akbar inquired contemptuously.

'That is my affair.' He looked at his stepson. 'Will you ride with me, boy?'

Sivitraj hesitated. Laura, standing on the far side of the room with Nanja, stepped forward.

'Go with the Amir, Sivitraj, I beg of you.'

All three men turned to look at her.

Laura drew a long breath. 'I would beg of you, Prince Akbar, either to take me with you into the mountains, or send me to the British with my daughter.'

Akbar frowned. 'You are Prince Batraj's wife.'

'He has used me most shamefully, my lord.'

Akbar's frown deepened. 'Did you not give him my letter?'

'I did, my lord. And he ignored it.'

It was all or nothing now.

Akbar turned to Batraj.

'The woman lies, my lord,' Batraj said. 'Nanja will testify

258

that I have not laid a finger on her.' He smiled. 'You have my permission to examine her, if you choose.'

It was Akbar's turn to hesitate; clearly he was sorely tempted.

'I will be your slave,' Laura cried. 'Only take me away, my lord.'

That clearly tempted him even more. But however willingly he might have acquiesed when Batraj had offered her to him, he remained a man of the strictest orthodoxy when it came to possession. 'I am sorry, Highness,' he said. 'Prince Batraj is your husband. Until and unless he divorces you, I have no right to come between you.'

He looked at Batraj enquiringly.

'Why should I divorce my wife, my lord?' Batraj asked. 'I love my wife.'

Akbar turned back to Laura. 'You must accompany your husband wherever he chooses to go, Highness. Prince Sivitraj, I give you permission to ride with your stepfather. Now I must leave you to prepare your departure.'

'May I ask what you intend to do with Prince Shuja?' Batraj asked.

'I have already given orders for his execution,' Akbar said.

Laura anticipated another savage bout of punishment, and now she lacked even Akbar's protection. On the other hand, she had gained the protection of her son, who still remained Batraj's ultimate hope of returning to Sittapore in triumph.

Batraj was clearly disgusted by Akbar's decision not to hold on to Kabul, and was thus again forced to watch the collapse of all his plans.

She realised that, with another of those astonishing contradictions which dominated his character, he had quite forgiven her for running away, and was in fact as loving to her as he had always been. As ever in the past, his changes of mood left her confused. She hated him, yet he was her husband. Once again, there was an ambivalence to her feelings for him when he made love to her.

Yet she still desperately wanted to escape him, and she now

259

knew that the only way this could be accomplished would be through his death.

She wondered if she would ever have the resolution to kill him?

Kabul, 20 September 1841

We are in control of the city! Five days ago, we marched in after very little fighting. Akbar has fled, and his army and most of his people with him. Kabul is quite deserted.

Sir George, who has led us from victory to victory, and has shown these brigands what an English army can do when properly commanded, has decreed that there shall be no looting. Our vengeance is to be carried out in an orderly fashion. The Bala Hissar, the scene of the murder of poor McNaghton and Burnes, is to be burned to the ground. The Royal Palace is to be similarly treated. As this building has stood for many hundreds of years this may appear as an act of wanton destruction, but its demolition is intended to serve as indication that our war has been against the perfidious rulers of Afghanistan and not their people.

But now we have been informed that our expedition, and the previous one in 1839, and all the many lives that have been lost, have been to no purpose whatsoever. Dost Mohammed is to be returned to the throne! In fact this gentleman is apparently already on his way from his Indian exile to take up his position once more. His only inconvenience will be the necessity of building a new palace!

Can this be credited? Do not the bones of some ten thousand people – I do not include the Afghans in this total – who followed the Union Jack to and from this benighted spot, cry out in horror at such a waste?

The Company, it seems, has decided that it would be too costly to maintain our presence here. Undoubtedly pressure has been brought to bear by the Government in London, who possibly fear a full-scale confrontation with Russia. But why were these factors not previously considered? I fear such events are enough to turn a man into a cynic, or at least to make him question the abilities of those who so carelessly order us into battle.

It is said that Dost Mohammed has given the most concrete assurances that he will keep himself free of Russian influence. But we have heard assurances from Dost Mohammed before! Can it be that, after all our vacillations, our triumphs and our disasters, we shall one day have to mount yet another expedition into these mountains? Should this ever happen, then indeed the entire British establishment in India will stand condemned before history for its utter incompetence.

At least we have achieved something of value, in that we have regained all but one of the ninety-five surviving prisoners held by the Afghans. To tell the truth, these largely rescued themselves. They had been held at a fortress some distance from Kabul, and when news of the defeat of Akbar Khan's army was received, they boldly hoisted the Union Jack, disarmed their guards, and marched to meet us. This was a great relief to us all, of course, as we could not help but dread the massacre of the women and children. Instead, those who survived the march are all in excellent health, led, it seems unnecessary to say, by the redoubtable Florentia Sale. If women ever receive campaign medals, she should certainly head the list.

Indeed Sale, his wife, and his poor widowed daughter, are about the only people who have come out of this sad affair with any credit, other than the gallant Dr Bryden. Elphinstone is dead, of dysentery, it appears. Well, I cannot help but suppose he would have been courtmartialled for his handling of the business had he survived. Shelton has been recalled. His future remains uncertain. He was never allowed a free hand until it was too late, but his inability to inspire his people with any spark of loyalty or vigour must remain a blot upon his career.

And Shah Shuja, the man for whom all of this misery was undertaken, was shot to death in his palace some weeks ago; his body remained mouldering for us to find.

Akbar may well be returning to Kabul. Batraj will not. We have learned that he and the Prince have quarrelled, and that he has taken himself off with his entire family, including Laura. No-one knows where they have gone, only that they rode to the west. The Thug's destination may be Persia, or even Turkey. Who can say? At least I know that Laura is still alive, but it would seem that she is more lost to me than ever.

What is particularly galling is that, thanks to the reports of both Lady Sale and Dr Bryden, of my beloved's heroism during the retreat and of her vain attempts to warn McNaghton and Elphinstone, her name has been entirely cleared. There can be no question but that she would be welcomed back to Bombay with open arms.

This is not the first time I have had the cup of sheer heaven dashed most cruelly from my lips.

And yet my personal affairs prosper. I seem to have again covered myself with glory during some of the skirmishes we fought on our march here, and am to get my own regiment.

Rufus the Second did not disappoint me, and has blooded his excellent set of teeth upon Afghan hides, to their great discomfort.

As to the future, I cannot say what it will hold.

12

The Flight

Batraj and his party left Kabul a week before the British marched in. There were twelve of them: Batraj and five men who were loyal to him; Laura, Nanja, Wu Li and Nanja's twelve-year-old daughter Sharita, Sivitraj and Mary, who was now fully recovered from her injuries.

They made off to the south-west, taking the road over the high mountains, which even in September were cold and bleak as they climbed more than five thousand feet.

Every member of the party had a horse, and there were several pack mules; if Batraj refused to confide in anyone where he was going, he was certainly prepared for a lengthy journey.

So once again I am on my travels, Laura thought, being dragged around the subcontinent like the chattel I am.

Batraj himself was in a fine good humour, despite the fact that he was again a fugitive.

'Those Afghans were never truly dedicated to driving the British out of India,' he declared. 'I wasted more than ten years of my life, trying to goad them into action. We are well rid of them.'

And what of my wasted years? Laura wondered. She was in her thirty-fifth year. The twenty-year-old who had dazzled Bombay as Rani of Sittapore might never have existed. Now both her mind and her body were toughened until she could stand almost anything, as she had had to do so often. She still stood straight, and her figure still seemed to attract men like flies to the honeypot. Her golden hair still tumbled down her back, longer then ever as it was never cut. And she still had her children. But where they, and she, were now bound, she had no idea. Most of the time she preferred not even to think about it.

They belonged to Batraj. And Batraj belonged to a dream rooted in the past.

From Kabul to Ghazni they climbed over the mountains; it was a horrendous journey. Often they proceeded in single file along narrow ledges with sheer drops of more than a thousand feet beside them, forced to trust entirely to the sure-footedness of their mounts. That Batraj had made this journey before and was apparently totally confident provided only the smallest reassurance.

Five days after leaving Kabul they came to Ghazni, situated in a mountain valley watered by its own river. Ghazni had in fact once been the principal city of Afghanistan, having been founded in the fourth century BC by Alexander the Great. There was little trace of Greek architecture still to be seen, but the city in the tenth century had become the headquarters of a Muslim dynasty whose most famous ruler Mahmud of Ghazni had been one of the most feared warriors in all Asia. Mahmud had raided into North India on fifteen separate occasions, apparently never seeking to establish an Indian empire, as he could so easily have done, but using the riches of the sub-continent merely as an inexhaustible reservoir of wealth and slaves.

Ghaznavid power had declined in succeeding centuries. The city was far more compact than Kabul, and was defended by high, thick walls. Yet its inhabitants were in a state of agitation, wondering if they were again to be visited by the fearsome bayonets of the Company army. Batraj had many friends here, for it was outside these walls that he had fought and been wounded, but even these friends were anxious for the fugitives to be on their way as quickly as possible.

A journey of another two hundred miles lay between Ghazni and Kandahar; Batraj estimated it would take three weeks. From Ghazni, they were able to descend to the valley of the Tarnak River, and the going became easier.

Batraj had one great fear, that of being captured by the British and publicly hanged as a murderer. Thus throughout the journey to Ghazni they had been able to do nothing more than replenish their provisions. Once they reached the Tarnak, however, he felt secure from pursuit, and allowed them more time to rest.

They were even able to enjoy the luxury of a bathe in the river, although the water was very nearly ice cold, as September was now dwindling into October, and the lowering clouds of winter were beginning to appear.

The idea of being caught in these mountains in the dead of winter, remembering as she did the horrors of the previous January, was terrifying to Laura, but Batraj merely grinned.

'We shall be on lower ground before the first snow,' he promised her.

Laura did not find this entirely reassuring.

That night they slept together for the first time since leaving Kabul. They had nothing more than a bivouac, as Batraj had not had time to organise an elaborate caravan. Hitherto on the journey Laura had slept with Mary in her arms, seeking warmth and comfort from the girl, but now Mary was sent to sleep with Sharita.

'Will you not tell me where we are going, now?' Laura asked.

'South.'

'South? But . . .'

'Oh, it is necessary to travel to the west first. But soon we will turn to the south. I have friends in the south.'

'Friends like the Afghans?'

He grinned and kissed her. 'Better friends than the Afghans. Perhaps I should have gone to them first.'

They had encountered quite a few people between Kabul and Ghazni, mainly fugitives like themselves, who had exchanged nothing more than the latest information on the supposed position of the British. West of Ghazni, however, there were fewer people to be seen, although there could be no doubt that they were being watched by the hill men to whom all travellers were prospective prey. Batraj made his entire small force which, including Sivitraj, totalled seven men, ride with their weapons always at the ready, and every night two sentries were posted.

Laura realised that the Hindus felt no more secure in relation to the Muslim tribesmen than did the British, but it did her spirits good to see the way in which Sivitraj took to his responsibilities and seemed to enjoy the prospect of danger.

She felt that she had to a large extent lost her son to his stepfather, but this would have come with manhood in any event; at least there had been no time for Batraj to make him into a Thug. She was happy that he sat with her each evening for half an hour.

Every night he shared his tent with Wu Li.

Batraj also clearly thought deeply about the boy. 'It is time to think of a wife for him,' he remarked one evening.

'He is not yet sixteen!' she protested.

'Had we been able to return to Sittapore, he would have been married long ago,' he pointed out.

'Well, we have not been able to return to Sittapore. And there is no wife available for him in these mountains. His requirements are attended to by Wu Li.'

'Wu Li is a slave. The boy needs a wife. I am thinking of Sharita. She is a pretty little thing.'

'Sharita!' Laura cried. 'I will not have that creature Nanja as my son's mother-in-law.'

Batraj grinned. 'Because she has been unswervingly faithful to me, while you have betrayed me time and again?'

She ignored that. 'You must see it is impossible for me, Batraj.'

'The impossibility is in your mind,' he said enigmatically.

Laura was afraid he might seek to unite the couple immediately, although anything like a proper ceremony would be impossible, but the next day they encountered a group of tribesmen who informed them that a British force was marching through the vaalley, en route from Kandahar to Ghazni and thence to Kabul, to join Pollock's army.

'We must take to the hills,' Batraj decided.

Thus the relative comfort of the valley was abandoned, and they dismounted to lead their horses up a narrow defile into the mountains which overshadowed them to either side. They had not climbed very high when Batraj called a halt, and they made camp.

That evening Batraj and Sivitraj climbed out on to a spur overlooking the river, to watch for the British. Laura went with them, Batraj raising no objection: any attempt to betray their position could lead to the death of Sivitraj, and he knew she was not going to risk that.

Soon enough they heard the drums and pipes, and the redcoats could be seen. They numbered several hundred Sepoys with mounted British officers, marching along behind their band.

'They make war as if it were a parade,' Batraj growled, contempt mingling strangely with admiration and respect in his voice.

Laura glanced at her son. Sivitraj's face was consumed with passion. Yes, she thought sadly, I have lost him. She would have to work very hard to get him back.

The British camped for the night beneath them, and they listened to bugle calls and shouts of command which echoed up into the mountains. Laura wondered what they would give to know that Batraj the Thug was only a few hundred yards away.

For their part, they could light no fire and had to eat scraps of cold food. Nor did Batraj allow them to move for a good twenty-four hours after the British had gone on their way.

Then he decided that it would be too risky to proceed all the way to Kandahar, where there was apparently still a British garrison. This disappointed Laura, who had hoped to see the famous city, founded like Ghazni by Alexander. Indeed the name, Kandahar, was a corruption of Iskandar, which was itself a corruption of Alexander. Instead they turned south, and began a long and bitter climb over the Hada mountains.

The track they followed ascended to some six thousand feet, and even higher peaks rose to either side. It began to rain heavily as they began the ascent, and the ground became slippery; they were forced to dismount and lead their animals. Even so one lost its footing and went crashing down the hillside. Its piteous neighing followed them for some time and left them all gloomy and depressed.

They then climbed into the very clouds, and found themselves in a dank and frightening world where the wind constantly buffeted at them; sometimes they had to lean against each other to resist it. 'It is not far,' Batraj kept telling them.

It was actually some sixty miles from where they left the Khandahar road to the village of Spin Buldak on the Dori river, and on the second day they had to ford the fast-running Arghastan River, a tributary of the Dori, which rushed down through a mountain pass in a flail of white foam.

There was a rope bridge across the river, but Laura felt sick as she watched it swaying in the wind, hardly more than six feet above the tumbling water.

'It is best we do not all cross together,' Batraj decided, and sent two of his men ahead, both to make sure the bridge was safe, and to hold the far side against any brigands who might dispute their passage. This done, the rest of the party began to cross. Sivitraj accompanied his mother and sister and Wu Li, apparently reflecting, as Laura was, that if they were going to drown, it was best they all drown together. Slowly they inched their way forward, while the bridge heaved and bucked beneath them, all sound drowned by the roar of the water: anyone falling in would not survive a second, Laura knew.

They reached the far side safely, and threw themselves on the ground as they watched the rest of the party and the animals being brought over. Batraj was as ever a bundle of energy and confident strength, crossing and recrossing the swaying bridge several times, encouraging and exhorting. Laura wondered if he was really any different from men like Mahmud and Genghis, Timur and Babur, who had ranged these mountains before him, slaughtering thousands, raping and pillaging, and yet by their energy, daring and fearlessness, carving immortal names for themselves in the pages of history.

It was not beyond the bounds of possibility that Batraj might yet still do likewise.

Then came the mountains, which made all that had gone

before seem as nothing. When Laura remembered how she had found the journey through the jungles of the Deccan almost too much for her she wanted to laugh. She would gladly give all of her jewellery to be down there again, rather than in this increasingly icy roof of the world.

They awoke one morning to find themselves shivering and their tents half covered with snow.

'You said we would escape this,' Laura reminded Batraj.

'We would have, had we been able to stay on the road,' he argued.

The snow was at least not as heavy as in January, but they were much higher up than on the road from Kabul to the Khyber Pass, and there was a good deal of ice. But they struggled on, shawls held across their faces, huddling round the campfires at night, and now also running out of food, for they saw no game.

'You should be used to this, Laura,' Batraj chided.

She shuddered. 'I had hoped never to experience it again,' she said.

She worried for the children, but both Sivitraj and Mary had constitutions as strong as her own. Wu Li was a different matter. Always thin and undernourished, no matter how well she had been fed in Kabul, the Chinese girl lacked the reserves of strength to combat exhaustion and extreme cold; Laura sometimes wondered if she had ever recovered from the ordeal of January.

Two days after the first snowfall Wu Li was definitely ill, and Laura insisted that she be allowed to ride. Batraj grumbled. 'We have no room for weaklings,' he said.

Laura ignored him, sure of Sivitraj's support in this instance. Indeed the Rajah led Wu Li's horse himself, and spoke to her constantly, begging her to believe that they were only a day or two away from warmth and safety. Thus encouraged, Wu Li clenched her tiny mouth and fought on.

In fact Sivitraj was proved right; within the week they began to descend to Spin Buldak. This was even more dangerous than climbing up, for the mountain trails were slippery, and as they came down through the clouds the snow turned to rain.

However, they made it to the valley of the Dori without loss, and that night found refuge in a small caravanserai outside the town.

Here there was soon a roaring fire, and Batraj managed to purchase a young goat, which was roasted to provide the most satisfying meal Laura could ever remember, while the villagers and their children gathered in the entrance to gaze at these strange beings who had appeared from the mountains, and most of all at the golden-haired woman.

'It is not far to the pass now,' Batraj assured them. 'But we will rest here for the next two days.'

This sounded heavenly, but next morning it was clear that Wu Li was dying. She had summoned all her strength to make the descent into safety; now she had none left.

Sivitraj was deeply upset, and sat beside the bed of straw on which the girl lay, holding her hand and gazing at her with sombre eyes. Batraj spent most of the day with the village elders, who were anxious to have news of what was happening in the rest of the country, and clearly did not much like what he had to tell them.

During the night Wu Li died.

There were no facilities in the village for cremation, so Wu Li was buried outside the caravanserai wall. Laura doubted that any of the party save herself, Sivitraj and Mary truly mourned the unhappy Chinese woman; to Batraj she had been just another appendage.

'Actually, it is best she is gone,' Batraj confided to Laura that evening. 'Now we can bring Sivitraj and Sharita together.'

At the end of their three-day rest, feeling much refreshed and with their stores replenished, they set out again, following now the valley of the Dori for the Khojak Pass.

It was like leaving a secure port to put to sea in a storm, for the rain continued to teem down, the river was swollen and boisterous, and the pass itself nothing more than a cleft in the mountain wall which led them to more mountains. Now the rain changed again to snow, and it was obvious that Batraj's

271

prediction that they would leave the mountains behind before the onset of winter had been unduly optimistic.

With increasing difficulty they struggled onwards. It was only sixty-odd miles from the pass to the village of Quetta, but it took them more than a week, and when they again reached safety, in the midst of a blinding snowstorm, Laura begged Batraj to allow them to spend the winter in shelter. But he refused, and two days later they were again on their way, for the Bolan Pass into Sind.

This took several more days of hard slogging, but once through this last gateway they were descending into the Valley of the Indus. They reached the lower ground at the beginning of December, to enjoy the unfamiliar warm air, the subtropical vegetation, and to look back at the huge mountains, almost lost behind the great black clouds, through which they had come.

'It is all easy now,' Batraj assured them.

They were now in the land of the Baluchis, fierce desert warriors who rode to battle in vast brigades of cavalry, wielding sword and spear. Batraj told Laura how Sind had once been part of the empire of Seleucus, one of Alexander's generals, but how before that it had been, according to legend, the seat of one of the earliest civilisations.

Laura found this hard to credit as she gazed at the miles of sandy desert across which they were making their way. But for all its aridity, Sind was watered by the mighty Indus. The river irrigated the land for some distance to either side, and enabled the Baluchis to prosper.

Now they had to worry about the British.

Sind was officially outside Company control, being broken up into several independent amirates, but as it bordered Company territory to the east it had long been 'invaded' by Company Residents seeking favourable treaties. The uneasy relations between the Baluchis and the British had come to a head three years before, when the Company had been forced to march through Sind to gain Afghanistan. Naturally they had resolved to use the river as much as possible, but when the Baluchis disputed this, their fort at Kurrachee had been

272

bombarded and captured, and their capital of Hyderabad, some thirty miles up-river, had also been taken. The amirs had been forced to sign treaties of peace and co-operation with the Company, a Residency had been established in Hyderabad, and a fortress with a strong garrison at Sukkur, a further hundred and fifty miles to the north.

Laura now began to understand Batraj's purpose. It was evident that the Baluchis deeply resented their enforced friendship with the Company, and Batraj might well hope to find friends and even allies amongst them.

But first it was necessary to reach the river, and this they did before Christmas. Here they were able to find places on a caravan of boats proceeding downstream. They sold their remaining horses and heaved their belongings on board. It was such a relief to be able to sit down and watch the banks drifting by, rather than having to force oneself to place one foot in front of the other, time and time and time again.

'Where are we going?' Laura asked lazily.

'Hyderabad.'

'Hyderabad?' she cried.

He grinned. 'This is not the Hyderabad in the Deccan. This is the Hyderabad at the mouth of the Indus. I have friends in this Hyderabad.'

Batraj was, apparently, well known all along the river, and at every stopping place went ashore to talk with the local head man. Sometimes these grim characters came back to the boat with him, to send shivers up and down Laura's spine as they gazed at her or, even worse, at Mary.

They were tall, gaunt men, with straggling beards and moustaches, who wore long kaftans and turbans, and carried fearsome curved swords and daggers. They made Dost Mohammed seem like an English country gentleman.

'Are they a united people?' she asked Batraj.

'They should be. And they will be,' he replied. 'All they need is leadership.'

'Which you hope to provide.'

He grinned. 'Am I not a born leader of men?'

*

273

Their way downriver naturally took them past the fortress of Sukkur. They concealed themselves in the boats as best they could, while Laura gazed longingly at the red-coated Sepoys patrolling the battlements above the river. But she no longer had any great faith in the power of the British to control native affairs, however triumphantly they might have returned to Kabul.

What awaited her in Hyderabad, she had no idea.

Hyderabad turned out to be a town of considerable size, situated mainly on the left or eastern bank of the river. Laura observed with a leap of the heart that immediately north of the city was a large compound surrounded by a white paling fence, from the main building of which there flew a Union Jack. Batraj had not told her there were Englishmen here.

Like Afghanistan, Sind was mainly a Muslim community and, Laura gathered from the numbers of mosques and veiled women, a much more orthodox one than Kabul.

'They take their religion very seriously here,' Batraj said. 'You will all wear the veil.'

So once again the women concealed themselves, and remained on the boat after it had been tied up alongside the wooden dock, while Batraj and Sivitraj went ashore to seek Batraj's friends.

Nanja sat beside Laura. 'His Highness has spoken with me about the matter of the Rajah's marriage,' she confided.

Laura continued gazing at the shore, and the people moving to and fro with their flocks of sheep, their chickens, their argicultural products, making for the marketplace.

'Your daughter is very young,' she remarked.

'Not so,' Nanja argued. 'Twelve is the right age for a wife to go to her husband. Sharita passes blood as a grown woman.'

'We will have to consider the matter,' Laura said.

They were escorted ashore to the home of one of the Baluchi chieftains. It was a spacious if somewhat ramshackle building on the right bank of the river. Here they were greeted by Abbas Ali Khan who, Batraj informed them, was a very powerful sheikh.

274

'He is my friend,' he told Laura. 'And I would make him more of one.'

'You did not tell me there were Company officials here,' she said.

'There are Company officials everywhere,' Batraj growled. 'But here, my dear Laura, they have even established what they call a Residency, which is a constant affront to my friends. Truly the arrogance of your people would be unimaginable, were it not real.'

'The people do not appear very resentful of the situation,' she remarked.

'They do not understand the perfidy of the Company,' he explained. 'For the moment, they believe their business is simply to trade. They do not realise that the Company intends to annexe their lands.'

'You cannot know that either,' Laura said.

'Have I not the evidence of my own eyes? The Resident has, as if he were some monarch, summoned all the amirs in southern Sind to come to Hyderabad at the beginning of next month in order to affirm their loyalty to the Company, and sign a proper treaty. My friends do not appreciate that at the very least the Company is seeking to establish what they call a protectorate, so that they can tell these people what they can and cannot do.'

'And you conceive it your duty to enlighten them on these matters?'

Batraj grinned. 'Why else would I be here? But first I have more important duties to perform. I must secure Abbas Ali Khan's support.' He gave her a sideways glance. 'One of his wives has recently died in childbirth. The poor fellow was quite upset. But his period of mourning is just ended. Is this not convenient?'

For a few moments what he had just said did not penetrate Laura's brain. She sat up very straight. 'No!'

'My dear Laura, Mary must be married. As she is my daughter, she must be married as advantageously as possible.'

'You would marry a twelve-year-old girl to that . . . that . . .'

'Abbas Ali Khan is a great chieftain, a wealthy man, and he is in the prime of life,' Batraj pointed out. 'Our daughter could

275

hardly make a more advantageous match, from every point of view. As for her age, she is certainly nubile. I am in fact about to marry Sivitraj to Nanja's daughter.'

'How can you marry a rajah to the daughter of a common woman?'

'Now, you know very well Nanja is by no means a common woman. Her father was a wealthy man. That she chose to follow her husband is to her credit. I am not suggesting that Sharita will be Sivitraj's only wife, or indeed his principal one, should things go well for us, but he needs a wife.'

'A creature of yours to bind him the more closely to you,' Laura said bitterly.

'A wife who will respect and honour him,' Batraj corrected.

As usual, Laura realised, she was utterly helpless.

Her only hope seemed to lie in her children themselves, and thus she had a talk with Mary.

'Has you father spoken with you, about marriage?' she asked.

'Oh, yes, Mama. Isn't it exciting?'

'Exciting?' Laura cried. 'How can it be exciting to marry a man four times your age?'

'Papa says it is right for a husband to be much older than a wife,' Mary said.

'He does, does he? Do you realise that you will have to become a Muslim?'

'I think that is a good religion, Mama.'

Laura sighed. 'I had so hoped you would marry an Englishman.'

'Why?' Mary asked with devastating simplicity.

'Well, because they are the best people in the world.'

'How can you say that, Mama? Papa says they are rude and arrogant, and aggressive and warlike. He says they seek to conquer the whole of India. He says they are only succeeding because of their superior weapons, and because the Indians will not unite against them. He says that when the Indians unite against them, they will be helpless, as we saw in Afghanistan.'

Laura was left speechless in the face of such a damning and accurate indictment.

'Besides,' Mary finished even more devastatingly. 'You did not marry an Englishman.'

Laura bit her lip, and tried her last resort. 'Have you any idea what marriage will entail?'

Mary smiled. 'Oh, yes, Mama. Sharita and I have often talked about it, and Aunt Nanja has told us about it too. She has even shown us what men do. I think it will be most enjoyable.'

Laura was utterly scandalised at the thought of Nanja *showing* her daughter what a man would do to her, but she knew it would be a waste of time complaining to Batraj. She sought out Sivitraj instead.

'Do you know what your stepfather is up to?' she demanded.

'My stepfather deals in many things,' Sivitraj said cautiously.

'Well, firstly, he means to stir up trouble against the British here in Hyderabad.'

'It is the only way we will ever drive them from India.'

'And you think that is desirable?'

'Should I not? I am a descendent of the Great Sivaji.'

Laura realised she must abandon that line immediately.

'Do you also know that he means to marry your sister off to Abbas Ali Khan?'

Sivitraj nodded. 'She is a fortunate girl. The Khan is a great man.'

Laura raised her eyes to heaven. 'He is old enough to be her grandfather. And how do you know he is a great man?'

'Well . . .' Sivitraj hesitated.

'Because Batraj has told you.'

'He has the aura of greatness,' Sivitraj said stubbornly. 'Many men call him Khan, a whole army of them. And he will help us in our designs. He will be our ally.'

Laura sighed. 'Prince Batraj also seeks to marry you to Sharita.'

Sivitraj's eyes gleamed. 'She is a pretty girl.'

'And will she also be your ally?'

'She will be my wife, Mother.'

*

277

Batraj was spending much of his time arranging for the two ceremonies, and conferring with Abbas Ali Khan and various other chieftains; once the news that Abbas was preparing to marry again got out, the Baluchi leaders had every reason to come to the town. The amirs were coming anyway, for the meeting with the Resident, which was set for 12 February. That Batraj was hatching some kind of a plot was obvious, however, and that the plot would involve an assault upon the British Residency seemed more obvious yet.

Left a good deal to herself, Laura took to walking out, duly wrapped up in a shawl and veil, and seeing what she could learn about the situation. She was now determined to oppose Batraj in every possible way, and to bring him down if it cost her her own life. She knew this would entail breaking her solemn promise to him, but that promise had been extracted under duress, because of her fears for Sivitraj, as in later years she had been constrained by her fears for Mary. But both Mary and Sivitraj now seemed irrevocably lost to her. She did not suppose that whatever she did would lead Batraj to harm them, however, he needed them both too much.

Besides, she had broken her promise before. Their relationship, such as it was, lay in ruins. Only vengeance was left to her.

She took to studying the Residency. It was certainly a large and imposing edifice, gleaming white in the sun, with a flat and castellated roof, above which the Union Jack flew proudly in the breeze. It was surrounded by a considerable number of outbuildings, and by the fence; but that could hardly be considered a defence. The fourth side faced the river, and consisted mainly of a dock, alongside which were two small paddlesteamers.

After careful observation, she concluded that the garrison consisted of about one hundred men, and that there were also a considerable number of officials and their wives and children. Her heart sank; was this going to be a repetition of the tragedy of Kabul?

The question was how to warn them of the danger hanging over their heads?

Her first opportunity came a week after their arrival, when she

278

was in the marketplace. Nanja and Mary and Sharita were with her, all heavily cloaked and veiled like the native women around them. But there were also two white women, in hooped skirts and poke bonnets, their faces exposed to the sun, examining the fruit before buying it.

Laura knew she had to grasp this chance, so she lingered behind Nanja, also appearing to examine the melons. Finally, she found herself standing beside the Englishwomen.

'It is very important that I speak with you,' she said in a low voice, in English, not looking at them.

Their heads jerked. One of them was quite young, in her mid-thirties, with a pretty freckled face and auburn curls peeping out from beneath her bonnet. The other was much older, and had a somewhat severe face.

'Please do not show surprise,' Laura said. 'I have news of great importance for the Resident.'

The Englishwomen looked at each other. But they were both sensible, and reacted well. They picked up some more fruit, apparently not noticing the woman beside them. 'Who are you?' asked the younger woman.

Laura took a deep breath. 'My name was once Laura Dean.' There was a muffled exclamation from beside her, and she hurried on. 'Do you come to the market regularly?'

'Every week,' said the other woman.

'Arrange a meeting for me with the Resident,' Laura said. 'I shall be here a week today for your answer.'

She could do nothing more; Nanja was looking over her shoulder, wondering where she had got to. Laura hurried off to join her.

Fortunately, Nanja was far too excited about the coming weddings to be suspicious about anything that might have happened in the market. The next week was a busy time, as saris were sewn and food was prepared. It was to be a double wedding, for the Rajah of Sittapore, as Batraj insisted upon calling Sivitraj, and the Princess Mary were to be married on the same day.

Laura, having once embarked upon her plan to warn the Residency, abandoned all attempt to oppose the weddings, and played her part as enthusiastically as any of the women. But she had an uneasy feeling that Batraj was only waiting for Abbas Ali Khan to become his son-in-law before inciting the Baluchis to action; time was very short.

She continued to be fortunate, however. The following week Nanja was too busy to go to the market, and Laura went with Mary, her heartbeat quickening as she saw the two women, who today had with them a man dressed in civilian clothes. He was obviously there for the purpose of speaking with her, from the way he looked at her expectantly as she came in sight.

'Wait here,' Laura told Mary. 'I wish to speak with those people.'

'English people?' Mary said contemptuously.

'I want news. It may be of use to your father,' Laura said, and went over to them.

'Are you really the Dowager Rani of Sittapore?' the man asked.

Laura could not take off her veil in public, but she pulled a strand of golden hair from beneath it for just a moment before tucking it out of sight again.

'My God!' the man commented.

'I must speak with the resident,' Laura said.

'What are you doing here?' the man asked.

'I am here with Prince Batraj. We have come here from Kabul.'

The man nodded, as if he had guessed that. 'And now you seek to escape him? We wish no trouble with the Baluchis, Your Highness. Perhaps you are unaware that they about to sign a treaty of amity with the Company's representatives.'

'For Heaven's sake, I am seeking to save your lives,' Laura said, vehemently. 'Why do you suppose Batraj is here? It is to make trouble between the Company and the Baluchis. Whatever treaty the amirs may sign with you will be meaningless.'

The man frowned at her.

'It is the truth,' Laura said.

'This so-called prince is your husband,' the man pointed out.

'Do you think I married him willingly? But yes, he is my husband. So I know what he is about. You *must* listen to me!'

280

She was growing desperate, because passers-by were glancing at them and she could tell that Mary was becoming impatient.

'I will certainly report what you have said to the Resident,' the man said. 'Have you details of what your husband proposes?'

'No. But I will obtain them. I will give my information to the Resident personally.' She could not take a chance on her warning being accepted and herself not; her very life was at stake now.

'Hm. Well, I will see what can be done. Will you be here a week today?'

Another week. These people seemed to have no sense of the urgency of the situation.

'No,' she said. 'Listen to me. I will come to the residency next Monday night.' It was the night of the wedding, but it would be her best chance of getting away.

'The treaty will have been signed by then. The amirs are meeting with the Resident on Sunday the twelfth.'

'And I have told you that whatever is agreed with the amirs will be meaningless. But nothing will happen until after Monday. Tell the Resident this, and that I will come to the Residency on Monday night. I do not know what time it will be. You must arrange for me to be admitted.'

The man was frowning again. 'How are we to know it is not some plot?'

'What am I supposed to do?' Laura asked, keeping her temper with great difficulty. 'I am a woman alone. Oh, have your people search me, if you wish. But please allow me to speak with the Resident.'

The man hesitated, but the younger of the two women now interfered. 'I am sure Miss Dean can be trusted, Walter,' she said. 'You have read what Lady Sale wrote of her.'

Florentia! 'Is Lady Sale safe?' Laura cried.

'Oh, indeed.' The woman touched Laura's hand. 'We will speak of it on Monday. It will be arranged, I promise you.'

Laura hurried away to rejoin Mary.

'They had much to say to you,' Mary commented.

281

'They had news of Afghanistan. Lady Sale is safe. Isn't that splendid?'

Laura had no idea how she was going to get away on the night of the wedding, but it seemed her best chance: she knew that however orthodox Abbas Ali Khan was it was certainly Batraj's intention to serve alcohol at his daughter's wedding.

More and more Baluchi tribesmen came to town, ostensibly to celebrate the wedding of their leader. Laura thought that the mere presence of so many men should alert the Resident, but there was no evidence of it, and on the Sunday the amirs duly attended the Residency and returned in great good humour having, they said, entirely satisfied the British requirements. Laura would have liked to ask them if the British had not inquired as to the presence of the wanted criminal Prince Batraj in their city, but she dared not.

On the Monday, the guests were a mass of finery and jewels. Laura, with her emeralds, outshone them all.

Batraj and Sivitraj both wore the uniforms of general officers in the Sittapore army. These had been freshly made for them by the seamstresses, and they both looked extremely handsome. Abbas Ali Khan wore a red kaftan decorated with green motifs, and kept darting glances at his prospective mother-in-law.

Laura looked at the other guests, all Baluchi chieftains, and thought that if only the British had been prepared to listen to her from the beginning, the Resident might have been able to arrest all of these men at one swoop. But they had just signed that vital treaty of amity.

The ceremonies were both Muslim and Hindu, and lasted for some time. Then there was a great feast, at which a good deal of alcohol was consumed. Laura pretended to drink with them, as most of the women were doing, while she watched her children with anxious eyes. But both Sivitraj and his sister were clearly enjoying themselves.

She could promise them nothing but hardship now. Yet she knew it had to be done.

After several hours she pretended to become visibly tired, yawned and even nodded off from time to time, to be shaken awake by Batraj.

'How long does this go on?' she asked.

'Until dawn at least,' he said.

'I must lie down,' she said. 'Or I will faint.'

He did not object and so, as unobtrusively as possible, she left the room and made her way along the corridors to the apartment she shared with Batraj. There she put on her veil, opened the door, and met Nanja.

'Where are you going?' Nanja inquired, her tone entirely lacking in respect. But then, Laura realised, we are now mothers-in-law.

'I need some fresh air,' she replied. 'I will not be long.'

'I will come with you,' Nanja said.

Laura hesitated, but to refuse her would be to arouse her suspicions even further. Moreover, she had told Batraj she was going to lie down.

'Very well,' she said.

She realised that she was approaching perhaps the most important moment of her life. Always, before, however irrevocably she might appear to have acted, she had always left herself an escape route. Had her marriage with Sitraj proved unhappy, she could have fled back to Bombay and her own people. When Batraj had carried her off, no matter how often she had rebelled, she had always known that she had but to surrender to him to survive. Even now, she had imagined she would be able to warn the Resident, and return to play her role as Batraj's wife.

Now she had to accept that that was impossible. Either she must abandon any idea of going to the Residency tonight, knowing there might never be another opportunity, or she must somehow eliminate Nanja while she escaped. And once she did that, she could never return.

She felt her heartbeat, which had been very quick, begin to slow. The decision was taken.

Nanja reappeared, also wrapped in a shawl. 'Where do you wish to go?'

'Somewhere quiet. I have a headache.'

'It is a great occasion.' Nanja walked beside her into the yard. 'Are you not proud?'

'What have I to be proud of?' Laura asked.

283

Nanja smiled. 'I am proud.'

'Well, you have every reason to be.' There was no moon, but it was a clear night, and the yard was a mingle of brightness and dark. Laura remembered that one of the servants had been chopping wood earlier that day, and walked casually towards the pile of cut timber. She still had no clear idea of what she was going to do. She had never actually hit anyone in her life.

'My daughter will make the Rajah a good wife,' Nanja declared, walking beside her. 'When he regains his throne, she will make an excellent Rani. She will give him many strong sons. You should be proud of that.'

'Do you really suppose Sivitraj will ever regain his throne?' Laura asked, stooping to select an appropriate length of wood, and discovering that the axe had been left with the pile.

'Of course. Our master has said so,' Nanja pointed out. 'What are you doing, Highness?'

Laura drew a long breath, and stood up, a length of wood held in both hands, turning and swinging as she did so. But in that moment Nanja had understood her danger and leapt away from her. The Indian woman tripped over her sari and fell to the ground, and Laura lunged after her.

'Help!' Nanja bawled, and rolled against the pile of wood.

Laura hesitated, but no-one had heard the shout. She moved forward again, and Nanja saw the axe. She closed both hands on the haft and swung it, parallel with the ground.

It was Laura's turn to leap backwards to avoid losing a leg, and equally her turn to trip over her sari and sit down so heavily that she lost her breath and the length of wood.

Nanja gave a cry of triumph and reached her feet, still holding the axe, which she now swung with all her strength. Desperately Laura rolled to one side, and the axe blade smashed into the earth. Nanja grunted and attempted to pull it free, but before she could do so Laura was on her knees. She threw both arms round Nanja's waist, heaving with all the force she could manage.

Nanja fell over, but retained her grip on the axe which came out of the ground. Now she tried to hit Laura again, but Laura had kept her grip on Nanja's thighs, and rolled again. Although they were much the same height, Laura was the stronger

284

woman, and Nanja thudded into the wood pile, at last releasing the axe.

Now she struck with her nails at Laura's face. Laura gasped in pain, released her grip, and rose to her knees, seizing the nearest piece of wood and hitting out with it. Nanja grunted and Laura struck her again and again, her blows loaded with all the anger she had felt against this woman for so long. Nanja's arms still flailed, reaching for her, and Laura struck her a fourth time. Nanja sighed, and lay still.

For several seconds Laura remained kneeling above her, panting, her breath coming in huge gasps. She could feel blood trickling down her cheek from where Nanja had scratched her, and she ached from a variety of other blows and bruises which she had not even noticed. She still held the wood, ready to hit again if Nanja moved. But Nanja did not move.

Once again Laura's heartbeat slowed. She grabbed at the Indian woman's wrist. There was no pulse there. She lowered her head to peer at Nanja's head, saw nothing but a mask of blood and distorted features.

'Oh, my God!' she whispered, and rose to her feet. She looked left and right, but the yard remained empty. No-one had heard the fight. She had indeed burned her bridges beyond repair.

Laura wrapped her torn shawl about herself, and hurried into the darkness.

Nowshera, 6 February 1843

Laura has been found, in the most amazing circumstances! And we are once more going to war!

The entire sub-continent is seething, following our Afghanistan adventure, and there is much work to be done.

After Batraj fled west from Kabul, taking Laura and her children with him, everyone assumed that he was abandoning India forever. Not a bit of it! The rascal has now turned up in Sind, of all places, with the intention of stirring up the Baluchis.

And I am here to meet him!

On my return from Afghanistan, I found myself seconded to the staff of General Sir Charles Napier, who had just been given command in Sind. I was happy to accept this posting, firstly because of the promise of action, and secondly because of the character of the man under whom I was going to serve, especially when I discovered that he had actually asked for me, as I had marched across this desolate country before and may therefore be presumed to know it.

Napier's is a glorious name. With his two brothers he served in the Peninsular war. During the gallant fight for Corunna, which cost Sir John Moore his life, Sir Charles, then a subaltern, was shot through the face and taken prisoner. As far as the British were concerned he was killed, and his Will was actually probated, before he returned from the dead. Since then his reputation for courage and eccentricity, has only grown. He was Governor of the Ionian Islands for a while, just when the Greek War of Independence was breaking out, and it was there that he met Lord Byron, of whom he is ever happy to

286

speak. Byron actually suggested to him that he abandon the British Army and take command of the Greek forces. Perhaps fortunately for us all, Sir Charles refused this dangerous honour, otherwise he might have died, like the poet, of a fever.

With his disjointed jaw, and various other ailments, he is a most odd figure of a man. He is also quite old, past sixty. Elphinstone, while younger than this, yet proved too old for his job. Napier is of different metal. I have related how, on our march north, we observed that the Baluchis were a sullen and mutinous lot, and it was to deal with this situation that Napier was given his command.

The Baluchis are two distinct peoples. The Upper Baluchis, under their head amir Rustum, appear to be loyal to the Company. The Lower, who follow the flags of men like Sher Mohammed, the Lion of Meerpure, and Abbas Ali Khan, are the troublemakers.

There were of course plenty of people, political officers in the main, who expressed the view that the Baluchis needed only firm but fair treatment to become loyal subjects. Our General holds a different view, and has no doubt at all that the amirs are bent on mischief. His intention therefore was to strike a decisive blow before the Baluchis could co-ordinate their resistance and so, with a small picked force, of which I had the honour to be a member, we crossed the Indus early last December and marched through the desert for the fortress of Emaum Ghur, the Baluchis' principal store of powder and shot. They were so surprised we captured the place without the loss of a man, where upon we blew it up with the most magnificent bang. That put the would-be rebels in a different frame of mind, and Sir Charles felt that now was the time to hold out the olive branch of peace. In his course he was encouraged by Major Outram, an experienced man in these parts, who had recently been appointed Resident in Hyderabad; he has a high opinion of the Baluchis, and a low opinion of the Company's 'aggression', as he terms it. Outram apparently had no doubt that he could persuade the recalcitrants to sit down and sign a lasting treaty of peace and friendship.

Then, unexpectedly, we received a message from Outram that Batraj was in the city.

Outram, of course, has never met Batraj, and he is of the opinion that the Thug's presence will make no difference to the acceptance of the proposed treaty by the amirs. He merely wished to ascertain whether or not the criminal should be placed under arrest. He wishes to postpone this step until after the treaty is signed, which is to take place next Sunday. He is, of course, fearful of arousing the Baluchis, to several of whose amirs Batraj is apparently known.

Most importantly, Outram says that he has been approached, indirectly, by a woman calling herself Laura Dean, Dowager Rani of Sittapore, who claims she has information of a vital character to impart to him. He tells us that he has not yet had a meeting with the lady, but that an appointment has been arranged for next Monday night. Most fortunately, he was acquainted with Laura in Bombay, and has always been one of those who believes she was hard done by. Thus he apparently intends to assist her, if she wishes it, to escape her husband and return to Bombay.

I was amongst the first to hear this news, for Sir Charles sent for me as soon as the despatch was received, to ask me what I made of it. I was forced to put forward the view that wherever Batraj appears there is likely to be trouble, that I felt Outram was somewhat sanguine in believing the Baluchis would proceed with the treaty, and that it was very likely we were within a few days of an uprising. This was an opinion Sir Charles was pleased to hear, as it coincided with his own, and thus he immediately determined to march with every available man on Hyderabad, to overawe the Baluchis, ensure the safety of the Residency, and arrest Batraj, and thus save Laura. Needless to say I shall accompany this force, and thus at last achieve my greatest ambition.

After eighteen years.

13

The Siege

Laura reached the river bank without mishap; it seemed all of Hyderabad was celebrating the Khan's wedding. Once there, having got her nerves back under control, she considered the situation. There were people on the bridge, but she could not tell in the darkness whether they were from the Residency or the City. There were lights glowing in the Residency, certainly, and beneath the wall there were also lights showing from the steamers that lay alongside the Residency dock a little downriver. She wondered if she could reach the steamers before being swept under the bridge.

However, it seemed obvious that the only safe way across was to swim. She took off her sari, wrapped it round her waist and between her legs and fastened it into a makeshift dhoti. Her jewellery would have to take its chances. Then she slid down the bank and entered the water, which was remarkably cool.

She did not hesitate, but struck out from the bank in a steady breaststroke, only her head showing. No-one on the bridge seemed to notice her, as she made almost no noise.

The current was very strong, and swept her downriver. She began to tire, but there was nothing for it but to keep going. She kept on swimming, and then saw the bulk of the bridge looming above her. She was nearly there. A few minutes later her feet touched mud, and she dragged herself into the shallows, to lie exhausted, the water flowing past her shoulders, listening to the voices, tensing herself to react if anyone had heard her.

But apparently no-one had. She was so tired she almost fell asleep, but was awakened by an outburst of noise from the far side of the river; someone had found Nanja's body.

The men left the bridge to go and see what was happening, and Laura crawled up the bank, every muscle twitching with fatigue, into the darkness. She was on the northern outskirts of the city, about half a mile downriver from the Residency. She was dripping wet and half naked, and felt quite incapable of moving another step. But there was no time for rest. The noise from across the river grew louder, punctuated by gunshots, and she could see torches flaring as people searched for the assassin.

She picked her way through the bushes that lined the bank, her face twisting as pebbles and thorns struck at her bare feet, keeping her gaze fixed on the palisade surrounding the Residency, in which more lights had appeared as the sentries listened to the racket from the city.

It took her nearly an hour to get right up to the palisade, and she could see the shako of a Sepoy patrolling up and down. She unwound her sari and put it on, wet and muddy and torn as it was, then found a pebble and threw it at the wood. It made quite a loud noise, and the sentry was immediately alerted.

'Who goes there?' he demanded in Hindustani, thrusting his musket through the palisade.

'The Dowager Rani of Sittapore,' Laura told him. 'I have come to see the Resident.'

The man hesitated, then called for his sergeant, to whom Laura repeated the request.

'You must come to the gate,' the havildar said.

'Where?'

'Go round so.'

He pointed to the east, and Laura wearily made her way along the palisade, again tormented by the stony ground on her bare feet, until she reached a small postern gate. Here not only the sergeant but a white officer waited for her.

'Am I expected?' she asked.

'His Excellency is awake,' the officer said.

She was allowed in, then escorted across some kind of a parade ground to the main building. Here there were more sentries, and more English officers, and she was inspected by the light of flaring torches. She hugged her sari closer to herself, knowing that she must resemble something the cat had dragged in.

'You had best come with me,' said a man in civilian clothes. She was allowed into the Residency itself, taken up a flight of stairs, and shown into an office, where a somewhat short but strongly-built man, fair-haired and moustached, waited. He stared at her in amazement, while she regarded him with delight.

'James Outram!' she cried.

'Laura Dean!' he said, amazed.

She had known Outram more than twenty years previously, when he had first come to Bombay as a subaltern in the 19th Foot. Of course she had only been a young girl then, but they had met on several occasions in the couple of years before she had married Sitraj, although his duties had taken him away from the city for considerable periods.

Outram came round his desk to take her hands. 'How very good to see you. But . . .' he peered at her face, 'you're hurt.'

Laura put up her hand, and it came away wet with blood. 'I was scratched. James . . . I am in the most dire trouble. But so are you all.'

'We will have to talk about that. But I think, first of all, you should be given a hot bath and something proper to wear.' He smiled. 'Otherwise you will be setting my people by the ears.'

'Let me speak first, James, I beg of you.'

He hesitated, then nodded, and gestured her to a settee against the wall.

'I am very wet.'

'I can see that. But you cannot stand. You look done in.'

Indeed Laura's legs were all but giving way, and Outram had to escort her to the seat.

'Brandy, Phillips,' he told the secretary. 'And perhaps you could find out if Mrs Fisher is awake.'

The drinks were brought; Laura thought she had never tasted anything quite so delicious in her life. While she sipped, and felt the warmth tracing its way down to her stomach, she told Outram about Batraj's plans.

He listened, frowning. 'I am bound to say, Laura, that I find what you have to say difficult to accept. Abbas Ali Khan signed the treaty only yesterday.'

'He is now Batraj's son-in-law, James.'

'Hm. Well, if you are right and I am wrong – and I hope and pray it may be the other way around – they have missed their opportunity. As soon as I learned that that scoundrel Batraj was in Hyderabad, I informed Sir Charles Napier at Nowshera, and asked for instructions as to whether I should apprehend him. Sir Charles has replied to say that I am to do nothing until he gets here with his army, which will be within the next seventy-two hours.'

'Thank God for that,' Laura said.

'It is a matter of how much time we have. Can you tell me the reason for that hubbub over there?'

Laura drew a long breath. 'Today was the wedding of my son and daughter, my son to a creature of Batraj's, my daughter to Abbas Ali Khan.'

'I knew of these marriages, but not that your children were involved. That noise does not sound like a celebration . . .'

'It is not. To get here, I had to kill a woman. My son's mother-in-law.'

Outram frowned at her. 'You *killed* her?'

Laura sighed. 'I did not intend to. She wished to prevent my departure, and we fought. I . . . I suppose I hit her too hard.'

'My God!'

Laura gave a twisted smile. 'So once again, you will have to put me under arrest.'

'There's no chance of that. Do you not realise that you are a considerable heroine, since Afghanistan?'

'Me?'

'Oh, indeed. Florentia Sale has been singing your praises to all the world. Now I shall have to do the same. Do you know, I was actually with Keane's force, but I was not with the people who entered Kabul, and in fact when I did get there I spent only a day or two before being sent off again. Anyway, by then, I gather, you were seeing quite a lot of Guy Bartlett.'

'I only wish to God either you or Guy had been enabled to remain, and avoid such a tragedy.'

'Amen.'

'I am dreadfully sorry to have brought this crisis upon you.'

'If you are right in your fears, I suspect it was going to happen anyway. Would you believe that a month ago I was about to embark for England?'

'You? Leaving India?'

'Well, it was not entirely my own choice. But my poor wife . . . did you know I was married?'

'I have been rather out of touch with events in Bombay recently.'

'Quite. Well, I married a few years ago, but my wife could not stand the climate here and had to be invalided home. I was to join her this year. But almost the moment I was to step on the ship Napier sent for me and asked me to postpone my departure in order to take up the post here, as the Baluchi chieftains were being difficult. As you know, I talked them into signing a peace treaty yesterday, and had supposed the matter done with. I am still hoping that is the case. On the other hand, the presence of your . . . is he your husband?'

Laura gazed at him. 'In Hindu law, yes. But it would not have mattered if he were not; I have been his slave for fifteen years.'

He gave a faint flush. 'Yes. I spoke with Guy quite recently.'

'Oh! How is he?'

'Very well. Divorced, as you may know. And very much in love with you. Did you know that he is in Nowshera, on Napier's staff?'

Laura's heart gave a great bound. 'Guy?'

'The very man.'

She bit her lip, and it was her turn to flush. 'Do you suppose . . .'

'Oh, I shall certainly deliver you to him, if that is what you wish, Laura. But . . . you mentioned your children.'

Laura sighed. 'I am afraid they are lost to me.'

'Even the Rajah?'

'I fear so.'

'I'm sorry. Ah, Jenny.' He stood up as a woman entered the room. 'I'm sorry to disturb you. You've met the Dowager Rani?'

Jenny Fisher was the younger of the two women from the

293

market; she had clearly dressed in a great hurry. 'Yes, I have. My dear . . .' she held out her hands. 'You look most terribly done up.'

'She is,' Outram told her. 'Will you attend to her for me?'

Laura was escorted to Jenny Fisher's bungalow. Her husband, Daniel Fisher, the financial officer of the Residency, goggled at the blood and mudstained woman with the flowing golden hair, and at the glittering emeralds which still hung round her neck and gleamed on her fingers, then he excused himself. Laura's wet and filthy clothes were taken away and she was ensconced in a hot bath, while Jenny and one of her Indian maids applied creams to her torn cheek.

'I am terribly afraid there is going to be a scar,' Jenny said. 'It is a deep gouge. Whoever did it?'

'An old enemy,' Laura told her. 'Just before I killed her.'

Jenny's mouth formed a huge O, but she made no comment. 'I expect it will fade, in time,' was all she said.

Laura was put to bed, and slept heavily. She was utterly worn-out, and although she knew that full understanding of what she had done would come in the morning, nothing would keep her awake now.

When she opened her eyes the sun was streaming through the window, and Jenny Fisher was in the room with a tray of toast and coffee.

'I've had a look round to see if I can find something for you to wear,' Jenny said. 'But I'm afraid there is no one in the Residency quite your size. So I've had your sari and other things washed and dried, and my girl is mending them now.'

'You're very kind.'

'They'll never be the same again, I'm afraid.'

'Is there news from the city?'

'It's all quiet. Dan says they're sleeping it off.'

'And any word from Sir Charles Napier?'

Jenny shook her head. 'But we are sure he is on his way.'

At midday there came from the city the mournful beating of

294

drums and clashing of cymbals, punctuated by the firing of muskets: Nanja was being buried.

The sentries had been doubled on the walls, and the entire garrison was standing by, while the Resident himself toured the perimeter and checked the defences.

'Our principal problem is a shortage of ammunition,' he told Laura, whom he entertained to luncheon. 'I was appalled when I arrived here and discovered it, and immediately put in a requisition for more, but it has not yet arrived.'

'And I have brought this trouble on you,' she said.

He smiled. 'You have probably done us a great favour. If you are right in assuming that the marriage of the Princess Mary to Abbas Ali Khan was to be the signal for an uprising, then the funeral of the woman Nanja has clearly put that back at least twenty-four hours. And Napier will be with us in forty-eight hours, I have no doubt at all.'

He was reassuring, but clearly not everyone in the Residency shared his optimism. In her sari and with her height and golden hair, Laura would have drawn attention in any event, but the news of why and how she had come to be there had spread. From the stares she noticed, she understood that most of the English population were fervently wishing she would go away again.

'They are all terrified,' Jenny Fisher told her.

'And aren't you?'

'Well, yes, I suppose I am. But General Napier is coming, is he not?'

They all had such sublime faith in the old general, but Laura could only remember Kabul. The British had had an old general there too, and more than twice as many troops as Napier apparently commanded, against the same number of the enemy.

But Outram himself remained utterly confident, and no-one could doubt that his Sepoys worshipped him. Not for nothing had he been given the sobriquet, by Napier himself, the Bayard of India.

Yet obviously even he was anxious about the situation, and that afternoon mounted to the roof of the Residency with his

295

glass to study the plains to the North. He could see nothing at all.

That evening, just before dusk, a group of men was seen approaching under a white flag.

'Prince Batraj and the Rajah Sivitraj of Sittapore wish to speak with Major Outram,' reported the orderly.

Outram glanced at Laura.

'I should like to speak with my son,' she said.

'And so you shall Highness. Accompany me to the gate, but stay out of sight until I call you.'

News of Batraj's approach had quickly spread, and all the inhabitants of the Residency, even the children, had turned out, whispering to each other as they watched Laura accompany Outram across the parade ground as the gate was thrown open.

The six Indians paused about fifty feet short of the gate. Outram stepped through.

'Greetings, Your Excellency,' Batraj said. 'You will know why I am here.'

'I am surprised you *are* here, Prince,' Outram said. 'Have you forgotten there is a warrant out for your arrest on a charge of murder?'

'I am under the protection of my friends, the Baluchis,' Batraj said. 'As well as a flag of truce.'

'You would do well to remind your friends that they, and those they protect, are under the protection of the Company,' Outram said. 'As agreed in the treaty we signed but two days ago.'

'You would protect us, with a hundred men?' Sivitraj demanded contemptuously.

'The Rajah is young, and hot-headed,' Batraj said hastily. 'He is also very distraught. He was married only yesterday.'

'So I understand,' Outram said. 'My congratulations, Your Highness.'

'But last night his mother-in-law was murdered,' Batraj said. 'Could any man be more unfortunate?'

'You have my sympathy, Your Highness.'

296

'The murderess was the Rajah's own mother,' Batraj said. 'She has now taken refuge in your Residency.'

'You have proof of this, Your Highness?'

'Do you deny that the Dowager Rani is in your house, Your Excellency?'

'She is here, certainly. I asked if you have proof that she committed the murder.'

'Who else could it have been? The Dowager Rani is the only person who was at the wedding who has now fled. She is also my wife. On both of these grounds I have come, with Rajah Sivitraj, to demand her return to us.'

'For execution?'

'For trial, certainly.'

Outram looked at Sivitraj. 'You wish to execute your own mother?'

'My stepfather has said that my mother must be tried,' Sivitraj said. 'She has committed a crime. The sentence will not be death.'

'I see. Some kind of perpetual imprisonment? Well, Prince, I have to inform you that the Dowager Rani claims to have killed the woman Nanja in self-defence, and that I believe her. I shall, of course, conduct a full inquiry into the affair, and if a crime has been committed it will be tried in a Company court. As will yours, sir. Since we are discussing cases of alleged murder, will you not now surrender to my jurisdiction?'

Batraj stiffened. 'Do you take me for a fool?'

'No, sir. But I do take you for the villain you are.'

Batraj glared at him. 'You will regret those words, Your Excellency.' He waved his arm. 'I have thousands of men at my beck and call.'

'I should have thought your Afghan adventure would have taught you not to risk unleashing thousands of enemies, Your Highness,' Outram said quietly. 'I assume you and your – ah – protectors are aware of the proximity of Sir Charles Napier?'

'Bah,' Batraj declared. 'An old man, like Elphinstone. His coup at Emaum Ghur was pure chance. Now he is exhausted. This is well known.'

'I hope for your sake you are correct,' Outram said. 'Rajah Sivitraj, would you care to speak with your mother?'

Sivitraj hesitated, and Outram beckoned Laura forward.

'I killed Nanja in self-defence,' Laura told him. 'I beg your forgiveness, Sivitraj, I also beg you to dissuade that evil man from doing anything which might lead to fighting between the Baluchis and the British. That way lies disaster, and it will end forever any chance you may have of regaining the throne of Sittapore.'

'You are a murderess,' Sivitraj said implacably.

Laura sighed, and turned away.

'And you are my wife,' Batraj called. 'When you are returned to me, as you will be, I will make you suffer for this crime.'

'If I were you, Prince Batraj,' Outram said. 'I should leave Hyderabad while you can. The arm of the Company is long, and it is stretching out behind you at this very minute.' He stepped back inside. 'Close the gate, Captain.'

'Perhaps you should have handed me over.' Laura said miserably. 'That would have delayed an assault even longer.'

'While they tortured you to death? Perhaps I should have told them Napier was on the way. But that is a double-edged sword; it might force them to attack immediately. And if Napier for any reason is *not* coming . . .'

'Then you and all your people are lost, because of me.'

'Never because of you, Laura. And we shall take a few of them with us.'

The garrison was stood to, the non-combatants sent to the cellars.

'You'll not forget I have tended wounded men before,' Laura reminded Outram.

'I would willingly assist,' Jenny Fisher said.

'Dr White will call upon you, should he need you,' Outram promised.

They ate their dinner, and waited. The night was very quiet; hardly a sound came from the city. The women and children were all in one cellar, where they lay on charpoys most uncomfortably; some of the children wailed constantly and no-one slept.

The atmosphere was somewhat bitter. 'It is intolerable that such a situation should have arisen,' someone said, 'because of, well . . .' she sniffed.

298

'I really think Major Outram could have handled things differently,' said another, hugging her weeping daughter to her breast.

'What you mean is, he should have handed the Dowager Rani over to the Baluchis,' Jenny said fiercely.

'Well, my dear, if she is guilty of murder . . .'

'She is *not* guilty of murder,' Jenny shouted.

'It is her word against everyone else's. Against that of her own son! And *we* must all suffer for it.'

Laura put a pillow over her ears. She had nothing to say to them. There was nothing she *could* say. She could only thank God for Outram's support, and Jenny's, and give way to despair. She had lost her children.

Just before dawn the next morning, 15 February, they were roused by the beating of drums and the blowing of bugles, countered by a bugle call from just above their heads and the thud of booted feet as the garrison took up its positions. Laura got up and went to the door.

'Where are you going?' Jenny asked.

'Outside. I don't think I can stand this much longer.'

'I'll come with you.' Neither had undressed; it was just a matter of pulling on their boots. They paused in the corridor for a moment, listening to the noise coming closer.

'Hold your fire,' an officer was shouting above their heads. 'Hold your fire. Make every shot count.'

Laura took Jenny's hand and led her along the corridor to the door. There was a Sepoy sentry.

'Ladies must stay under cover,' he said apologetically.

'I am not a lady,' Laura pointed out. 'I am the Dowager Rani of Sittapore.'

The man hesitated, and they slipped past him into the courtyard of the Residency; it was in darkness and seemed deserted, but for a gleam of light from the billiard room, which had been converted into a surgery.

The Baluchis were now very close, and the night was beginning to fade.

'Open fire,' came the command. 'By volleys. Section One!'

299

The muskets exploded, and Laura ran to the arched gateway.

The entire garrison was at the palisades, firing by sections. Outram was there as well, walking up and down behind the gate, where the main assault was clearly going to be launched. The volley firing and the speed with which the highly trained Sepoys could reload had temporarily driven the Baluchis back.

Laura and Jenny dashed up the outside staircase to the first floor verandah, then up the next flight to the flat roof. Here they crouched by the parapet to prevent themselves from being seen as the darkness turned to grey. They could look out and see the masses of Baluchis surging forward against several parts of the wall at once; they could see the gleaming swords and the muskets. Immediately beneath them a thin circle of company soldiers stood against the palisade, awaiting orders to fire.

Laura strained to see if she could discern Batraj or Sivitraj but she could not make them out in the crush.

Now men were being hit, as the Baluchis came again and again. The orderlies helped several back to the Residency.

'We had best go down,' she said.

But she cast a last look at the northern horizon. To the east, at the very edge of the plain, the sun was just rising with dazzling brilliance. And to the north, closer to the earth tiny slivers of silver were gleaming in the dawn . . .

Her heart missed a beat. She blinked her eyes and looked again. It was no illusion. But the pinpoints were a very long way away.

Jenny was already halfway down the steps, and Laura hurried after her into the billard room, which was already foul with blood and stench.

'Ladies!' Dr White objected.

He was operating on a Sepoy who had been wounded in the thigh. The poor man stretched on the bloodstained billiard table, was naked from the waist down, and Jenny Fisher gave a little gasp and stepped back.

'We are here to assist you, sir,' Laura said firmly, and knelt beside another wounded Sepoy, who had received a sword slash in the arm. The wound had been bound up, but was still seeping blood; Laura swabbed it dry and gave the man a drink of water.

White returned to his operating table. The wounded man gave a fearful shriek as the probe went in search of the bullet.

Jenny ran from the room, and Laura could hear her vomiting on the verandah. Three more men were brought in.

'This is really no place for women,' White grumbled; having removed the bullet he was now dressing the wound.

Laura ignored him, and turned her attention to the next new arrival. Her sari was by now soaked with blood. A few minutes later, she discovered Jenny kneeling beside her.

'Good girl,' she said, and hugged her briefly.

They worked there for over an hour. All around them the firing continued and the casualties grew, while the sun rose higher and the air became hotter and more sultry. But as yet no Baluchi had got inside the compound. And surely those pinpoints of light were coming ever closer?

It was an hour later that Outram himself came to the surgery. Both Laura and White looked up, alarmed that the commander might have been hit. But Outram was unhurt, although smoke-stained and grave. He beckoned Laura outside. The air was thick with dust and smoke, and she could hear the screams of anguish and shouts of defiance.

'Are they not magnificent?' Outram asked.

'Yes indeed. How many Baluchis are there?'

'Hardly less than eight thousand. And we have given not an inch. But now, Laura . . . we are running out of ammunition.'

'Oh, my God! But General Napier is coming.'

'If only we could be sure of that.'

'I saw him, this morning.'

He frowned at her.

'I saw pin-points of light, in the sunrise.'

Outram ran up the steps to the roof, levelled his glass.

'Are they there?' Laura followed him.

The sun was now high, and scorching down on the plain.

'Do you not see them?'

'Perhaps. Yes, there is something out there, moving and glittering.'

'It is General Napier.'

'Still perhaps twenty-four hours away. And we have not enough ammunition for more than another hour.'

To die, at such a time, with help so near . . . Laura sighed, and went over to the parapet, to look down at the two little steamers, still alongside the dock.

She grasped Outram's arm. 'The steamers!'

'Eh?'

'Could we not abandon the Residency for the steamers?'

'The Baluchis will simply follow. They have horses; they can gallop faster than those tubs can move, especially against the current and with more than a hundred people on board.'

'It is a matter of time,' Laura said. 'If we take to the water, they will find it more difficult to get at us. And if we can steam upriver, no matter how slowly, all the while General Napier will be coming closer.'

'By God! You're right!' he said. 'It might do.'

'It is better than sitting here waiting to be cut to pieces. Can you hold out long enough for the captain to raise steam?'

'We must,' he said. 'All right, Laura, I put you in charge of evacuating the women and children. Get them aboard.'

Laura shook her head. 'You will have to give that task to Jenny Fisher. The women will never listen to me.'

He nodded. 'Perhaps you are right. Then you go and tell the skipper to get up steam.' He hurried down the stairs and into the operating theatre. 'We are about to evacuate the Residency and take to the steamers. Women and children first, then the wounded. Haste, now, haste!'

He returned to the fighting. Jenny ran down to the cellar. It took her some time and a great deal of shouting to get the women to leave the comparative safety of the stone walls and venture out among the shrieks and screams of flying bullets, but she managed it at last, and shepherded them down to the dock and onto the steamers, apparently unnoticed by the Baluchis.

By then Laura was already aboard. Captain Brown, who was also the engineer, had already started to raise steam. He grinned when he heard the orders. 'Sure, and I was thinking of getting out meself, if things got any rougher. But did you say everybody's coming? Where am I to put them all?'

The little ship was only fifty feet long, but she had two decks.

'She'll heel over,' Brown said. 'And if she don't, she'll run aground. This time of year the river's at its lowest.'

'Can't we use the other ship as well?'

'She has engine trouble. She'll not raise steam in time.'

'Then we'll have to keep stable by placing most of the people on the lower deck,' Laura told him. She went to hurry the women trailing down the dock.

'I've been hit,' a woman wailed. 'I've been hit.'

Laura examined her quickly, but saw no blood. 'The bullet was spent. Now, please arrange yourself amidships, and sit on the deck.'

'On the deck?'

'That way there will be less chance of you really being hit. No, no, please . . .' she stood in front of the ladder as several of the women went towards it. 'You cannot go on the upper deck.'

'But I always travel on the upper deck,' the first woman said haughtily. 'The lower deck is for natives and animals.'

'Today, you are travelling on the lower deck,' Laura said firmly. 'Jenny . . .'

'The Dowager Rani is right,' Jenny said. 'Ladies, you simply must co-operate.'

White and his orderlies assisted the wounded down the dock. This provoked a fresh outbreak of complaints.

'They're not putting those men with us?'

'Ugh!'

'I'm going to be sick, I know it.'

'Those men were hit defending you,' Laura snapped.

White arranged his people on the deck, which immediately became stained with blood; the women and children huddled together, well away from them. Laura looked up towards the Residency. The flag still flew from the roof, but the firing was unabated. Surely Outram would know they were ready.

The Baluchis had seen them. Men ran onto the bridge, pointing at the smoke issuing from the steamer's funnel. One or two fired muskets, but fortunately the range was too great for accuracy, even had they been expert marksmen. But the steamer was a large target, and every so often there was the

303

crunch of lead into wood, or the clang of a bullet striking metal. Sooner or later someone was going to be hit.

'I'm going up to see what's happening,' Laura told Brown. 'Dangerous,' the Scotsman remarked. 'But it's getting late.'

Laura gathered up her sari to her knees and ran along the dock and up the slope. The Sepoys had abandoned the perimeter, and were holding the Residency building itself, from which there was direct access to the dock. The Baluchis had swarmed across the palisade and the parade ground, but were still restrained by the deadly volley firing of the Sepoys who retreated in sections, one firing, one reloading, and one withdrawing. Their courage and precision were totally admirable. Their British officers, Conway and Outram, stood at the end of the firing line, encouraging and commanding. Yet they were so few. If the Baluchis were to launch a concerted attack they were bound to be overrun.

Outram looked round and saw her. He raised his hand briefly in acknowledgement, and issued his orders.

Now it was a time for haste. The Sepoys fired a last time, then broke and ran. For a moment the Baluchis hesitated, then uttered a great shout of triumph and flooded into the Residency, the steamers forgotten.

It seemed as if the fleeing Sepoys would be overrun, but the Residency itself proved too great a temptation for the attackers. Some climbed up on to the roof to haul down the Union Jack; others invaded Outram's private apartments in search of loot. Others had already spread yelling and shouting, to the various bungalows.

The Sepoys ran down the dock and hastily boarded the steamer. Conway immediately sent men to the upper deck to resume firing.

Outram came last. He grasped Laura's arm and raced her along the dock, slipping and panting, while bullets hummed around them and the shricks of the Baluchis were only feet away. The steamer had already been cast off, and they leapt across the widening gap as the current pulled the ship away from the dock.

The Baluchis yelled their rage at the escape of their victims,

304

but crowded together they presented an easy target, and several fell into the water as they were hit.

Captain Brown put his head out of the wheelhouse and grinned down at the Resident. 'Now where d'you wish to go, Major?' he inquired.

Their danger was not over yet. Within half an hour Baluchi horsemen were galloping along both banks, shooting at the little steamer as it moved slowly upstream.

The Sepoys did not reply. They were saving the last of their ammunition.

'How much fuel do you have, Mr Brown?' Outram asked.

'Maybe eight hours.'

'Which will take us where?'

'Well, we must be making all of two knots against this current. Sixteen miles, if we don't touch bottom.'

'And the Baluchis can watch us every foot of the way. Very good, Captain Brown. Just keep going.'

'What happens if we run out of fuel before General Napier reaches us?' Laura asked.

'We shall anchor in the middle of the river and sit it out.'

The prospect was grim, but conditions on board the steamer were grimmer yet. There was no room to move on the lower deck, and the upper was reserved for fifty of the Sepoys and their officers. The enormous weight meant that the ship was lower in the water than usual, and once or twice there was a grating sound as she scraped across a sandbank. There was no food and only a little water, and as the sun rose higher it became extremely hot.

But there were few complaints. Most of the women and children were simply too exhausted, and besides, they could see the smoke rising behind them from the Residency as it was set on fire.

At five o'clock that afternoon, the steamer's funnel ceased to belch smoke. Brown promptly gave the order to drop anchor, and the steamer *Satellite* came to a halt in the middle of the river, riding to the current. The Baluchis, who had easily kept pace with them, uttered whoops of exultation.

'We have them confused, anyway,' Outram remarked.

'But they seem quite happy with the situation,' Laura pointed out.

The afternoon drifted by. Now that they had stopped, they presented an easier target, and one or two of the women were hit by ricocheting bullets. Outram ordered his men to return fire, but soon darkness fell, and there was no moon. The Baluchis on the banks kept up an enormous hullabaloo, punctuated by the firing of muskets.

'Do they never sleep?' Laura asked Outram.

'They are covering other noises, I would say,' Outram said. 'But they are not natural sailors.'

He kept every man on the alert, and sure enough, shortly before midnight several boats loomed out of the darkness.

'The ladies will lie down,' Outram ordered; this time he was obeyed without question. The Sepoys on the upper deck opened fire with the last of their cartridges; those on the lower deck met the attack with bayonets. For several minutes after the boats came alongside there was a desperately fierce fight. Men screamed and shouted as they hacked and cut and clubbed; some even fought with fists and fingers. After several of the Baluchis had fallen or been thrown overboard, the rest lost heart and went after them.

The cost had been severe, however. Four Company men had been killed and another dozen wounded. The tiny force was reduced to less than half its original number. Most of the women were in a state of near hysteria as Dr White, assisted by Laura and Jenny and his orderlies, carried out emergency surgery by the light of a single lantern, his patients' screams echoing into the night.

When Laura was sent away for a breath of fresh air she climbed to the wheelhouse where Outram, Conway, and Brown were gazing out at the night.

'What happens tomorrow?' she asked.

'We will sit it out.'

'This is all my fault,' she observed.

Outram put his arm round her shoulders and hugged her. 'It was a good idea. The only idea. But I hope you haven't forgotten how to pray.'

*

Slowly the racket on the banks died. Even the Baluchis had to sleep some time.

Laura slept for a while, but she was back on duty just before dawn. Suddenly a chill breeze swept across the river, and immediately a mist arose, almost blotting out the banks. It would, she thought, have been a good time for the Baluchis to launch another attack, but the banks remained uncannily silent.

She returned to the upper deck to find Outram and Conway; neither man had slept.

'There's nobody out there,' Conway said. 'I'd swear to it. And listen.'

Out of the slowly lightening darkness to the east, there came the rhythm of drums, and the screech of fifes.

The Banks of the Indus, 17 February 1843.

As I sit here and write my journal by the light of a flickering candle, I am the happiest of men. My Laura sleeps but a few feet away from me.

Alas, we do not share the same tent. Sir Charles is a stickler for propriety and would have none of that, nor would I have dared suggest it. But nonetheless I have held her in my arms, looked into her lovely eyes, and assured myself both that she is well and that she loves me as much as ever.

The only sadness in our reunion is the absence of her children who, she fears, have been suborned by Batraj. Thus she cries out for vengeance upon the Thug, a vengeance which I will execute, tomorrow.

After we received a message from Outram to say that he was in touch with Laura and that he anticipated an assault upon the Residency within a few days, we set off immediately.

Outram's and Laura's forebodings were proven true, and the Residency is apparently still burning. But Outram, gallant fellow, evacuated his people, including Laura, on to a steamer and sought to make his escape up river. He could not go downstream, because the way was blocked. In any event, on account of the dry weather and the resulting shallowness of the water, his was a hazardous adventure, with the Baluchis controlling the banks to either side. He could thus proceed no more than a few miles, and then anchor and await our arrival. While at anchor his little band, less than a hundred fighting men, was assailed by a huge force of Baluchis.

They survived, however, and were there to greet us when we reached the bank in the small hours of this morning. Then was

I re-united with Laura, who is once again a heroine. It even appears that she killed an enemy female with her bare hands. I have not ascertained the truth of this, and there are those who claim it was murder, but who will believe such a tale?

Certainly Sir Charles will not entertain the notion for a moment. He is in any event more concerned with dispersing the rebels who, we are informed, have taken up a position some half-dozen miles north of Hyderabad to await our assault. Sir Charles has already given the command to prepare to march upon this place, which is apparently called Meanee. Laura is convinced that the devilish Batraj is there, spurring on the rebellion. Thus tomorrow will surely be the day of reckoning for that rascal. I only hope it is not also the day of reckoning for Rajah Sivitraj, but this entirely for Laura's sake. From all accounts he has become a proper Thug himself, and I can see little future for him.

14

The Battle

Laura was woken at three in the morning by the sound of bugles. She felt she had been sleeping more heavily than at any other time in her life; she was utterly exhausted. The women and children had been herded together into one section of the camp, several to a tent, and conditions were nearly as uncomfortable as they had been in the Residency cellar or on board the steamer. But here they were safe in the midst of a British army, a small army, to be sure, less than three thousand strong, of which no more than a fifth were actually British. But all served the Company, and all were quite sure that, properly led, they could deal with any number of Baluchis.

That they were going to be properly led no one could doubt. Once she had got over her initial shock at General Sir Charles Napier's bristling beard and the strangely lop-sided face, Laura was deeply impressed by his energy and obvious strength of character.

He, for his part, knew all about her. 'Highness,' he said. 'It must be the ambition of every soldier in India to meet the celebrated Dowager Rani of Sittapore. I am a most fortunate fellow.'

'The Rani warned us of the impending attack, Sir Charles,' Outram said. 'And then played a most gallant part in the defence.'

'Would you have expected anything else?' Napier asked, and Laura realised that he was not above a gentle flirtation. 'I should be pleased if you would have luncheon with me, Highness, as I am sure you have a great deal to tell me about the Baluchis and especially about this fellow Batraj, your husband.'

'Yes,' Laura agreed. 'My husband.'

310

'Quite so. Incidentally, there is an officer on my staff who is most anxious to renew his acquaintance with you. Do you recollect a Colonel Guy Bartlett?'

She retained her composure. 'Indeed I do, Your Excellency.'

'Then I'll ask you to observe the proprieties while in my encampment, Highness,' the General said drily, indicating that he also knew all about their affair in Kabul.

Laura bowed.

Guy kissed her hands, and looked into her eyes.

It was not possible to do any more than behave as old friends re-united, surrounded as they were by British officers. Napier carefully seated them well apart during the luncheon, which was served on trestle tables erected between the officers' tents; Laura sat on the General's right, and they talked about her experiences in Sind, and her estimation of the Baluchis' capabilities.

'And what of your husband's capabilities, Highness?' the old General asked.

'Prince Batraj has considerable talent as a soldier, Your Excellency, at least as a guerilla.'

'You mean commanding small bodies of troops in difficult country? He does not seem to have distinguished himself as a general in the assault on the Residency.'

'Fortunately for us all,' Laura agreed.

'You understand, Highness, that it is my duty, and my intention, either to kill your husband in battle or to take him prisoner so that he may be hanged.'

'Yes,' Laura said.

'You will, no doubt, be pleased to be free of him.'

'Yes,' Laura said.

'So that you may marry Colonel Bartlett?'

'I would hope to do so, certainly.'

'A strange conversation,' Napier remarked, half to himself. 'But these are strange times, and this is a strange country. Do I then understand that you have little regard for what we might call Christian morality?'

Laura did not take offence. 'I have seen precious little of it practised during the past seventeen years, Your Excellency. But I would like to think I am close to resuming such a way of life.'

Napier's eyes twinkled. 'Provided you are allowed to shape your future as you think best.'

'Of course,' she answered gravely.

Napier crumbled a piece of bread between his fingers. 'What of your children?'

'I would hope to regain them, Your Excellency. My daughter is married to Abbas Ali Khan. Do you not also intend to dispose of him?'

'If he and his people are in arms against me, certainly. Would that also please you?'

'I would like to regain my daughter, Your Excellency.'

'Madam, you frighten me. What of your son?'

'I am afraid he has been suborned by Batraj.'

'You understand that if he too is in arms . . .'

She sighed. 'I know. But you will not condemn me for fighting for his life?'

'Of course not. As you have fought for your own.'

She had wondered when that was coming.

'Yes, Your Excellency. It was her life or mine. She was trying to kill me.'

'As the only witnesses are hostile, I will accept that.'

Laura gazed at him levelly. 'There were no witnesses, Your Excellency.'

Napier smiled. 'Then I certainly accept your word.'

Guy managed to have a word with her during the afternoon, but it was brief, as the army was making ready to march on Meanee. They met in full view of the rest of the camp.

'I love you,' he said.

'As I love you. Do you have to fight tomorrow?'

'That's why I'm here.'

She sighed. 'To have waited so long, travelled so far . . . were anything to happen to you now . . .'

'I've survived so far. Laura, darling . . . tomorrow must settle it.'

'I know,' she said.

*

The bugles sounded, and Laura got up and went outside with Jenny Fisher to watch the army move out into the darkness.

Since he had to leave his encampment adequately protected, Napier could take no more than two thousand men against the Baluchi force, which was estimated by his scouts to number not less than twenty thousand. Some of the scouts placed it at almost double that.

The British had twelve guns commanded by Major Lloyd, and served by fifty Madras sappers; the British regiment was the 22nd, commanded by Colonel Pennefather, less than five hundred strong, but composed in the main of fighting Irishmen; there were three native Bombay regiments, the 25th, 12th and 1st Grenadiers. They were followed by the 9th Bengal Cavalry, commanded by Colonel Pattle, and a contingent of the Sind Horse under Major Jacob.

Guy rode with the General, immediately in front of the infantry. He blew a kiss to Laura as the little force disappeared into the darkness.

The sun was rising by the time the Company army came in sight of the village of Kattree, having marched south from Muttara along the left bank of a small tributary of the Indus, the Fullallee. The country was broken up by a succession of dry water courses, known as nullahs, which not only slowed the march but made any effective cavalry work quite impossible.

The Fullallee was dry at this time of year, but the lie of the land prohibited any flank manoeuvres. Napier surveyed the village through his glass. Flashes of light and movement outside the village could just be seen.

'You'll halt the men, Colonel, while we have a look at those fellows,' the General decided. Guy sent the necessary orders back and Napier cantered forward, leaving his officers no choice but to follow him. As they left the main body, firing broke out in front of them. But the General continued to move forward until he was within a thousand yards of the Baluchi position, when he drew rein and calmly levelled his glass, while his staff struggled to keep their horses under control, for the

313

dust was flying as bullets sang past them, and the horses danced and whinnied nervously.

The Baluchi commander clearly realised that the British had marched themselves into a cul-de-sac, and had made his dispositions with this in mind. Close to, the Baluchi position appeared even stronger, for here the Fullallee made an almost reverse left-handed bend before swinging back to form a rough S. In the crook of the first bend there was a *shikargar*, or hunting park of trees and bushes, fronted by a wall over six feet high, while there was another shikargar in the upper crook. The road led between the two to a ford which made use of an island in the middle of the river before resuming its way to the south bank.

There was a considerable force in the first shikargar, which threatened the British line of advance, although the wall itself presented an obstacle to any rapid enveloping movement for there was only one narrow gateway in the stonework. The Baluchis also lined the far side of the canal on the left, while a strong contingent held the north bank which made a natural fortification, blocking the ford. Here they also had a battery of field guns. Immediately to the right of these was the little village, which was full of tribesmen. From all of these positions muskets were being fired at the little British party.

On the far, southern bank of the river the Baluchi cavalry were gathered under a host of banners, to indicate that their chieftains were also over there. For all the evidence, Guy did not believe they intended to fight a purely defensive battle. Their strategy seemed obvious. By presenting so strong a front, they hoped to force the Company troops into retreat, whereupon they would attempt to surround and overwhelm them by sheer weight of numbers. On the other hand their numbers were far less than he had been led to suppose, not much more than fifteen thousand men.

'Very good, gentlemen,' Napier said, and cantered back to the British lines. 'Mr Robertson, you are bleeding; have that wound attended to. Anyone else who has been hit has my permission to fall out.' He waited for a moment until he was satisfied that everyone present was fit for battle. 'Now, gentlemen, those fellows are well posted. But there do not

314

seem as many as we were warned of earlier. As our room for manoeuvre is limited, I therefore propose to advance and clear the river bank in front of us, and the batteries emplaced there, and force our way across the river so that we may assail the enemy camp, thus opening the road to Hyderabad. In my experience this is the quickest way to discomfort these people. We will carry out the assault in our order of march, extending obliquely to our right. Thus you, Major Lloyd, will anchor our right with your guns.'

Lloyd nodded.

'The 22nd will lead the advance,' Napier went on, 'with the Bombay regiments in echelon on their left. There will be no deployment until we approach the enemy position. Colonel Pattle, the ground between our present position and the village appears quite suitable for cavalry, but it is a very narrow front. For the time being you will hold your horse in reserve and make sure none of the enemy crosses the canal. Should they attempt to do so, charge them. It is on the right flank that we will be vulnerable. I can spare but a single company as flank guard. Captain Tew, when we advance, take your company and line that wall with your people. You must hold that gateway, and confine the Baluchis to this side of the river. Understood?'

'Understood, sir,' Tew agreed.

'Very well. Then let us be at it.'

Having made his dispositions, Napier decided there were no more tactical questions to be considered; only leadership remained. Thus he waited for his company and regimental commanders to rejoin their people, then walked his horse out in front of the troops, and drew his sword.

'The army will advance,' he shouted. Then he wheeled his horse and trotted back towards the enemy, with Guy at his elbow.

The Baluchi fire had slackened after the British officers withdrew, but now it was resumed again as the entire army advanced on the double. The enemy firing remained wild, however, and few of the Company army were hit. The 22nd deployed into line and charged with fixed bayonets uttering blood-curdling cries, then suddenly ceasing their shouting and coming to a halt.

Guy gasped in amazement. Earlier it had appeared that the riverbank behind the guns was thinly held, but now it could be seen that the river bed itself was dry, and in it was a huge mass of twenty thousand warriors, waving their swords as they surged forward.

The young Irishmen ceased their advance, and the native regiments further back also stopped, although they could have no idea what the problem was; they had not yet deployed.

For a moment the outcome of the battle hung in the balance even before it had been properly joined. It needed but one man to turn and run, and the whole British force would disintegrate. But before anyone could do that, Napier once again rode to the front, waving his sword.

'Come on, the 22nd!' he shouted. 'Follow me.'

He rode at the enemy.

'Follow the General!' Guy bellowed, and rode behind Napier.

The 22nd uttered a huge shout, and surged forward once more. Instantly the Bombay Sepoys resumed their advance as well, and the Company troops charged up to and through the Baluchi guns, which had quite failed to dominate the field, and up the bank.

But the Baluchis were made of tougher mettle than the Afghans, and were not afraid of the bayonets; they also had the confidence of numbers, and came swarming up the bank in turn. The two forces met with a tremendous clash of arms, and the morning became hideous with smoke and steel, shrieks and curses, blood and sweat.

Now was the time for the Baluchis, with their great superiority in manpower, completely to envelop the tiny Company army, but the too-rigid plan adopted by their commanders played them false. Those on the banks of the canal feared to cross lest they be caught piecemeal by the British cavalry, which remained motionless on the left wing. Soon they even ceased firing; so dense was the mêlée that they stood every chance of hitting their own people.

To the west, six thousand Baluchis came out of the trees, but were checked by the wall and met by the cool volley-firing of Tew's company. They were driven back in disorder. They came again, and were again repulsed. Tew fell dead, but his men continued their disciplined resistance.

Without them, the battle would certainly have been lost, but even so it was difficult to see how it was to be won. Far from driving the Baluchis in disorder across the dry river and back on their encampment as they had intended, the British force had been brought to a halt on the edge of the bank, where it formed a large, irregular, but determined block, muskets and bayonets thrust forward, against which the Baluchis hurled themselves time and again.

Musketry gave the British troops some advantage. The men loaded and fired with impressive speed, and the range was so close that every bullet struck home. When the Baluchis managed to get to close quarters, tulwar clashed on bayonet or sword, and men glared into each other's eyes from a distance of no more than a foot. A miasma of heat rose above the struggling mass, but neither side would give an inch. When the Baluchis withdrew from sheer exhaustion, it was always but a matter of a few minutes before a fresh onslaught began.

Guy fought with the 22nd, cutting and slashing, thrusting and shouting encouragement as his throat went dry and blood dribbled from a tulwar cut on his left arm. After about an hour every British officer was either dead or wounded, even the indomitable General, who was here, there and everywhere, encouraging his people. There could be only one end to so unequal a struggle. Even if six Baluchis fell to every Company soldier, the odds yet favoured the tribesmen. As exhaustion began to set in, the British would sustain tremendous casualties, while the Baluchis still had fresh troops to hurl into the conflict.

Guy found Napier at his elbow, during one of the brief lulls as the Baluchis regrouped.

'We must end this business, now, or it will be lost,' Napier said, his voice hoarse.

'Yes, sir,' Guy said doubtfully. There was no prospect of getting the exhausted foot soldiers to advance, and to attempt a retreat would mean the total disintegration of the little force.

317

'The cavalry,' Napier said. 'Ride back to Pattle, and tell him to charge these fellows on their right when next they come at us. Full charge, now, Bartlett, on their right. Nothing else will do. It's good ground.'

Guy swallowed. 'Three hundred men, sir?'

Napier's smile was grim. 'Fresh troops, Colonel. Fresh troops. The secret of victory.'

Guy ran back from the line. The officers' horses were held at the rear of the British force by half a dozen orderlies. Guy mounted, and a moment later he was galloping back across the plain, trying to avoid trampling the Company wounded.

One or two Baluchis on the far side of the canal fired at him, but more in derision than anger. They thought he was running away.

He was back with Pattle within ten minutes. The cavalry commander was walking his horse up and down in front of his men, swatting at flies with his crop, and every so often peering at the distant battle.

'What the devil is going on over there, Bartlett?' he demanded. 'You fellows don't seem able to make any progress.'

'You're right. The General wishes you to charge the Baluchi right and see if you can break them up.'

Pattle stared at the mass of men to the left of the British position.

'It's good ground,' Guy assured him. 'I have just ridden over it.'

Pattle nodded. 'You had best stay here, now; you are bleeding.'

'I'll ride with you, if I may.'

Pattle grinned. 'If you can keep up, Colonel.' He rose in his stirrups. 'Major Jacob! We are to disperse the enemy right wing. Your people will form the third line.'

'Yes, sir,' Jacob responded.

Pattle drew his sword. 'Cavalry will advance.'

With a jingle which made Guy's blood tingle the two lines of Bombay cavalry walked their horses forward, taking their lances from their rests as they did so. The Sind Horse, armed only with swords, followed. Guy took his place at Pattle's right shoulder, beside the bugler, who was no more than a lad, his face agleam with determination.

'Trot!'

The speed was increased.

'Canter!'

The Baluchis had observed the advance, but they could not believe that a few hundred men were going to charge at such odds. For the moment they supposed the cavalry were merely moving up to support their infantry.

'Bugler, sound the charge!' Pattle cried, and then leaned forward over his horse's head, sword arm thrust forward, twisted and locked.

Guy followed his example, and the entire force raced forward. A screen of musketeers was hastily thrown out before the Baluchis' position, but the cavalry burst through them as if they had been paper, and careered into the mass beyond. Lances smashed into flesh and bone to send men tumbling to the ground, whereupon the wooden shafts were abandoned, swords were drawn, and the horsemen slashed and cut their way deep into the enemy ranks.

As Napier had foreseen, the cavalry charge was the small weight which, thrown into the balance, turned the scales of battle in his favour. The Baluchis who actually received the charge found themselves driven back and down the embankment, and those engaged in again assaulting the dwindling British force checked to look over their shoulders.

'Now, the 22nd!' Napier shouted, raising his helmet. 'Now, my gallant Bombay boys! Now's your chance.'

Summoning the last of their energy, the British force advanced, and the Baluchis could not recover. Driven to the edge of the bank, they tumbled down into the river bed. Napier now brought his men back under control, ordered them to load their muskets and fire into the mass below them.

Meanwhile the cavalry had cut their way right through the Baluchis, careered down the slope into the river bed, crossed to the southern bank, and ridden right through the enemy encampment, cutting at everything that moved. The camp followers fled in every direction accompanied by the tribesmen, as they finally broke and streamed away to the south.

The bugler sounded the recall, and the horsemen wheeled and cantered back to the river, while more Baluchis fled away from this apparently irresistible force.

Napier came down to congratulate them. 'That was brilliantly done, Colonel Pattle. Colonel Bartlett, you carried out my instructions to the letter. But you are wounded.' He peered at Guy. 'In three places, I would say. Have yourself attended to.'

'They are but scratches, Sir Charles,' Guy protested. 'And there is a lot to be done.'

He wished to go amongst the Baluchi dead, and see if he could discover either Batraj or Sivitraj. It was an immense task, for there were several thousand corpses scattered over the battlefield and in the river. The British casualties were also severe. Twenty officers had been wounded, and six of them were dead. Two hundred and fifty men had gone down, and of these more than fifty were dead. The medical orderlies were having a busy time as they roamed to and fro, gathering the dead, succouring the wounded.

A hasty search convinced Guy that neither of the men he sought had fallen, and by now it was time to attend Napier again, for an envoy had arrived from some of those amirs who had escaped the battle, seeking terms for a peace settlement.

'I demand the surrender of Hyderabad,' the old General told the Baluchi. 'Now. Immediately. This morning.'

'On what terms, Your Excellency?'

'Terms? Why, I will grant life to anyone who does not oppose me, death to anyone who does. Those are my terms.'

The envoy bowed, and Napier continued. 'Excluded from this amnesty is the Thug, Batraj. I wish him delivered to me before the surrender of the city.'

The army was still burying its dead, when six amirs rode into the British position, and offered Napier their swords.

'Is Hyderabad surrendered?' the General demanded.

'The city is yours, General. Abbas Ali Khan, encouraged by Prince Batraj, is determined to continue the fight, and has fled to join the army of Sher Mohammed, who is known as the "Lion of Meerpure".'

'I have heard of this Lion,' Napier said. 'Where is he now?'

'His army lies not ten miles from here.'

Napier frowned. 'Then why did he not take part in the battle?'

The Amir gave a deprecatory shrug. 'When he saw how many were our people, and how few yours, he said he would not fight as it would detract from the glory of our victory.'

'Ha, ha!' Napier cried. 'Then what does he say now?'

'That he will avenge this day for the glory of our people, Your Excellency.'

'Well, I promise you, he will have the opportunity. Meanwhile, we will march on Hyderabad as soon as my people have buried their dead.'

Guy spoke with one of the amirs. 'You say Prince Batraj is still with your people?'

'Yes, to our misfortune, Colonel sahib. He it is who inspires our compatriots to fight on.'

'And the Rajah of Sittapore?'

'He follows his stepfather.'

'You spoke also of Abbas Ali Khan.'

'He is the creature of the Thug, Colonel sahib. Batraj is his father-in-law.'

Guy sighed with exhaustion. Everything needed to be done all over again.

The encampment was broken to allow the remainder of the little army, and the essential medical supplies, to be brought forward. The women and children naturally accompanied them, as Napier intended to send them back to Bombay and safety by ship.

This pleased Guy, although Laura was horrified to learn that he had been wounded.

Meanwhile, the army entered Hyderabad with a tremendous display of pomp, Napier being carried in a palanquin, wearing full dress uniform and all of his ribbons and honours. The onlookers were probably less impressed by his appearance than by the fact that their army had been routed; there were a lot of very glum faces in the watching crowd.

Guy obtained an escort for Laura, and together they went to the house of Abbas Ali Khan, but it was deserted. Mary and Sharita had either fled with their menfolk, or been carried off. In some ways this was a relief, since though Napier forbade the sacking of the city, he nonetheless issued orders that all valuables were to be confiscated for the Company's coffers in order to pay the expenses of the war. This gave the soldiery the right to enter any house they chose, and to force the inhabitants to submit to a search, which included stripping the proud ladies of the harems to the accompaniment of much and ribald laughter.

Outram, of course, also came up, and made a strong protest at this invasion of Muslim custom, but Napier refused to be moved. 'Did they not encourage their menfolk to make war on us?' he demanded. 'There has been no rape.'

'That, sir, is a matter of opinion,' Outram remarked.

Napier was more interested in calling his officers together to hear their views of the military situation.

'I know this fellow Sher Mohammed,' Outram said.

'The Lion,' Napier remarked drily.

'Oh, he is a fierce fighter,' Outram agreed. 'But he is also a fellow of the most remarkable quirks and fancies, given to quite unexpected acts of chivalry, such as his refusal to add to the odds against you at Meanee, Sir Charles.'

'He is a fool then,' Napier said bluntly.

'No doubt. However, I believe I can persuade him that it is now too late to take up arms against us, if you will give me permission, sir.'

Napier considered. He had intended to lead his men directly against the Lion's troops, but he was well aware that the odds would probably be as great as at Meanee, that the Lion's men were entirely fresh while his own were exhausted, and that he had a substantial number of wounded, for whom a few days' rest was essential.

He also needed a brief cessation in the campaign to enable him to summon reinforcements from the garrison at Sukkur.

'Very well, Major,' he said. 'But my terms remain

unchanged. I wish the unconditional surrender of all Baluchi arms, and also of Prince Batraj.'

An envoy was immediately despatched to Sher Mohammed's camp, and the army settled down to prepare itself for whatever lay ahead. Messengers were also immediately sent up to Sukkur.

Meanwhile, Napier moved his people out of the city to the north, to prepare a fortified camp on the bank of the Indus, which was reasonably easy to do because of all the natural defences. The artillery were emplaced, wells and latrines were dug, and the army made itself as comfortable as it could.

'I am concerned about the ladies,' the General confided to Guy. 'But they will just have to sit it out until a ship arrives.' He glanced at his chief-of-staff. 'I suppose that pleases you?'

'I am sure the Dowager Rani prefers to be here, close to her children, than in Bombay, sir,' Guy replied.

Napier snorted.

'Will there be another battle?' Laura asked, as they walked outside the encampment.

'That depends on Sher Mohammed. Or should I say, more likely on Batraj.'

Laura shuddered. 'Then there will be another battle. Oh, Guy, what will become of us?'

'Why, if there is another battle, we shall beat them again.'

'And a lot more men will be killed.'

'That is inevitable. Believe me, I will do everything in my power to see that your son survives.'

Laura sighed. 'And perhaps die yourself in the attempt.'

'Well, they haven't made a very good job of killing me yet. I doubt they'll improve.'

'But why, Guy? Why? What do we wish with this . . . this desert? It is the Baluchis' country. Why cannot they be left in possession of it? Surely we have enough of India for even our greedy needs?'

He raised his eyebrows. 'You are starting to talk like one of the missionary wallahs. Left to themselves, and stirred up by

323

Batraj, the Baluchis would soon be crossing into British India and forcing us to beat them all over again.'

Laura knew she would never persuade any Company officer otherwise. But Guy could see her distress.

'From our point of view, beating Sher Mohammed is the only possible way of ever regaining your children.'

'Our point of view?'

'Your hopes are my hopes, Laura. You know my wife's petition of divorce has been granted by the Lords?'

'I did not know.'

'It is very unusual for a woman to be granted a decree against her husband. I suspect it has only happened because the Dowager Rani of Sittapore has become quite a well-known figure in the English press.'

'You mean I am pilloried there, too.'

'You have your detractors, certainly, but also your staunch supporters. Florentia Sale is certainly one of your leading defenders, and she is a formidable advocate. Laura, what I am trying to say is that I am now a free man. Will you marry me?'

'But that would ruin your career.'

He smiled. 'Not even you can do that to me now, Laura. I am quite a famous solider. The General intends to mention me in despatches yet again. There is every possibility of a brigadier-generalship.'

'Not if you marry me.'

'If I am prepared to remain in India, if *you* are prepared to remain in India, we have only success to look forward to.'

Laura could not meet his eyes. 'I am dedicated to restoring my son to his inheritance.'

'I'm afraid that will have to wait on circumstances. He is doing his cause no good at the moment. However, I will lend you, and him, all the support in my power.'

'Will you?' Her head came up, and then drooped again. 'But I am married to Batraj.'

Guy put his finger beneath her chin to raise her face, and lightly kissed her lips. 'That also needs to be attended to.'

He was so confident, so different from the boy she remembered.

Marriage to Batraj had been a long and painful captivity, in which only hatred had sustained her.

Now, at last, she was sure of one man's love and understanding.

Outram returned from his meeting with Sher Mohammed somewhat chastened.

'The Lion refuses to consider any terms, Sir Charles, save that of your surrender.'

'What did you say?' Napier inquired.

'Sher Mohammed bids me tell you that he commands thirty thousand men whose only dream is to come to grips with John Company, but that if you agree to surrender, he will permit us, together with the women and children, to evacuate Sind, on condition that we never again seek to invade his lands or those held by his compatriots.'

'The devil!' Napier swore.

Outram looked thoroughly distressed. 'There is one proviso, sir.'

'Only one? What is it?'

'That the Dowager Rani of Sittapore be handed over to answer for her crimes and submit to Baluchi justice.'

Napier glanced at Guy.

'Batraj!' Guy said.

'Of course.'

'What answer shall we send to Sher Mohammed, sir?' Outram inquired.

'Tell him my terms are the same as before,' Napier said.

The two armies then settled down to a waiting game. Even though he claimed to command thirty thousand men, the Lion was not apparently disposed to attack a well-entrenched British force. And while Napier had every intention of carrying the fight to the enemy as soon as it became possible, he needed his reinforcements from Sukkur. He was in no hurry; he had sufficient water and food for a lengthy stay. He controlled the river, so that he could always withdraw his people if he chose, having now accumulated sufficient boats and small ships, including the two steamers.

From Guy's point of view the waiting meant he could see Laura, even if it was frustrating to have to behave with the utmost propriety. To an extent he shared her distraction as to what might be happening to her children: Mary had now been married for well over a month.

A ship came upriver from Kurrachee, and the women and children were embarked.

'I am to go to Bombay alone?' Laura asked in dismay.

'Outram is accompanying you. And Jennie Fisher will look after you,' Guy said reassuringly. 'Until I get there.'

She smiled bravely, but he knew she was thinking: what if you never do arrive there?

The reinforcements from Sukkur arrived on the morning of 23 March, and brought the British strength up to five thousand men. Two cavalry regiments came with them, so Napier now had a thousand mounted men, as well as nineteen guns.

The rest of the day was spent in teaching the new troops the tactics he intended to use. At dusk a further emissary arrived from Sher Mohammed, once again demanding that the British force surrender, or the Lion would march upon them.

Napier merely smiled. 'You have been to our camp before,' he told the envoy.

'Oh yes, General sahib.'

'And do you remember what you saw?'

The envoy looked nervous. 'I remember some things, General sahib?'

'Nonsense,' Napier told him. 'You remember everything. That is part of the business of being an envoy. Now my aide, Colonel Bartlett, is going to take you through the camp. I wish you to tell what you have seen to the Lion. He will be interested.'

The envoy followed Guy as he was led through the various detachments, most of which were standing to. Then the unhappy Baluchi was brought back before Napier.

'You will have seen that my numbers have been doubled since last you were here,' the General said. 'Be sure you tell the Lion of this. And tell him also, he has no need to come to me. I intend to come to him. Tomorrow.'

The envoy mounted his horse and rode from the camp as fast as he could.

Napier smiled at his officers. 'Tomorrow, gentlemen.'

Hyderabad, 23 March 1843

We join battle again tomorrow morning.

Batraj still keeps the field. He has now allied himself to a chieftain who calls himself the Lion of Meerpure, and is reputed to command the usual astronomical numbers of followers. But as our strength has recently been doubled, we approach the coming conflict with total confidence.

Laura has been sent to Bombay with the other women and the children, and is thus removed from all danger, to my great relief. Outram went with them, bristling with indignation at what he regards as the indecent and impolitic treatment of the Baluchis who surrendered to us, particularly their womenfolk. In fact, much as I admire the General for his determination and his warlike qualities, I feel he was a little harsh in his approach to the Baluchi ladies, apparently regarding them as being every bit as guilty of insurrection as their husbands. No doubt there will be a great to-do when Outram's report reaches London. By then, however, this campaign will surely be completed.

How many times have I claimed to have Batraj in my sights? But now at last I have a general who is determined to bring him down, no matter what it takes.

15

The Pursuit

Having established that the Lion was to be found near the village of Dubba to the north-east of the city, with twenty-five thousand men, Napier determined to repeat the strategy which had stood him in good stead at Meanee, and march straight at him. Reveille was sounded at three in the morning, and the Company army moved out soon after.

The column was led by the Poona Horse, followed by the 9th Cavalry. Then came the five infantry regiments, the 22nd, now under the command of Major Poole, and the Bombay Native Brigade commanded by Major Woodburn, consisting of the 25th, the 21st, the 12th and the 8th. The 3rd Cavalry and the Sind Horse brought up the rear. Of the guns, five were horse artillery at the rear of the column, the other fourteen were at the head.

It promised to be as hot as usual, and the men sweated and cursed, but were nonetheless impatient to get at the enemy.

Some five hours after they left the encampment, they were back at the Fullallee, this time fording it unopposed at the village of Chilgheree. Beyond it they saw the Baluchi army.

The river here made a huge slow right-handed bend, in the semi-circle of which were the two villages of Chilgheree and Dubba two miles apart. Thus there was no river barrier held by the Baluchis, as they had attempted at Meanee.

The land was broken up by nullahs, some more than twenty feet wide and as much as eight feet deep. The Baluchis were extended along several of these stretching south from Dubba. The Lion was totally confident of victory, and banners fluttered over the gaily coloured tents of his harem behind the village.

Napier rode forward to inspect the enemy position, and gave

orders for the army to deploy to the left as they crossed the river, thus taking up a front opposite the tribesmen.

'They are strongly posted, and this Lion has a formidable reputation as a soldier,' he said. 'We must see if we can lure them out of their position, and into an attack.'

The Poona Horse and the 9th Cavalry therefore set off almost due north to reach the river bank at the top of the loop. The infantry followed, the 3rd Cavalry and the Sind Horse continuing to act as rearguard at the ford. Once all his men were in position, Napier arranged the guns in three batteries evenly spaced along his front, and told them to commence firing, which they promptly did. Napier then rode up the line to join the 22nd, who were again to lead the assault, although this time on the left of the British order of battle.

'Now, my brave boys,' he urged them, 'Now . . .'

He was interrupted by an outbreak of shouts and firing from the far end of the British position. He turned, levelling his glass. The rearguard horse, quite without orders, were charging at the Baluchi line, which was situated at the edge of a small wood and which Major Stack, the cavalry commander, had observed becoming restless under the artillery bombardment. Their way lay across several nullahs, but they were jumping these with tremendous elan, cheering and shouting.

Without a word, Napier put spurs to his horse and galloped off, Guy at his heels. They drew rein when they saw the horsemen crashing into the surprised Baluchis, who now were most certainly giving way.

'By God,' Napier muttered. 'One learns, all the time. We must take advantage of this. The entire army will advance on the double, Colonel.'

They set off back along the line, waving their swords and summoning the men who, with a deafening shout, immediately charged at the Baluchis.

Again the tribesmen were surprised. They rose out of the first nullah, to be met by the thrusting bayonets and sent tumbling back in dismay. The Irish and the Sepoys followed them, bursting across the second nullah, up to the houses of Dubba itself.

Here some of the Baluchis rallied, but the Lion was already

330

in flight, abandoning his tents and most of his women, although from the shrieks in the distance it seemed he had taken his favourites. He was hotly pursued by the British cavalry, who were hacking down and spearing the fugitives. Napier himself went in pursuit for a couple of miles, before calling his men to order and returning to the village to consolidate his victory.

Dubba was one of the briefest and yet most vicious actions ever fought by the British army in India. After only a couple of hours, five thousand Baluchis had been killed in the field or in the pursuit. Two hundred and seventy officers and men of the Company army had also fallen, of whom more than half were from the 22nd.

'Well, Colonel Bartlett,' Napier said. 'I would say that is the end of all organised resistance from these people. Not that I intend to let the Lion get away. We'll mount a pursuit. But the campaign is effectively over. I must send a despatch back to Bombay at the earliest moment. What shall I tell them, do you suggest?'

'That you came, you saw, you conquered, sir?'

'*Veni, vidi, vici,* eh? That confounded fellow Caesar used it damn near two thousand years ago. I shall have to improve on that.' He smiled. 'I shall amuse their lordships. They sent me to conquer Sind. Well then . . . *peccavi*. You know your Latin, Bartlett?'

'*Peccavi*! I have sinned.'

'Is that not brilliant? Yes, indeed. *Peccavi*.'

'What are your orders now, sir?'

'We mustn't give those rascals time to recover. I want as many fresh men as can be found sent off immediately, to keep them on the run. How many people do you estimate fled with Sher Mohammed?'

'If we include his women, several hundred. But I doubt more than two hundred fighting men, although he may well recruit from among the fugitives. I would like permission to command the pursuit, sir.'

'You, Bartlett?' Napier stroked his chin. 'It is an unChristian morality, to wish to hunt down the husband of your mistress. You do not even know that Batraj accompanied Sher Mohammed.'

'He is certainly not here. And I cannot pretend to have any Christian feelings towards Batraj, General. But there is an even more personal matter involved. Fourteen years ago the Thug made a fool of me and destroyed the company I was commanding.'

'Revenge is also an unChristian self-indulgence,' Napier said. 'You are sure he will not make a fool of you again?'

'I will endeavour to make sure, sir. It also appears that Rajah Sivitraj has fled with his stepfather, and Abbas Ali Khan is also apparently with the Lion.'

'With the Dowager Rani's daughter. I cannot help but feel that you are too personally involved in this business, Bartlett.'

'I merely need to know your mind, sir: whom do you consider the more important, Batraj or Sher Mohammed? Supposing they divide their forces?'

Napier considered for a few minutes. 'Batraj is the true troublemaker. He must be got rid of. You'll take an adequate force; as you say, he may have been accompanied by only two hundred men when he left the field, but he will certainly have regained some support on the road. You will need two squadrons of lancers, two companies of Sepoys mounted on mules, and two field guns. Organise it.' He pointed. 'Colonel Bartlett! We want to end this business as quickly and cheaply as possible. Any amir who offers to surrender with his people is to be accommodated. That includes Sher Mohammed himself.'

'Does that also apply to Prince Batraj, sir?'

'No, it does not. Just make sure that this time you beat the beggar. And remember that I am moving to your support.'

Guy had no means of telling Laura what he was doing, but he had no doubt she would approve; both of her children were with Sher Mohammed. He rode immediately to where Pattle and his men were resting, and gave them Napier's orders.

Pattle nodded. 'You'll want volunteers,' he decided. 'Major Brewster, call out the men.'

When the regiment was assembled and told of the mission, every man stepped forward.

'Good lads,' Pattle said. 'Very well. A Troop, Captain Onslow; B Troop, Captain Kelly. Now, lads, you'll be under the command of Colonel Bartlett, and you'll obey him as you would obey me. The Colonel is not a cavalryman, but you'll remember that he rode with us at Meanee and proved himself as good as any cavalryman there ever was. Good fortune, and good hunting.'

The men gave a cheer. Equally satisfying was the response from the infantry; the allotted companies were commanded respectively by Captains Brotherton and Avery. Lieutenant Barker commanded the two horse artillery pieces. Guy also called for two loyal Baluchi guides, Samji and Mudha Ali; they would follow the trail for him.

By now the commissariat wagons had come up, and Guy was able to draw three days' rations for his men. He knew there was some pretty rugged country ahead of them, but he didn't intend to lose an hour. By mid afternoon the little brigade of three hundred men was ready to march out.

Many of the Baluchis had fled south and west, but from information given by prisoners Guy already knew that the Lion had fled north along the river, apparently making for Rajputana. One of the captured amirs said that Batraj had gone with him, another that he had not. But Abbas Ali Khan had certainly accompanied Sher Mohammed, and there had been several women with the party. That Batraj had gone with them, and almost certainly Sivitraj and Mary as well, seemed certain.

It was Batraj Guy wanted, even more than did Napier. He was not sure if he wanted Sivitraj or not. He wished to cause Laura as little grief as possible, but Sivitraj had certainly taken up arms against the Company. If he now surrendered his life at least would be safe. If he chose to follow his stepfather, then he must meet the same fate.

The first part of the pursuit was simple enough. It was merely a matter of following the discarded weapons of the fleeing Baluchis; often enough there were men lying dead or dying as

333

well. The road led through a succession of villages, many of which were deserted as the inhabitants had run off at the news that the dreaded John Company had won another victory.

The column camped for the night at one of these, and next morning resumed their march an hour before dawn. Now they were on the edge of the true desert, the Thar, which stretched for hundreds of miles to the east. Beside the river, however, the land remained reasonably fertile.

They halted again at noon, and rested for three hours until the heat had gone out of the sun, then pressed on again. Now the land began to rise, and they were among low, barren hills. Guy had no intention of being ambushed again, and threw out a flanking patrol as well as an advance guard.

Onslow, the senior captain, was having similar thoughts. 'Good place for an ambush,' he commented.

'Something at which Batraj is adept,' Guy agreed.

Next day they came upon the naked bodies of three women by the side of the trail. They had been mutilated and their throats had been cut. Guy's stomach rolled as he peered at them, but all were definitely too dark and too old to be Mary.

'What do you make of it?' Onslow asked.

'They're getting rid of the unwanted,' Guy told him.

The men mounted and rode on, their faces grim.

That afternoon they saw flashes of light ahead of them, and soon the advance guard returned, with one man killed and three wounded.

'They came at us sudden like, sir,' the sergeant explained.

'How many?'

'A good number, sir. Several hundred.'

'Are they still there?'

'Reckon so, sir. They was firing at us as we rode off.'

Guy rode out a little way to survey the possible battlefield through his glass. Batraj was definitely in command, he decided; he had chosen a similar position to that north of Sittapore, with one vital difference. The road led between the river and the hills, making it almost obligatory for the pursuing force to pass beneath the hillside; if the entire brigade turned off to flank the hill, not only would a great deal of time be

334

wasted, Batraj would be able to watch its every move. His position was nowhere as strong as fourteen years ago, yet it was a reasonable place for an ambush, and there was no telling how much support he had accumulated during the past twenty-four hours.

Would he remain there or, his position now being known to the pursuers, pull out? Guy thought he would remain there, and wait for the pursuers to challenge him.

Guy called his officers together. He knew they were a little uneasy; the story of his ambush and defeat fourteen years before was fairly common knowledge.

'We'll pitch camp here. If Batraj is in command, that's what he'd expect us to do. But this time we'll do some ambushing of our own. Captain Kelly, as soon as it is dark I wish you to take your squadron off to the right, walking your horses for the first two miles, until you are out of earshot of the enemy. Then see if you can work your way round that hill. The rest of us will advance one hour before dawn. If you do find a way, Captain, hold any offensive action until you hear our bugle.'

Kelly nodded, and went off to speak with his eighty-odd men. The other two hundred and fifty pitched camp in full view of the enemy, and ate their evening meal as the sun sank into the mountains beyond the river to the west, while Guy allowed himself to reflect how convenient it would be if Batraj were to attack.

'You don't think it could be a trap?' Onslow inquired over dinner. 'We don't know how many men he has.'

'True. But the Baluchis have a healthy respect for Company troops. Oh, they'd have liked us to enter the defile blind, but that didn't work. As we're here, they'll expect us to force the road tomorrow.'

'And you intend to oblige.'

'Oh, indeed.'

At three in the morning the brigade was stood to. It was a still night, and there was little hope of concealing their movements, so Guy did not attempt to try. He left a platoon to hold the camp, and ordered a general advance. When they reached the defile, he called a halt and went forward, accompanied by the sergeant, to have a closer look through his binoculars. It was now broad daylight.

'They came from up there on the right, sir.'

Guy studied the rocks. If Batraj was in command, he thought, he did not have his people as well in hand as he had had his Thugs, so long ago. Quite apart from the alerting of the advance guard, he could make out several gleams of light amidst the bushes and rocks on the shallow hillside. He suspected that Batraj would probably use the same tactical plan as before, especially in such similar terrain.

He rode back to his officers.

'Dismount your infantry, Captain Brotherton, Captain Avery,' he said. 'Take them forward to just within musket shot. When the command is given, advance and clear the hillside. Lieutenant Barker, unlimber your guns, and throw some shot on to that right hand slope. Captain Onslow, you will hold your men for the charge.'

Guy then went forward with Barker to see the two guns emplaced. They were still out of musket range of the hillside, but Guy estimated there were several hundred men up there.

By now Brotherton and Avery had taken their eager Sepoys forward. The Baluchis could restrain themselves no longer. Puffs of smoke began to appear amidst the rocks as they opened fire.

The cannon exploded, and shrapnel shells burst over the Baluchi position.

'Two more, Mr Barker.'

Once again the shells burst amidst shrieks and screams from the Baluchis. The firing from the hillside was now very ragged. 'Sound the charge,' Guy ordered, and Brotherton and Avery, now a good quarter of a mile in front of the artillery, led their men at the double up the hill, bayonets fixed.

The Baluchis rose from concealment to meet them, but were soon fleeing for their horses on the far side of the hill. Guy summoned Onslow and his horsemen and rode forward behind the infantry, leaving Barker to limber up his guns and follow.

The last of the Baluchis were now in full flight and Guy led Onslow's men into a canter. Kelly brought his men round in a wide sweep, and charged the fleeing men.

When it was all over, Guy was amazed to find that he had lost only the one man of the advance guard, while thirty Baluchi tribesmen lay dead.

Several prisoners had been taken. One in particular was richly dressed, a sullen-looking man with a drooping moustache.

'Your name?' Guy demanded.

'I have no name.'

Guy looked round at the other men. 'His name?' he said. 'Or I will have one of you hanged.'

The men shuffled their feet.

'I will give you five seconds . . .'

'I am Abbas Ali Khan,' the man said.

'Ah,' Guy commented. 'You had best come and sit with me, Your Excellency. We must talk.'

'Where is the Lion?' Guy asked.

'He flees north, for Rajputana,' Abbas said.

'With Prince Batraj? Was Batraj here?'

'He was. But he left.'

'You mean he ran away. How far away is the Lion's encampment?'

'Not far.'

'Where is your wife?'

'She is with the Lion, and Batraj.'

'Whose idea was it to stop and fight us?'

'Batraj's. The Lion has given him command of his soldiers. Batraj said we would stop you here, that you would abandon the pursuit. But as soon as things went badly . . .'

'He rode off. Was Rajah Sivitraj with him?'

Abbas Ali Khan shook his head. 'The Rajah was wounded in the fight at Dubba.'

Guy frowned. 'Badly?'

'No. But he cannot use his right arm.'

'Hm. And your young wife. Is she well?'

'She is well.'

'Good. Well, Your Excellency, I am going to release you to rejoin your wife and family.'

Abbas gazed at him apprehensively.

337

'I will allow you some three hours' start before I resume my march. When you catch up with Prince Batraj, tell him that this pursuit column is commanded by Colonel Guy Bartlett. Remind him that Colonel Bartlett pursued him once before, unsuccessfully, but that this time he intends to overtake him and capture him and carry him back to Bombay for execution, no matter how long it takes. Do you understand this?'

Abbas swallowed. 'I understand.'

'Good. I would also like you to speak with Rajah Sivitraj, and tell him that should he abandon the Lion and Batraj, he will be welcomed by General Napier. The same goes for yourself.'

'I *have* abandoned them,' Abbas protested. 'I willingly surrender myself to the jurisdiction of the Company.'

'I will not allow you to do so until after you have delivered my message,' Guy told him.

'Batraj will kill me if I attempt to desert.'

'Batraj will wish to stand and fight, when he learns that it is I who pursue him,' Guy said. 'You will stand and fight with him. How many men does he command?'

'There are eight hundred men with the Lion,' Abbas said. 'It is a question of how many will follow Batraj?'

'And how many of them will follow you?'

'Two hundred of them are my people.'

'Good. Then when battle is joined, you will turn your men on Batraj and fight for me.'

Abbas licked his lips.

'There is no need to worry about the safety of your wife,' Guy told him. 'Batraj will hardly slay his own daughter. But be sure that if you play me false, I will have you hanged beside the Prince.'

Abbas licked his lips again.

'Captain Kelly, provide His Excellency with a horse,' Guy commanded.

Abbas, obviously in a highly nervous state, mounted and rode off.

'We will camp for three hours,' Guy told his officers, 'and then resume our march.'

'Will Batraj really stand and fight this time?' Onslow asked.

'I am certain of it.'

'And you have suborned part of his command. By God, Colonel, that has a touch of Robert Clive about it.'

'Why, yes, so it does,' Guy agreed.

'A lone horseman,' Sivitraj said, stepping outside the tent.

His arm, broken in a fall from his horse, was in a sling, and the pain was making him restless. He was also still distressed by Sher Mohammed's decision to murder three of his older concubines merely because they were complaining. But he was not alone in his unhappiness. Gloom hung over the Baluchi encampment. In vain Batraj had tried to remind everyone that he had sought only to check the British, and cause them casualties. But the plan had gone disastrously wrong. In vain he railed against his son-in-law, who had allowed his people to open fire long before the proper time, and so alerted the enemy. Thus, far from inflicting heavy casualties on the British, they had suffered heavy casualties themselves, and been driven from the field in rout. And they had lost Abbas Ali Khan.

Mary was inconsolable. In the month she had been married she had grown fond of her husband. Now she stared at her father with angry eyes.

Batraj and Sher Mohammed came out to join Sivitraj. They peered into the darkness, and listened to the challenge from the sentries.

'Abbas Ali Khan,' came the shouts. 'It is Abbas Ali Khan.'

'My husband!' Mary shrieked, and ran to throw herself into Abbas' arms. 'Oh, my dear love! We thought you dead.'

Abbas hugged her, and glared defiantly at the waiting princes.

'Where have you been?' Batraj demanded.

'I was taken by the British. And I was released, to give you this message: that the commander of the force pursuing you is Colonel Guy Bartlett . . .'

'Bartlett?' Batraj spat.

' . . . and that he intends to pursue you to the death, and avenge both his defeat of fourteen years ago, and the wrongs you have inflicted upon the Dowager Rani of Sittapore. He sends too a message to Rajah Sivitraj, that the Company will welcome his surrender, and see that he is re-united with his mother.'

'You know of this man?' Sher Mohammed inquired of Batraj.

'Oh, yes,' Batraj growled. 'He is an old friend. Once I had him at my mercy, because he was a fool. I spared his life, because I was a fool. I suspect he is a fool still, to send me such a message. But I am no longer a fool.'

'He defeated you this morning,' Sher Mohammed pointed out. The Lion was probably the only man in all India who would have dared remind Batraj of that.

'Because of the stupidity of Abbas Ali Khan's people,' Batraj declared. 'But now I know who opposes me . . . why, we will end this pursuit. How many men does Bartlett command?' he asked Abbas Ali Khan.

'Less than three hundred. But he has two guns.'

'Two guns,' Batraj said contemptuously. 'He has learned something, since our last meeting, but not enough. Bring me the map.'

He returned to his tent, and the map was spread on the carpet.

'How far is Bartlett behind us?' Batraj asked Abbas.

'Only a few hours.'

'Then we must break camp immediately.' He prodded the map. 'I wish to reach Aymalia by dawn. We will wait for Bartlett there.'

'Aymalia is to the east,' Sher Mohammed objected. 'It is in the desert.'

Batraj nodded. 'Yes. But when Bartlett follows us, he will be in the desert too. He must reach the oasis, and gain possession of it, or perish with all his people. We will already hold the oasis.'

Sher Mohammed pulled thoughtfully at his beard. 'I wish to go north,' he said. 'There is nothing in the desert.'

'We will go north again when we have dealt with Bartlett,' Batraj told him.

'And if we are defeated? There is nowhere to run in the desert.'

340

'You think only of defeat, of running,' Batraj said contemptuously. 'How came you by the name of Lion?'

Sher Mohammed glared, but said nothing.

'We are not going to be defeated,' Batraj asserted. 'We outnumber Bartlett by three to one.'

'We outnumbered Napier by five to one at Dubba,' Sivitraj pointed out. 'And at Meanee by ten to one.'

His stepfather glared at him.

'I am going north,' Sher Mohammed said.

'Very well. Leave me sufficient men to deal with Bartlett. Six hundred will be enough.'

'Then I will have only my escort.'

'You will need nothing more.'

'And suppose Bartlett ignores you and follows me?'

Batraj smiled. 'He will follow me. You may be certain of that. I am important to him.'

'He may divide his force, and follow us both,' Abbas Ali Khan suggested.

'Will that not be to our advantage, since we can then destroy him piecemeal? But I do not think he will do that, not when he knows where I have gone. It is I whom he seeks,' Batraj said proudly, 'both because there is a price on my head, and because he wishes to marry my wife. Oh, yes, it is I whom he seeks. Now, let us make haste.'

'My wives will not like it,' Sher Mohammed grumbled. 'They are weary, and want a good night's sleep.'

'Is it you, or your wives, who commands?' Batraj inquired. 'Well then, stay here and wait for Bartlett. I will take my men and ride for Aymalia.'

'I will ride with you,' Abbas Ali Khan said grudgingly.

After three hours the column continued on its way, but at dusk Guy called a halt.

'What will the Thug do?' Onslow asked.

'He will seek the best defensive position, and hope to lure us into some kind of a trap,' Guy said.

The next day, they had not ridden very far when they came upon the most recent Baluchi encampment. The guides

341

sniffed around. 'It is ten, maybe twelve hours since they left, Colonel sahib,' Samji said.

'And then the party split in two,' Mudhas Ali explained, pointing to the diverging sets of tracks. 'The party travelling north has the women and the camels. That making west has horses and mostly men, but I think there are some women with it as well.'

The river was still close, and the north-leading tracks followed its course. The other tracks headed into the desert.

'Where is the nearest water to the east?' he asked Samji.

'There is water at Aymalia, Colonel sahib. It is twenty miles to the east.'

'And it is now held by the enemy, I would say,' Onslow suggested.

'Oh, indeed. But at least we know where he is. Twenty miles. Very good, gentlemen. We will camp here for the rest of the day. Make sure all your men, and particularly the horses, are well rested and watered. We will move out at dusk and march through the night. Captain Kelly, take your squadron and continue to the north, just to make sure it is no part of Sher Mohammed's plan to double back.'

'With respect, sir, but that will reduce our effective force to two hundred and fifty men,' Onslow protested.

'We will have enough. Make sure that your men have their canteens full when we leave, and that the skins for the horses are also full. Thank you, gentlemen.'

All now depended upon Abbas Ali Khan playing his part.

The people of Aymalia glared sullenly as the tribesmen took over their village. They were Baluchis, but here in the north had played no part in the recent uprising. They wished no part of it now, yet it had been brought to their doorstep. The headman had protested, and had been told to shut up and mind his own business. Now the goats had been brought in from pasture, and the tribesmen were digging themselves in on the outskirts of the village.

'It is possible that Bartlett may attempt another flank manoeuvre,' Batraj said. 'You, Abbas Ali Khan, will hold the north side of the village with your people. Remember that no man is to fire until I give the command. Bertus Khan, you will hold the south side with fifty men. Jodas Khan, you will take twenty-five men to guard the east. But the main force will be here on the west with me, because this is where the British will come.'

The amirs nodded, and took their positions.

'You have no post for me,' Sivitraj remarked.

'You are wounded. You will be useless,' Batraj told his stepson. 'And perhaps you secretly wish to be re-united with your mother, as Bartlett has offered.'

'I will not desert you,' Sivitraj said.

'Do not even think of it,' Batraj told him. 'Now go to the women.'

Sivitraj was seething with rage as he joined his sister and Abbas Ali Khan's other wives who, with Sharita and Batraj's two women, were occupying the headman's house.

'Are the British here?' Mary asked anxiously.

'Not yet.'

'My husband has told me he does not wish to have to fight them,' Mary whispered to her brother, casting anxious glances at the other women.

'Has he told your father this?'

She shook her head. 'He is afraid to do so.'

'With good reason.'

'But Sivitraj . . .' she clung to his arm. 'I do not wish him to fight either. He was nearly killed the last time he fought. My father rode away and left him to be captured.'

'Well,' Sivitraj said. 'Your father cannot ride away now, because there is nowhere to go.' But he put his good arm round her shoulder to hug her, for he was genuinely fond of his little half-sister. 'I believe he may well win, today.'

'It is going to be hot,' Onslow remarked, unnecessarily; it was already hot.

'All according to Batraj's plan,' Guy told him. 'He must be rubbing his hands with glee.'

'But you have a better plan,' Onslow said, hopefully. 'Do you trust Abbas Ali Khan?'

Guy grinned at him. 'I have no choice.'

If his plan failed, he knew, he could lose his whole force. The men had so far responded well, and had followed their orders to be very sparing with their water. But that had been during the night. Once the heat really grew fierce, they would consume their supplies much more rapidly. Then it would be a case of taking the oasis or dying. Guy did not suppose many of them would make it back to the river, especially with Batraj's people at their heels.

He called for Samji. 'How much further?'

'It is near now, Colonel sahib.'

'It had better be,' Guy growled.

An hour later the oasis came into sight. Guy called a halt, and told the men to eat.

'Captain Onslow, you will hold your cavalry on the left wing, just out of musket range. Your business will be to charge the Baluchis should they attempt to come at us, and to make sure none of them escape to the east. We must finish this business today.'

Onslow nodded.

'Captain Brotherton, Captain Avery, you will dismount your men and advance to musket range, taking advantage of all possible cover. The artillery will provide a barrage, and I wish you to continue to work your way forward, as steadily as possible.'

The two captains exchanged glances.

'How far are we to advance, sir?'

'You will advance, Captain Brotherton, until you are told to stop, or until the charge is sounded. Understood?'

'Yes, sir.' Samji had told Browning that there were more than six hundred men in the oasis. Neither of the infantry officers knew of Guy's bargain with Abbas Ali Khan, but even Onslow, who did know of it, felt apprehensive. There was no telling whether or not the amir would betray them in turn.

Guy rode forward with Barker to site the guns.

'There will be women and children in the oasis, Colonel,' the Lieutenant pointed out.

'I know. But it can't be helped.' Guy replied. 'I will see what can be done.'

He called for Samji and a lancer trooper, tied his spare shirt

344

to the lance as a flag of truce, and walked his horse forward, Samji to one side and the trooper to the other. Behind him the infantry quietly took up their positions before the guns.

Knowing he was in the sights of several hundred muskets, Guy advanced until he was within fifty yards of the oasis. He took a long breath.

'Prince Batraj!' he shouted. 'This is Colonel Guy Bartlett. You are wanted by the Company for the crimes of rebellion and murder. There can be no escape for you. We have hunted you the length and breadth of this land, but now you can flee no more. You are cornered, and must surrender or die. Why waste the lives of your people, of your women and children? Have not sufficient of your warriors fallen in battle, at Meanee and Dubba? Surrender, and put an end to this conflict.'

There was some movement and for a moment he thought he might have gained a point. Then Batraj shouted. 'You must come and get me, Bartlett. If you can.'

'If that is your decision,' Guy said. 'But I will give you one hour to evacuate your women and your children and your wounded. Then I intend to bombard the oasis.'

'Our women and children fight and die with us,' Batraj bellowed.

Guy waited a further minute, then walked his horse back to the Sepoys. 'Nonetheless,' he told his officers. 'We will give them the full hour. Tell your men to rest without leaving their positions.'

'You are a fool,' Abbas Ali Khan remarked. 'You should have let the women and children go.'

'We are here to fight and win,' Batraj insisted. 'All of us. Let Bartlett bombard the oasis. He will run out of water, and then we will destroy him.'

'The women and children have no part in our quarrel,' Abbas insisted. 'They are innocent. Why should they suffer?'

'They are traitors who would not support our cause,' Batraj snarled. 'They should suffer more than anyone else. Do not let me hear any more of your coward's talk, Abbas Ali Khan. Prepare to fight like a man.'

Abbas got up and walked away through the trees. He met

345

Sivitraj, who had been listening to the exchange between Batraj and Guy.

'Your stepfather is bent upon destruction,' Abbas remarked.

'Destruction of the British,' Sivitraj suggested.

'The British will not be beaten,' Abbas told him. He looked as if he might say more, then changed his mind. 'Sivitraj, brother-in-law, care for my wife, your sister, no matter what happens.'

'The British do not make war upon women,' Sivitraj told him.

Abbas caught his arm. 'Nonetheless, care for her. I make this your charge. Care for her.'

Guy studied his watch. The sun was now high and scorching, and the red tunics of the Sepoys were stained with sweat.

'One hour,' he said. 'You will open fire, Mr Barker. May God have mercy on their souls.'

The order was given, and the two field pieces exploded.

The first shells burst amongst the trees, and caused a tremendous chorus of screams and shrieks, and the barking of dogs. Sivitraj instinctively ducked, and hurried back towards the house where Sharita and Mary and the other women were huddled together, their hands over their ears.

'We will all be killed!' Sharita wailed. 'We will all be killed.'

Yet more shells burst overhead. Sivitraj could hear the whistle of the shrapnel as it cut through the trees, the cries of men who had been hit. He dropped to his knees and watched the little force out there in the desert, the line of red-coated Sepoys moving forward, sometimes running, sometimes crawling, disappearing from sight as they found shelter in shallow depressions or behind rocks, every so often pausing to deliver a volley.

The Baluchis were replying, but their firing was far less accurate.

Sivitraj went to Batraj. 'Why do you not simply charge those people?' he asked. 'We outnumber them by two to one. And this is not like Meanee; here we can surround them.'

'You are a foolish boy,' Batraj told him. 'That is just what

346

Bartlett wishes us to do, leave our sheltered position so that he can send his cavalry to charge us in the flank. All we need to do is wait.'

Sivitraj made his way to where Abbas Ali Khan and his men guarded the northern perimeter of the oasis.

Abbas Ali Khan was walking up and down between the trees; no shells had burst here as yet.

'What is happening?' he asked Sivitraj.

'The Company infantry are advancing, while their guns blow the oasis to pieces. But my stepfather is still sure of victory.'

'It will soon be time,' Abbas Ali Khan said. 'Perhaps it is time now. Listen, Rajah Sivitraj, you have sworn to protect my wife, who is your sister.'

'If it is possible.'

'Then go to her, and protect her. Now.'

'But . . .'

'Go,' Abbas Ali Khan insisted. 'You have given me your word.'

Sivitraj hesitated, then hurried back to the village, pausing only to duck when a shell burst above his head.

Guy levelled his telescope, but could discern very little. As the Sepoys approached the trees men were being hit, red blotches on the brown of the sand. Guy could not tell whether they were inflicting any casualties on Batraj's people. It was time for Abbas Ali Khan to turn on Batraj, for if the Sepoys actually reached the oasis they could easily be overwhelmed by Batraj's superior numbers.

'Sound the charge!' he said.

The two Sepoy companies responded immediately, rising from their concealment to stand shoulder to shoulder, bayonets fixed.

At the same time Onslow led his horsemen forward.

From the oasis there came a volley, and several of the Sepoys fell. Suddenly, there was firing from the Baluchi right, and shouts of surprise and anger as Abbas Ali Khan sent his people through the trees to fall on Batraj's rear.

347

The Sepoys charged. Guy drew his sword and dashed forward to be in at the kill.

When he saw his men fall, and Abbas Ali Khan, tulwar drawn, waving his people forward, Batraj thought he would explode with rage and frustration. But then his habitual good sense took over. This battle was lost thanks to his son-in-law's treachery, but he would live to fight another day, and would have his revenge.

'Shoot them down!' he bellowed at his wavering men. 'Shoot them down.'

He dashed into the trees, threw himself down as if hit, and began to crawl unseen back towards the village as the Sepoys reached the oasis.

He scrambled to his feet and ran towards the houses. He went first to the house where the women were.

'Where is Sivitraj?' he demanded of Mary.

'He went outside. What is happening, Father?'

'Your husband has betrayed me,' Batraj said. 'I will have my revenge.'

He leapt at her, swinging his tulwar. Mary screamed and hurled herself across the room.

'Father!' she shouted. 'I am your daughter!'

He stood over her. 'You are a hateful thing,' he snarled, 'a creature of that she-devil's womb! You are no daughter of mine!'

He grasped her hair and dragged her head back. She screamed again. Sharita sprang across the room, and pulled at her father-in-law's sword arm. He turned and lunged furiously at her, his tulwar slashing across her throat. For a moment, Sharita looked down at the gushing blood in total bewilderment. Then her knees gave way and she hit the ground, dead.

Mary screamed again as Batraj turned back to her, murder in his eyes. Then the door burst open, and Sivitraj rushed in, a tulwar in his left hand.

'You shall die too,' Batraj spat, and struck at him. Sivitraj defended himself as best he could, but was hampered by his injured arm, and in any event he was no match for his

348

stepfather as a swordsman. He was forced against the wall of the hut, while the women huddled in the corner.

'I shall leave all of that viper's brood for her to weep over,' Batraj snarled, as Sivitraj's sword fell from his fingers.

But the doorway was darkened again. Guy Bartlett stood there, a pistol in one hand, his sword in the other.

'Drop the tulwar, Batraj,' Guy said, 'or you are a dead man.'

Batraj hesitated. Sivitraj threw himself forward, striking the weapon from his stepfather's hand, then picked it up and swung it threateningly.

'No,' Guy snapped.

'He killed my wife!'

'You cannot kill an unarmed man,' Guy told him. 'That would be murder, a crime of which your stepfather is guilty, and for which he will pay, according to British justice. You have my word.'

Laura waited in the hall of the Fishers' Bombay house and watched Sivitraj crossing the floor towards her. She made herself stand absolutely still until he had reached her, then she could take him in her arms.

'Your shoulder . . .'

'It is healed.' He demonstrated the ease with which he could move it. 'I have spoken with the Governor, Mother,' he said. 'He now accepts that I was kidnapped, in 1828, and was therefore prevented from taking my proper place as Rajah of Sittapore, and that I have been prevented from returning ever since. He has agreed that Partaj should be set aside, although left as heir to my throne until I have a son of my own.' His face twisted, and Laura knew he was thinking of Sharita.

'I am so pleased for you,' she said.

'There is a proviso,' he added, watching her face.

'What is it?'

'The Governor-General considers it would be unwise for you to return, in view of your escape from suttee. You knew of this?'

She nodded. 'I was told as soon as I arrived here. I shall not go back to Sittapore. I shall make my home in Bombay. Perhaps you will be able to visit me from time to time. Is there news of Mary?'

349

'She has remained with her husband. I am sure she would like to see you, should you decide to revisit Hyderabad.' Sivitraj drew a long breath. 'Prince Batraj has asked to see you.'

Laura glanced at Guy, seeking guidance.

'The decision is yours,' he said. 'I can at least promise that you will be well protected.'

Laura hesitated. She had suffered at Batraj's hands for fifteen years. Yet he was the father of her daughter, even if that daughter was now irrevocably lost to her. She had hated him; she hated him still. Yet he had lived for an ideal, and fought for it; now he had been condemned to death for it.

And he was her husband.

'When?' she asked.

It was the most miserable time of the year. The monsoon winds blew, and successive rainsqualls swept across Bombay.

The gaol was always a depressing place, but in the monsoon it became a reeking quagmire. Laura held her skirts above her ankles as she squelched through the mud beneath an umbrella held by Guy. Her boots and stockings were soaked through by the time she reached the outer office.

The English warden was waiting for them. 'Do you wish to see your husband alone, Your Highness?' he inquired.

Again Laura looked at Guy for guidance.

'As long as he is secured, and we can see what is happening,' Guy said.

'Of course,' the warden agreed.

They were shown into a room, bare save for a table and two chairs, with a barred window looking out at yet another courtyard. The air was heavy with the stench of the prison, and they could hear screams and shouts, the steady rhythm of a whip.

Laura shuddered.

'They need discipline,' the warden said with a cold smile.

The door opened and four men came in, marching Batraj between them. He wore a dhoti and nothing more, and there were recent weals on his shoulders; his wrists were manacled behind his back.

350

The gaolers stepped away and stood against the far wall. The warden also withdrew.

Batraj looked at Guy. 'Can I not speak with my wife?'

'You may,' Guy said. 'But I shall remain in the room, and if you attempt to touch her . . .'

Batraj smiled bitterly. 'You will shoot me down. Would that not be a better death than hanging?'

'You are going to die by hanging, Your Highness,' Guy told him.

He went to stand with the four guards.

Batraj looked at Laura. 'Will you not sit down?'

Laura allowed her knees to give way, and sank into a chair. Batraj also sat, on the far side of the table.

'Were you at my trial?'

The Company authorities had decided not to tread the risky legal ground of calling Laura as a witness; although she and Batraj had never been married according to Christian ritual, nevertheless Batraj claimed her as his wife, and it might have provided grounds for an appeal against the sentence. In any event, they had secured sufficient depositions from captured Thugs to convict him, and this had been done.

'No,' she said.

'But you know that I am to die, by hanging.'

'And now you are afraid,' she remarked.

'Yes, I am afraid. It is a shameful way to die, for a warrior. Why do they not give me a sword and let me die like a man?'

'Did you give all the people you murdered the chance to die like men?'

'They are afraid to give me a sword,' Batraj went on. 'Because they are afraid that I shall die like a hero, and become a legend to my people. But I will yet be a legend. Prince Batraj will be remembered, and remembered too, on the day that the British are finally driven out of India.'

'That day will never come,' Laura told him. 'You will be forgotten.'

'Laura,' he said. 'Did you never love me at all?'

'You saved my life, once,' she said. 'I have always been grateful for that.'

She rose and left the room.

351

Laura heard footsteps in the hall, and rose from the window-seat, her heart pounding.

Jenny came in first, stripping off her gloves.

'Well?' Laura asked.

Jenny shrugged. 'It seems such a . . . such a to-do, for something that is finished in five minutes. Less.'

'Was it . . . did he. . . ?'

'He actually seemed quite composed. Just before they put the noose round his neck he shouted something about India, but I don't think very many people heard what he said. Oh, Laura . . .' she held her hands as tears sprang to Laura's eyes. 'I know, only too well, that you were forced to live as his wife, but he was dreadfully evil.'

'I know,' Laura said.

Guy was hovering in the doorway. 'It is all over,' he said.

She shrugged.

He hesitated, then smiled at her. 'It has stopped raining. No-one ever goes to the beach during the monsoon. But I wondered if you would like to walk . . . Rufus the Second would like to meet you.'

Bombay, 1 September 1843

Six months ago I brought Batraj to heel; three months ago I saw him hang.

One month ago I received my brigade or, to be more precise, the rank; I am now commander of the Bombay garrison.

Two weeks ago Regina gave birth to six handsome pups; Rufus the Second is delighted, as am I.

And one week ago, Laura and I were married. I doubt there is a happier couple in all India.

Much as we would like to return home, we shall be remaining in Bombay for the foreseeable future. Here our various adventures are known, appreciated, and understood. We are not sure this would be the case in England.

Besides, there is a great deal to be done. When I compare the state of India now with when I arrived here, a callow youth, eighteen years ago . . . The whole vast sub-continent is at our mercy, but has also become our responsibility. All of the Deccan is ours save for the dominions of the Nizam of Hyderabad, but he accepts our dominance in everything. Bengal and all of the east of the country are directly under our rule, as are Sind and Baluchistan in the west. In the north, the Mughal Emperor still rules in Delhi, but by virtue of our bayonets, and at the behest of our Commissioners. Rajasthan and Rajputana remain ruled by native princes, but as our clients. We are about to undertake a war to bring the proud Sikhs to heel. I have not volunteered for this conflict, as I feel I have played my part in the conquest of India, and wish to spend as much time as possible with my wife: I have no doubt that the

353

campaign, which is to be conducted by Hugh Gough, will be entirely successful.

When Kashmir and the Punjab are ours, all the lands south of the great mountain barriers, the Himalayas and the Hindu Kush, will be subservient to Great Britain, save only for the tiny mountain kingdoms of Nepal and Bhutan, and they will understand their dependance on the all-prevailing power of the Company.

This is truly an Empire we have created for ourselves.

Its story is mine and Laura's. Our love is as hard-forged as India's frontiers, and as impregnable. Built to last, my wife laughs.

How little I thought when, as a boy, I dreamed of fine adventures, that I would experience such extremes of defeat and victory, of pride and shame, of hate and, most importantly, of love? Laura and I have earned our happiness, we have paid for it in blood and tears.

It has taken us nearly twenty years to win it.